FROM LAB MATERIALS TO PRINT AND AUDIO TOOLS... RESOURCES THAT HELP YOU SUCCEED

This online tool includes 14 modules with 130 activities that give you virtual experience gathering data and performing experiments through engaging simulations. Change parameters to see what happens in each simulation, generate your own data, and write up results. Each experiment includes a general introduction followed by a series of interactive laboratory activities, each with its own set of questions. With an easy-to-use design and unparalleled flexibility, **Virtual Biology Laboratory 3.0** will make you feel like you're in a real lab!

The following experimental modules are available for purchase at academic. cengage.com/biology:

Choose from the following lab modules:

- Biochemistry
- Cell Chemistry
- Cell Division
- Cell Membranes
- Cell Respiration
- Cell Structure
- Ecology
- Evolution
- Genetics
- Microscopy
- Molecular Biology
- Pedigree Analysis
- Photosynthesis
- Population Biology

ALSO AVAILABLE

Study Guide
This interactive workbook pairs text-specific concepts with questions, illustrations, and exercises that promote active learning, as well as topic maps, study strategies, and case studies to help you study more efficiently.

BIOLOGY

Exploring the Diversity of Life

First Canadian Edition

Volume One

Peter J. Russell

Stephen L. Wolfe

Paul E. Hertz

Cecie Starr

M. Brock Fenton
University of Western Ontario

Heather Addy
University of Calgary

Denis Maxwell
University of Western Ontario

Tom Haffie
University of Western Ontario

Ken Davey
York University (Emeritus)

NELSON / EDUCATION

NELSON / E D U C A T I O N

Biology: Exploring the Diversity of Life, First Canadian Edition, Volume One
by Peter J. Russell, Stephen L. Wolfe, Paul E. Hertz, Cecie Starr, M. Brock Fenton, Heather Addy, Denis Maxwell, Tom Haffie, Ken Davey

Vice President, Editorial Director:
Evelyn Veitch

Editor-in-Chief, Higher Education:
Anne Williams

Executive Editor:
Paul Fam

Senior Marketing Manager:
Sean Chamberland

Managing Editor, Development:
Alwynn Pinard

Photo Researcher:
Indu Arora

Permissions Coordinator:
Indu Arora

Content Production Manager:
Christine Gilbert

Production Service:
PrePress PMG

Copy Editor:
Holly Dickinson

Proofreader:
Martha Ghent

Indexer:
Cindy Coan

Production Coordinator:
Ferial Suleman

Design Director:
Ken Phipps

Managing Designer:
Franca Amore

Interior Design:
Dianna Little

Cover Design:
Johanna Liburd, Cover Concept;
Jennifer Leung, Cover Design

Cover Image:
Main image (bat): Photo courtesy of
M. Brock Fenton

Background image (DNA double helix):
Grant Faint/Stone/Getty Images

Compositor:
PrePress PMG

Printer:
Courier

ISBN-13: 978-0-17-650229-4
ISBN-10: 0-17-650229-7

About the Cover: A flying little brown bat frozen in mid-wing stroke moves through the blackness of an underground passage. Echolocation allows the bat to collect information about its surroundings or to locate flying insects. In the background is the elegantly sinuous double helix of DNA, a widely recognized vernacular icon for life itself. The blurred DNA connotes the generative activity inherent in the molecule that carries the genetic code of all life into the future.

For, and because of, our generations of students.

About the Canadian Authors

M.B. (BROCK) FENTON received his Ph.D. from the University of Toronto in 1969. Since then, he has been a faculty member in biology at Carleton University, then at York University, and then at The University of Western Ontario. In addition to teaching parts of first-year biology, he has also taught vertebrate biology, animal biology, and conservation biology, as well as field courses in the biology and behaviour of bats. He has received awards for his teaching (Carleton University Faculty of Science Teaching Award, Ontario Confederation of University Faculty Associations Teaching Award, and a 3M Teaching Fellowship, Society for Teaching and Learning in Higher Education) in addition to recognition of his work on public awareness of science (Gordin Kaplan Award from the Canadian Federation of Biological Societies; Honourary Life Membership, Science North, Sudbury, Ontario; Canadian Council of University Biology Chairs Distinguished Canadian Biologist Award; The McNeil Medal for the Public Awareness of Science of the Royal Society of Canada; and the Sir Sanford Fleming Medal for public awareness of Science, the Royal Canadian Institute). He also received the C. Hart Merriam Award from the American Society of Mammalogists for excellence in scientific research. Bats and their biology, behaviour, evolution, and echolocation are the topic of his research, which has been funded by the Natural Sciences and Engineering Research Council of Canada (NSERC).

HEATHER ADDY is a graduate of the University of Alberta and received her Ph.D. in plant–soil relationships from the University of Guelph in 1995. During this training and in a subsequent postdoctoral fellowship focusing on mycorrhizas and other plant–fungus symbioses at the University of Alberta, she discovered a love of teaching. In 1998, she joined the Department of Biological Sciences at the University of Calgary in a faculty position that places emphasis on teaching and teaching-related scholarship. In addition to teaching introductory biology classes and an upper-level mycology class, she has led the development of investigative labs for introductory biology courses and the introduction of peer-assisted learning groups in large biology and chemistry classes. She received the Faculty of Science Award for Excellence in Teaching in 2005 and an Honourable Mention for the Student's Union Teaching Excellence Award in 2008.

DENIS MAXWELL received his Ph.D. from the University of Western Ontario in 1995. His thesis under the supervision of Norm Hüner focused on the role of the redox state of photosynthetic electron transport in photoacclimation in green algae. Following his doctorate, he was awarded an NSERC postdoctoral fellowship. He undertook postdoctoral training at the Department of Energy Plant Research Laboratory at Michigan State University, where he studied the function of the mitochondrial alternative oxidase. After taking up a faculty position at the University of New Brunswick in 2000, he moved in 2003 to the Department of Biology at The University of Western Ontario. His research program, which is supported by NSERC, is focused on understanding the role of the mitochondrion in intracellular stress sensing and signalling. In addition to research, he is passionate about teaching biology and science to first-year university students.

TOM HAFFIE is a graduate of the University of Guelph and the University of Saskatchewan in the area of microbial genetics. Currently the learning development coordinator for the Faculty of Science at the University of Western Ontario, Tom has devoted his 20-year career to teaching large biology classes in lecture, laboratory, and tutorial settings. He led the development of the innovative core laboratory course in the biology program, was an early adopter of computer animation in lectures and, most recently, has coordinated the implementation of personal response technology across campus. He holds a UWO Pleva Award for Excellence in Teaching, a UWO Fellowship in Teaching Innovation, a Province of Ontario Award for Leadership in Faculty Teaching (LIFT), and a national 3M Fellowship for Excellence in Teaching.

KEN DAVEY is a graduate of the University of Western Ontario and received his Ph.D. from Cambridge University. He is an emeritus professor of biology at York University and has by preference taught elementary courses in zoology at McGill and York and more advanced courses in invertebrate physiology, parasitology, and endocrinology. He has held a number of academic administrative positions at York. His research interests include invertebrate physiology and the endocrinology of insects and parasitic worms, supported by NSERC. Ken has accumulated a number of academic awards, including the Canadian Council of University Biology Chairs Distinguished Canadian Biologist Award and the Wigglesworth Award for Service to Entomology of the Royal Entomological Society. He is a Fellow of the Royal Society of Canada and an Officer of the Order of Canada.

About the U.S. Authors

PETER J. RUSSELL received a B.Sc. in Biology from the University of Sussex, England, in 1968 and a Ph.D. in Genetics from Cornell University in 1972. He has been a member of the Biology faculty of Reed College since 1972; he is currently a Professor of Biology. He teaches a section of the introductory biology course, a genetics course, an advanced molecular genetics course, and a research literature course on molecular virology. In 1987 he received the Burlington Northern Faculty Achievement Award from Reed College in recognition of his excellence in teaching. Since 1986, he has been the author of a successful genetics textbook; current editions are *iGenetics: A Mendelian Approach, iGenetics: A Molecular Approach,* and *Essential iGenetics.* He wrote nine of the BioCoach Activities for The Biology Place. Peter Russell's research is in the area of molecular genetics, with a specific interest in characterizing the role of host genes in pathogenic RNA plant virus gene expression; yeast is used as the model host. His research has been funded by agencies including the National Institutes of Health, the National Science Foundation, and the American Cancer Society. He has published his research results in a variety of journals, including *Genetics, Journal of Bacteriology, Molecular and General Genetics, Nucleic Acids Research, Plasmid,* and *Molecular and Cellular Biology.* He has a long history of encouraging faculty research involving undergraduates, including cofounding the biology division of the Council on Undergraduate Research (CUR) in 1985. He was Principal Investigator/Program Director of an NSF Award for the Integration of Research and Education (AIRE) to Reed College, 1998–2002.

STEPHEN L. WOLFE received his Ph.D. from Johns Hopkins University and taught general biology and cell biology for many years at the University of California, Davis. He has a remarkable list of successful textbooks, including multiple editions of *Biology of the Cell, Biology: The Foundations, Cell Ultrastructure, Molecular and Cellular Biology,* and *Introduction to Cell and Molecular Biology.*

PAUL E. HERTZ was born and raised in New York City. He received a bachelor's degree in Biology at Stanford University in 1972, a master's degree in Biology at Harvard University in 1973, and a doctorate in Biology at Harvard University in 1977. While completing field research for the doctorate, he served on the Biology faculty of the University of Puerto Rico at Rio Piedras. After spending 2 years as an Isaac Walton Killam Postdoctoral Fellow at Dalhousie University, Hertz accepted a teaching position at Barnard College, where he has taught since 1979. He was named Ann Whitney Olin Professor of Biology in 2000, and he received The Barnard Award for Excellence in Teaching in 2007. In addition to his service on numerous college committees, Professor Hertz was Chair of Barnard's Biology Department for 8 years. He has also been the Program Director of the Hughes Science Pipeline Project at Barnard, an undergraduate curriculum and research program funded by the Howard Hughes Medical Institute, since its inception in 1992. The Pipeline Project includes the Intercollegiate Partnership, a program for local community college students that facilitates their transfer to 4-year colleges and universities. He teaches one semester of the introductory sequence for Biology majors and preprofessional students as well as lecture and laboratory courses in vertebrate zoology and ecology. Professor Hertz is an animal physiological ecologist with a specific research interest in the thermal biology of lizards. He has conducted fieldwork in the West Indies since the mid-1970s, most recently focusing on the lizards of Cuba. His work has been funded by the National Science Foundation, and he has published his research in such prestigious journals as *The American Naturalist, Ecology, Nature,* and *Oecologia.*

CECIE STARR is the author of best-selling biology textbooks. Her books include multiple editions of *Unity and Diversity of Life, Biology: Concepts and Applications,* and *Biology Today and Tomorrow.* Her original dream was to be an architect. She may not be building houses, but with the same care and attention to detail, she builds incredible books: *"I invite students into a chapter through an intriguing story. Once inside, they get the great windows that biologists construct on the world of life. Biology is not just another house. It is a conceptual mansion. I hope to do it justice."*

BEVERLY McMILLAN has been a science writer for more than 20 years and is coauthor of a college text in human biology, now in its seventh edition. She has worked extensively in educational and commercial publishing, including 8 years in editorial management positions in the college divisions of Random House and McGraw-Hill. In a multifaceted freelance career, Bev also has written or coauthored six trade books and numerous magazine and newspaper articles, as well as story panels for exhibitions at the Science Museum of Virginia and the San Francisco Exploratorium. She has worked as a radio producer and speechwriter for the University of California system and as a media relations advisor for the College of William and Mary. She holds undergraduate and graduate degrees from the University of California, Berkeley.

Preface

Welcome to an exploration of the diversity of life. The main goal of this text is to guide you on a journey of discovery about life's diversity across levels ranging from molecules to genes, cells to organs, and species to ecosystems. Along the way, we will explore many questions about the mechanisms underlying diversity as well as the consequences of diversity for our own species and for others.

At first glance, the riot of life that animates the biosphere overwhelms the minds of many who try to understand it. One way to begin to make sense of this diversity is to divide it into manageable sections on the basis of differences. In this book, we highlight the divisions between plants and animals, prokaryotes and eukaryotes, protostomes and deuterostomes, but we also consider features found in all life forms. We examine how different organisms solve the common problems of finding nutrients, energy, and mates on the third rock from our Sun. What basic evolutionary principles inform the relationships among life forms regardless of their different body plans, habitats, or life histories? Unlike many other first-year biology texts, this book has chapters integrating basic concepts such as genetic recombination, the effects of light, nutrition, and domestication across the breadth of life from microbes to mistletoe to moose. As you read this book, you will be referred frequently to other chapters for linked information that expands the ideas further.

Evolution provides a powerful conceptual lens for viewing and understanding the roots and history of diversity. We will demonstrate how knowledge of evolution helps us appreciate the changes we observe in organisms. Whether the focus is the conversion of free-living prokaryotes into mitochondria and chloroplasts or the steps involved in the domestication of rice, selection for particular traits over time can explain the current condition.

We hope that Canadian students will find the subject of biology as it is presented here accessible and engaging because it is presented in familiar contexts. We have highlighted the work of Canadian scientists, used examples of Canadian species, and referred to Canadian regulations and institutions, as well as discoveries made by Canadians.

Although many textbooks use the first few chapters to introduce and/or review background information, we have used the first chapters to convey the excitement and interest of biology itself. Within the centre of the book, we have placed important background information about biology and chemistry in the reference section entitled *The Chemical and Physical Foundations of Biology*. These pages are distinct and easy to find with their purple edges and have become affectionately known as the "Purple Pages." These pages enable information to be readily identifiable and accessible to students as they move through the textbook rather than information that is tied to a particular chapter. The purple background makes the pages easy to find when you need to check a topic. This section keeps background information out of the mainstream of the text, allowing you to focus on bigger pictures.

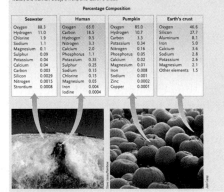

In addition to presenting material about biology, this book also makes a point of highlighting particular people, important molecules, interesting contexts, and examples of life in extreme conditions. Science that appears in textbooks is the product of people who have made careful and systematic observations, which led them to formulate hypotheses about these observations and, where appropriate, design and execute experiments to test these hypotheses. We illustrate this in each chapter with boxed stories about how particular people have used their ingenuity and creativity to expand our knowledge of biology. We have endeavoured to show not just the science itself but also the process behind the science.

Although biology is not simply chemistry, specific chemicals and their interactions can have dramatic effects on biological systems. From water to progesterone, amanitin, and DDT, each chapter features the activity of a relevant chemical.

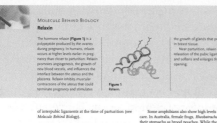

of interpubic ligaments at the time of parturition (see *Molecule Behind Biology*).

39.1 Housing and Fuelling Developing Young

Some animal parents invest significant energy in housing and feeding their developing young. This is one aspect of the genetically selfish drive to ensure that their genes are represented in future generations.

39.1a Housing: Providing a Place in Which the Embryo Can Develop

There is a recurring tendency across phyla for parents to put eggs and developing young in situations that minimize their exposure to predators and parasites while maximizing favourable conditions for growth and development. Many species of birds use nests to house their eggs and unfledged young. Parents of other species, such as some species of scorpions (see Figure 3.22a), frogs, and insects, carry their young with them, often on their backs. This allows the parent (parents) to avoid or actively deter would-be predators.

An escalation in parental investment is moving eggs and young inside the parent's body (vivipary and ovovivipary; see Chapter 38). This approach to parental care has several different stages (see Chapter 38, *On the Road to Vivipary*). Although we associate vivipary with mammals, many species of fish are mouth-breeders, keeping eggs and, for a time, developing young in their mouths. Other fish, such as sea horses and pipefish (family Syngnathidae, order Gasterosteiformes; **Figure 39.1**), keep eggs and developing young in specialized incubation areas, called brood pouches, located on the tail or trunk of the male. "Pregnancy" in male sea horses represents an increase in parental investment. It also allows males to be confident about the paternity of the young they raise.

Some amphibians also show high levels of parental care. In Australia, female frogs, *Rheobatrachus silus*, use their stomachs as brood pouches. While the young are developing, they secrete prostaglandin E₂, which inhibits its secretion of gastric acid in the stomach and saves the developing young from being digested. On Mount Nimba in west Africa, female toads *Nectophrynoides occidentalis* harbour developing young in their uterus, where the young feed on uterine secretions in the absence of a placenta. The gestation period for these toads is nine months, and newborns are 7 to 8 mm long and weigh 30 to 60 mg. Retention of developing embryos in the oviducts has evolved independently in each of the three living groups of Amphibia: Anura, Urodela, and Gymnophiona (see Chapter 27).

39.1b Feeding: Aiding and Abetting Developing Young

Almost everyone has seen pictures of parent birds feeding their young (see Figures 40.2 and 40.4). In many species, both males and females deliver food to the nestlings. Some fruit-eating adult birds feed insects to their young

Figure 39.1
A male sea horse gives birth.

To help frame the material with an engaging context, we begin each chapter with a section called "Why It Matters." In addition, several chapters include boxed accounts of organisms thriving "on the edge" at unusual temperatures, pressures, radiation dosages, salt concentrations, etc. These brief articles explain how our understanding of "normal" can be increased through study of the "extreme."

Examining how biological systems work is another theme pervading this text and underlying the idea of diversity. We have intentionally tried to include examples that will tax your imagination, from sea slugs that steal chloroplasts for use as solar panels, to hummingbirds fuelling their hovering flight, to adaptive radiation of viruses. In each situation, we examine how biologists have explored and assessed the inner workings of organisms from gene regulation to the challenges of digesting cellulose.

Solving problems is another theme that runs through the book. Whether the topic is gene therapy to treat a disease in people, increasing crop production, or conserving endangered species, both the problem and the solution lie in biology. We will explore large problems facing planet Earth and the social implications that arise from them.

Science is by its nature a progressive enterprise in which answers to questions open new questions for consideration. Each chapter presents unanswered questions as well as questions for discussion to emphasize that biologists still have a lot to learn—topics for you to tackle should you decide to pursue a career in research.

"Study Breaks" occur after each section in the chapters. They contain questions written by students to identify some of the important features of the section. The answers are embedded in the "Review" section at the end of each chapter. Also included at the end of each chapter is a group of multiple-choice self-test questions, the answers to which can be found at the end of the book. "Questions for Discussion" at the end of each chapter challenge you to think more broadly about biology. You are encouraged to use these in discussions with other students and to explore potential answers by using the resources of the electronic library.

To maximize the chances of producing a useful text that draws in students (and instructors), we sought the advice of colleagues who teach biology (members of the Editorial Advisory Board). We also asked students (members of the Student Advisory Boards) for their advice and comments. Both groups read draft chapters and provided valuable feedback, but any mistakes are ours. The members of the Student Advisory Boards also wrote the Study Break questions found throughout the text.

We hope that you are as captivated by the biological world as we are and are drawn from one chapter to another. But don't stop there—use electronic resources to broaden your search for understanding.

multiple auxotrophic *E. coli* mutants here; the idea is the same.) As for the homologous chromosomes pair, they are held together tightly by a protein framework called the **synaptonemal complex (Figure 10.15, p. 220)**. Supported by this framework, segments of homologous chromatids exchange segments, producing new combinations of alleles (see Figure 10.14, step 2). Recall that the exchange process is very precise and involves the breakage and rejoining of DNA molecules by enzymes (Figure 10.1). When the exchange is complete toward the end of prophase I, the synaptonemal complex disassembles and disappears. If you now follow meiosis I and II through to the end in your mind, notice that each of the four resulting nuclei receives one of these four chromatids (see Figure 10.14, step 3); two receive unchanged chromatids, and two receive chromatids that have new combinations of alleles due to recombination.

The physical effect of recombination can be seen later in meiosis I, when increased condensation of the chromosomes thickens the chromosomes enough to make them visible under the light microscope (see Figure 10.11, steps 3 and 4). Regions in which nonsister chromatids cross one another, called **crossovers** or **chiasmata** (singular, *chiasma* = crosspiece), clearly show that two of the four chromatids have exchanged segments. Because of the shape produced, the recombination process is also called **crossing-over**.

Note that illustrations of recombination usually show chromosomes "paired" side by side, with only the closest chromatids participating in recombination (see Figure 10.14); however, chromosomes actually pair "one on top of the other" such that any two of the four chromatids can participate in a given recombination event. Recombination takes place largely at random, at almost any position along the chromosome arms.

Several events likely occur at various locations along all chromatids.

Notice in Figure 10.14 that a recombination event does not just "switch" the alleles of a given gene in a localized area. All of the DNA sequence stretching from the site of recombination to the ends of the participating chromatids is exchanged.

Random Segregation. Random segregation of chromosomes of maternal and paternal origin accounts for the second major source of genetic variability in meiosis. Recall that the maternal and paternal members of each homologous pair are different in that they typically carry different alleles of many of the genes on that chromosome. During prometaphase I, spindle microtubules make connections to kinetochores. For each homologous pair, one chromosome makes spindle connections leading to one pole and the other chromosome connects to the opposite pole. In making these connections, all the maternal chromosomes may connect to one pole and all the paternal chromosomes may connect to the opposite pole. Or, as is most likely, a random combination of maternal and paternal chromosomes may be segregated to a given spindle pole (**Figure 10.16, p. 221**).

The number of possible combinations depends on the number of chromosome pairs in a species. For example, the 39 chromosome pairs in dogs allow 2^{39} different combinations of maternal and paternal chromosomes to be delivered to the poles, producing potentially 500 billion genetically different gametes from this source of variability alone. Note that this random partitioning of maternal and paternal chromosomes is responsible for the independent assortment of the alleles of two genes in Mendel's experiments with garden peas described in Chapter 11.

But some F₁ hybrids are healthy, vigorous, and fully fertile and can breed with other hybrids and with both parental species. Sometimes the F₁ generation, produced by matings between F₁ hybrids, or between F₁ hybrids and either parental species, may exhibit reduced survival or fertility, a phenomenon known as **hybrid breakdown**. Experimental crosses between fruit fly (*Drosophila*) species may produce functional interspecific hybrids, but their offspring experience a high rate of chromosomal abnormalities and harmful types of genetic recombination. Thus, reproductive isolation is maintained between the species because there is little long-term mixing of their gene pools.

18.8 Geography of Speciation

Geography has a huge impact on whether gene pools have the opportunity to mix. Biologists define three modes of speciation based on the geographic relationship of populations as they become reproductively isolated: allopatric speciation (*allo* = different; *patria* = homeland), parapatric speciation (*para* = beside), and sympatric speciation (*sym* = together).

18.8a Allopatric Speciation: New Species Develop from Isolated Populations

Allopatric speciation can occur when a physical barrier subdivides a large population or when a small population becomes separated from a species' main geographic distribution. Allopatric speciation, probably the most common mode of speciation in large animals, occurs in two stages. First, two populations become geographically separated, preventing gene flow between them. Then, as the populations experience distinct mutations as well as different patterns of natural selection and genetic drift, they may accumulate genetic differences that isolate them *reproductively*.

Geographic separation sometimes occurs when a barrier divides a large population into two or more

Supplementary Materials

An extensive array of supplemental materials is available to accompany this text. These supplements are designed to make teaching and learning more effective. For more information on any of these resources, please contact your local Nelson Education sales representative or call Nelson Education Limited Customer Support at 1-800-268-2222.

Instructor Resources

These resources are available to qualified adopters. Please consult your local Nelson Education sales representative for details.

Instructor's Resource DVD

The *Instructor's Resource DVD* contains the following resources:

Instructor's Resource Manual

The *Instructor's Resource Manual* for this First Canadian Edition has been dramatically revised by Tanya Noel, Tamara Kelly, and Julie Clark from York University to include tips on teaching using cases as well as suggestions on how to present material and use technology and other resources effectively, integrating the other supplements available to both students and instructors. This manual doesn't simply reinvent what's currently in the text; it helps the instructor make the material relevant and engaging to students.

ExamView® Computerized Test Bank

Create, deliver, and customize tests (both print and online) in minutes with this easy-to-use assessment and tutorial system. ExamView® offers both a Quick Test Wizard and an Online Test Wizard that guide you step-by-step through the process of creating tests, while its "what you see is what you get" capability allows you to see the test you are creating on the screen exactly as it will print or display online. You can build tests of up to 250 questions using up to 12 question types. Using *ExamView's* complete word-processing capabilities, you can enter an unlimited number of new questions or edit existing questions.

Nelson Education Testing Advantage

 Nelson Education Testing Advantage

In most postsecondary courses, a large percentage of student assessment is based on multiple-choice testing. Many instructors use multiple-choice testing reluctantly, believing that it is a methodology best used for testing what a student *remembers* rather than what she or he has *learned*.

Nelson Education Ltd. understands that a good-quality multiple-choice test bank can provide the means to measure *higher level thinking* skills as well as recall. Recognizing the importance of multiple-choice testing in today's classroom, we have created the Nelson Education Testing Advantage program (NETA) to ensure the value of our high-quality test banks.

The *Test Bank* to accompany *Biology*, adapted by Ivona Mladenovic of Simon Fraser University and Ian Dawe of Selkirk College, offers the Premium Nelson Education Testing Advantage. NETA was created in partnership with David DiBattista, a 3M National Teaching Fellow, professor of psychology at Brock University, and researcher in the area of multiple-choice testing. NETA ensures that subject-matter experts who author test banks have had training in two areas: avoiding common errors in test construction and developing multiple-choice test questions that "get beyond remembering" to assess higher level thinking. In addition, Professor DiBattista confirms the subject-matter expert's understanding of and adherence to the NETA principles through a review.

All Premium NETA test banks include David DiBattista's guide for instructors, "Multiple Choice Tests: Getting Beyond Remembering." This guide has been designed to assist you in using Nelson test banks to achieve your desired outcomes in your course.

Customers who adopt a Premium Nelson Education Testing Advantage title may also qualify for additional faculty training opportunities in multiple-choice testing and assessment. Please contact your local Nelson Education sales and editorial representative for more details about our Premium NETA.

Microsoft PowerPoint® Slides This one-stop lecture tool makes it easy to assemble, edit, publish, and present custom lectures. Adapted by Jane Young of the University of Northern British Columbia, this resource brings together text-specific lecture outlines, art, video, and animations, culminating in a powerful, personalized, PowerPoint® presentation.

Also included on the *Instructor's Resource DVD* are Word files of the *Test Bank,* as well as a full *Image Bank* of the art and photos from the text book. ISBN: 978-0-17-647529-1.

Student Resources

Study Guide

The *Study Guide* for the First Canadian Edition has been adapted by Colin Montpetit of the University of Ottawa, Julie Smit of the University of Windsor, and Wendy J. Keenleyside of the University of Guelph. The *Study Guide* contains unique case studies to integrate the concepts within the text, study strategies, interactive exercises, self-test questions, and more. ISBN: 978-0-17-647474-4.

CengageNOW™   CENGAGENOW

CengageNOW Personalized Study is a diagnostic tool (featuring a chapter-specific Pretest, Study Plan, and

Post-test) that empowers students to master concepts, prepare for exams, and be more involved in class. Results to *Personalized Study* provide immediate and ongoing feedback regarding what students are mastering and why they're not to both the instructor and the student. *CengageNOW Personalized Study* links to an integrated eBook so that students can easily review topics and also contains animations, links to websites, videos, and more as part of their Study Plan. *CengageNOW* has been adapted by Dora Cavallo-Medved, University of Windsor; Todd Nickle, Mount Royal College; and Edward Andrews, Sir Wilfred Grenfell College.

CengageNOW with Premium eBook

Want to take your biology experience to the next level? Our *Premium eBook* allows students access to an integrated, interactive learning environment with advanced learning tools and a user interface that gives students control over their learning experience. *CengageNOW Personalized Study* is included with the Premium eBook for the ultimate online study experience.

JoinIn™ on TurningPoint®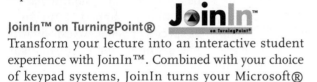
Transform your lecture into an interactive student experience with JoinIn™. Combined with your choice of keypad systems, JoinIn turns your Microsoft®

PowerPoint® application into audience response software. With a click on a handheld device, students can respond to multiple-choice questions, short polls, interactive exercises, and peer-review questions. You can also take attendance, check student comprehension of concepts, collect student demographics to better assess student needs, and even administer quizzes. In addition, there are interactive text-specific slide sets that you can modify and merge with any of your own PowerPoint® lecture slides. These have been adapted by Jane Young of the University of Northern British Columbia and contain poll slides and pre- and post-test slides for each chapter in the text. This tool is available to qualified adopters at **http://www.turningtechnologies.com/**.

Students and Instructors

Visit the website to accompany *Biology: Exploring the Diversity of Life*, First Canadian Edition, at **http://biologyedl.nelson.com**. This website contains quizzes, flashcards, weblinks, and more.

Prospering in Biology

Using This Book

The following are things you will need to know in order to use this text and prosper in Biology.

Names

What's in a name? People are very attached to names—their own names, the names of other people, the names of flowers and food and cars, and so on. It is not surprising that biologists would also be concerned about names. Take, for example, our use of scientific names. Scientific names are always italicized and Latinized.

Castor canadensis Kuhl is the scientific name of the Canadian beaver. *Castor* is the genus name, *canadensis* is the species name, and Kuhl is the name of the person who described the species. "Beaver" by itself is not enough because there is a European beaver, *Castor fiber*, and an extinct giant beaver, *Castoides ohioensis*. Furthermore, common names can vary from place to place (*Myotis lucifugus* is sometimes known as the "little brown bat" or the "little brown myotis").

Biologists prefer scientific names because the name (Latinized) tells you about the organism. There are strict rules about the derivation and use of scientific names. Common names are not so restricted, so they are not precise. For example, in *Myotis lucifugus*, *Myotis* means mouse-eared and *lucifugus* means flees the light; hence, this species is a mouse-eared bat that flees the light.

Birds can be an exception. There are accepted "standard" common names for birds. The American robin is *Turdus migratorius*. The common names for birds are usually capitalized because of the standardization. However, the common names of mammals are not capitalized, except for geographic names or patronyms (*geographic* = named after a country; *patronym* = named after someone; e.g., Canadian beaver or Ord's kangaroo rat, respectively).

Although a few plants that have very broad distributions may have accepted standard common names (e.g., white spruce, *Picea glauca*), most plants have many common names. Furthermore, the same common name is often used for more than one species. Several species in the genus *Taraxacum* are referred to as "dandelion." It is important to use the scientific names of plants to be sure that it is clear exactly which plant we mean. The scientific names of plants also tell us something about the plant. The scientific name for the weed quack grass, *Elymus repens*, tells us that this is a type of wild rye (*Elymus*) and that this particular species spreads or creeps (*repens* = creeping). Anyone who has tried to eliminate this plant from their garden or yard knows how it creeps! Unlike for animals, plant-naming rules forbid the use of the same word for both genus and species names for a plant; thus, although *Bison bison* is an acceptable scientific name for buffalo, such a name would never be accepted for a plant.

In this book, we present the scientific names of organisms when we mention them. We follow standard abbreviations; for example, although the full name of an organism is used the first time it is mentioned (e.g., *Castor canadensis*), subsequent references to that same organism abbreviate the genus name and provide the full species name (e.g., *C. canadensis*).

In some areas of biology, the standard representation is of the genus, for example, *Chlamydomonas*. In other cases, names are so commonly used that only the abbreviation may be used (e.g., *E. coli* for *Escherichia coli*).

Units

The units of measure used by biologists are standardized (metric or SI) units, used throughout the world in science.

Definitions

The science of biology is replete with specialized terms (sometimes referred to as "jargon") used to communicate specific information. It follows that, as with scientific names, specialized terms increase the precision with which biologists communicate among themselves and with others. Be cautious about the use of terms because jargon can be a veneer of precision. When we encounter a "slippery" term (such as species or gene), we explain why one definition for all situations is not feasible.

Time

In this book, we use c.e. (Common Era) to refer to the years since year 1 and b.c.e. (Before the Common Era) to refer to years before that.

Geologists think of time over very long periods. A geologic time scale (see Table 1.1) shows that the age of Earth could be measured in years, but it's challenging to think of billions of years expressed in days (or hours, etc.). With the advent of using the decay rates of radioisotopes to measure the age of rocks, geologists adopted 1950 as the baseline, the "Present," and the past is referred to as b.p. ("Before Present"). A notation of 30 000 years b.p. (^{14}C) indicates 30 000 years before 1950 using the ^{14}C method of dating.

Other dating systems are also used. Some archaeologists use PPNA (PrePottery Neolithic A, where A is the horizon or stratum). In deposits along the Euphrates River, 11 000 PPNA appears to be the same as 11 000

B.P. In this book, we use B.C.E. or B.P. as the time units, except when referring to events or species from more than 100 000 years ago. For those dates, we refer you to the geologic time scale (see Table 1.1 on page xiv).

Sources

Where does the information presented in a text or in class come from? What is the difference between what you read in a textbook or an encyclopedia and the material you see in a newspaper or tabloid? When the topic relates to science, the information should be based on material that has been published in a scholarly journal. In this context, "scholarly" refers to the process of review. Scholars submit their manuscripts reporting their research findings to the editor (or editorial board) of a journal. The editor, in turn, sends the manuscript out for comment and review by recognized authorities in the field. The process is designed to ensure that what is published is as accurate and appropriate as possible. The review process sets the scholarly journal apart from the tabloid.

There are literally thousands of scholarly journals, which, together, publish millions of articles each year. Some journals are more influential than others, for example, *Science* and *Nature*. These two journals are published weekly and invariably contain new information of interest to biologists.

To collect information for this text, we have drawn on published works that have gone through the process of scholarly review. Specific references (citations) are provided, usually in the electronic resources designed to complement the book.

A citation is intended to make the information accessible. Although there are many different formats for citations, the important elements include (in some order) the name(s) of the author(s), the date of publication, the title, and the publisher. When the source is published in a scholarly journal, the journal name, its volume number, and the pages are also provided. With the citation information, you can visit a library and locate the original source. This is true for both electronic (virtual) and real libraries.

Students of biology benefit by making it a habit to look at the most recent issues of their favourite scholarly journals and use them to keep abreast of new developments.

M. Brock Fenton
Heather Addy
Denis Maxwell
Tom Haffie
Ken Davey

London, Calgary and Toronto
February 2009

Table 1.1 The Geological Time Scale and Major Evolutionary Events

Eons (Duration drawn to scale): Cenozoic, Mesozoic, Paleozoic (Phanerozoic); Proterozoic

Eon	Era	Period	Epoch	Millions of Years Ago	Major Evolutionary Events
Phanerozoic	Cenozoic	Quaternary	Holocene	0.01	
			Pleistocene	1.7	Origin of humans; major glaciations
		Tertiary	Pliocene	5.2	Origin of ape-like human ancestors
			Miocene	23	Angiosperms and mammals further diversify and dominate terrestrial habitats
			Oligocene	33.4	Divergence of primates; origin of apes
			Eocene	55	Angiosperms and insects diversify; modern orders of mammals differentiate
			Paleocene	65	Grasslands and deciduous woodlands spread; modern birds and mammals diversify; continents approach current positions
	Mesozoic	Cretaceous		144	Many lineages diversify: angiosperms, insects, marine invertebrates, fishes, dinosaurs; asteroid impact causes mass extinction at end of period, eliminating dinosaurs and many other groups
		Jurassic		206	Gymnosperms abundant in terrestrial habitats; first angiosperms; modern fishes diversify; dinosaurs diversify and dominate terrestrial habitats; frogs, salamanders, lizards, and birds appear; continents continue to separate
		Triassic		251	Predatory fishes and reptiles dominate oceans; gymnosperms dominate terrestrial habitats; radiation of dinosaurs; origin of mammals; Pangaea starts to break up; mass extinction at end of period

Eon	Era	Period	Millions of years ago	Events
Phanerozoic (continued)	Paleozoic	Permian	290	Insects, amphibians, and reptiles abundant and diverse in swamp forests; some reptiles colonize oceans; fishes colonize freshwater habitats; continents coalesce into Pangaea, causing glaciation and decline in sea level; mass extinction at end of period eliminates 85% of species
		Carboniferous	354	Vascular plants form large swamp forests; first seed plants and flying insects; amphibians diversify; first reptiles appear
		Devonian	417	Terrestrial vascular plants diversify; fungi and invertebrates colonize land; first insects appear; first amphibians colonize land; major glaciation at end of period causes mass extinction, mostly of marine life
		Silurian	443	Jawless fishes diversify; first jawed fishes; first vascular plants on land
		Ordovician	490	Major radiations of marine invertebrates and fishes; major glaciation at end of period causes mass extinction of marine life
		Cambrian	543	Diverse radiation of modern animal phyla (Cambrian explosion); simple marine communities
Proterozoic			2500	High concentration of oxygen in atmosphere; origin of aerobic metabolism; origin of eukaryotic cells; evolution and diversification of protists, fungi, soft-bodied animals
			3800	Evolution of prokaryotes, including anaerobic bacteria and photosynthetic bacteria; oxygen starts to accumulate in atmosphere
Archaean			4600	Formation of Earth at start of era; Earth's crust, atmosphere, and oceans form; origin of life at end of era

Acknowledgements

We thank the many people who have worked with us on the production of this text, particularly Paul Fam, Executive Editor, whose foresight brought the idea to us and whose persistence saw the project through. Thanks go to those who reviewed the U.S. text to provide us with feedback for the Canadian edition including Logan Donaldson, York University; Robert Holmberg, Athabasca University; and Thomas H. MacRae, Dalhousie University. We also are grateful to the members of the Editorial Advisory Board and the Student Advisory Board, who provided us with valuable feedback and alternate perspectives (special acknowledgements to these individuals are listed below). We also thank Richard Walker at the University of Calgary, who began this journey with us but who was unable to continue. We thank Carl Lowenberger for contributing Chapter 44 (on defences). We are especially grateful to Alwynn Pinard, Managing Developmental Editor, and James Polley, who kept us moving through the chapters at an efficient pace, along with Tracy Duff, Project Manager, and Christine Gilbert, Content Production Manager. We thank Rosemary Tanner, who provided a thoughtful substantive edit of the entire manuscript, Holly Dickinson for her careful copy editing, and Sandra Peters, who did a cold read as a further check on our presentation. Finally, we thank Sean Chamberland, Senior Marketing Manager, for making us look good.

Brock Fenton would like to thank Allan Noon, who offered much advice about taking pictures; Laura Barclay, Jeremy McNeil, Tony Percival-Smith, C.S. (Rufus) Churcher, and David and Meg Cumming for the use of their images; and Karen Campbell for providing a critical read on the domestication chapter.

It is never easy to be in the family of an academic scientist. We are especially grateful to our families for their sustained support over the course of our careers, particularly during those times when our attentions were fully captivated by bacteria, algae, fungi, parasites, or bats. Saying "yes" to a textbook project means saying "no" to a variety of other pursuits. We appreciate the patience and understanding of those closest to us that enabled the temporary reallocation of considerable time from other endeavours and relationships.

Many of our colleagues have contributed to our development as teachers and scholars by acting as mentors, collaborators, and, on occasion, "worthy opponents." Like all teachers, we owe particular gratitude to our students. They have gathered with us around the discipline of biology, sharing their potent blend of enthusiasm and curiosity that leaves us energized and optimistic for the future.

Editorial and Student Advisory Boards

We were very fortunate to have the assistance of some extraordinary students and instructors of biology across Canada who provided us with feedback that helped shape this textbook into what you see before you. As such, we would like to say a very special thank you to the following people:

Editorial Advisory Board

Mark Brigham, University of Regina
Dion Durnford, University of New Brunswick
Wendy Keenleyside, University of Guelph
Marty Leonard, Dalhousie University
Cindy Paszkowski, University of Alberta
Carol Pollock, University of British Columbia
Kevin Scott, University of Manitoba
Paula Wilson, York University

Student Advisory Boards
University of Western Ontario (pictured above)
Rachael Danielson
Dalal Dharouj
Yvonne Dzal
Liam McGuire
Aimee McMillan
Errin Pfeiffer
Max Rachinsky
Nina Veselka
Ivana Vilimonovic
Marisol Wilcox

University of Calgary (pictured above)
Kristina Birkholz
Jobran Chebib
Liam Cummings

Aravind Ganesh
Shaista Hashem
Colleen Michael
Simon Sun
Camilla Tapp
Anita Tieu
Sahar Zaidi

University of New Brunswick
Maria Correia
Kelvin Gilliland
Jonathon Neilson
Allison Ritcey
Faith Shannon
Brittany Timberlake
Coleman Ward
Corey Willis

Thanks go as well to the high school students who participated, Meghan Harris and Lindsay Patton. Anne Duguay, a teacher from Queen Elizabeth High School in Calgary, and her student, Saskia, also participated. They provided a unique perspective on what entering students would expect from a text for an introductory course in biology. Finally, we wish to thank the student review boards from the University of Victoria, University of Toronto, Erindale Campus, Ryerson University, Sir Wilfred Grenfell College, and the University of Windsor. High school students, university students, and university instructors together provided us with an amazingly diverse array of feedback that allowed us to understand our audience and create a resource best suited to their needs.

Brief Contents

Contents

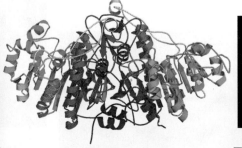
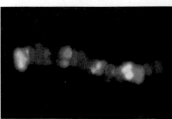
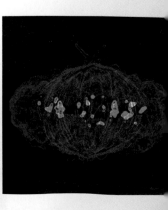

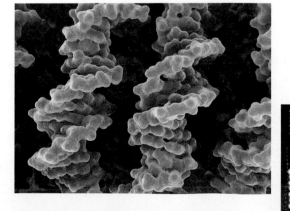

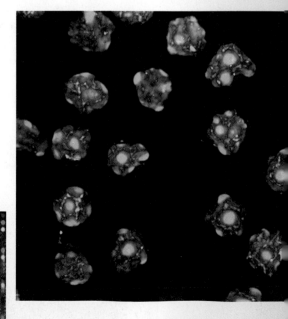

a.

b.

Paintings by Claude Monet (1840-1926). Compared to his early works including The water-lily pond **(a)** his later paintings including the Japanese footbridge **(b)** bordered on the abstract with almost complete loss of light-blue. Monet suffered from vision degenerative disease cataracts which was diagnosed in 1912.

1 Light and Life

WHY IT MATTERS

Claude Monet (1840–1926), a French painter, is considered by many to be the master of the impressionist form that rose to prominence in the late nineteenth century. Other well-known impressionists include Edgar Degas and Paul Cézanne. Impressionism as an art movement was characterized by the use of small visible brush strokes that emphasized light and colour, rather than lines, to define an object. The artists used pure, unmixed colour, not smoothly blended, as was the custom at the time. For example, instead of physically mixing yellow and blue paint, they placed unmixed yellow paint on the canvas next to unmixed blue paint so that the colours would mingle in the eye of the viewer to create the "impression" of green. The Impressionists found that they could capture the momentary and transient effects of sunlight and changing colour of a scene by painting *en plein air*, in the open air, outside of the studio, where they could more accurately paint the reflected light of an immediate scene.

Interestingly, compared with his early works, which included the Water Lily Pond (1899), Monet's later paintings verge on the abstract, with colours bleeding into each other and a lack of rational shape and perspective. For example, "The Japanese Footbridge" is an explosion of orange, yellow, and red hues, with heavy, broad brush strokes, leaving the viewer barely able to discern the vague shape of the arched bridge. In many of Monet's later works, the colours in his paintings became more muted, far less vibrant and bright, with a pronounced colour shift from blue-green to red-yellow and an almost total absence of light blues. The sense of **atmosphere** and light that he was famous for in his earlier works disappeared.

Although the change in Monet's paintings could easily be explained by an intentional change in style or perhaps an age-related change in manual dexterity, Monet himself realized that it was not his style or dexterity that had changed but, rather, it was his ability to see. Monet suffered from cataracts, the vision-deteriorating disease that was diagnosed in both eyes by a Parisian ophthalmologist in 1912 when Monet was 72. A cataract is a change in the lens of the eye, making it more opaque. The underlying cause is a progressive **denaturation** of one of the **proteins** that make up the lens. The increased opaqueness of the lens absorbs certain wavelengths of light, decreasing the transmittance of blue light. Thus, to a cataract sufferer such as Monet, the world appears more yellow.

1.1 The Physical Nature of Light

Light serves two important functions for life on Earth: First it is a source of energy that sustains all life. Second, light provides organisms with information about the physical world. An excellent example of an organism that uses light for both energy and information is the green alga *Chlamydomonas reinhardtii* **(Figure 1.1)**. *C. reinhardtii* is a single-celled photosynthetic eukaryote that is commonly found in ponds and lakes. Each cell contains a single large **chloroplast** that harvests light energy and uses it to make energy-rich molecules through the process of photosynthesis. In addition, each cell contains a light sensor called an *eyespot* that allows it to sense both light direction and light intensity.

Regardless of whether the light is used as a source of energy or information about the environment, both rely on the same fundamental properties of light and require the light energy to be captured by the organism.

1.1a What Is Light?

The reason there is life on Earth and, as far as we know, nowhere else in our solar system has to do with distance—specifically, the distance of

150 000 000 km separating Earth from the Sun **(Figure 1.2)**. By converting hydrogen into helium at the staggering rate of some 3.4×10^{38} hydrogen nuclei per second, the Sun converts over 4 million tonnes of matter into energy every second. This energy is given off as electromagnetic radiation, which travels at the speed of light (1 079 252 848 km/h) and reaches the Earth in just over 8 minutes. Electromagnetic radiation moves in the form of two waves, one electrical and one magnetic, which are oriented at 90° to each other **(Figure 1.3)**. Scientists often distinguish electromagnetic

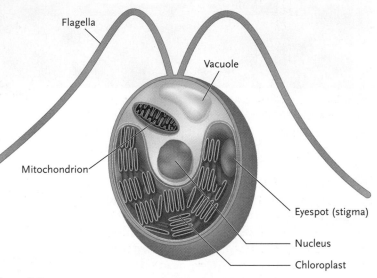

Figure 1.1

Chlamydomonas reinhardtii. A drawing of *Chlamydomonas reinhardtii*, a green alga. Each cell contains a single chloroplast used for photosynthesis as well as an eyespot for sensing light in the environment.

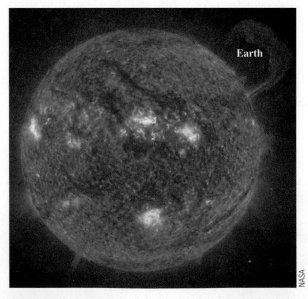

Figure 1.2

The Sun. The sun is a star with a surface temperature of approximately 5000°C. It generates electromagnetic radiation by the nuclear fusion of hydrogen nuclei into helium. Note the superimposed image of the Earth used to illustrate the relative size.

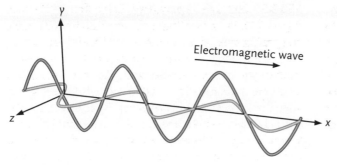

Figure 1.3
Electromagnetic radiation. Electromagnetic radiation can be considered as self-propagating waves which consist of both electrical and magnetic waves which are oriented at 90° to each other. A wave consists of discrete packets of energy called photons.

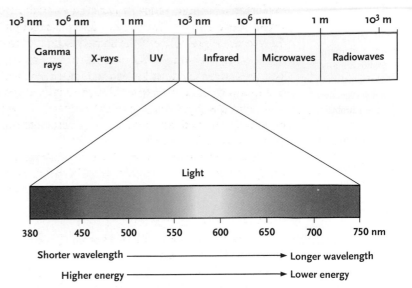

Figure 1.4
The electromagnetic spectrum. Is the grouping of all types of electromagnetic radiation according to wavelength. It ranges from very short wavelengths characteristic of gamma rays to the long wavelengths associated with radio waves. The shorter the wavelength of the electromagnetic radiation the higher the energy of each photon it contains. Light represents only a small portion of the total electromagnetic spectrum.

radiation by its **wavelength**, the distance between two successive peaks. The wavelength of electromagnetic radiation ranges from less than one picometre (10^{-12} m) for cosmic rays to more than a kilometre (10^6 m) for radio waves.

Okay, but what is light? **Light** can be defined as the portion of the **electromagnetic spectrum (Figure 1.4)** that humans can detect with their eyes. Light, or visible radiation, is a narrow band of the electromagnetic spectrum spanning the wavelengths in nanometres (1 nm = 10^{-9} m) from 400 nm (blue light) to about 700 nm (red light). To avoid confusion, wavelengths just outside this range should not be referred to as light but rather as ultraviolet and infrared *radiation*.

One reason that light is a bit of an enigma and hard to characterize is that although it can be described as a wave, it also behaves as a stream of energy particles. These discrete particles or packets of energy are referred to as **photons**. Unlike atoms, photons have no mass, but each contains a precise amount of energy. The amount of energy in a photon is inversely related to its wavelength. Looking just at visible light (see Figure 1.4), this means that blue light, with a shorter wavelength, consists of photons that have higher energy than longer wavelength red light. It is important to realize that although one photon contains a very small amount of energy (red light: 3.01×10^{-19} joules/photon; blue light: 4.56×10^{-19} joules/photon), on a clear summer's day, approximately 10^{21} photons hit each square metre of Earth each second.

1.1b Light Interacts with Matter

Although light has no mass, it is able to interact with and change matter. These changes allow light to be used by living things. When photons of light hit an object, the photons have three possible fates. They can be (1) reflected off the object, (2) transmitted through the object, or (3) absorbed by the object **(Figure 1.5).** For most objects exposed to sunlight, all three of these processes come into play.

Although light can be reflected or transmitted by an object, to be used by an organism the photons of light must be absorbed. A molecule that can absorb photons of light is called a **pigment,** and individual pigments differ in the wavelengths of light they can absorb. For example, some pigments absorb only blue light and others only green light, whereas others absorb light of a number of different wavelengths. There is a large diversity of pigments **(Figure 1.6, p. 4),** including chlorophyll *a*, which is involved in photosynthesis; retinal, which is involved in vision; and indigo, which is used to dye jeans their distinctive blue colour.

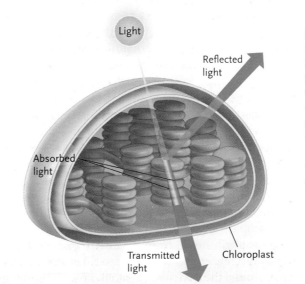

Figure 1.5
Light interacting with matter. When photons of light interact with matter the light energy has three possible fates. It can be reflected by the matter, transmitted through the matter or the energy may be absorbed by the matter.

Figure 1.6
Structure of some common pigments. Chlorophyll *a*, photosynthesis. **11-cis-Retinal,** vision: **Indigo,** dye: **Phycoerythrobillin,** red photosynthetic pigment found in red algae: **Carmine,** scale pigment found in some insects. **Beta carotene,** an orange accessory photosynthetic pigment. A common feature of all these pigments that is critical for light absorption is the presence of a conjugated system (shown in red) of double/single carbon bonds. The conjugated system is the actual portion of the pigment involved in light absorption.

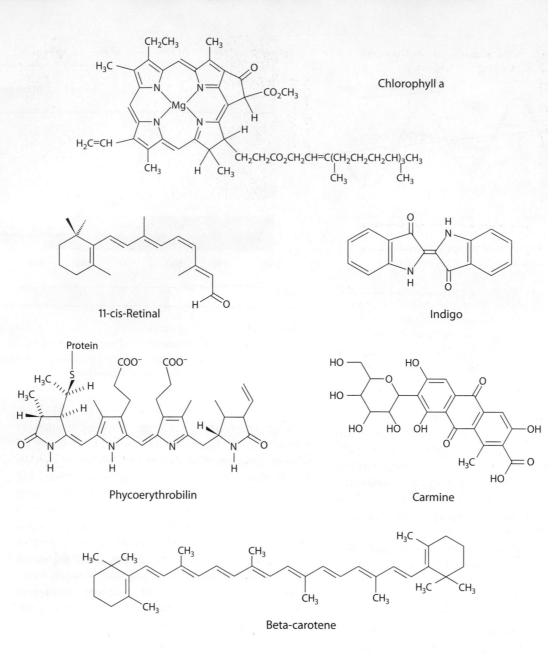

Chlorophyll a

11-cis-Retinal

Indigo

Phycoerythrobilin

Carmine

Beta-carotene

What is it about pigments that enable them to capture light? At first glance, the pigments shown in Figure 1.6 seem to be very different from each other structurally; however, they all share a common feature critical to light absorption: a region where carbon atoms are covalently bonded with alternating single and double bonds. This bonding arrangement is called a *conjugated system* and results in the delocalization of electrons. None of these electrons are closely associated with a particular atom, and because of this, they are more available to interact with a photon of light.

1.1c Why Chlorophyll Is Green

Absorption of light occurs when the energy of a photon is transferred to an electron of the pigment molecule. For example, **Figure 1.7** shows this in a single molecule of **chlorophyll**. Recall from chemistry that electrons occupy discrete energy levels, or excited states, in their orbits around the nucleus of an **atom**. Before absorbing

a photon of light, an electron exists in the ground state, which we can designate as 0. Upon absorption of a photon of light, the energy is transferred to the electron, moving it from the ground state to a higher energy, excited state. For a chlorophyll molecule, the electron involved in photon capture can exist in two, and only two, excited states (see Figure 1.7). The lower excited state, designated as 1, is reached by chlorophyll absorbing a photon of red light. The higher excited state, designated as 2, is reached by the absorption of a photon of blue light. Absorption of blue light excites an electron to a higher energy state than absorption of red light because blue photons contain more energy.

Two important principles must be kept in mind when thinking about light absorption by pigments: first, a single photon results in the excitation of one, and only one, electron in a pigment molecule. Second, the energy of the photon must match the energy *difference* between the ground state and one of the excited states in order for the photon to be absorbed. If the energies do not match,

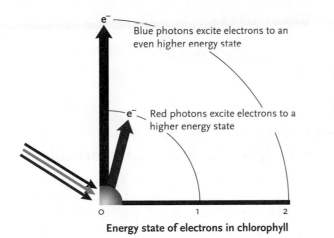

Figure 1.7
Absorption of light by chlorophyll a. Absorption of a photon by a chlorophyll a molecule results in transfer of energy to an electron raising it to a higher energy level. Blue photons raise electrons to a higher energy level because they contain more energy than red photons. Green photons cannot be absorbed since the molecule does not have an energy state which matches the energy contained in a green photon. Because of this, green photons get transmitted through the pigment or reflected by the pigment molecule giving chlorophyll its green colour.

the photon is not absorbed. In the chlorophyll molecule, the energy of a blue photon or a red photon matches perfectly with the energy required for an electron to reach either the first or the second excited state.

So why is chlorophyll green in colour? The colour of a pigment is determined by the wavelengths of light it *cannot* absorb. Chlorophyll is green because although it can trap photons of blue light and red light, it cannot absorb photons of green light. As shown in Figure 1.7, a chlorophyll molecule cannot absorb a photon of green light because it does not have an energy level matching that of a green photon. Whereas red and blue photons are captured, green photons are reflected or transmitted, giving chlorophyll (and plants) its distinctive green colour.

Because pigments do not absorb all wavelengths of light equally, the effectiveness of light in driving processes that use the absorbed light, such as photosynthesis or vision, varies depending on the wavelength of the light. A plot of the effectiveness of different wavelengths of light on a biological process is called an **action spectrum. Figure 1.8** illustrates the action spectrum for photosynthesis in the leaf of a plant.

Figure 1.8 shows that red and blue wavelengths of light are more effective at driving photosynthesis than green wavelengths are. This fits well with what we know about the wavelengths of light that are absorbed by chlorophyll. You may notice in Figure 1.8 that some photosynthesis still occurs under green light. This is because photosynthesis involves a number of accessory pigments that can absorb wavelengths of light between the red and blue wavelengths used by chlorophyll.

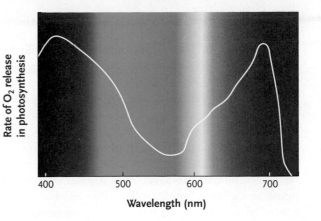

Figure 1.8
Action spectrum shows the relative effectiveness of different wavelengths of light on photosynthesis. The characteristics of the action spectrum reflect the fact that the major photosynthetic pigment, chlorophyll a preferentially absorbs blue and red photons of light.

STUDY BREAK

1. What form does light take?
2. What do the structures of all pigment molecules have in common?

1.2 Light as a Source of Energy

We have already seen that after a photon of light is absorbed, an electron within a pigment molecule is raised to a higher excited state. This excited state electron is a source of potential energy that can be used to do work. As we will see in Chapter 7, this potential energy is used in photosynthetic electron transport to synthesize energy-rich **compounds** NADPH (the reduced form of nicotinamide adenine dinucleotide phosphate) and adenosine triphosphate (ATP), which are used to convert carbon dioxide into carbohydrates **(Figure 1.9)**. In

Figure 1.9
Photosynthesis sustains almost all life. Photosynthesis uses the energy in sunlight to build sugar molecules from carbon dioxide and water, releasing oxygen as a byproduct. The products of photosynthesis not only sustain photosynthetic organisms but through the process of cellular respiration are used by the vast majority of organisms on Earth as a usable form of energy

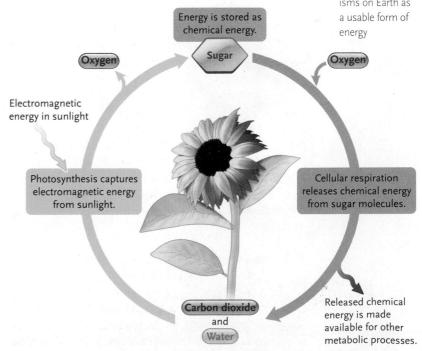

addition, some of the chemical energy is used to synthesize other biological molecules, such as lipids, proteins, and nucleic acids, from simple building blocks found in the environment. Although the energy of a single photon is very small, the photosynthetic apparatus within the chloroplast of a single *C. reinhardtii* cell, for example, absorbs millions of photons each second.

Organisms use light as a source of energy in other processes, but to avoid confusion, these are generally not referred to as photosynthesis. A good example is found in a group of **prokaryotes** called *Halobacterium*, which live in some of the most extreme environments on Earth **(Figure 1.10)**. *Halobacterium* contains a protein complex called bacteriorhodopsin, which functions as a light-dependent **proton pump**.

STUDY BREAK

How do pigment molecules trap the energy of light?

1.3 Light as a Source of Information

As the deterioration of Monet's eyesight illustrates, organisms also use light to sense their environment—as a source of information. The experience of trying to perform even the simplest of tasks in a dark room makes one quickly realize how important the ability to sense light has become for many forms of life.

a. *Halobacterium salinarium*

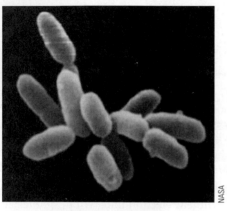

NASA

b. Hutt Lagoon, Western Australia

L. Lodwick

c. A model of bacteriorhodopsin

d. Bacteriorhodopsin-driven ATP formation

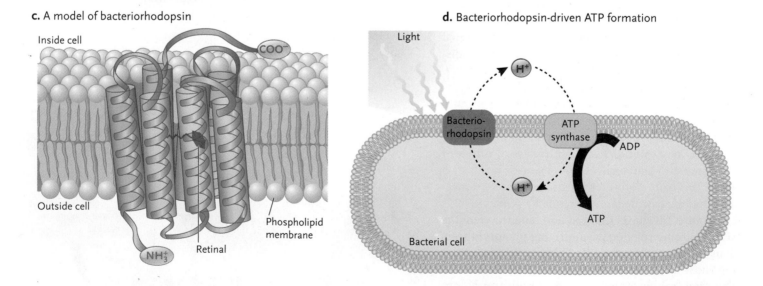

Figure 1.10
Halobacteria are a group of prokaryotes that contain bacteriorhodopsin. **(a)** Electron micrograph of a colony of cells. **(b)** Halobacteria are extremophiles and are found in hypersaline environments like Hutt Lagoon in Australia. The pink colour is due to the presence of bacteriorhodopsin. **(c)** model of bacteriorhodopsin which is composed of the protein, bacteriorhodopsin, and the bound pigment, retinal. **(d)** Bacteriorhodopsin functions as a light-driven proton pump, the proton gradient being used to synthesis ATP.

The change in Monet's eyesight also demonstrates that not every person, and certainly not every species, sees the world in the same way.

1.3a Rhodopsin, a Highly Conserved Photoreceptor

The basic light-sensing system, found almost universally in all organisms, is the photoreceptor. By far the most common photoreceptor in nature is rhodopsin **(Figure 1.11),** which is not only the basis of vision in animals but also the photoreceptor used by many other organisms, including *C. reinhardtii*, where it serves as the light-sensing unit of the eyespot. Each rhodopsin molecule consists of a protein called **opsin** that binds a single pigment molecule called retinal. Opsins are membrane proteins that span a membrane multiple times and form a complex with the retinal molecule at the centre (see Figure 1.11). As the name implies, rhodopsin is very similar to the bacteriorhodopsin found in *Halobacterium* and other prokaryotes. As shown in Figure 1.11, absorption of a photon of light causes the retinal pigment molecule to change shape. This change triggers alterations to the **opsin** protein, which, in turn, triggers downstream events, including alterations in intracellular ion concentrations and electrical signals. As we will see in Chapter 34, in the case of vision, these electrical signals are sent to the visual centres of the **brain**. In humans, capturing of light by the eye involves about 125 million photoreceptor cells (rods and cones) that line the **retina**. Each photoreceptor cell contains thousands of individual rhodopsin molecules.

Rhodopsin is the most common photoreceptor found in nature, but it is not the only one. Both plants and animals have a range of other photoreceptors that absorb light of particular wavelengths. It remains a mystery why rhodopsin became the most common photoreceptor. Perhaps its widespread occurrence is the result of it developing very early in the evolution of life. Interestingly, whereas vision and smell (olfaction; see Chapter 34) are different senses, proteins very similar to opsins are used in olfaction, suggesting that specific aspects of opsin proteins are particularly useful for sensory perception.

1.3b Sensing Light Without Eyes

When we think about sensing light, we automatically think about our ability to see with our eyes. However, many organisms can sense the light in their surroundings even though they lack eyes. This includes plants, algae, invertebrates, and even some prokaryotes. As an example, let's take a closer look at the eyespot of *C. reinhardtii*. The eyespot, a structure approximately 1 μm in diameter, is located within the chloroplast of a C. reinhardtii cell, in a region closely associated with the cell membrane **(Figure 1.12).** Although it is

in the chloroplast, the eyespot does not play a role in photosynthesis, instead the photoreceptors of the eyespot allow the cell to sense light direction and intensity. Using a pair of flagella, *C. reinhardtii* cells can respond to light by swimming toward or away

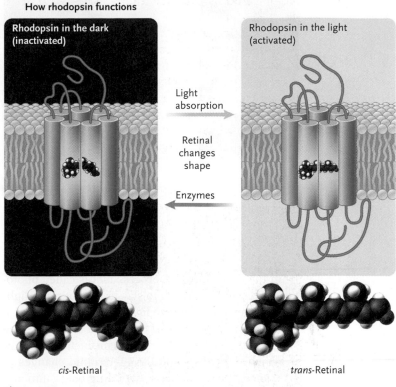

How rhodopsin functions

Rhodopsin in the dark (inactivated)

Rhodopsin in the light (activated)

Light absorption

Retinal changes shape

Enzymes

cis-Retinal

trans-Retinal

Figure 1.11
Model of the photoreceptor rhodopsin. Rhodopsin consists of a protein (opsin) which binds a pigment molecule (retinal). Upon absorption of a photon of light retinal changes shape which triggers changes to the opsin molecule. These changes trigger signalling events which allow the organism to respond to the light.

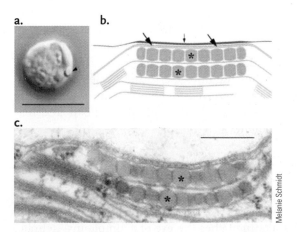

a.

b.

c.

Melanie Schmidt

Figure 1.12
An eyespot. Schematic representation of the eyespot found in *Chlamydomonas*. The cell **(a)** is about 10 μM in diameter, **(b)** Drawing of the eyespot apparatus with the asterisks indicating the orange pigment-rich globule layers which are found inside the chloroplast outermembrane (indicated by large arrow). The plasma membrane is indicated by the small arrow. **(c)** Transmission electron micrograph of same area drawn in B.

photomorphogenesis

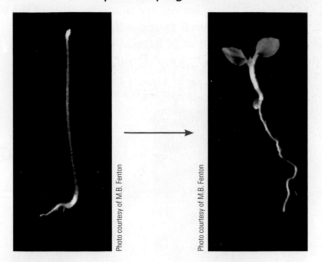

Photo courtesy of M.B. Fenton

Photo courtesy of M.B. Fenton

Figure 1.13

Photomorphogenesis. Shifting seedlings from darkness to light triggers a developmental program called photomorphogenesis. Light sensed by the photoreceptor phytochrome initiates the program which involves the activation of hundreds of genes.

from the light source, a process that is called phototaxis. This allows the cell to stay in the optimum light environment to maximize light capture for photosynthesis. Light absorption by the eyespot is linked to the swimming response by a signal transduction pathway, in which light absorption triggers rapid changes in the concentrations of ions, including potassium and calcium, which generate a cascade of electrical events. These, in turn, change the beating pattern of the flagella used for locomotion.

In plants, a different photoreceptor, called phytochrome, senses the light environment and is critical for photomorphogenesis, the normal developmental process activated when seedlings are exposed to light **(Figure 1.13).** Phytochrome is present in the cytosol of all plant cells, and when the plant is exposed to wavelengths of red light, phytochrome becomes active and initiates a signal transduction pathway that reaches the nucleus. In the nucleus, these signals activate hundreds of genes, many of which code for proteins involved in photosynthesis and leaf development.

1.3c The Eye

The **eye** can be defined as the organ animals use to sense light. It is described in detail in Chapter 34. What distinguishes the eye of a simple invertebrate, for example, from the eyespot of *C. reinhardtii* is vision. The process of vision not only requires an eye but it also requires a brain or at least a simple nervous system that interprets signals sent from the eye. The eye and brain are thought to have co-evolved because detailed visual processing occurs in the brain rather than in the

eye. Essentially, we "see" not with our eyes but, rather, with our brain.

The simplest eye is the ocellus (plural, ocelli), which consists of up to 100 photoreceptor cells lining a cup or pit. In planarians, for example, photoreceptor cells in a cuplike depression below the epidermis are connected by bundles of nerves to the cerebral ganglion **(Figure 1.14).** Each ocellus is covered on one side by a layer of pigment cells that blocks most of the light rays arriving from the opposite side of the animal. As a result, most of the light received by the pigment cells enters the ocellus from the side it faces. Through integration of information transmitted to the cerebral ganglion from the eyecups, planarians orient themselves so that the amount of light falling on the two ocelli is equal and diminishes as they swim. This reaction carries them directly away from the source of the light and toward darker areas, where the risk of predation is smaller. Ocelli occur in a variety of animals, including a number of insects, arthropods, and molluscs.

In many ways, the eye of a planaria is not much more advanced than the eyespot of *C. reinhardtii*. In both cases, the eye is used to sense light intensity and direction to a light source but little else. The greatest advance in vision came with more sophisticated eyes that produced an actual image of the lighted environment for discerning objects and shapes. These "image-forming eyes" are found in two distinctly different types: compound eyes and **single-lens eyes**.

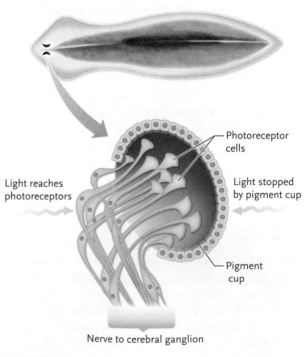

Photoreceptor cells

Light reaches photoreceptors

Light stopped by pigment cup

Pigment cup

Nerve to cerebral ganglion

Figure 1.14

The ocellus of *Planaria*, a flatworm, and the arrangement of photoreceptors cells on which its orientation response is based.

Compound eyes are common in arthropods such as insects and crustaceans, and each contains hundreds to thousands of ommatidia (*omma* = eye), units fitted closely together **(Figure 1.15)**. Each ommatidium samples only a small part of the visual field as light entering an ommatidium is focused onto a bundle of photoreceptor cells. From these signals, the brain receives a mosaic image of the world. Because even the slightest motion is detected simultaneously by many ommatidia, compound eyes are extraordinarily adept at detecting movement, a lesson soon learned by fly-swatting humans.

Some invertebrates and most vertebrates have eyes with single lenses, "camera eyes" **(Figure 1.16)**. Light enters this eye through the transparent cornea, a lens concentrates the light, and a layer of photoreceptors at the back of the eye, the retina, records the image. We will learn more about the structural and functional aspects of eyes in Chapter 34.

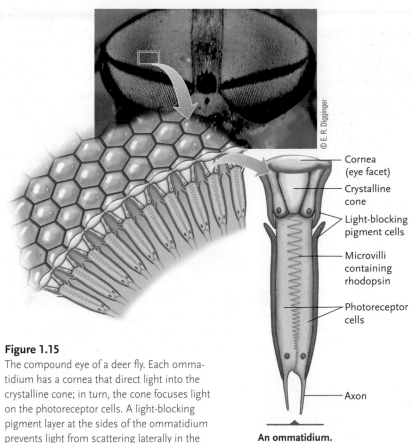

Cornea (eye facet)
Crystalline cone
Light-blocking pigment cells
Microvilli containing rhodopsin
Photoreceptor cells
Axon

An ommatidium.
The unit of a compound eye

Figure 1.15
The compound eye of a deer fly. Each ommatidium has a cornea that direct light into the crystalline cone; in turn, the cone focuses light on the photoreceptor cells. A light-blocking pigment layer at the sides of the ommatidium prevents light from scattering laterally in the compound eye.

1.3d Darwin and the Evolution of the Eye

When Charles Darwin presented his theory of evolution by natural selection in *On the Origin of Species by Means of Natural Selection* (1859), he recognized that "organs of extreme perfection," such as the eye, would present a problem:

> To suppose that the eye, with all its inimitable contrivances for adjusting the focus to different distances, for admitting different amounts of light, and for the correction of spherical and chromatic aberration, could have been formed by natural selection, seems, I freely confess, absurd in the highest possible degree. Yet reason tells me, that if numerous gradations from a perfect and complex eye to one very imperfect and simple, each grade being useful to its possessor, can be shown to exist; if further, the eye does vary ever so slightly, and the variations be inherited, which is certainly the case; and if any variation or modification in the organ be ever useful to an animal under changing conditions of life, then the difficulty of believing that a perfect and complex eye could be formed by natural selection, though

insuperable by our imagination, can hardly be considered real.

Darwin found a way out of this dilemma by proposing that the eye as it exists in humans and other animals did not appear suddenly but evolved by variation (mutation) and natural selection over time from a simple, primitive eye.

How long would it take for an eye to evolve? Starting with a patch of light-sensitive cells on the skin, a recent study predicted that about 2000 small improvements over time would gradually yield a camera-type eye in less

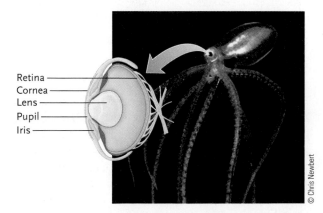

Retina
Cornea
Lens
Pupil
Iris

Figure 1.16
The eye of an octopus a cephalopod mollusc

than half a million years **(Figure 1.17)**. Considering that animals with primitive eyes appeared in the fossil record about 500 million years ago, the camera-type eye found in humans could have evolved more than 1000 times. Eye evolution is explained by the huge advantage an improved eye would give to an organism. For example, the development of heightened visual ability in a predator would force comparable eye improvements in both prey and potential other predators. Rapid eye development would therefore be critical to survival (see Chapter 34). This being said, an optically refined eye is no good unless the brain of the organism improves at the same time, allowing for more advanced neural processing of the information being sent by the optic nerve.

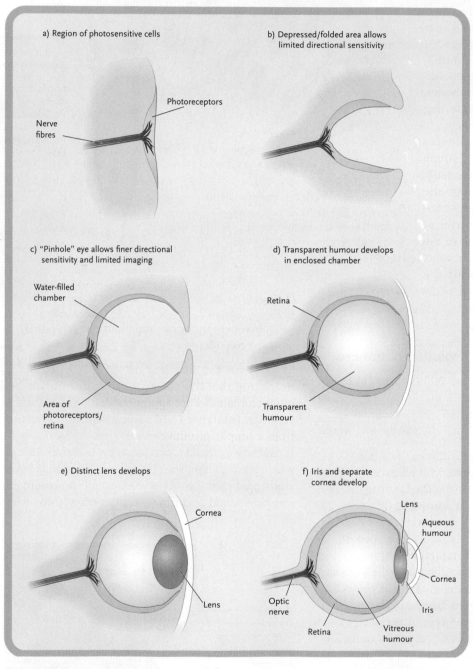

a) Region of photosensitive cells

Photoreceptors

Nerve fibres

b) Depressed/folded area allows limited directional sensitivity

c) "Pinhole" eye allows finer directional sensitivity and limited imaging

Water-filled chamber

Area of photoreceptors/ retina

d) Transparent humour develops in enclosed chamber

Retina

Transparent humour

e) Distinct lens develops

Cornea

Lens

f) Iris and separate cornea develop

Lens

Aqueous humour

Cornea

Iris

Optic nerve

Retina

Vitreous humour

Figure 1.17

The evolution of the eye. Starting with a layer of light-sensitive cells, recent research suggests that a camera eye could evolve in less than 500 million years. The evolution of a more sophisticated eye can be explained by the huge advantage improved eye sight would give an organism.

STUDY BREAK

1. What is a photoreceptor?
2. Why, historically, has the eye posed a problem for evolutionary biologists?

1.4 Light Can Damage Biological Molecules

Light is a very small portion of the total electromagnetic spectrum (look back at Figure 1.4), yet this small portion of the spectrum is essential to life on Earth. These wavelengths, from about 400 to 700 nm, are the only wavelengths used for photosynthesis, vision, phototaxis, navigation, and many other light-driven processes.

Is it just a coincidence that all of these processes depend on such a narrow band of the electromagnetic spectrum? According to the Harvard physiologist and Nobel laureate George Wald (1906–1997), it is not a coincidence at all. Wald reasoned that light is used by organisms because it is the most dominant form of electromagnetic radiation reaching Earth's surface **(Figure 1.18)**. Shorter wavelengths of electromagnetic radiation are absorbed by the ozone layer high in the atmosphere, whereas wavelengths longer than those in the visible spectrum are absorbed by water vapour and carbon dioxide in the atmosphere.

Another reason life uses light and not other wavelengths of electromagnetic radiation has to do with the energy it contains. Remember that living things are made up of molecules held together by chemical bonds. Radiation of shorter wavelengths than light contains enough energy to destroy these bonds. Absorption of high energy photons wouldn't just excite electrons within a pigment but actually oxidize the molecule producing ions. Because of this, shorter wavelengths of electromagnetic radiation are often refered to as ionizing radiation.

Alternatively, wavelengths longer than those comprising light would not supply enough energy to excite the electrons necessary for photochemistry. Furthermore, longer wavelengths are readily absorbed by water, which is the bulk of all living things. Even if life evolved on some other planet, Wald suggests, it would still use the same narrow range of electromagnetic wavelengths it uses on Earth.

1.4a Damage by Light: Direct Effects

Although not as energetic as some forms of electromagnetic radiation, light is still a form of energy, with the potential to damage biological molecules, both directly and indirectly. However, regardless of how the damage is caused, all organisms that are exposed to

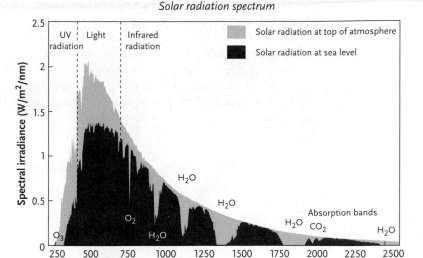

Solar radiation spectrum

Figure 1.18

Electromagnetic radiation reaching the Earth's surface. Compared to the electromagnetic radiation that reaches the outer atmosphere, the radiation reaching the earths surface is reduced in both short wavelengths and long wavelengths of the electromagnetic spectrum.

sunlight have developed mechanisms either to help prevent light-induced damage or to repair it quickly if damage occurs.

A good example of the direct damaging effects of light on a biological process is found with photosynthesis. As we will see in Chapter 7, the photosynthetic apparatus is composed of photosystems **(Figure 1.19)**, pigment–protein complexes that trap the energy of light and convert it to chemical energy. Normal chloroplasts contain hundreds of photosystems, each trapping the energy of approximately

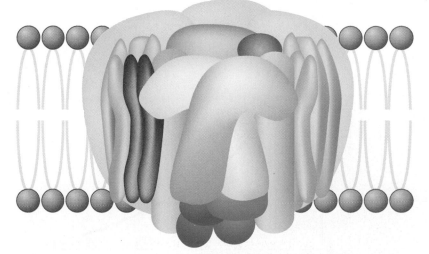

Figure 1.19

Photosystem II is constants being damaged by light. A single Photosystem II complex involved in the light reactions of photosynthesis can absorb approximately 10,000 photons of light each second. The energetic nature of this results in photosystem II complex constantly being inactivated by light-induced damage to specific proteins. Overall, high rates of photosynthesis are maintained by the presence of a very efficient repair system for damaged photosystems.

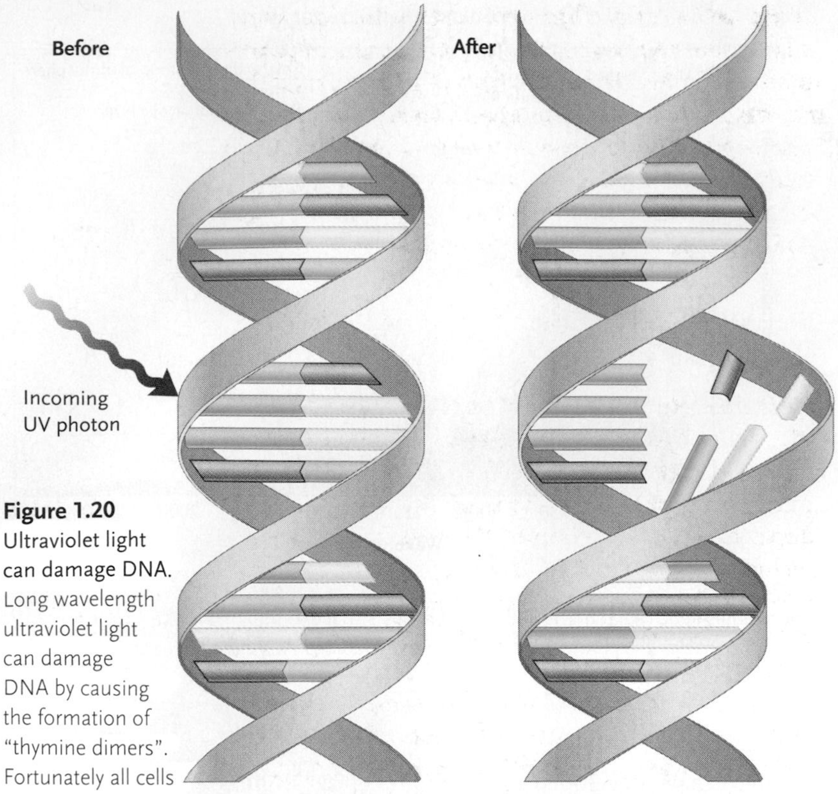

Before   **After**

Incoming
UV photon

Figure 1.20
Ultraviolet light
can damage DNA.
Long wavelength
ultraviolet light
can damage
DNA by causing
the formation of
"thymine dimers".
Fortunately all cells
have an efficient
mechanism to
repair damage to
DNA.

10 000 photons of light each second. Although a photosystem is very efficient at converting light energy into chemical energy, the high-energy environment within its core often results in damage to its protein components. Although damage to photosystems is unavoidable, rapid repair of damaged photosystems developed early during the evolution of life so that the rate of photosynthesis can be maintained even under high light conditions.

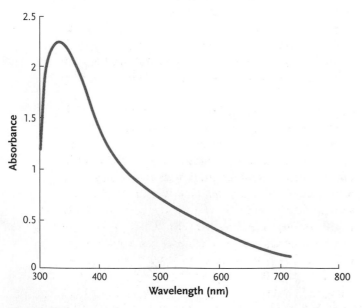

Figure 1.21
Absorption spectrum of melanin. The skin pigment melanin strongly absorbs photons of electromagnetic radiation which are in the ultraviolet region of the spectrum.

Besides an active repair system, all photosynthetic organisms have **carotenoids**, accessory pigments that can protect the photosynthetic apparatus from high light levels by absorbing excess light and safely dissipating the energy as heat. Although carotenoids are not nearly as abundant as chlorophyll, they are absolutely required to protect the photosynthetic apparatus. Plants unable to synthesize carotenoids turn white when exposed to sunlight because their chlorophyll becomes oxidized and its light-harvesting capabilities destroyed.

1.4b Damage by Light: Indirect Effects

Light from the sun is potentially harmful to life indirectly because of the ultraviolet radiation that accompanies it. This is the electromagnetic radiation between blue light and x-rays, consisting of wavelengths between 200 and 400 nm. Life on Earth is protected from the most damaging form of ultraviolet light, UV-C, by the atmosphere's ozone layer. However, longer wavelengths of harmful ultraviolet radiation, including UV-B and UV-A, do reach Earth's surface.

Because of its high energy, ultraviolet radiation can randomly ionize the atoms in a range of molecules, including pigment molecules and proteins. However, the structural integrity of deoxyribonucleic acid (DNA) is particularly vulnerable to damage **(Figure 1.20)**. The interaction of ultraviolet light with nucleotide bases that make up DNA can result in the formation of a "dimer" when two neighbouring bases become covalently linked. Dimers can change the shape of the double-helix structure of DNA and prevent its replication, as well as hinder gene expression (see Chapter 12). Although cells have evolved elaborate mechanisms to repair this damage, dimer formation can give rise to genetic mutations, some of them harmful.

For most organisms, exposure to sunlight and therefore the damaging effects of ultraviolet radiation is unavoidable. Therefore, organisms use a range of behavioural, physiological, and biochemical mechanisms to protect themselves. Animals may avoid intense sunlight and/or shield their skin with fur or feathers. However, organisms with naked skin, such as humans, rely on producing melanin as an important protective mechanism.

Melanin is a pigment that absorbs ultraviolet radiation. This is shown by an absorption spectrum of pure melanin in solution **(Figure 1.21)**. An **absorption spectrum** is a plot of the amount of light a pigment absorbs in relation to the wavelength of light. (We discuss absorption spectra related to photosynthesis in Chapter 7.) Figure 1.21 shows that melanin preferentially absorbs photons of electromagnetic radiation in the ultraviolet region of the spectrum. Humans synthesize melanin in specialized skin cells called

Figure 1.22
Human populations vary in regards to the amount of melanin.

melanocytes. In general, people from countries receiving a lot of sunlight (equatorial regions), such as Uganda, have more melanin in their skin than people from regions receiving less direct sunlight, such as Sweden **(Figure 1.22)**. The presence of melanin prevents the DNA damage in skin cells that is linked to the development of skin cancer. Melanin prevents ultraviolet radiation from penetrating the skin and destroying the essential B vitamin folate.

Since melanin protects us from ultraviolet light, *why don't all humans have high melanin levels?* Although melanin filters out damaging ultraviolet wavelengths, humans require some ultraviolet radiation to synthesize vitamin D, which is critical for normal bone development. People with high melanin levels who live in regions that do not receive abundant sunlight are susceptible to vitamin D deficiency, such as someone of African descent living in Sweden. In much of the developed world, inadequate vitamin D intake is rare because many foods, such as milk, yogurt, and grain products (cereals and bread), are fortified with vitamin D. Interestingly, Inuit who are native to the Arctic have retained their relatively dark skin even though they inhabit a sun-poor environment. This can be explained by the fact that their traditional diet is dominated by fish and other marine life that is naturally high in vitamin D.

STUDY BREAK

1. What biological molecule is particularly susceptible to damage by ultraviolet radiation?
2. What wavelengths of electromagnetic radiation does melanin absorb?

1.5 Role of Light in Ecology and Behaviour

Nature provides a great range of light environments, ranging from the total darkness of caves or the ocean depths to the stark brightness of deserts and snowscapes. Differences in the intensity and spectral composition of the light coincide with organisms' adaptations to the specific light environment of particular habitats. For photosynthetic organisms, this means adjustments in light-harvesting properties of photosynthetic pigments. For many animals, it leads to unique colorations that may serve to attract members of the same species while making them potentially less visible to potential predators.

1.5a Using Light to Tell Time: Circadian Rhythms

Because Earth rotates on its axis once every 24 hours, life has evolved under a constant rhythmic cycle of light and dark. Many physiological and behavioural phenomena possess 24-hour rhythmicity: they vary depending on the time of day. Such phenomena include sleep-wake cycles, body temperature, locomotion, metabolic processes, cell division, and the behaviours associated with foraging for food and mating (see Chapters 40 and 41).

Many physiological and behavioural responses geared to Earth's day-night cycle are called **circadian rhythms** (*circa* = "around"; *diem* = "day") because they oscillate with a period of approximately 24 hours **(Figure 1.23, p. 14)**. A defining characteristic of circadian rhythms is that they are NOT direct responses to changes in the external light environment but instead are controlled by an internal (endogenous), organism-based clock. This "biological clock" is set by the external light environment, but it can run a long time without any input from outside the organism. That circadian rhythms can be "free running" without daily input from the sun was first discovered in 1729 by the French astronomer Jean-Jacques d'Ortous de Mairan. He found that the daily rhythmic movements of certain plant leaves continued when he placed the plants in complete darkness. In humans, daily fluctuations in hormone levels, for example, are controlled by a circadian clock and will occur even if a subject is placed in conditions of constant light or darkness.

The importance of being able to predict the daily fluctuations of light is shown by the fact that circadian rhythms are found in all forms of life, from single-celled bacteria to plants and animals. Being able to keep track of day and night allows organisms to anticipate when a process occurs most efficiently during the 24-hour day and prepare accordingly. For example, in photosynthetic organisms, many proteins needed for photosynthesis are synthesized before dawn. This allows photosynthesis to occur at maximum efficiency during the daylight. It is thought that circadian rhythms originated to protect replicating DNA from damaging ultraviolet radiation during the day. As a result, the process of DNA replication is under circadian control and in many organisms occurs only at night.

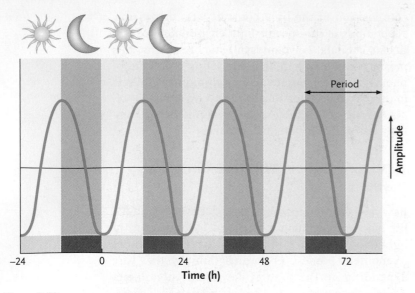

Figure 1.23
Circadian rhythms are oscillations in behaviour and physiology which have a period of approximately 24 hours. These rhythms are controlled by an endogenous biological clock.

In most animals, the central biological clock controlling many circadian rhythms is found within the suprachiasmatic nucleus, a region of the brain within the hypothalamus **(Figure 1.24).** The suprachiasmatic nucleus receives light inputs directly from the eye via the optic nerve, which it uses to set the biological clock. This clock, in turn, regulates a wide range of bodily functions, including the secretion of melatonin, a hormone, from the pineal gland. Melatonin is thought to have a role in controlling our sleep-wake cycles as its synthesis is active at nighttime but inhibited during the day (see Chapters 40 and 41).

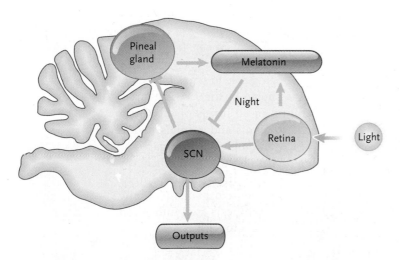

Figure 1.24
In humans circadian rhythms are controlled by a central biological clock which is found in the superchiasmatic nucleus of the brain. Changes in physiology and/or behaviour are linked to the central clock through changes in the levels of the hormone melatonin.

Several conditions can interfere with normal circadian cycling. Probably the best example is jet lag, which occurs when you travel rapidly across many time zones, putting your circadian clock out of synchronization with the external light environment. For example, if you take a five hour flight from Halifax to Vancouver starting at 6 P.M. when you arrive in Vancouver the local time is 7 P.M. The feeling of jet lag occurs because while it is only 7 P.M. your biological clock is telling you to go to bed because it thinks it is 11 P.M. Symptoms related to jet lag include lack of appetite, fatigue, insomnia, and mild depression. The physiological consequences of jet lag clearly indicate the number of processes that are linked to circadian time keeping. They also show that the circadian clock cannot be automatically reset to the new light conditions but may take a few days to become readjusted or entrained.

Many plants and animals show cycles of seasonal activities as well as daily cycles. In plants, this includes the timing of flowering and dormancy. In animals, this includes migration or hibernation (see Chapter 40). In some parts of the world, changes in day length (photoperiod) herald changes in seasons. Plants and animals in these regions mainly depend on the photoperiod to prepare for changes in their seasonal activities. What better way to measure the relative length of day and night than by enlisting the machinery by which circadian rhythms are entrained?

1.5b Avoiding Detection: Camouflage

Camouflage works when one animal fails to distinguish another from the background. Pattern and behaviour play central roles in camouflage. The female duck sitting on her nest is hard to distinguish from the background because of the pattern of colour in her feathers and because she does not move **(Figure 1.25).**

The importance of background in camouflage is demonstrated by the case of the peppered moth, *Biston betularia.* Prior to the Industrial Revolution in England, light-coloured peppered moths were considered "typical" and dark-coloured individuals were exceptions prized by moth collectors. Light colour made the moths inconspicuous when resting on lichen-covered tree trunks during the day **(Figure 1.26a).** The situation changed after the Industrial Revolution, when many tree trunks became dark-coloured from deposits of soot and because air pollution killed the lichens. In this setting, light-coloured moths were easily detected by hunting birds and dark-coloured individuals quickly became the most common form **(Figure 1.26b).** Today, as a result of clean air legislation and reduced air pollution, the ratio

a.

c.

b.

Figure 1.25
From a distance, **(a)** it is easy to overlook the duck (*Anas* spp.) sitting on her nest in an urban graveyard. Up close **(b)**, the pattern on her feathers breaks up her body outline, making her difficult to see, particularly when she does not move. As usual, looking for eyes can be a good way to see animals you otherwise might have overlooked, such as the Scops Owl **(c)** (*Otus scops*).

a.

b.

Figure 1.26
An example of camouflage in the peppered moth, *Biston betularia*. The moth is found in one of two forms: lightly-coloured or darkly-coloured. During the industrial revolution pollution darkened the bark of trees **(a)** that were part of the moth's habitat. This resulted in increased predation of the light-coloured moth. Following anti-pollution measures, trees returned to being lightly coloured **(b)** which resulted in an increase in the numbers of the moths that are similarly coloured.

of light- to dark-coloured moths has returned to the pre–Industrial Revolution norm in some areas. The case of the peppered moth is clear and has become an often-cited example of evolution by natural selection (see Chapters 3 and 18).

1.5c Using Colour as Signals

Animals often use bright colours to signal that they are distasteful and/or armed and dangerous. As animals that make extensive use of vision, we humans are familiar with colourful warning signals **(Figure 1.27, p. 16)**. To be effective, a signal must be received, so if the signal receiver is blind to colour **(Figure 1.28, p. 16)**, the signal is of no use. But animals use other media, and most North Americans are familiar with the odour of a skunk or the buzz of a bee, not to mention the rattle of a rattlesnake. Monarch butterflies (*Danaus plexippus*) use a distinct red and black pattern to warn of their bad taste **(Figure 1.29, p. 16)** (see Chapter 47). Bees and wasps, with their black and yellow stripes as warning signals, are other examples of dangerous animals. Some animals mimic the warning signals of others (see Figures 47.6 and 47.10 and Chapter 47).

Figure 1.27
The red signal on a traffic light sends an unmistakable signal **(a)** that is completely lost on a species or individual that is blind to colour **(b)**.

M.B. Fenton

a.

M.B. Fenton

b.

Figure 1.28
Comparing a colour **(a)** and grey scale **(b)** view of a chart designed to assess colour vision in humans is one way to demonstrate the impact of colour blindness.

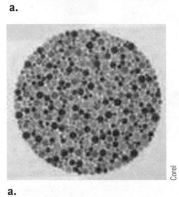

Corel

a.

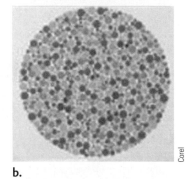

Corel

b.

M.B. Fenton

a.

M.B. Fenton

b.

M.B. Fenton

c.

M.B. Fenton

d.

M.B. Fenton

e.

M.B. Fenton

f.

Figure 1.29
The colourful warning signal of a bee **(a)** or a monarch butterfly **(b)** loses its impact when viewed in greyscale (**c** and **d**). The situation is further complicated by their predators. Whereas a Bluejay **(e)** has excellent colour vision, a hedgehog **(f)** does not.

Although humans marvel at the diversity of colours and patterns of flowers, biologists correctly conclude that such displays were not designed to please humans but rather to attract animal pollinators (see Chapter 30). Pollination involves the movement of pollen from the **anthers** (male parts) of one flower to the stigma (female parts) of the same or other flowers to effect fertilization and production of seeds (see Chapters 30 and 47). Pollinators obtain sugar-rich nectars and protein-rich pollen at flowers.

Plants that use animals as pollinators must attract the correct candidates to ensure that they are pollinated and do not waste pollen and nectar. The characteristics of flowers (shape, colour, smell) make them more attractive to specific groups of potential pollinators, reflecting differences in pollinator behaviour. Potential pollinators differ in their perception of light of different wavelengths, so they are attracted by flowers of specific colours. Birds such as hummingbirds are attracted to red flowers, whereas bees are attracted primarily to blue and yellow flowers (see Figure 18.18). Bees are important pollinators that also perceive ultraviolet light and are attracted to flowers with ultraviolet-reflecting pigments **(Figure 1.30)**.

a.

b.

Figure 1.30
Flower colour is geared to the visual acuity of specific pollinators, suggesting that the two co-evolved. While Hummingbirds are attracted to red-coloured flowers **(a)**, Bees which can perceive ultraviolet wavelengths of light are attracted to flowers with ultraviolet-reflecting pigments **(b)**.

1.5d Light in Aquatic Habitats

Water attenuates light rapidly, and almost no light penetrates below about 150 metres. Furthermore, water selectively scatters and absorbs longer wavelengths of light more effectively than shorter wavelengths, so below about 30 metres, light is essentially monochromatic, consisting solely of blue wavelengths. Red algae **(Figure 1.31)** thrive at a greater depth in the oceans than many other photosynthetic organisms because they have phytoerythrin, an accessory photosynthetic pigment not found in land plants. Phytoerythrin preferentially absorbs blue wavelengths of light, giving red algae their distinctive colour.

Fish living in shallow marine waters tend to be brilliantly coloured, whereas species that live deeper tend to have black backs and silver underbodies, making them less conspicuous when viewed from both above and below.

1.5e Ecological Light Pollution

The electric light bulb is considered one of the greatest inventions because it allowed people to carry on pursuits at night that otherwise would not have been possible. However, rapid proliferation of artificial lighting that illuminates public buildings, streets, and signs has resulted in "light pollution," which has transformed the nighttime environment over significant portions of Earth's surface. In the United States, only about 40% of people live where it truly gets dark at night **(Figure 1.32, p. 18)**.

Ecologists have begun to study the sometimes devastating consequences of light pollution on natural populations. The presence of artificial light disrupts orientation in nocturnal animals otherwise accustomed to operating in the dark. For example, newly hatched sea turtles emerge from nests on sandy beaches and orient themselves and move toward the ocean because it is

Figure 1.31
Why are red algae....red? Red algae preferentially absorb shorter wavelength blue light-red photons are reflected. Blue light is the dominant wavelengths of light that reach deep in the water column where red algae are found.

Figure 1.32
An example of light pollution.

Thomas Hawk

Figure 1.33
The blind mole rat (*Spalax* sp.) is subterranean rarely venturing above ground. They are functionally blind.

Reprinted by permission from Macmillan Publishers Ltd: Nature, vol. 427, Issue 6973, copyright 2004.

brighter than the silhouette of dark dunes. However, with increased beachfront lighting, hatchlings become disoriented, head inland, and die. The nocturnal lives of many species of frogs and salamanders have been disrupted by light pollution. We know that artificial lighting has a negative effect on migrating birds. Hundreds of thousands of migrating birds are killed each year when they collide with lighted buildings and towers.

Other animals, such as bats and geckos, benefit from night lights that attract insects, effectively concentrating their prey.

STUDY BREAK

1. What is a circadian rhythm?
2. How does water affect the properties of light?

1.6 Life in the Dark

Humans see very well by day, but our visual powers quickly falter at night, when light levels may be 100 million times dimmer than daylight. With decreasing light levels, we first lose our ability to see colour, followed by our ability to distinguish shapes. Animals that are nocturnal, such as moths, fish, bats, and frogs, see very well under dim light.

In some environments, such as caves and ocean deeps, animals live in complete darkness. Many of these animals cannot see even though their ancestors had functional eyes. The blind mole rat spends all of its life in underground darkness, only rarely venturing above ground (Figure 1.33). Twenty-five million years of adaptation to life in the dark has resulted in the natural degeneration of the blind mole rat's visual system to the point at which the mole rat is effectively blind. Their eyes are not only small (less than 1 mm in diameter) but also are covered by several layers of tissue. Behavioural and physiological studies have shown that the photoreceptors of the eye remain functional even though the image-forming part of the brain is dramatically reduced. *So what purpose do these functional photoreceptors have?* Since individual mole rats are exposed to brief periods of natural light, the photoreceptors allow entrainment or setting of their biological clocks and control of their circadian rhythms. Although the image-producing portion of the brain in these mole rats is greatly reduced, the suprachiasmatic nucleus is well developed and receives information from the eyes.

Another good example of the degeneration of the eye over time is found in the Mexican cavefish, which occurs as two morphological types: a surface-water form that has eyes and skin pigment (Figure 1.34a) and a cave-dwelling form that lacks eyes and pigment (Figure 1.34b). The ancestors of the cavefish lived on the surface, and both eyes and pigment have been lost over approximately 10 000 years.

STUDY BREAK

Do the eyes of the blind mole rat have a function?

1.7 Organisms Making Their Own Light: Bioluminescence

Many organisms, including certain bacteria, algae, fungi, insects, squid, and fish, are **bioluminescent**: they produce light (Figure 1.35). Bioluminescence has developed many times during evolution but always involves the same basic biochemical reaction. Recall that in the process of light absorption by a pigment, the energy of a photon is transferred to an electron, raising it from the ground state to an excited state. Bioluminescence is essentially the same process in reverse. Chemical energy in the form of ATP excites an electron in a substrate molecule to a higher excited state, and when the electron returns to the ground state, the energy is released as a photon of light. Bioluminescence

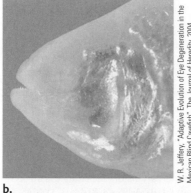

a.

b.

Figure 1.34
If you don't use it you lose it. An example of eye degeneration in the Mexican cave fish, *Astyanax mexicanus*. The single species exists as a surface-dwelling form (left) and a blind cave-dwelling form (right).

W. R. Jeffery, "Adaptive Evolution of Eye Degeneration in the Mexican Blind Cavefish", The Journal of Heredity, 2004, vol. 96, issue number 3, pp. 186, by permission of Oxford University Press.

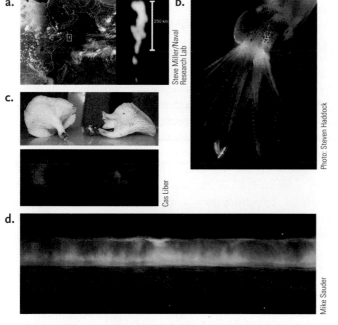

a.

b.

Steve Miller/Naval Research Lab

c.

Cas Liber

d.

Mike Sauder

Photo: Steven Haddock

Figure 1.35
Examples of bioluminescence. **(a)** Satellite image of a "milky sea" a bloom of bioluminescent bacteria off the east coast of Africa. **(b)** bioluminescent octopus. **(c)** A type of fungus in the light (top) and dark (bottom) showing bioluminescence **(d)** A beach in California showing a wave of bioluminescence caused by the presence of billions of cells of a group of unicellular algae called dinoflagellates.

reactions are remarkably efficient. Although up to 95% of the energy of a light bulb is lost as heat, less than 5% of the energy used for bioluminescence is given off as heat. This extraordinary efficiency is essential because high heat production would be incompatible with life.

Why do bioluminescent organisms invest so much energy in light production? Bioluminescent organisms use light to attract a mate, for camouflage, to attract prey, or to communicate. Dinoflagellates are unicellular algae that use bioluminescence as an "alarm bell" to scare off potential predators. In these tiny organisms, bioluminescence is triggered simply by disturbance of the water surrounding them. When a predator such as a small fish swims close to a dinoflagellate at night, the resulting burst of light produced by all the dinoflagellates in the vicinity lights up the water around the fish. This defensive behaviour makes the fish clearly visible to its own predators.

Some marine bacteria use bioluminescence in a type of communication called quorum sensing. Individual bacteria often release compounds into their environment at concentrations too low to elicit a response from their neighbours. However, as a bacterial population grows its size reaches a threshold, a quorum, whereby the concentration of compounds is high enough to elicit a physiological response in all members of the population. The response results in the activation of certain genes, including those that encode for proteins required for bioluminescence. Quorum sensing is now believed to be the basis for what are termed "milky seas" (see Figure 1.35). This strange phenomenon of luminescence from the surface of the ocean has been reported many times over the past several hundred years by sailors, including a mention in Jules Verne's classic book *Twenty Thousand Leagues under the Sea.*

If you have ever walked through a forest at night, you may have seen glowing light here and there on the forest floor. This light, known as "foxfire," is part of many ghost stories and folktales, but it is produced by bioluminescent fungi growing in rotten wood. Unlike bioluminescence in other organisms, we do not yet understand how fungi produce light or what role bioluminescence plays in their lives. One suggestion is that the fungi produce light to attract insects that will disperse spores, but this cannot always be the case as at least some bioluminescent fungi use wind to disperse their spores. In many bioluminescent fungi, the vegetative body produces light, not the spore-producing structure. Fungal bioluminescence remains a mystery (see Chapter 24).

Bioluminescent light must be perceived by another organism in order to be useful to the organism producing it. Therefore, organisms that use bioluminescent signals must have light-sensing organs. We presume, perhaps correctly, that bioluminescence evolved later than light sensing.

Most bioluminescent organisms are marine and are most abundant below 800 metres, a depth to which sunlight does not penetrate. Bioluminescence has not been reported in land plants or higher vertebrates. Why is bioluminescence absent in these organisms? We do not yet have the answers to this or other questions about bioluminescence, reminding us how much there is still to discover about life on Earth.

In closing, this introductory chapter discussed one phenomenon, light, and how it impinges on the biology of Earth. From absorption of a single photon by a pigment molecule in a single cell to affecting the composition of entire ecosystems, the influence of light spans all levels of biological organization. This chapter touched on many topics, from physics and chemistry, photosynthesis, genes and proteins, evolution and natural selection to ecology and behaviour. As you work through the remaining chapters of this textbook, you will learn much more about these topics and many others.

STUDY BREAK

1. What is bioluminescence?
2. Bioluminescence is found in many organisms found in which habitat?

UNANSWERED QUESTIONS

Is there any hope for the development of a "bionic eye"?

For most of us, having good vision throughout our lives is something we take for granted. However, a number of diseases result in diminished vision and often progressively lead to blindness. These include retinitis pigmentosa and age-related macular degeneration, two diseases that have genetic links for which there is no foreseeable cure. Recent data indicate that about one-third of people between 55 and 74 years of age will develop age-related macular degeneration.

Both age-related macular degeneration and retinitis pigmentosa lead to a loss of vision because they both result in degeneration of the photo-receptor cells (rods and cones) found in the retina at the back of the eye. We will learn much more about eye structure and function in Chapter 34. The rods and cones convert light into electrical impulses, which are carried by the optic nerve to the brain, where images are formed.

For years, the development of an artificial "bionic eye" that could restore at least some vision to people who are otherwise blind has been the realm of science fiction—an unattainable dream for both scientists and those with vision degeneration. However, a great deal of research has been carried out in recent years, specifically in the development of an artificial retina since this is the part of the optic system that is damaged in many forms of vision degeneration. The most significant advances have come with the production of a functional artificial retina through research carried out by Mark Humayun, professor of ophthalmology and biomedical engineering, and his associates at the Doheny Eye Institute at the University of Southern California.

Current versions of the artificial retina, which has been successfully implanted in a number of patients, consist of a flexible, wafer-thin, square grid of 16 electrodes surgically attached in the back of the eye. The system also consists of a miniature camera mounted on a pair of sunglasses. The retina and camera are interfaced by a small external wallet-size computer that converts the information from the camera into electrical signals, which are then sent wirelessly to the artificial retina. From there, the current passes through the optic nerve to the brain. The implant has allowed patients to regain some rudimentary vision, including the ability to detect motion and to distinguish between dark and light.

Given the tremendous technological and engineering hurdles that have been overcome to develop this artificial retina, the results for vision may seem relatively primitive. These problems reflect the highly impressive ability of the vision system to process information. Human vision is remarkably sensitive to a wide range of wavelengths and light intensities and can differentiate subtleties in colour, shading, and depth. There are roughly 1.2 million fibres in the optic nerve, each connected to a neuron, which can fire 200 pulses per second. A single eye can send the brain up to 200 million bits of information per second. Although the current technology does not come close to the staggeringly fast rate of information transfer, the current system is rapidly improving. Advancements include reducing the size and power demands on the camera such that it can be placed within the eye itself. Researchers have also successfully moved from implanting a 16-electrode retina to a more advanced 60-electrode device. Researchers are currently developing a 1000-electrode implant that should allow recipients of the retina to gain facial recognition capabilities.

Review

Go to CENGAGENOW™ at http://hed.nelson.com/ to access quizzing, animations, exercises, articles, and personalized homework help.

1.1 The Physical Nature of Light

- For organisms, light serves as a source of energy and as a source of information.
- Light can be defined as electromagnetic radiation that humans can detect with their eyes.
- Light can be thought of as a wave of discrete particles called photons.
- To be used, light energy must be absorbed by molecules called pigments.
- Colour is the result of wavelengths of light that are not absorbed by a pigment.

1.2 Light as a Source of Energy

- The absorption of light by a pigment results in electrons becoming excited. This represents a source of potential energy.
- Photosynthesis is the dominant process on Earth that uses pigments to capture light energy and uses it to convert carbon dioxide into energy-rich carbohydrates.

1.3 Light as a Source of Information

- The basic light-sensing system is called the photoreceptor.
- A photoreceptor (e.g., rhodopsin) consists of a pigment molecule (retinal) bound to a protein (opsin).

- The *C. reinhardtii* eyespot allows the organism to sense both light direction and intensity and respond by swimming toward or away from the light (phototaxis).
- The eye can be defined as the organ animals use to sense light.
- Vision requires a brain to interpret signals sent from the eye.
- The simplest eye is the ocellus found in planarians. It enables the sensing of light direction and intensity.
- Image-forming eyes include compound eyes found in arthropods and single-lens eyes found in some invertebrates and most vertebrates, including humans.
- Because it was thought to be an organ of "extreme perfection," Darwin initially had a difficult time explaining how it could have arisen by evolution.
- The relatively rapid evolution of the eye is explained by the huge advantage an improved eye would give an organism.

1.4 Light Can Damage Biological Molecules

- Photosynthesis, vision, and most other light-driven processes use only a narrow band of the electromagnetic spectrum. This may be because shorter wavelengths are more harmful (higher energy) and longer wavelengths tend not to reach Earth's surface.
- Light is a form of energy; thus, too much light can damage biological molecules.
- The photosynthetic apparatus is constantly being damaged by light and the damage repaired.
- Ultraviolet radiation, because of its high energy, is particularly harmful to biological molecules, particularly DNA.
- Human skin cells are protected by the pigment melanin that absorbs ultraviolet radiation.

1.5 Role of Light in Ecology and Behaviour

- Organisms are adapted to specific light environments from total darkness to bright light.

- Many physiological and behavioural responses are geared to the daily changes in light and darkness and are called circadian rhythms.
- Circadian rhythms are found in all forms of life and evolved to enable organisms to anticipate changes in the light environment.
- Many organisms use colour to attract, warn, or hide from other organisms.
- Aquatic habitats have an altered light environment because water rapidly attenuates longer wavelengths (red) of light. Below 30 m, only blue wavelengths of light penetrate; below about 150 m, there is a total absence of light.
- The widespread use of artificial lighting has been shown to disrupt numerous biological phenomena, including bird migration and the orientation of nocturnal animals.

1.6 Life in the Dark

- Unlike humans, many nocturnal animals (moths, fish, bats, frogs) see very well under dim light conditions.
- Some animals, such as the blind mole rat, are functionally blind yet are descended from ancestors that had functional eyes.

1.7 Organisms Making Their Own Light: Bioluminescence

- A range of organisms can use chemical energy to make light—bioluminescence.
- Bioluminescent organisms use light to attract a mate, for camouflage, to attract prey, or to communicate.

Questions

Self-Test Questions

1. Which of the following statements about light is NOT correct?
   a. Light is a form of electromagnetic radiation.
   b. Organisms use light as a source of energy and information.
   c. Light can be considered a wave composed of packets of energy called photons.
   d. Electromagnetic radiation moves in the form of two waves.
   e. The longer the wavelength, the more energy the photons of light contain.

2. Chlorophyll appears green because it
   a. reflects red light.
   b. absorbs green and blue wavelengths of light.
   c. reflects blue light.
   d. does not absorb green photons.
   e. contains an excited state that matches the energy of a green photon.

3. To be used as a source of information or energy, a photon of light must
   a. have sufficient energy to oxidize a molecule.
   b. first be absorbed by a pigment molecule.
   c. interact with a protein in the plasma membrane.
   d. be reflected off a substance.
   e. None of the above statements are correct.

4. A photoreceptor consists of
   a. a pigment molecule bound to a protein.
   b. a protein that is involved in photosynthesis.

   c. a group of many pigment molecules.
   d. a molecule of chlorophyll.
   e. None of the above is correct.

5. Compared to the eyespot of *C. reinhardtii*, the human eye
   a. is composed of photoreceptors.
   b. can detect changes in light intensity.
   c. can activate a signal transduction pathway when it absorbs light.
   d. is not damaged by ultraviolet radiation.
   e. is image forming.

6. Which of the following statements is NOT correct?
   a. Rapid eye evolution is explained by the huge advantage an improved eye would give an organism.
   b. The ocellus is common in a number of insects, arthropods, and molluscs.
   c. "Vision" requires not only eyes but also a brain.
   d. All eyes consist of a single large photoreceptor cell.
   e. The ommatidium of insects is very adept at detecting movement.

7. Light represents only a very narrow region of the electromagnetic spectrum, yet it is used for a diversity of processes, including vision, photosynthesis, phototaxis, and navigation. This is because
   a. light contains the most energy.
   b. light can excite molecules without destroying them.
   c. all other wavelengths of light are too destructive to biological molecules.

d. light is the dominant form of radiation that reaches Earth's surface.

e. Both b and d are correct.

8. Which of the following statements about circadian rhythms is correct?

a. They have a period of approximately 12 hours.

b. They stop if an organism is placed in complete darkness.

c. They are found only in animals and plants.

d. They enable organisms to anticipate changes to their light environment.

e. They are not affected by airplane travel.

9. The Mexican cavefish illustrate that

a. animals can still see in complete darkness.

b. you don't need eyes for vision.

c. eyes can still function without photoreceptors.

d. organs that are no longer of use can degenerate over time.

e. None of the above is correct.

10. Bioluminescence is

a. the process whereby organisms capture light and then release it.

b. the production of light energy from chemical energy.

c. found only in bacteria.

d. commonly found in organisms that are found in the deep ocean.

e. Both b and d are correct.

Questions for Discussion

1. In writing this chapter, the authors found it difficult to define the "eye." Why do you think this was difficult?

2. Are eyes perfect?

3. What is the biochemical basis of circadian rhythms and biological clocks? What are the components of this clock, and how does it work?

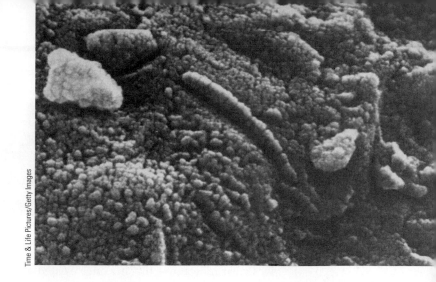

Scanning electron microscope image of a portion of the meteorite ALH84001. The elongate structure may represent a fossilized microorganism.

Time & Life Pictures/Getty Images

2 Origins of Life

WHY IT MATTERS

In 1984, a group of scientists in the Antarctic discovered a 1.9 kg meteorite that they catalogued as ALH84001. Initial studies of the meteorite showed that it was about 4.5 billion years old, which is about the same age as the solar system. As well, its chemical composition indicated that it had originated from Mars and had impacted Earth approximately 13 000 years ago. The meteorite garnered headlines around the world in 1996 when an article was published in the prestigious journal *Science* with evidence that ALH84001 contained distinct evidence that life had at one time existed on Mars.

Chemical analysis showed that, when on Mars, ALH84001 had at one time been fractured and subsequently infiltrated by liquid water. Using scanning electron microscopy, the coauthors of the article observed very small, elliptical, ropelike, and tubular structures in the fractured surfaces of ALH84001 that look very similar to fossilized prokaryotes. Furthermore, the scientists found microscopic mineral "globules," which bear strong resemblance to mineral alterations caused by primitive prokaryotes on Earth. One last piece of evidence is that the meteorite contains an abundance of polycyclic aromatic hydrocarbons (PAHs). These compounds are commonly formed when microorganisms die and break down.

Figure 2.1
Red-eyed treefrog on a rock.

Analysis of ALH84001 continues as it remains controversial as to whether the evidence presented gives clear indications that life once existed on Mars. However, taken together, the PAHs, unusual mineral deposits, and bacteria-like structures were all located within a few micrometres of one another, suggesting a relationship that may be due to life.

Figure 2.2
The seven characteristics of life.

2.1 What Is Life?

Picture a frog sitting on a rock, slowly shifting its head to follow the movements of insects flying nearby (Figure 2.1). You know instinctively that the frog is alive and that the rock is not. However, if you examine both at the molecular level, you will find that the differences between them blur. The types of atoms and molecules found in living things are no different from those found in nonliving forms of matter. Furthermore, living cells obey the same fundamental laws of chemistry and physics as does the **abiotic** (nonliving) world. For example, the biochemical reactions that take place within living cells, although seemingly remarkably complex, are only modifications of reactions that take place in the abiotic world.

2.1a Seven Characteristics that All Forms of Life Share

Although life seems relatively easy to recognize, it is not easy to define using only a single sentence. Instead, all forms of life share a set of attributes that collectively differentiate them from nonliving things. The seven fundamental characteristics that are common to all forms of life are listed below and shown in **Figure 2.2**.

a. Display order: All forms of life including this flower are arranged in a highly ordered manner, with the cell being the fundamental unit of life.

b. Harness and utilize energy: Like this hummingbird, all forms of life acquire energy from the environment and use it to maintain their highly ordered state.

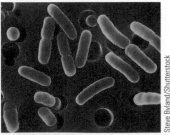

c. Reproduce: All organisms have the ability to make more of their own kind. Here, some of the bacteria can be seen having just divided into two daughter cells.

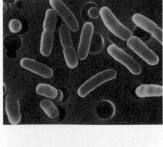

d. Respond to stimuli: Organisms can make adjustments to their structure, function, and behaviour in response to changes to the external environment. A plant can adjust the size of the pore on the surface of a leaf (a stomata) to regulate gas exchange.

e. Exhibit homeostasis: Organisms are able to regulate their internal environment such that conditions remain relatively constant. Sweating is one way in which the body attempts to remove heat and thereby maintain a constant temperature.

f. Growth and development: All organisms increase their size by increasing the size and/or number of cells. Many organisms also change overtime.

g. Evolve: Populations of living organisms change over the course of generations to become better adapted to their environment. This snowy owl illustrates this perfectly.

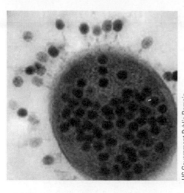

US Government Public Domain

Figure 2.3
Bacteriophage (a type of virus) infecting a bacterium. A virus is not considered to be alive.

Is a virus alive? A handful of biological entities straddle the definition of life, and the best example of these is a virus **(Figure 2.3)**. Viruses seemingly display many of the properties of life, including the ability to reproduce and evolve over time. However, the characteristics of life that a virus possesses are based on its ability to infect living cells. Although viruses contain nucleic acids, they lack the cellular machinery to synthesize their own proteins. They essentially highjack the machinery and metabolism of a living cell in order to reproduce. For this reason, most scientists do not consider a virus alive.

2.1b The Fundamental Unit of Life Is the Cell

By the middle of the nineteenth century, observations by biologists using light microscopy (see *The Chemical and Physical Foundations of Biology* pages) yielded three profound generalizations about the organization of living organisms. Together, these have become known as the three tenets of the **cell theory:**

1. **All organisms are composed of one or more cells.** Some types of organisms, such as prokaryotes, are composed of only a single cell. In these **unicellular** organisms, the one cell is a functionally independent organism capable of carrying out all life activities. In more complex multicellular organisms, including plants and animals, major life activities are divided among varying numbers of specialized cells. Individual cells of mul-

ticellular organisms are potentially capable of surviving by themselves if placed in a chemical medium that can sustain them.

2. **The cell is the smallest unit that has the properties of life.** If cells are broken open, the property of life is lost: they are unable to grow, reproduce, or respond to outside stimuli in a coordinated, potentially independent fashion. Scientists can learn a lot about how a cell functions by doing experiments on disrupted cells, examining only a single component of the cell.

3. **Cells arise only from the growth and division of preexisting cells.** Although deoxyribonucleic acid (DNA) and **ribonucleic acid (RNA)** contain the information required to manufacture a vast array of biological molecules, they cannot orchestrate the formation of an entire cell. New cells can arise only from the division of preexisting cells.

As shown by the examples in **Figure 2.4,** there are many different kinds of cells.

STUDY BREAK

Why are viruses not considered a form of life?

2.2 The Chemical Origins of Life

Recall that the third tenet of the cell theory states that cells arise only from the growth and division of preexisting cells. This tenet has probably been true for hundreds of millions of years, yet there must have been a time when this was not the case. There must have been a time when no cells existed, when there was no life. Over the course of hundreds of millions of years, cells with the characteristics of life arose out of a mixture of molecules that existed on the primordial Earth. In the next few sections, we discuss how life arose on Earth. For parts of this discussion, the theories have been firmly supported by experimentation; for other parts, all we have are vague hypotheses.

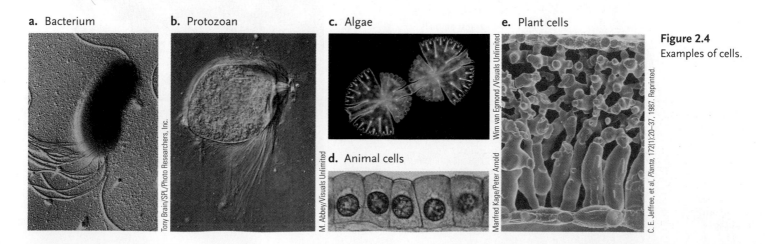

a. Bacterium   **b.** Protozoan   **c.** Algae   **d.** Animal cells   **e.** Plant cells

Tony Brain/SPL/Photo Researchers, Inc.   M. Abbey/Visuals Unlimited   Wim van Egmond /Visuals Unlimited   Manfred Kage/Peter Arnold   C. E. Jeffree, et al, *Planta,* 172(1):20–37, 1987. Reprinted.

Figure 2.4
Examples of cells.

2.2a 4.6 Billion Years Condensed into 1

Earth is approximately 4.6 billion or 4 600 000 000 years old. To give us some sense of this immense length of time and the relative timing of some major events in the history of life on Earth, **Figure 2.5** condenses the entire history of Earth into a unit of time that we are familiar with—one year. By condensing 4.6 billion years into a single year, each day represents an interval of 12.6 million years.

According to this analogy, Earth was formed on January 1 at 12:00 A.M., however, the earliest chemical evidence of life doesn't occur until mid-March, with the first fossil evidence of prokaryotic life appearing in late March. It is not until early July, however, that the first eukaryotic cells appear. Animals do not make an appearance until mid-October and land plants until the following month. Using our calendar, the extinction of dinosaurs, which we discuss in Chapter 20, does not occur until late December. What about humans? We may think humans, *Homo sapiens*, have been around a long time, but relative to other forms of life, the roughly 150 000 years that modern humans have existed is a very short period of time. Using our year analogy, modern humans have existed only since December 31—more precisely, December 31 at 11:42 P.M.

2.2b Conditions on Primordial Earth

Evidence using a range of dating methods has firmly established that Earth, the Sun, and the other planets of the solar system all formed at about the same time. According to the most widely accepted hypothesis, the solar system was formed by the gravitational condensation of matter present in a molecular cloud, which initially consisted mostly of hydrogen. Intense heat and pressure generated in the central region of the cloud formed the Sun, whereas the remainder of the spiralling dust and gas condensed into the planets. Astronomers agree that this series of events is typical for the vast majority of the estimated 400 millions stars in our galaxy, the Milky Way, and that since planet formation is a natural consequence of the condensation of interstellar gas, which leads to the formation of stars **(Figure 2.6)**, our galaxy most likely contains many millions of planets.

Figure 2.5
The history of Earth condensed into one year.

January
1	2	3	4	5	6	7
8	9	10	11	12	13	14
15	16	17	18	19	20	21
22	23	24	25	26	27	28
29	30	31

← Earth forms

February
1	2	3	4
5	6	7	8	9	10	11
12	13	14	15	16	17	18
19	20	21	22	23	24	25
26	27	28

March
1	2	3	4
5	6	7	8	9	10	11
12	13	14	15	16	17	18
19	20	21	22	23	24	25
26	27	28	29	30	31

← Earliest prokaryotes

April
| 1 |
2	3	4	5	6	7	8
9	10	11	12	13	14	15
16	17	18	19	20	21	22
23	24	25	26	27	28	29
30

May
1	2	3	4	5	6
7	8	9	10	11	12	13
14	15	16	17	18	19	20
21	22	23	24	25	26	27
28	29	30	31

← Oxygen increases in atmosphere

June
1	2	3
4	5	6	7	8	9	10
11	12	13	14	15	16	17
18	19	20	21	22	23	24
25	26	27	28	29	30

July
| 1 |
2	3	4	5	6	7	8
9	10	11	12	13	14	15
16	17	18	19	20	21	22
23	24	25	26	27	28	29
30	31

← Earliest eukaryotes

1 day = 12.6 million years
1 second = 143 years

August
1	2	3	4	5
6	7	8	9	10	11	12
13	14	15	16	17	18	19
20	21	22	23	24	25	26
27	28	29	30	31

September
1	2
3	4	5	6	7	8	9
10	11	12	13	14	15	16
17	18	19	20	21	22	23
24	25	26	27	28	29	30

October
1	2	3	4	5	6	7
8	9	10	11	12	13	14
15	16	17	18	19	20	21
22	23	24	25	26	27	28
29	30	31

← Earliest animals

← Earliest land plants

November
1	2	3	4
5	6	7	8	9	10	11
12	13	14	15	16	17	18
19	20	21	22	23	24	25
26	27	28	29	30

December
1	2
3	4	5	6	7	8	9
10	11	12	13	14	15	16
17	18	19	20	21	22	23
24	25	26	27	28	29	30
31

← Extinction of Dinosaurs

← Earliest humans (Dec. 31st at 11:43 pm)

Figure 2.6

A galaxy. Andromeda (M31) is similar to the Milky Way in being a spiral galaxy. Andromeda is estimated to contain about 1 trillion stars.

World Perspectives/Getty Images

Once Earth was formed, its early history was marked by bombardment of rock from the still-forming solar system and extensive volcanic and seismic activity **(Figure 2.7)**. Over time, Earth radiated away some of its heat and surface layers cooled and solidified into the rocks of the crust. Because of its size, Earth's gravitational pull was strong enough to hold an atmosphere around the planet. The atmosphere was derived partly from the original dust cloud and partly from gases released from the planet's interior as it cooled. It is estimated that it took approximately 500 million years for Earth to cool to temperatures that could nurture the development of life.

The atmosphere of 4 billion years ago was vastly different from the one today. The primordial atmosphere probably contained an abundance of water vapour from the evaporation of water at the surface, as well as large quantities of hydrogen sulphide (H_2S), carbon dioxide (CO_2), ammonia (NH_3), and methane (CH_4). Some of these compounds were formed spontaneously by reactions in the atmosphere, whereas others were the result of volcanic eruptions. From these basic building blocks, the molecules essential to the formation of life are thought to have formed.

In the 1920s, two scientists, Aleksander Oparin and John Haldane, independently proposed that organic molecules essential to the formation of life—including **amino acids**, sugars, and the nucleotide bases that form DNA and RNA—could have been made in the absence of life (abiotic synthesis), given the conditions and simple molecules thought to be present on primordial Earth.

A critical aspect of what is known as the Oparin–Haldane hypothesis is that the early atmosphere was a *reducing atmosphere* because of the presence of large concentrations of molecules such as hydrogen (H_2), methane, and ammonia. These molecules contain the maximum possible number of electrons and hydrogen and are said to be fully reduced (see *The Chemical and Physical Foundations of Biology* pages). A rich source of electrons that can be easily donated makes reactions possible that lead to the building up, or synthesis, of large and complex organic molecules. By comparison, today's atmosphere, which contains 21% O_2, is an *oxidizing atmosphere*. The presence of O_2 prevents complex, electron-rich molecules from being formed because oxygen is a strong oxidizing molecule.

2.2c The Miller–Urey Experiment

The lack of oxygen in the primordial atmosphere meant that there was no ozone (O_3) layer to partially block the Sun's energetic ultraviolet light from reaching Earth's surface. Oparin and Haldane hypothesized that the ultraviolet light, along with abundant lightning, provided the energy that, combined with the reducing conditions present in the atmosphere, would lead to the accumulation of the simple "building blocks" required for life.

Experimental evidence in support of the Oparin–Haldane hypothesis came in 1953 when Stanley Miller, a graduate student of Harold Urey at the University of Chicago, created a laboratory simulation of the reducing atmosphere believed to have existed on early Earth. Miller placed components of a reducing atmosphere—hydrogen, methane, ammonia, and water vapour—in a closed apparatus and exposed the gases to an energy source in the form of continuously sparking electrodes **(Figure 2.8)**. Water vapour was added to the "atmosphere" in one part of the apparatus and subsequently condensed back into water by cooling in another part. After running the experiment for only a week, Miller found a large assortment of organic compounds in the water, including urea, amino acids, and lactic, formic, and acetic acids. In fact, as much as 15% of the carbon that was originally in the methane (CH_4) was now in the form of organic compounds.

Other chemicals have been tested in the Miller–Urey apparatus, including hydrogen cyanide (HCN) and formaldehyde (CH_2O), which are considered

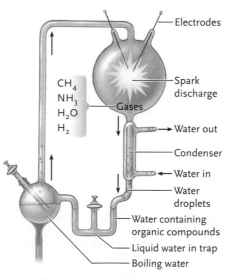

Figure 2.8
The Miller–Urey apparatus demonstrating that organic molecules can be synthesized spontaneously under conditions simulating primordial Earth. Operation for 1 week converted 15% of the carbon in the "atmosphere" inside the apparatus into a surprising variety of organic compounds.

Figure 2.7
An artist's depiction of Earth during its early cooling stage.

Figure 2.9
Deep sea vent.

likely to have been among the earliest substances formed in the primitive atmosphere. When HCN and CH_2O molecules were added to the simulated primitive atmosphere in Miller's apparatus, all the building blocks of complex biological molecules were produced—amino acids; fatty acids; the **purine** and **pyrimidine** building blocks of nucleic acids; sugars such as glyceraldehyde, ribose, glucose, and fructose; and phospholipids, which form the lipid bilayers of biological membranes.

Considerable debate exists in the scientific community as to whether the atmosphere of primitive Earth contained enough methane and ammonia to provide the reducing characteristics necessary to yield the results found with Miller–Urey experiments. However, besides the primordial atmosphere, highly reducing conditions would have been found near volcanoes and near the hydrothermal vents found on the ocean floor **(Figure 2.9)**. Today, the areas around these vents support a wide range of organisms that are of tremendous scientific interest because of their ability to thrive under extreme conditions of pressure and the total absence of light. Besides releasing geothermally heated water, the vents also release methane and ammonia, which could have led to the formation of the building blocks of life on primitive Earth.

Regardless of the specifics, the significance of the Miller–Urey experiment cannot be overstated. It showed that molecules critical to life, such as amino acids (the building blocks of proteins), as well as many other biologically important molecules, could be produced abiotically, and that they could be produced relatively simply. At the time, this finding was remarkable and laid the groundwork for further research into the origins of life.

2.2d The Synthesis of Polymers from Monomers

Given that primordial Earth contained very little oxygen, it is thought that after the organic molecules were synthesized, they could have existed for much longer than would be possible in today's oxygen-rich world. That being said, it is important to realize that the key building blocks of life, such as nucleic acids and proteins, are not individually synthesized molecules, called monomers. Instead they are macromolecules, built up from large numbers of subunit monomers coming together to produce what are called polymers. Nucleic acids are polymers of nucleotides, proteins are polymers of amino acids, and many carbohydrates are polymers of simple sugars (see *The Chemical and Physical Foundations of Biology* pages). Today, the synthesis of proteins and nucleic acids, for example, requires protein-based catalysts called enzymes and results in macromolecules, which are very large, often consisting of hundreds to many thousands of monomers linked together.

So how do you make the polymers that are required for life without sophisticated enzymes? Given that the earliest forms of life were probably nowhere near as elaborate as even the simplest prokaryote, scientists hypothesize that a polymer that consists of even 50 monomers may have been of sufficient length to impart a specific function (like a protein) or store sufficient information (like a nucleic acid) to make their formation advantageous to an organism. It is, however, doubtful that **polymerization** could have occurred in the aqueous environment of primordial Earth as macromolecules would have been quickly broken down or hydrolyzed. An **alternative hypothesis** is that solid surfaces, especially clays, would have provided a unique environment for polymerization to occur. In fact, numerous experiments have demonstrated the formation of short nucleic acid chains and polypeptides on the surface of clay. Clay would have been present in evaporating tidal pools, for example, on early Earth. Clays consist of very thin layers of minerals separated by layers of water only a few nanometres thick. The layered structure readily absorbs ions and organic molecules and promotes their interactions, including condensations and other assembly reactions. Clays can also store potential energy and therefore could have channelled some of that energy into reactions taking place in them.

2.2e Protobionts: The First Cells

The next key factor we need to consider on the way to life is the development of a boundary that would separate the polymers required for life from the external environment. A **protobiont (Figure 2.10)** is the term given to a group of abiotically produced organic molecules that are surrounded by a membrane or membrane-like structure. The development of protobionts was important because it allowed for an internal environment to develop that was distinctly different from the external environment: the concentration of key

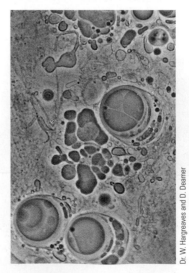

Figure 2.10
An electron micrograph of vesicles of various sizes and shapes assembled from phospholipids synthesized under simulated primordial conditions. Such molecules may have been the precursor protobionts of living cells.

molecules could be higher, and molecules could attain more order in a closed space. Laboratory experiments have shown that protobionts could have formed spontaneously, given the conditions of primordial Earth. For example, liposomes, which are small membrane-bound spheres, can be formed when lipid molecules accumulate in an aqueous environment. Lipid molecules are hydrophobic and consequently can spontaneously aggregate into spheres in which the lipid molecules form a **bilayer** very similar to cell membranes. Liposomes are also selectively permeable, allowing some molecules to move in and out. As well, liposomes can swell and contract depending on the osmotic conditions of their environment.

STUDY BREAK

In trying to understand the origin of life, what was the significance of the Miller–Urey experiment?

2.3 The Origins of Information and Metabolism

Of the several critical events necessary for the development of life, two stand out: the development of a system for the storage, replication, and translation of information for protein synthesis and the development of metabolic pathways that would capture and harness energy for metabolism.

2.3a The Origin of the Information System

All organisms contain **deoxyribonucleic acid (DNA)**. DNA is a large, double-stranded, helical molecule that contains a unique alphabet that provides the instructions for assembling many of the important components of a cell organism from simpler molecules. DNA functions similarly in all organisms—the information in DNA is copied onto molecules of a related substance, **ribonucleic acid (RNA)**, which then directs the production of protein molecules **(Figure 2.11)**. Even the simplest of cells contains thousands of proteins, each coded for by a unique DNA sequence. This flow of information from DNA to RNA to protein is common to all forms of life (see Figure 2.11). Enzymes are required to catalyze the replication of DNA, the transcription of DNA into RNA, and, subsequently, the translation of the RNA into protein. This information pathway is preserved from generation to generation by the ability of DNA to direct its own replication so that offspring receive the same basic molecular instructions as their parents have. Changes in the DNA, regardless of how

they are brought about, are what contribute to evolutionary change over generations.

2.3b Ribozymes Are Biological Catalysts that Are Not Proteins

A fundamental question about the flow of information from DNA to RNA to protein is *how did such a system evolve when the products of the process, proteins, are required to catalyze each step of the process?* For years, scientists struggled to come up with a reasonable hypothesis for how this system could have evolved. A breakthrough in our thinking came in 1979, Thomas Czech and his coworkers discovered a group of RNA molecules that could themselves act as catalysts. This group of RNA molecules, called **ribozymes,** can catalyze reactions on the precursor RNA molecules that lead to their own synthesis, as well as on unrelated RNA molecules **(Figure 2.12, p. 30)**. The property of RNA that makes some able to act as catalysts is that they are single-stranded molecules that can fold into very specific shapes. Ribozyme function depends on how it is folded, similar to protein function, which is achieved only after the amino acid chain acquires a precise three-dimensional shape (see *The Chemical and Physical Foundations of Biology* pages).

The discovery of ribozymes revolutionized thinking about the origin of life. Instead of the contemporary system that requires all three molecules—DNA, RNA, and protein—early life may have existed in an "RNA world," where a single type of molecule could serve as both a carrier of information (in its

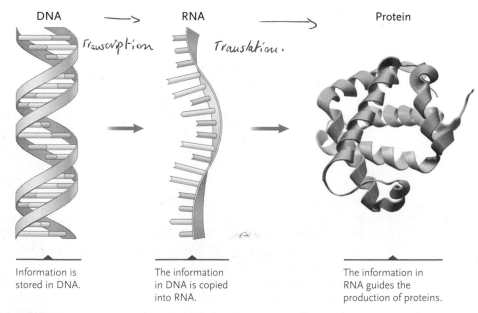

DNA   RNA   Protein

Transcription   *Translation.*

| Information is stored in DNA. | The information in DNA is copied into RNA. | The information in RNA guides the production of proteins. |

Figure 2.11
The pathway of information flow in living organisms. Information stored in DNA is copied into RNA, which then directs the construction of protein molecules.

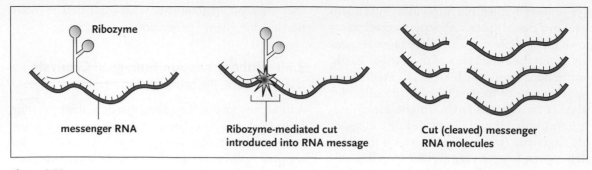

Figure 2.12

An example of a ribozyme binding to a RNA molecule and catalyzing its breakage. WIthin a cell such a reaction may help control gene expression by altering the abundance of functional messenger RNA molecules.

nucleotide sequence) and a catalyst (due to its ability to form unique three-dimensional shapes). Prior to the discovery of ribozymes, enzymes, which are proteins, were the only known biological catalysts. Chapter 4 is devoted to this very important group of molecules.

2.3c   The Evolution of Proteins and DNA

If life developed in an "RNA world" and RNA served as both an information carrier and a catalyst, why is life today dominated by DNA and proteins? The simple answer, which we discuss further below, is that they do the respective jobs of information storage (DNA) and catalysis (protein) far better than RNA does by itself; thus, the evolution of these molecules would have given organisms that had them a distinct advantage over others that used only RNA.

A possible scenario for the development of today's system of information transfer is shown in **Figure 2.13.** The first cells may have contained only RNA, which was self-replicating and could catalyze

a small number of reactions critical for survival. It is hypothesized that, subsequently, a small population of RNA molecules evolved that could catalyze the formation of very simple proteins, independent of the ribosome (the organelle in contemporary organisms required for protein synthesis). It is interesting to note that the modern ribosome, which plays a key role as an intermediate between RNA and protein, is composed of about two-thirds RNA and one-third protein. Interestingly, it has recently been shown that the RNA of the ribosome, not the protein, actually catalyzes the incorporation of amino acids onto a growing peptide chain. Thus, the ribosome may be considered a type of ribozyme.

RNA molecules that developed the ability to synthesize even small proteins would be at a tremendous advantage because proteins are far more versatile than RNA molecules, for two main reasons. First, the catalytic power of most enymes is greater than that of any known ribozyme. That is, a typical enzyme can catalyze the same reaction using a pool of substrate molecules many hundreds and even thousands of times a second. Second, proteins are much more diverse compared with ribozymes. Twenty different kinds of amino acids can be incorporated into a protein, whereas an RNA molecule is composed of only four nucleotide bases. As well, amino acids can interact chemically with other amino acids in bonding arrangements not possible between nucleotides. Because of the tremendous diversity in the structure of proteins, they are the dominant structural and functional molecule in the cell.

In the RNA world, DNA would have developed after the development of proteins (see Figure 2.13). Compared with RNA, molecules of DNA are more complex. Not only is DNA double stranded, it also contains the sugar deoxyribose, which is more difficult to synthesize than the ribose found in molecules of RNA. At first, DNA nucleotides may have been produced by random removal of an oxygen atom from the ribose subunits of the RNA nucleotides. At some point, the DNA nucleotides paired with the RNA informational molecules and were

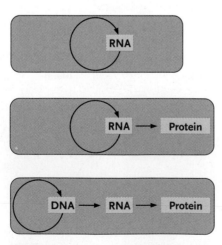

Figure 2.13

Possible scenario for the evolution of the flow of information from DNA to RNA to protein.

L1 Ligase Ribozyme

RNA molecules may have been critical in the development of life on Earth since it is thought that they not only could store information but also could act as biological catalysts prior to the evolution of DNA and proteins. However, to replicate RNA, individual nucleotide triphosphate monomers need to be joined, or ligated, together to form an RNA polymer.

Today, this ligation reaction, carried out by a group of protein enzymes called polymerases, can result in RNA strands being many thousands of nucleotides in length. How this polymerization reaction would have been catalyzed in an RNA-only world stumped scientists for years.

Using what is called *in vitro* evolution and selection, scientists recently produced a range of synthetic ribozymes that do not currently exist in nature. One of these synthetic ribozymes is called the L1 ligase ribozyme, and it has been shown to catalzye the joining of two RNA monomers together. This finding clearly suggests that, although not currently found in nature, a ribozyme capable of ligating nucleotides together may have existed on primitive Earth.

assembled into complementary copies of the RNA sequences. Some modern-day viruses carry out this RNA-to-DNA reaction using the enzyme reverse transcriptase (see Chapter 22). Once the DNA copies were made, selection may have favoured DNA as it is a much better way to store information than RNA, for three main reasons:

- Each strand of DNA is chemically more stable than a strand of RNA. This is due to the presence of the sugar deoxyribose instead of ribose.
- The base uracil found in RNA is not found in DNA; it has been replaced by thymine. It is thought that the reason for this is that a common mutation in DNA is the conversion of cytosine into uracil. By utilizing thymine in DNA, any uracil is easily recognized as a damaged cytosine and can be repaired.
- DNA is double stranded, so in the case of a mutation, the complementary strand can be used to repair the damaged strand.

The stability of DNA makes it an excellent molecule to store and preserve genetic information. This is reflected by the fact that, using the polymerase chain reaction, intact DNA can be successfully extracted and amplified from tissue that is many thousands of years old.

Many unanswered questions remain concerning the origin of life and how the first cells came about. A wide range of theories exist, with different degrees of experimental support. What is indeed frustrating is that we simply do not know the specifics of what happened because we lack evidence—both fossil evidence and otherwise. Sifting through the various models and theories, we can perhaps agree that there were some basic steps:

1. the abiotic (nonliving) synthesis of organic molecules such as amino acids
2. the assembly of complex organic molecules from simple molecules, including protein, RNA, or both
3. the aggregation of complex organic molecules inside membrane-bound protobionts

2.3d The Development of Energy-Harnessing Reaction Pathways

Oxidation–reduction reactions were probably among the first energy-releasing reactions of the primitive cells. In our cells, we *oxidize* food molecules (e.g., sugars) and use some of the liberated energy (electrons) to *reduce* other molecules, for example, those needed to synthesize proteins. In primitive cells, the electrons removed in an oxidation would have been transferred directly to the substances being reduced, in a one-step process. This, however, is not very efficient and leads to a lot of wasted energy. Over time, multistep processes would have evolved, whereby the energy from an oxidation is slowly released. A good example of this is cellular respiration, which is discussed in Chapter 6. The greater efficiency of stepwise energy release would have favoured development of intermediate carriers and opened the way for primitive electron transport chains.

As part of the energy-harnessing reactions, adenosine triphosphate (ATP) became established as the coupling agent that links energy-releasing reactions to those requiring energy. ATP may first have entered early cells as one of many organic molecules absorbed from the primitive environment. Initially, it was probably simply hydrolyzed into adenosine diphosphate (ADP) and inorganic phosphate, resulting in the release of energy. Later, as cells developed, some of the energy released during electron transfer was probably used to synthesize ATP directly from ADP and inorganic phosphate. Because of the efficiency and versatility of energy transfer by ATP, it gradually became the primary substance connecting energy-releasing and energy-requiring reactions in early cells.

$ATP = ADP + P_i$

STUDY BREAK

1. What are ribozymes, and what is their significance in our understanding of the origins of life?
2. In what ways was DNA better than RNA as a means of storing genetic information?

2.4 Early Life

2.4a Earliest Evidence of Life

The earliest conclusive evidence of life is found in the fossilized remains of structures called stromatolites, which have been dated to about 3.5 billion years ago. **Stromatolites** are a type of layered rock that is formed when microorganisms bind particles of sediment together, forming thin sheets **(Figure 2.14)**. Confidence that fossil stromatolites were formed by microbial activity comes from the fact that modern-day stromatolites although rare, do exist in habitats characterized by warm shallow water, and do harbour microbial life (see Figure 2.14).

Modern-day stromatolites are formed by the action of a group of photosynthetic prokaryotes called cyanobacteria. As we discuss in a later section, cyanobacteria possess a sophisticated metabolism that suggests that earlier life forms must have preceded their evolution. Indirect (nonfossil) evidence of life existing as early as 3.9 billion years ago comes from research looking at the carbon composition of ancient rocks. Early organisms would have required the ability to take CO_2 from the atmosphere and "fix it" by incorporating it into various organic forms (sugars, amino acids, etc.). Interestingly, organisms preferentially incorporate the carbon-12 isotope over other isotopes, see *The Chemical and Physical Foundations of Biology*, such as carbon-13. Researchers have discovered sedimentary rocks, originating from the ocean floor, that contain deposits that are depleted in ^{13}C. This finding suggests that the deposits are remnants of ancient microbes.

2.4b Could Life Have Come to Earth from Space?

It is a well-regarded hypothesis that life on Earth could have had an extraterrestrial origin. Panspermia is the name given to the hypothesis that very simple forms of life are present in outer space and may have seeded early Earth. Two points of discussion support the extraterrestrial origin of life on Earth:

- Although life seems very complex, it arose relatively quickly after the formation of Earth. The Earth formed 4.6 billion years ago, and we have clear fossil evidence of life dated to about 3.5 billion years ago and chemical evidence to about 3.9 billion years ago. Given that primordial Earth had to cool after being formed, many scientists argue that this window for the development of life is very narrow.

- Research in the past decade has shown that life is far more resilient than previously thought and could possibly survive for years in space. Extremophiles, which are mostly prokaryotes, can thrive under very harsh conditions of temperature, pressure, and nutrients and might be able to survive in a dormant state in interstellar space. Prolonged dormancy is a property of the spores of a range of organisms, including a number of prokaryotes and simple eukaryotes. Spores are highly resistant to changes in the external environment and can be restored to active growth after exposure to high levels of radiation, water deficiency, and/or exposure to extreme temperatures. Given this, one cannot discount the possibility that simple life forms came to Earth about 4 billion years ago and initiated the evolution of life as we know it.

2.4c Prokaryotes Have Properties Common to All Cells

All forms of life are based on two fundamentally distinct types of cells: prokaryotic and eukaryotic. The earliest forms of life, including those found in stromatolites, are the simplest organisms known, prokaryotes **(Figure 2.15)**. As we discuss in Chapter 21,

Figure 2.14
(a) Stromatolites exposed at low tide in Western Australia's Shark Bay. These mounds, which consist of mineral deposits made by photosynthetic cyanobacteria, are about 2000 years old; they are highly similar in structure to fossil stromatolites that formed more than 3 billion years ago. As a result of photosynthesis by cyanobacteria, oxygen began to accumulate in the atmosphere. **(b)** Structures that are believed to be a strand of fossil prokaryote cells in a rock sample 3.5 billion years old.

a.

b.

5 μm

Bill Bachmann/Photo Researchers Inc.

Bill Bachmann, Photo Researchers, Inc.

Stanley M. Awramik

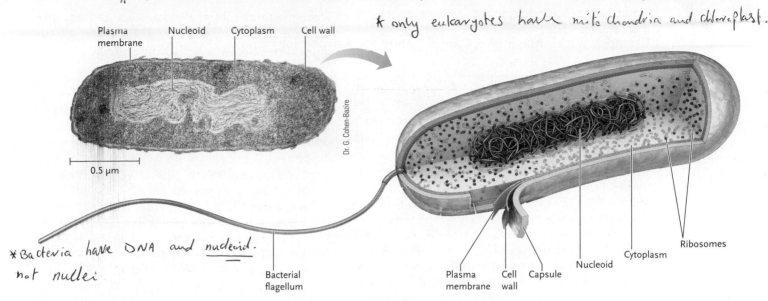

*All three domain of life have plasma membrane and ribosome and chromosome.
*only eukaryotes have mitochondria and chloroplast.

*Bacteria have DNA and nucleoid.
not nuclei

Figure 2.15

Prokaryotic cell structure. An electron micrograph (left) and a diagram (right) of the bacterium *Escherichia coli*.

prokaryotic organisms are found in two domains of life: the bacteria and the Archaea. Although the lack of a nucleus makes prokaryotes distinctly different from eukaryotic cells, it is important to realize that all cells share many fundamental features. All cells possess a selectively permeable *plasma membrane*, which separates the external environment from the **cytoplasm** of the cell. The cytoplasm consists of the **cytosol**, which is mostly water, salts, and various organic molecules, along with the various structural features within the cell, including **organelles**. The plasma membrane contains protein complexes that allow the controlled transport of materials into and out of the cells. In addition, the prokaryotic plasma membrane also contains protein complexes that form electron transport chains, used to link the oxidation of various molecules to the synthesis of ATP. In photosynthetic prokaryotes, the plasma membrane, or internal membranes derived from the plasma membrane, are the sites of photosynthetic electron transport chains, which harvest light energy for the synthesis of energy-rich molecules, including ATP. We will see that in **eukaryotes**, energy transduction machinery is found in organelles called mitochondria and chloroplasts.

The DNA of both prokaryotic and eukaryotic cells is organized into *chromosomes*. However, as you will learn in subsequent chapters, the structure of the chromosome is distinctly different between prokaryotes and eukaryotes. Lacking a nucleus, the DNA of a prokaryote is found localized in a central region of the cell called a **nucleoid**. The processes of transcription and translation, which are discussed in detail in Chapter 14, are also fundamentally similar in prokaryotes and eukaryotes relying on ribosomes for the synthesis of proteins from an RNA template.

2.4d Prokaryotes Display Remarkable Diversity

Prokaryotic cells are usually not much more than a few micrometres in length and a micrometre or less in diameter, which makes them about 10 times smaller than a typical eukaryotic cell. Also, prokaryotes have much less internal membrane organization, compared to eukaryotic cells. Although prokaryotic cells appear to be relatively simple, their simplicity is deceptive. As we discuss further in Chapter 21, prokaryotes display remarkable metabolic flexibility, being able to use a variety of substances as energy and carbon sources and to synthesize almost all of their required organic molecules from simple inorganic raw materials. In many respects, prokaryotes are biochemically more versatile than eukaryotes. Their small size and metabolic versatility are reflected in their abundance; prokaryotes vastly outnumber all other types of organisms and live successfully in almost all regions of Earth's surface, from the Antarctic to hot springs. Chapter 21 outlines the diversity of prokaryotes and extends the discussion of the prokaryotic structure.

2.4e Oxygenic Photosynthesis and the Rise of Atmospheric Oxygen

Geologic evidence indicates that the earliest prokaryotic cells relied on anaerobic metabolism as the atmosphere of Earth lacked molecular oxygen. Evidence for an increase in atmospheric O_2 starting about 2.5 billion years ago is found by the presence of a type of sedimentary rock called banded iron. It is thought that this type of rock was formed in the sediments of lakes and oceans as dissolved oxygen reacted

PEOPLE BEHIND BIOLOGY

Chandra Wickramasinghe, Cardiff Centre for Astrobiology

A professor of applied mathematics and astronomy at Cardiff University in the United Kingdom, Dr. Chandra Wickramasinghe is currently the director of the Cardiff Centre for Astrobiology. Along with Sir Fred Hoyle, Wickramasinghe is credited with the modern theory of panspermia—the idea that life on Earth was seeded by microbes from space. Although initially rejected as absurd, the concept of panspermia has come to be regarded as a plausible hypothesis for the starting of life on Earth.

Professor Wickramasinghe was born in Sri Lanka and educated at Royal College, Colombo, and later the University of Ceylon. He received his Ph.D. from the University of Cambridge in the United Kingdom, under the supervision of the late Sir Fred Hoyle. In 1964, he was appointed as a staff member of the Institute of Astronomy at the University of Cambridge, where he started his pioneering work on the nature of interstellar dust. In 1974, he first proposed the theory that dust in interstellar space and in comets was largely organic, a theory that has now been confirmed.

Through his research, Wickramasinghe is credited with developing the field of astrobiology as a serious academic program that includes biology, astronomy, and geology in the study of the origin, evolution, distribution, and future of life in the universe. This multidisciplinary field encompasses the search for habitable environments in our solar system and habitable planets outside our solar system, the search for evidence of prebiotic chemistry and life on Mars and other bodies in our solar system, laboratory and field research into the origins and early evolution of life on Earth, and studies of the potential for life to adapt to challenges on Earth and in space. Numerous universities around the world now have undergraduate degree programs in astrobiology.

---

with dissolved iron, which formed the precipitate, iron oxide (rust) **(Figure 2.16)**.

An obvious question to ask is *where did the O_2 come from?* The most primitive forms of metabolism probably included anaerobic respiration, fermentation, and photosynthesis. The earliest form of photosynthesis relied on compounds such as H_2S and ferrous iron (Fe^{2+}), which could be easily oxidized by energy trapped from sunlight. The liberated electrons, would in turn, be used to reduce CO_2 into sugars.

However, starting about 3 billion years ago a group of prokaryotes called cyanobacteria appeared that could use something more common than H_2S or ferrous iron as an electron donor for photosynthesis. Cyanobacteria could harness electrons from water **(Figure 2.17)**. A consequence of oxidizing water was that besides releasing electrons and **protons**, the "splitting of water" resulted in the formation of O_2, which was released and over millions of years slowly accumulated in the atmosphere. Because it releases O_2, photosynthesis that relies on the oxidation of water is termed *oxygenic photosynthesis*. As discussed in detail in Chapter 7, the evolution of oxygenic photosynthesis represents a remarkable energetic feat since water is not an easy molecule to oxidize.

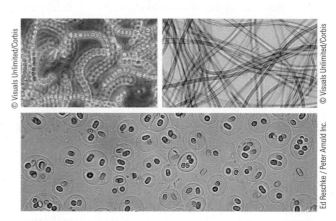

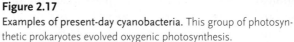

Figure 2.17
Examples of present-day cyanobacteria. This group of photosynthetic prokaryotes evolved oxygenic photosynthesis.

Figure 2.16
The rust layers in banded iron formations provide evidence for the rise of atmospheric oxygen.

The huge advantage afforded to cyanobacteria by utilizing oxygenic photosynthesis has, interestingly, nothing to do with oxygen but everything to do with water. Unlike compounds such as H_2S and Fe^{2+}, water was, and remains, far more abundant in the environment. This meant that cyanobacteria could thrive virtually anywhere there was sunlight. As you would expect, the evolution of oxygenic photosynthesis resulted in an explosion of life as cyanobacteria quickly became a dominant life form on early Earth. Although it evolved about 3 billion years ago, oxygenic photosynthesis remains the dominant form of photosynthesis used by all plants and algae, as well as present-day cyanobacteria.

The development of oxygenic photosynthesis was also a critical event in the evolution and diversification of life on Earth because the rise in atmospheric O_2 led quite rapidly to the evolution of prokaryotic cells, which are able to undergo aerobic respiration. We discuss this in detail in Chapter 6, but for now remember that in aerobic respiration, energy is extracted from food molecules, with O_2 acting as the final electron acceptor. Aerobic respiration allowed organisms to extract a much greater amount of energy from food molecules than respiration that does not use O_2 (anaerobic respiration). As you will see in the next few sections, the rise in atmospheric O_2 by the development of oxygenic photosynthesis was a key factor that led to the development of eukaryotic cells.

STUDY BREAK

1. What is panspermia?
2. What was the advantage gained by oxygenic photosynthesis?

2.5 Eukaryotic Cells

Figure 2.18 shows a typical eukaryotic cell. All present-day eukaryotic cells have several interrelated characteristics that distinguish them from prokaryotes:

- the separation of DNA and cytoplasm by a nuclear envelope
- the presence in the cytoplasm of membrane-bound compartments with specialized functions: mitochondria, chloroplasts, endoplasmic reticulum (ER), and the Golgi complex, among others
- highly specialized motor (contractile) proteins that move cells and internal cell parts

In this section, we discuss how eukaryotes most probably evolved from associations of prokaryotes.

2.5a The Endomembrane System Is Derived from the Plasma Membrane

Eukaryotic cells are characterized by an **endomembrane system** (*endo* = within), a collection of interrelated internal membranous sacs that divide the cell

motor proteins move cells and internal cell parts.

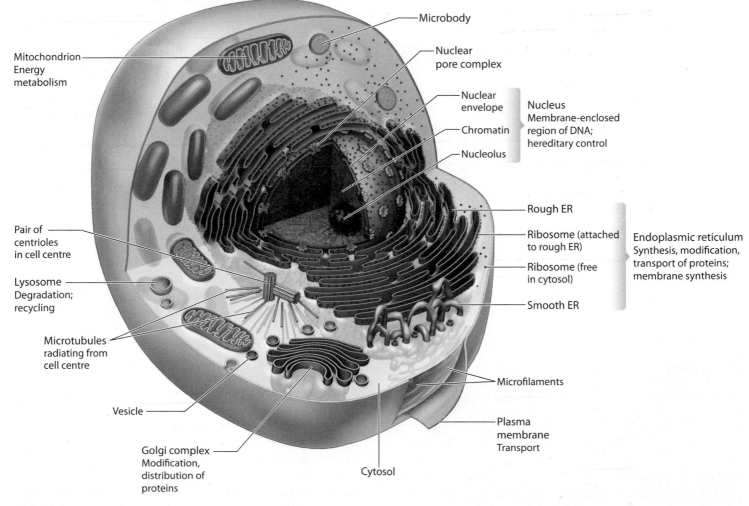

Figure 2.18
Eukaryotic cell.

Microbody

Nuclear pore complex

Nuclear envelope
Chromatin
Nucleolus

Nucleus
Membrane-enclosed region of DNA; hereditary control

Mitochondrion
Energy metabolism

Pair of centrioles in cell centre

Lysosome
Degradation; recycling

Microtubules radiating from cell centre

Vesicle

Golgi complex
Modification, distribution of proteins

Cytosol

Rough ER
Ribosome (attached to rough ER)
Ribosome (free in cytosol)

Endoplasmic reticulum
Synthesis, modification, transport of proteins; membrane synthesis

Smooth ER

Microfilaments

Plasma membrane
Transport

into functional and structural compartments called organelles. The major membrane components include the nuclear envelope, the ER, and the Golgi complex. Infolding of the plasma membrane is believed to be responsible for the evolution of all of these structures (Figure 2.19, left illustration). Researchers hypothesize that, in cell lines leading from prokaryotes to eukaryotes, pockets of the plasma membrane may have extended inward and surrounded the nuclear region. Some of these membranes fused around the DNA, forming the nuclear envelope and, hence, the nucleus. The remaining membranes formed vesicles in the cytoplasm that gave rise to the ER and the Golgi complex (Figure 2.19, right illustration).

The membranes of the endomembrane system (Figure 2.20) are connected either directly, in the physical sense, or indirectly by vesicles, which are small membrane-bound compartments that transfer substances between parts of the system. The nuclear envelope controls the movement of both proteins and RNA molecules into and out of the nucleus. The ER and the Golgi complex together serve a variety of functions, including the synthesis and modification of proteins, their transport into membranes or to the outside of the cell, the synthesis of lipids, and the detoxification of harmful compounds. Let's look into the structure and function of these two parts of the endomembrane (see Figure 2.20) in more detail:

1. **Endoplasmic reticulum.** The **endoplasmic reticulum (ER)** is an extensive interconnected network (*reticulum* = little net) of membranous channels and vesicles. Each vesicle is formed by a single membrane that surrounds an enclosed space called the lumen of the ER. The ER occurs in two forms, rough ER and smooth ER, each with a specialized structure and function. The **rough ER** gets its name from the many ribosomes that stud its outer surface. Proteins synthesized on the rough

ER are destined for the plasma membrane or for release outside the cell. After being synthesized, these proteins enter the lumen where they fold into their final form. The proteins are then delivered to the cell surface within vesicles that pinch off from the ER and move to join with the Golgi complex. In comparison, the **smooth ER** does not have ribosomes attached to its surface. Instead of protein synthesis, the smooth ER serves various functions, including the synthesis of lipids that become part of cell membranes.

Proteins made by the ribosomes that are freely suspended in the cytosol remain in the cytosol, pass through the **nuclear pores** to enter the nucleus, or become parts of mitochondria, chloroplasts, the cytoskeleton, or other cytoplasmic structures.

2. **Golgi complex.** The **Golgi complex** consists of a stack of flattened membranous sacs and is usually located between the rough ER and the plasma membrane. The Golgi complex receives proteins made in the ER and transported to the complex in vesicles. Within the Golgi complex, further chemical modifications of the proteins occur. The modified proteins are then sorted into other vesicles that pinch off from the margins of Golgi sacs on the side of the complex that faces the plasma membrane. The Golgi complex regulates the movement of several types of proteins. Some are secreted from the cell, others become embedded in the plasma membrane, and yet others are placed in lysosomes. For example, proteins secreted from the cell are transported to the plasma membrane by **secretory vesicles**, which release their contents to the exterior by **exocytosis**. Vesicles may also form by the reverse process, called **endocytosis**, which brings molecules into the cell from the exterior.

2.5b The Theory of Endosymbiosis Suggests that Mitochondria and Chloroplasts Evolved from Ingested Prokaryotes

Besides the extensive endomembrane system, another clear characteristic of eukaryotic cells is the presence of energy-transducing organelles: the chloroplast and the mitochondrion (plural = mitochondria). From the last section, recall that all the membrane structures of the endomembrane systems are thought to have been derived from an infolding of the plasma membrane. By comparison, a large body of evidence supports a model of eukaryotic evolution that involves endosymbiosis—the mitochondria and chloroplasts are descendants of free-living prokaryotes (Figure 2.21, p. 38). The established **theory of endosymbiosis** states that the prokaryotic ancestors of modern mitochondria and chloroplasts were engulfed by larger prokaryotic cells, forming a mutually advantageous relationship called a symbiosis, and that slowly, over time, the host cell and the endosymbionts became inseparable parts of the same organism.

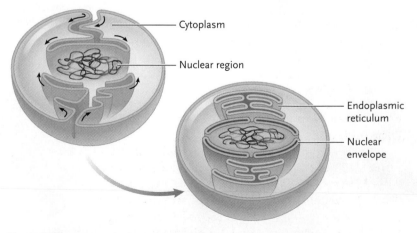

Figure 2.19
A hypothetical route for formation of the nuclear envelope and endoplasmic reticulum, through segments of the plasma membrane that were brought into the cytoplasm by endocytosis.

Cytoplasm

Nuclear region

Endoplasmic reticulum

Nuclear envelope

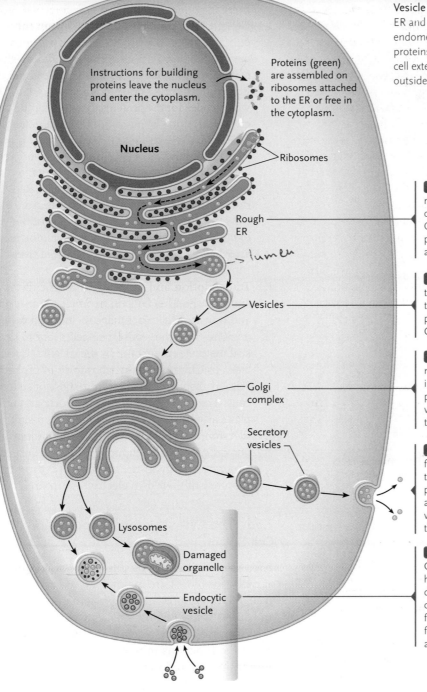

Figure 2.20
Vesicle traffic in the cytoplasm. The ER and Golgi complex are part of the endomembrane system., which releases proteins and other substances to the cell exterior and gathers materials from outside the cell.

Instructions for building proteins leave the nucleus and enter the cytoplasm.

Proteins (green) are assembled on ribosomes attached to the ER or free in the cytoplasm.

Nucleus

Ribosomes

Rough ER

lumen

Vesicles

Golgi complex

Secretory vesicles

Lysosomes

Damaged organelle

Endocytic vesicle

1 Proteins made by ER ribosomes enter ER membranes or the space inside ER cisternae. Chemical modification of some proteins begins. Membrane lipids are also made in the ER.

2 Vesicles bud from the ER membrane and then transport unfinished proteins and lipids to the Golgi complex.

3 Protein and lipid modification is completed in the Golgi complex, and products are sorted into vesicles that bud from the complex.

4 Secretory vesicles budding from the Golgi membranes transport finished products to the plasma membrane. The products are released by exocytosis. Other vesicles remain in storage in the cytoplasm.

5 Lysosomes budding from the Golgi membranes contain hydrolytic enzymes that digest damaged organelles or the contents of endocytic vesicles that fuse with them. Endocytic vesicles form at the plasma membrane and move into the cytoplasm.

The rise in atmospheric O_2 is thought to be a key factor in the occurrence of endosymbiosis. Mitochondria carry out aerobic respiration; thus, it is thought their ancestors were free-living aerobic prokaryotic cells. These cells would have been able to generate far more ATP from the same amount of food as a comparable anaerobic cell. Endosymbiosis of these small aerobic cells would give a larger anaerobic cell a distinct energy advantage compared with other anaerobic cells. In the same way, the modern chloroplast is thought to be derived from endosymbiotic events involving cyanobacteria. Because cyanobacteria are photosynthetic, the host cell would be able to utilize sunlight as a source of energy. Additionally, because cyanobacteria carry out *oxygenic* photosynthesis, the host cell could easily supply the water needed to drive photosynthesis.

Whereas virtually all eukaryotic cells contain mitochondria, only plants and algae contain both mitochondria and chloroplasts. This fact indicates that endosymbiosis occurred in stages, with the event leading to the evolution of mitochondria occurring first. Once eukaryotic cells with the ability for aerobic respiration developed, some of these became photosynthetic after taking up cyanobacteria. This lineage developed into the plants and algae of today.

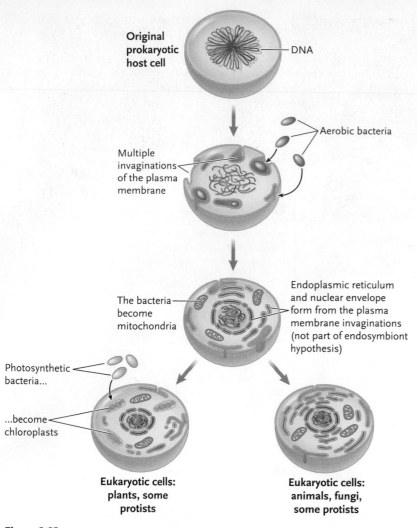

Original prokaryotic host cell

DNA

Aerobic bacteria

Multiple invaginations of the plasma membrane

The bacteria become mitochondria

Endoplasmic reticulum and nuclear envelope form from the plasma membrane invaginations (not part of endosymbiont hypothesis)

Photosynthetic bacteria...

...become chloroplasts

Eukaryotic cells: plants, some protists

Eukaryotic cells: animals, fungi, some protists

Figure 2.21

The endosymbiont hypothesis. Mitochondria and chloroplasts of eukaryotic cells are thought to have originated from various bacteria that lived as endosymbionts within other cells.

2.5c   Several Lines of Evidence Support the Theory of Endosymbiosis

If the endosymbiont theory is correct and both mitochondria and chloroplasts are descendants from prokaryotic cells, then these organelles should share some clear structural and biochemical features with modern prokaryotes. Five lines of evidence suggest that these energy-transducing organelles do have distinctly prokaryotic characteristics that are not found in other eukaryotic cells:

1. **Morphology.** The form or shape (morphology) of both mitochondria and chloroplasts is similar to that of a prokaryotic cell. Mitochondria resemble aerobic prokaryotes, and chloroplasts resemble cyanobacteria.

2. **Reproduction.** A cell cannot make a mitochondrion or a chloroplast. Just like free-living prokaryotic cells, mitochondria or chloroplasts are derived only from preexisting mitochondria or chloroplasts. Both chloroplasts and mitochondria divide by

binary fission, which is how prokaryotic cells divide (see Chapter 9).

3. **Genetic information.** If the ancestors of mitochondria and chloroplasts were free-living cells, then one could predict that these organelles should contain their own DNA. This is indeed the case. Both mitochondria and chloroplasts contain DNA, which codes for the proteins essential for the organelle's function. Whereas a free-living bacterium contains a few thousand protein-coding genes, the DNA found in energy-transducing organelles contain less than a hundred. The reason for this is that many of the genes have been relocated to the nucleus. The protein encoded by the gene is still the same, but the movement of some of the genes to the nucleus is thought to have given the nucleus and thus the host cell better control of overall cell function.

4. **Transcription and translation.** Both chloroplasts and mitochondria contain a complete transcription and translational machinery, including a variety of enzymes and the ribosomes necessary to synthesize the proteins encoded by their DNA. As you will learn in Chapter 13, the ribosomes of prokaryotic cells are distinctly different from those of eukaryotic cells. The ribosomes of mitochondria and chloroplasts are similar to the type found in prokaryotes.

5. **Electron transport.** Similar to free-living prokaryotic cells, both mitochondria and chloroplasts can generate energy in the form of ATP through the presence of their own electron transport chains.

2.5d   The Cytoskeleton Supports and Moves Cell Structures

The characteristic shape and internal organization of each type of cell are maintained in part by its **cytoskeleton**, the interconnected system of protein fibres and tubes that extends throughout the cytoplasm. The cytoskeleton also reinforces the plasma membrane and functions in movement, both of structures within the cell and of the cell as a whole. The cytoskeleton of animal cells contains three major types of structural elements: microtubules, intermediate filaments, and microfilaments **(Figure 2.22).** Plant cytoskeletons contain only microtubules and microfilaments. As shown in Figure 2.22a, **microtubules** are microscopic hollow tubes. **Intermediate filaments** (see Figure 2.22b) are fibres that occur singly, in parallel bundles, and in interlinked networks, either alone or in combination with microtubules, microfilaments, or both. **Microfilaments** (see Figure 2.22c) are thin fibres that consist of two rows of protein subunits wound around each other in a long spiral.

Eukaryotic cell movements are generated by "motor" proteins that push or pull along microtubules or microfilaments. One end of a motor protein is firmly fixed to a cell structure such as a vesicle, a

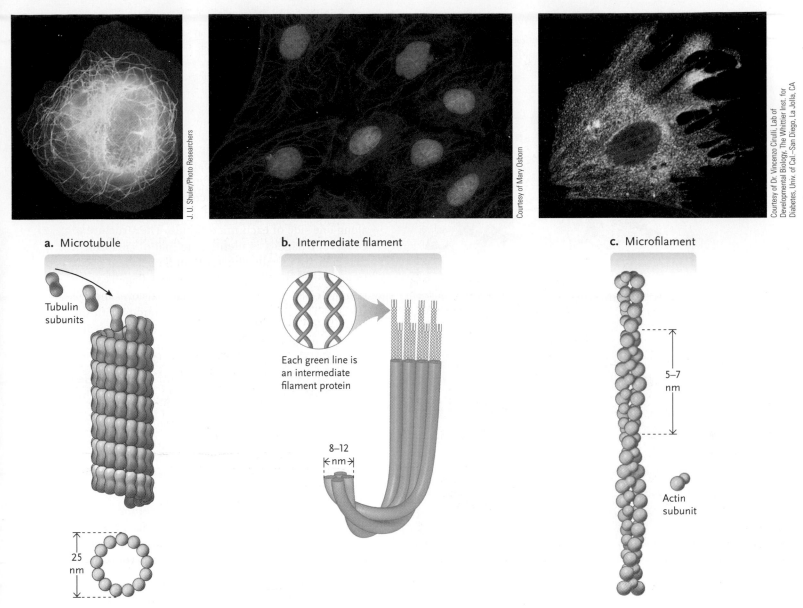

a. Microtubule

Tubulin subunits

25 nm

b. Intermediate filament

Each green line is an intermediate filament protein

8–12 nm

c. Microfilament

5–7 nm

Actin subunit

J. U. Shuler/Photo Researchers

Courtesy of Mary Osborn

Courtesy of Dr. Vincenzo Cirulli, Lab of Developmental Biology, The Whittier Inst. for Diabetes, Univ. of Cal.–San Diego, La Jolla, CA

Figure 2.22
The major components of the cytoskeleton as visualized by specific staining and light microscopy (TOP) and molecular models (BOTTOM). **(a)** Microtubules are stained yellow in a pancreatic cell. Microtubules are assembled from individual tubulin subunits. **(b)** Intermediate filaments assembled from keratin proteins in cells of the kangaroo rat. The nucleus is stained blue in these cells. In intermediate filaments eight protein chains wind together to form each subunit shown as a green cylinder. **(c)** Microfilaments (red) in a migrating mammalian cell. A microfilament is assembled from two rows of actin proteins, wound around each other into a double helix.

microtubule, or a microfilament. The other end has reactive groups that "walk" along another microtubule or microfilament by making an attachment, forcefully swivelling a short distance, and then releasing **(Figure 2.23, p. 40)**. ATP supplies the energy for the walking movements.

Some cell movements, such as the whipping motions of sperm tails, depend entirely on microtubules and their motor proteins. Microfilaments are solely responsible for other types of movements, including *amoeboid motion*, the actively flowing motion of cytoplasm called *cytoplasmic streaming*, and the contraction of muscle cells (the roles of myosin and microfilaments in muscle contraction are discussed further in Chapter 36). When animal cells divide, both microtubules and microfilaments are active—the chromosomes are divided and moved by microtubules, and the cytoplasm is divided by microfilaments (see Chapter 11 for further discussion).

2.5e The Flagella of Eukaryotes and Prokaryotes Are Not Evolutionarily Related

Flagella (singular = flagellum) are long, hair-like structures that project from the cell surface and function in cell movement. Flagella are common on single-celled prokaryotes and numerous eukaryotic cells. Although they superficially look the same and serve the same function, the flagella of eukaryotes and prokaryotes are structurally different. A bacterial

a. "Walking" end of a kinesin molecule

Connects to cell structure
such as a vesicle

One "foot" of
motor protein

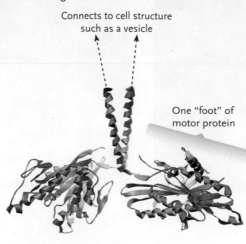

b. How a kinesin molecule "walks"

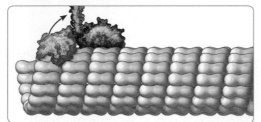

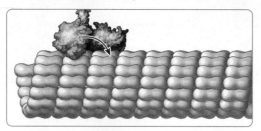

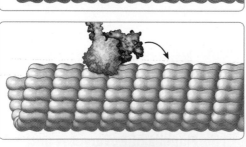

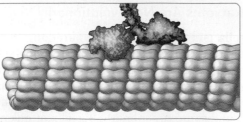

Analogous => Same function,
not share evol. history

Homologous => Do share
evolutionary history.

Figure 2.23

The microtubule motor protein kinesin. **(a)** Structure of the end of a kinesin molecule that "walks" along a microtubule, with alpha-helical segments shown as spirals and beta strands as flat ribbons. **(b)** How a kinesin molecule walks along the surface of a molecule by alternately attaching and releasing its "feet."

flagellum **(Figure 2.24),** which is made of a single protein called flagellin, moves the cell by rotating like the propeller of a boat. In comparison, the flagella of a eukaryote are constructed of microtubules, and their movement is whiplike. The actual flagellum bends in response to the movement of a protein called dynein along one side of each microtubule. The structure of eukaryotic flagella is identical to that of cilia except that cilia are usually shorter than flagella and occur in greater numbers on cells. Whereas flagella serve to move cells, cilia act to move materials over the cell surface. The plasma membrane surrounds both the cilia and flagella of eukaryotic cells, whereas prokaryotic flagella protrude through the membrane.

A bundle of microtubules extends from the base to the tip of a eukaryotic flagellum or **cilium (see Figure 2.25).** In the bundle, a circle of nine double microtubules surrounds a central pair of single microtubules, forming what is known as the *9 + 2 complex.* Dynein motor proteins slide the microtubules of the 9 + 2 complex over each other to produce the flagellar or ciliar movements **(Figure 2.26, p. 42).**

Because the flagella of eukaryotes serve the same purpose as the flagella of prokaryotes, combined with the fact that they look similar, you may think that the two are evolutionarily related, that the **prokaryotic flagellum** was the ancestor of the flagellum of eukaryotes. This, however, is not the case. At the molecular level, there is nothing similar between the two structures. The proteins involved are distinctly different, being encoded by different genes, and as we have seen, they function in distinctly different ways. Structures that perform the same function but do not share a common evolutionary history are said to be analogous structures. Structures that are similar because they *do* share a common evolutionary history are said to be homologous. You will learn much more about analogous and homologous structures in Chapter 10.

2.5f Why Are Eukaryotic Cells Larger than Prokaryotic Cells?

The size of a cell is determined primarily by its *surface area* being able to supply its *volume* with the necessary metabolic requirements for life. The cubes in **Figure 2.27, p. 42** can be used to represent single cells. Although the overall surface area of a cell increases as the square of its length, the cell's volume increases as the cube of that dimension. So, as a cell gets larger, its volume increases much more rapidly than its surface area does. In other words, its surface area to volume ratio decreases.

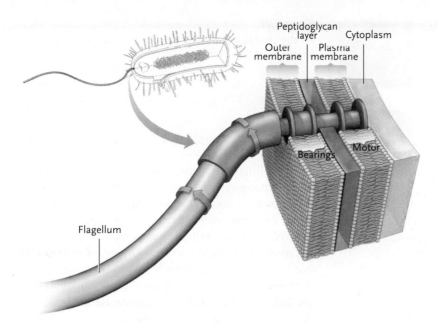

Peptidoglycan
layer
Outer
membrane
Plasma
membrane
Cytoplasm

Figure 2.24
A flagellum of a bacterium (prokaryote). The flagellum spins around its axis which causes the cell to move.

Bearings   Motor

Flagellum

a. Cross section of flagellum

b. Micrograph of flagellum

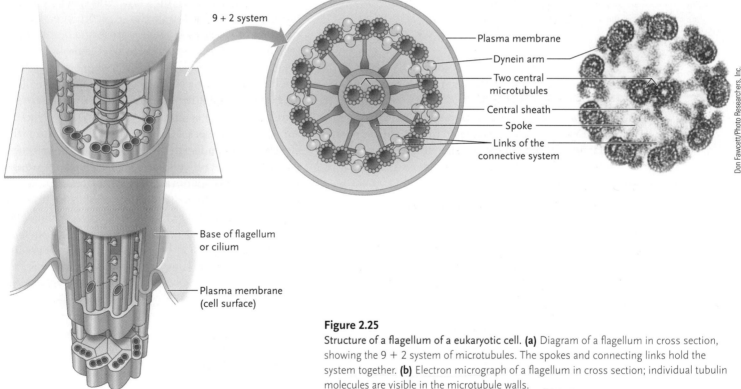

9 + 2 system

Plasma membrane
Dynein arm
Two central microtubules
Central sheath
Spoke
Links of the connective system

Don Fawcett/Photo Researchers, Inc.

Base of flagellum or cilium

Plasma membrane (cell surface)

Figure 2.25
Structure of a flagellum of a eukaryotic cell. **(a)** Diagram of a flagellum in cross section, showing the 9 + 2 system of microtubules. The spokes and connecting links hold the system together. **(b)** Electron micrograph of a flagellum in cross section; individual tubulin molecules are visible in the microtubule walls.

Think of the plasma membrane of a prokaryotic cell as the total surface area across which nutrients and waste products move into and out of the cell. It is also the location of the electron transport chains used to make ATP. Now think of the total volume of the cell. This volume needs to be supported by the energy produced by the electron transport chains and the nutrient/waste transport systems of the plasma membrane. As a cell increases in size and its surface area to volume ratio decreases, a point will be reached where the volume is too great to be supported by the processes occurring on the plasma membrane. The plasma membrane can hold only a finite number of transport proteins and only a limited number of electron transport chains.

Figure 2.28, p. 43 shows that the bacterial cells are much smaller than the pink epithelial cells (the lining of the nose). *Why can a eukaryotic cell be larger (and thus have a lower overall surface area to volume ratio) than a prokaryotic cell?* The answer is that a eukaryotic cell has a large area of internal membrane structures with specialized functions

a. Flagella beat in smooth, S-shaped waves that travel from base to tip.

Base

Tip

Lennart Nilsson

Figure 2.26
Flagellar and ciliary beating patterns. The micrographs show a few human sperm, each with a flagellum (top), and cilia from the lining of an airway in the lungs (bottom).

b. Cilia beat in an oarlike power stroke (dark orange) followed by a recovery stroke (light orange).

CNRI/SPL/Photo Researchers

c. The waves and bends are produced by dynein motor proteins, which slide the microtubule doublets over each other. An examination of the tip of a bent cilium or flagellum shows that the doublets extend farther toward the tip on the side toward the bend, confirming that the doublets actually slide as the shaft of the cilium or flagellum bends.

Straight

Link

Bent

that can support the larger cell volume. For example, a typical animal cell may contain hundreds of mitochondria, each one producing ATP to support the needs of the cell. As well, eukaryotic cells contain the endomembrane system, which allows the efficient movement of proteins and lipids throughout the cell and provides various compartments for synthesis and storage.

2.5g The Evolution of Multicellular Eukaryotes

One of the most profound transitions in the history of life was the evolution of multicellular eukaryotes. Besides consisting of at least two cells, a key trait of

a multicellular organism is that a "division of labour" exists among the cells of the organism. That is, the cells are not identical in structure and/or function. Some cells may specialize in harvesting energy, for example, whereas others may serve a specific role in the motility of the organism. The evolution of multicellularity meant that cells no longer needed to be autonomous (independent). In a multicellular system, the cells cooperate with one another for the benefit of the entire organism. Over evolutionary time, this specialization of cell function led to the development of the specialized tissues and organs that are so clearly evident in modern eukaryotes.

Like early prokaryotes and eukaryotes, there is little, if any, evidence in the fossil record of early multicellular organisms. How they arose and developed is still an area of intensive research. It is thought, however, that multicellularity arose independently along the lineages leading to fungi, plants, and animals. A very useful model for the study of multicellularity is found in a group of green algae called the volvocine. All of the members of this group are evolutionarily closely related and span the full range of size and complexity from the unicellular *Chlamydomonas*, through various colonial genera, to the multicellular *Volvox* **(Figure 2.29)**. Unlike a true multicellular organism, a cell colony is a group of cells that are all of one type; there is no specialization in cell structure or function. *Volvox* consists of a sphere of two to three thousand small, flagellated, *Chlamydomonas*-like cells that provide the individual *Volvox* with the ability to move. In

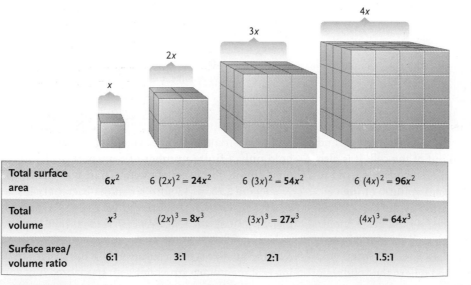

Figure 2.27
Relationship between surface area and volume. The surface area of an object increases as a square of the linear dimension, whereas the volume increases as a cube of that dimension.

	x	$2x$	$3x$	$4x$
Total surface area	$6x^2$	$6(2x)^2 = 24x^2$	$6(3x)^2 = 54x^2$	$6(4x)^2 = 96x^2$
Total volume	x^3	$(2x)^3 = 8x^3$	$(3x)^3 = 27x^3$	$(4x)^3 = 64x^3$
Surface area/ volume ratio	6:1	3:1	2:1	1.5:1

Figure 2.28

The yellow rods are bacteria covering the surface of skin cells lining the interior of a human nose. Why are the skin cells so large compared to the bacterial cells?

If prokaryotic cells first evolved some 3.5 billion years ago, it took up to 1.3 billion years for eukaryotic cells to evolve from prokaryotes (see Figure 24.2). If so, this long interval probably reflects the complexity of the adaptations required as prokaryotic cells evolved to become eukaryotic cells. Of course, it is possible that eukaryotic cells evolved more quickly and we have yet to find the evidence.

Overall, the events outlined in this chapter, leading from Earth's origin to the appearance of eukaryotic cells, may seem improbable. But as scientist and author George Wald of Harvard University put it, given the total time span of these events, more than 3.5 billion years, "the impossible becomes possible, the possible probable, and the probable virtually certain. One has only to wait; time itself performs the miracles." Some researchers go a step further and maintain that the evolution of life on our planet was an inevitable outcome of the initial physical and chemical conditions established by Earth's origin, among them a reducing atmosphere (at least in some locations), a size that generates moderate gravitational forces, and a distance from the Sun that results in average surface temperatures between the freezing and boiling points of water.

addition, within the sphere lie about 16 large nonmotile cells that serve a specialized role in reproduction.

2.5h Life May Have Been the Inevitable Consequence of the Physical Conditions of Primitive Earth

How long did it take for evolutionary mechanisms to produce fully eukaryotic cells? The oldest known fossil eukaryotes are 2.2 billion years old.

STUDY BREAK

1. What is the evidence in support of endosymbiosis?
2. What role is served by the cytoskeleton?
3. What are the key traits of a multicellular organism?

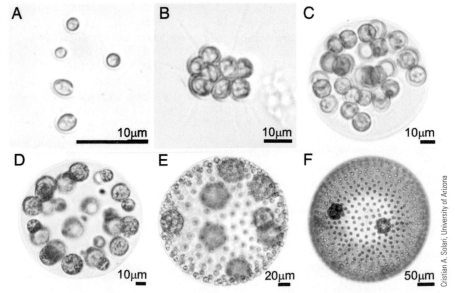

Figure 2.29

Examples of species of the volvocine that differ in cell number, colony size and degree of specialization.
(a) *Chlamydomonas reinhardtii*, a unicell (b) *Gonium pectorale*, a group of undifferentiated cells
(c) *Eudorina elegans*, a spherical colony of undifferentiated cells.
(d) *Pleodorina californica*, (e) *Volvox carteri* (f) *Volvox aureus*. In d.–f. two cell types are present - numerous smaller somatic cells and fewer larger reproductive cells.

UNANSWERED QUESTIONS

1. Does life exist elsewhere in our solar system? In our galaxy? | 2. Is it possible to synthesize life in the laboratory?

Review

Go to CENGAGENOW at http://hed.nelson.com/ to access quizzing, animations, exercises, articles, and personalized homework help.

2.1 What Is Life?

- All forms of life share seven characteristics: order, energy utilization, homeostasis, response to stimuli, growth, reproduction, and evolution.
- According to the cell theory, (1) all living organisms are composed of cells, (2) cells are the functional units of life, and (3) cells arise only from preexisting cells by a process of division.

2.2 The Chemical Origins of Life

- Earth and the rest of the solar system were formed about 4.6 billion years ago.
- The Oparin–Haldane hypothesis maintains that the organic molecules that formed the building blocks of life, such as amino acids, could have been formed given the conditions that prevailed on primitive Earth, including a reducing atmosphere that lacked oxygen.
- The Miller–Urey experiment demonstrated that abiotic synthesis of biologically important molecules is possible.
- The key macromolecules of life, such as proteins and nucleic acids, are polymers that were not formed by the Miller–Urey experiment. Instead, it is thought that polymerization reactions could have occurred on solid surfaces, such as clay.
- Organic molecules produced by chance in early Earth's environment formed aggregates that became membrane bound in protobionts, primitive cell-like structures with some of the properties of life. Protobionts may have been the precursors of cells.

2.3 The Origins of Information and Metabolism

- Living cells required the development of several critical components, notably energy-harnessing pathways, and a system based on nucleic acids that could store and pass on the information required to make proteins.
- Ribozymes are a group of RNA molecules that can catalyze specific reactions. Because they can store information and drive catalysis, it is thought that RNA was the first molecule from which both DNA and proteins developed.
- Because of their greater diversity and much higher rate of catalysis, proteins became the dominant structural and functional macromolecule of all cells.
- DNA is more stable than RNA and thus evolved as a better repository of genetic information.
- Early metabolism was probably based on simple oxidation–reduction reactions.

2.4 Early Life

- Stromatolites dated to 2.3 billion years ago represent the earliest fossil evidence of life.
- Panspermia is the hypothesis that very simple forms of life are present in space and seeded Earth soon after it cooled.
- Prokaryotic cells lack a nucleus, which is a characteristic of eukaryotic cells.
- Both prokaryotic and eukaryotic cells share common features: plasma membrane, electron transport chains, and transcription–translation machinery that relies on ribosomes.
- Some early cells developed the capacity to carry out photosynthesis using water as an electron donor; the oxygen produced as a by-product accumulated, and the oxidizing character of Earth's atmosphere increased. From this time on, organic molecules produced in the environment were quickly broken down by oxidation, and life could arise only from preexisting life, as in today's world.

2.5 Eukaryotic Cells

- Eukaryotic cells possess an endomembrane system that probably evolved from infolding of the plasma membrane. The endomembrane system consists of the nuclear envelope, the ER, and the Golgi complex.
- The ER occurs in two forms, rough and smooth. The ribosome-studded rough ER makes proteins that become part of cell membranes or are released from the cell. Smooth ER synthesizes lipids and breaks down toxic substances.
- The Golgi complex chemically modifies proteins made in the rough ER and sorts finished proteins to be secreted from the cell or embedded in the plasma membrane.
- The energy-transducing organelles—the chloroplasts and the mitochondria—are thought to have been derived from free-living prokaryotic cells.
- According to the theory of endosymbiosis, mitochondria developed from ingested prokaryotes that were capable of using oxygen for aerobic respiration; chloroplasts developed from ingested cyanobacteria.
- The cytoskeleton is a supportive structure built from microtubules, intermediate filaments, and microfilaments in animal cells but only from microtubules and microfilaments in plants.
- Motor proteins walking along microtubules and microfilaments produce most cell movements.
- Motor protein–controlled sliding of microtubules generates the movements of flagella and cilia of eukaryotes. The flagella of prokaryotes are functionally and structurally very different.
- Multicellular eukaryotes probably evolved by differentiation of cells of the same species that had congregated into colonies. Multicellularity evolved several times, producing lineages of several algae and ancestors of fungi, plants, and animals.

Questions

Self-Test Questions

1. Which of the following is not a characteristic of all living organisms?
   a. Genetic information is used for the synthesis of proteins.
   b. Genetic information is passed to the next generation.
   c. Has DNA that is contained within the nucleus.
   d. Energy is obtained from the surrounding environment.
   e. Populations of organisms change over generations.

2. According to the Oparin–Haldane hypothesis, the atmosphere when life began is thought to have been composed primarily of
   a. H_2O, N_2, and CO_2.
   b. H_2, H_2O, NH_3, and CH_4.
   c. H_2O, N_2, O_2, and CO_2.
   d. O_2 and no H_2.
   e. H_2 only.

3. The O_2 in the atmosphere comes from
   a. aerobic respiration.
   b. a type of photosynthesis that uses oxygen.
   c. a type of photosynthesis that oxidizes water.
   d. anaeorobic respiration.
   e. the formation of Earth.

4. The Miller–Urey experiment
   a. used an atmosphere rich in O_2.
   b. demonstrated that abiotic protein synthesis was possible.
   c. did not require a source of energy.
   d. did not require water as a reactant.
   e. demonstrated that abiotic synthesis of amino acids was possible.

5. The hypothesis that life on Earth developed from microbes from space (panspermia) is supported by the fact that
   a. life seemingly developed quickly after Earth was formed.
   b. life on Earth is similar to the forms of life found on Jupiter.
   c. DNA and proteins have been discovered in the tails of comets.
   d. prokaryotic cells have been shown to survive extreme conditions.
   e. Both a and d are correct.

6. Ribozymes may have played a critical role in the evolution of life because they
   a. carry genetic information.
   b. were the first polymers of amino acids.
   c. display catalytic activity.
   d. were double stranded like DNA.
   e. Both a and c are correct.

7. As part of the evolution of eukaryotic cells, infolding of the plasma membrane led to the formation of
   a. chromosomes.
   b. mitochondria.
   c. ribosomes.
   d. the nuclear envelope.
   e. microtubules.

8. Which of the following statements does NOT support the theory of endosymbiosis? Both mitochondria and chloroplasts
   a. are each about the same size and shape of many bacterial cells.
   b. are surrounded by a membrane.
   c. contain ribosomes.
   d. possess electron transport chains.
   e. contain DNA.

9. Compared with prokaryotic cells, eukaryotic cells tend to be larger because they
   a. contain DNA.
   b. contain ribosomes.
   c. contain a nucleus.
   d. grow faster.
   e. have an overall greater membrane surface area.

10. A key trait of multicellular organisms is
    a. different amounts of DNA among cells.
    b. division of labour among cells.
    c. the ability to photosynthesize.
    d. the presence of mitochondria.
    e. the presence of flagellated cells.

Questions for Discussion

1. What evidence supports the idea that life originated through inanimate chemical processes?

2. Most scientists agree that life on Earth can arise only from preexisting life, but also that life could have originated spontaneously on primordial Earth. Can you reconcile these seemingly contradictory statements?

3. What conditions would likely be necessary for a planet located elsewhere in the universe to evolve life similar to that on Earth?

4. What drove the evolution of the eukaryotic cell?

The symbols and arrows show how seasonal influenza A (H3N2) moves out from an area of overlapping epidemics in East and Southeast Asia.

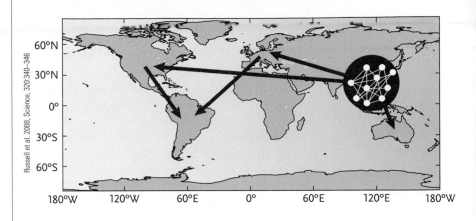

Russell et al. 2008, Science, 320:340–346

3 Selection, Biodiversity, and Biosphere

WHY IT MATTERS

Imagine yourself sitting in a crowded airplane bound from London, England, to Vancouver, Canada. The person sitting beside you has a runny nose, is sneezing and sucking on cough candies, and appears to have a fever. Your fellow passenger periodically dozes and does not eat anything during the flight. Recognizing that your seat mate is exhibiting many of the symptoms of influenza A, you hope that some of the other symptoms, such as vomiting and diarrhea, do not appear until after you have left the aircraft. You have just seen how influenza ("the flu") can affect people and how air travel can help it spread around the world.

At any given time, 5 to 15% of the global population of people exhibit the symptoms of influenza A. Every year, this strain of the influenza virus kills about 500 000 people. To study the spread of influenza A, Colin A. Russell and his colleagues analyzed about 13 000 human influenza A (H3N2) viruses, collecting viral material from infected people on six continents between 2002 and 2007. Their analysis revealed almost continuous circulation of H3N2 in East and Southeast Asia. This regional network of overlapping epidemics appeared to be the source of influenza outbreaks elsewhere in the world. These epidemics usually reached, in order, Oceania (Australia and other islands in the central and south Pacific), North America, and Europe, finally arriving in South America.

Since H3N2 was first reported in humans in 1968, it has undergone periods of relative stasis (evolutionary stability) lasting 3 to 8 years, followed by rapid changes. The evolution of H3N2 has been "punctuated" (see Chapter 20). The good news is that the virus changes relatively little once it has left Southeast Asia. This means that the World Health Organization has more opportunity to monitor the situation in East and Southeast Asia, allowing vaccines to be developed against the most threatening strains of H3N2. These vaccines offer us some protection from the illness.

This anecdote demonstrates evolutionary change in a virus, its dispersal around the world, and its impact on humans. Biology in action! Have you had your flu shot this year?

3.1 Biodiversity

The astonishing diversity of life in the biosphere is an array of riches. Measured as the number of species of organisms, **biodiversity** reflects the reality that life on Earth exists from the ocean floor to well into the atmosphere. The study of biology focuses on the levels of life, from molecules to organelles, cells, organisms, ecosystems, and the **biosphere (Figure 3.1)** (see Chapter 1). Exploring and understanding this reality can be one of the most rewarding challenges for humans in general and for biologists in particular.

In Chapter 1, we saw how access to light and energy are organizing factors for life on Earth. Now, examine the photographs in **Figure 3.2.** What organisms or parts of organisms appear in each photograph? What can these pictures tell us about the diversity of life? How can you relate them to the themes of light and energy? Speculate about which of these organisms are most closely related to one another. Look for more information about the members of this gallery as you proceed through this book.

How many different types of organisms live on Earth? There are different ways to answer this question, depending on how we define "type" of organism. If we take a taxonomic definition (see Chapter 18), we can consider the number of organisms in each

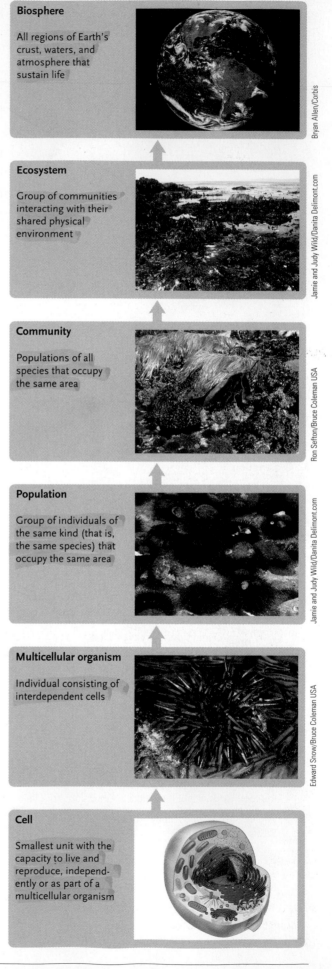

Biosphere

All regions of Earth's crust, waters, and atmosphere that sustain life

Bryan Allen/Corbis

Ecosystem

Group of communities interacting with their shared physical environment

Jamie and Judy Wild/Danita Delimont.com

Community

Populations of all species that occupy the same area

Ron Sefton/Bruce Coleman USA

Population

Group of individuals of the same kind (that is, the same species) that occupy the same area

Jamie and Judy Wild/Danita Delimont.com

Multicellular organism

Individual consisting of interdependent cells

Edward Snow/Bruce Coleman USA

Cell

Smallest unit with the capacity to live and reproduce, independently or as part of a multicellular organism

Figure 3.1

The hierarchy of life. Each level in the hierarchy of life exhibits emergent properties that do not exist at lower levels. The middle four photos depict a rocky intertidal zone on the coast of Washington State.

Figure 3.2

(a) Mushroom orchid (b) Scales of pangolin (c) Bird's nest fungus (d) Zombie worm (e) Fern sporangia (f) Sea anenome
(g) Barnacles (h) Insects caught by *Pinguicula*.

kingdom. Although these numbers are easier to determine for certain kinds of organisms than for others, we can determine an overview of life on Earth by group of organisms **(Figure 3.3, p. 50).** We have quite accurate information about the numbers of species of large, easily observed organisms such as mammals, birds, and flowering plants. We do not have accurate information about the numbers of species of microscopic organisms that live in habitats where they are hard to observe. We have only rough estimates of the numbers of species of soil fungi and aquatic prokaryotes.

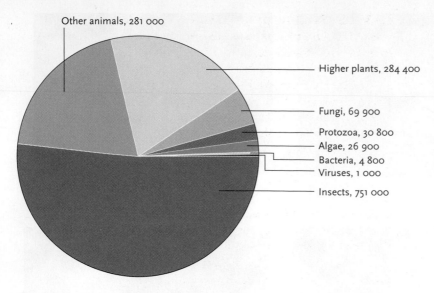

Other animals, 281 000
Higher plants, 284 400
Fungi, 69 900
Protozoa, 30 800
Algae, 26 900
Bacteria, 4 800
Viruses, 1 000
Insects, 751 000

Figure 3.3
Diversity of life. The approximate numbers of species in different groups of organisms.

When we group organisms by factors other than their taxonomic categories, we get a different picture of the diversity of life on Earth. One approach is to consider how organisms obtain carbon because carbon is the "backbone" of all organic molecules synthesized by an organism (see Chapter 47). Most plants are **autotrophs** (*auto* = self; *troph* = nourishment), which synthesize organic carbon molecules using inorganic carbon (CO_2). (Note that although CO_2 contains a carbon atom, oxides containing carbon are considered **inorganic molecules**.) All animals are heterotrophs, meaning that they obtain carbon from organic molecules, either from living hosts or from organic molecules in the products, wastes, or remains of dead organisms.

Organisms are also divided according to the source of the energy they use to drive biological activities. Chemotrophs (*chemo* = chemical; *troph* = nourishment) obtain energy by oxidizing inorganic or organic substances, whereas **phototrophs** obtain energy from light. Combining the carbon and energy sources allows us to group living organisms into four categories **(Table 3.1).**

Prokaryotes show the greatest diversity in their modes of securing carbon and energy. Note that prokaryotes are the only representatives of two of the categories, chemoautotrophs and photoheterotrophs; see Chapter 21 to find out more about the amazing metabolic diversity that exists among prokaryotes.

STUDY BREAK

Describe the differences among heterotrophs, autotrophs, photoautotrophs, and chemoautotrophs. Provide an example of each.

3.2 Selection

Selection occurs when some force or phenomenon affects the survival of individual organisms. An unexpected spring frost can kill many plants in your garden. Only the cold-resistant plants survive the selective force (temperature). When you hear about an outbreak of some disease in a hospital or care facility, you are often seeing an example of the outcome of selection. Bacteria that are resistant to **antibiotics**, for example, can survive and reproduce, overwhelming the defences of individuals and institutions. The same can be true with the emergence of pests that are resistant to pesticides, whether the targets are weeds, parasites, or insects.

Selection occurs when a large population of individuals is exposed to a lethal factor and only resistant individuals survive to reproduce. If resistance is inherited, then the offspring of survivors will be resistant. If the resistant population is able to reproduce quickly, there is the potential for explosive growth of a population of individuals who are immune to the lethal factor. When the target pests are bacteria, some of which can double their populations in minutes, it does not take long for resistant pests to take over (see Chapter 45). Imagine having 10 million toxic bacteria in your body. You take an antibiotic that kills 99.99% of them. The remaining 1000 bacteria are resistant to the antibiotic.

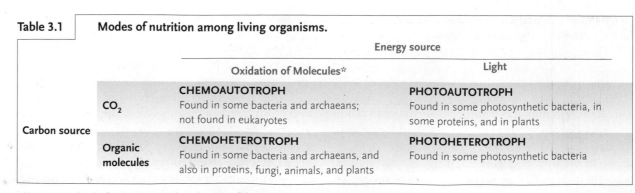

Table 3.1	Modes of nutrition among living organisms.		
		Energy source	
		Oxidation of Molecules*	Light
Carbon source	**CO_2**	**CHEMOAUTOTROPH** Found in some bacteria and archaeans; not found in eukaryotes	**PHOTOAUTOTROPH** Found in some photosynthetic bacteria, in some proteins, and in plants
	Organic molecules	**CHEMOHETEROTROPH** Found in some bacteria and archaeans, and also in proteins, fungi, animals, and plants	**PHOTOHETEROTROPH** Found in some photosynthetic bacteria

*Inorganic molecules for chemoautotrophs and organic molecules for chemoheterotrophs.

If their population doubles every 20 minutes, you will have over 10 million (now resistant) bacteria within 5 hours.

The key factors behind selection are a selective force (pressure) and the capacity for explosive population growth. When these factors coincide, we can be overrun by pests, such as antibiotic-resistant bacteria in hospitals or health care facilities, weeds in crop fields, or insect pests. When this happens, the consequences for humans can be deadly.

Selection is the major force responsible for evolution and biodiversity. A recurring theme in selection is genetic variation in the population put to the test by some selection pressure. Here are three examples of selection in action.

3.2a Case 1, Syphilis: Migration and Emergence of a Disease

Treponematoses are diseases caused by bacteria in the genus *Treponema*. *Treponema pallidum pallidum* is the bacterium that causes syphilis, a venereal disease also known as "the pox." Often the first signs of syphilis are small, painless sores (chancres) at the site of contact. This can progress to secondary stages (rash, fever, fatigue) and, if untreated, to tertiary syphilis, with symptoms that can include disfigurement, neurological disorders, and cardiovascular problems. *Treponema pallidum pertenue* causes yaws, a skin disease that usually afflicts people in hot, humid areas. The extinct *Treponema carateum* caused pinta, a skin disease confined to South and Central America. Perhaps also extinct, *Treponema pallidum endemicum* caused bejel, endemic syphilis that was limited to hot, arid climates in the Middle East. Genetic evidence indicates that *T. pallidum pertenue* is an older subspecies of *T. pallidum* than *T. pallidum pallidum* is, meaning that whereas yaws has afflicted people for a long time, syphilis caused by *T. pallidum pallidum* is relatively new. Syphilis and other treponemal diseases, except pinta, leave distinct marks on the skeleton, which have allowed paleoanthropologists to document the incidence of these diseases in human skeletal remains and determine their prehistoric distribution.

The first outbreak of syphilis in Europe occurred in 1495, and since then, it has killed tens of thousands of people. Syphilis has long been thought to have originated in the New World. In 2008, genetic analyses supported the hypothesis that a new strain of *T. pallidum (T. pallidum pallidum)* emerged in Europe in 1495, brought from the New World by members of Columbus's crew.

The history of *T. pallidum* appears to have involved three steps:

- First, *T. pallidum* appeared as a nonvenereal infection and spread with humans throughout the Middle East, Europe, and the New World. At that point, the pathogen caused yaws, which was spread by skin-to-skin contact.
- Second, European explorers brought a strain of *T. pallidum* from the New World to Europe, where it emerged as the progenitor of the modern *T. pallidum pallidum* that caused syphilis. When clothed European explorers, such as Columbus and his crew, met unclothed natives in the New World, yaws (caused by *T. pallidum*) could not readily spread between the two groups of people because of the lack of skin-to-skin contact. But the explorers could be exposed to the lesions of yaws (and *T. pallidum*) during sex.
- Third, although the strains or subspecies of *T. pallidum* that caused yaws were thwarted by clothes, variants that occurred in the genital area could be transferred during sex. This meant success for the bacterium, and syphilis was the result.

The pivotal discovery giving genetic support to the theory that syphilis came from the New World emerged when a Canadian physician (Michael S. Silverman), working in isolated settlements in Guyana (South America), spotted lesions caused by yaws. He obtained samples of bacteria from the lesions and set the genetics side of the story in motion.

The key elements were genetic variation, differences in transmission of the disease-causing agent, and the opportunity for *T. pallidum pallidum* to spread widely due to people's sexual behaviour. In 2008, syphilis became more common, suggesting that the process is still in play.

3.2b Case 2, Evolution of Whales: A Change from Hoofed Mammal to Whale

The first fossil whales were found in rocks in south Asia dated to the Eocene, about 50 million years ago. Paleontologists had presumed that the ancestor of whales lived a hippopotamus-like existence, retreating to the water to avoid predators and going ashore at night to eat vegetation. The fossil evidence also indicated that whales and modern hoofed mammals (ungulates) shared a common ancestor and that hippopotomi are ungulates. But the oldest hippo ancestors are 15 million years old and have been found only in Africa, so timing and location mean that hippos are not close relatives of whales.

In 2007, Hans Thewissen and his colleagues reported evidence of an ungulate ancestor that was closely related to whales. The candidates, raccoon-sized species in the genus *Indohyus* (family Raoellidae), were Eocene fossils found in Kashmir (India). Thewissen and his colleagues presented several lines of evidence supporting the proposal that *Indohyus* was aquatic, lived a hippo-like existence, and shared a close ancestor with whales. *Indohyus* had dense bones and high levels of oxygen isotopes (O^{18}), two features indicating an aquatic lifestyle. *Indohyus* had crushing basins in their molar teeth, and the levels of carbon isotopes (C^{13}) suggested that they ate terrestrial plants. Raoellids also shared cochlear structures (see Chapter 34) with whales, notably the presence of a ridge called the "involucrum."

In the Eocene in what is now Kashmir, *Indohyus* lived an amphibious existence, entering the water to avoid predators and going ashore to eat vegetation. At some point, *Indohyus* species started to eat fish, which became the mainstay of their diet; this was also true of the earliest whales but not the living ones. Thewissen's proposal explains the development of an aquatic mammal from a terrestrial one, a herbivore to a piscivore.

Again, genetic variation, survival of individuals that used the water to avoid predation, and selection of strains of individuals that switched their diets to fish were the key elements.

3.2c Case 3, Climbing Plants: Reaching for the Light

Plants such as trees reach for the sun by growing tall, at least as tall as their neighbours. An alternative way for plants to get their share of sunlight is to climb on a physical support. Climbing plants are known as vines or lianas, and those that find suitable support often have biomass and reproductive output that matches or exceeds that of the trees on which they grow. Climbing plants are successful because they grow quickly, depend on reduced biomass of supporting structures (compared with trees), achieve higher leaf biomass, and thus outcompete other plants when it comes to reaching for the sun. At least 130 families of plants include climbing species, and vines represent at least 40% of the plant diversity in tropical forests. Whereas vines such as morning glories (*Ipomoea* spp.) are herbaceous, others, such as grapevines (*Vitus* spp.), are woody. Herbaceous vines grow readily on pioneer species of trees that are rarely robust enough to support woody vines.

In 2004, Ernesto Gianoli compared 48 groups of plants in which there was enough information about evolutionary relationships to assess the relative diversity of climber and nonclimber sister groups. In 38 cases, climbing taxa were more diverse than nonclimbers. Gianoli concluded that climbing was a "key" development in plants because it resulted in a great increase in numbers of species.

The success and diversity of climbing plants are reflected in the variety of structures they use for climbing. Some use tendrils, modified stems or leaves, which coil around supporting structures. Others use modified roots, sometimes holdfasts, to attach to supports. In still others, the stem itself coils clockwise or anticlockwise around the support. Note that Charles Darwin was one of the first to study climbing plants.

STUDY BREAK

Selection is the force responsible for evolution and biodiversity. What key elements aid in the selection and survival of certain individuals and their genetic traits?

3.3 Evolution

Evolution, a gradual change in the characteristics of a population of organisms over time, can be the result of selection. Evolution is a central key to understanding the diversity of life on Earth (see Chapters 17, 18, 19, and 20). Although the theory of evolution is widely accepted today by educated people around the world, the levels of acceptance vary among countries (Figure 3.4), perhaps reflecting variation in the degree to which science has been politicized. Teaching of evolution is not permitted in some educational jurisdictions. In this book, we consider evolution to be an organizing force in life and the foundation of modern biology. Understanding evolution is central to understanding the elements of biodiversity, but it does not mean believing or accepting that humans evolved from apes or from amoebas.

The theory of evolution explains both the unity and the diversity of all life; it tells us that all organisms alive today descended from a common ancestor, which explains why all organisms share features such as the use of adenosine triphosphate (ATP) as a cellular energy source, deoxyribonucleic acid (DNA) as genetic material, and plasma membranes composed of lipid bilayers. But evolution also tells us that species change over time as a result of natural selection. The central ideas of Darwin's theory of evolution by natural selection can be summarized as follows:

- Individual organisms in a population vary in many heritable traits.
- Any population has the potential to produce far more offspring than the environment can support. Competition for limited resources means that only some individuals survive.
- Some individuals in the population have traits that give them an advantage in their local environment; these organisms are more likely to survive and reproduce.

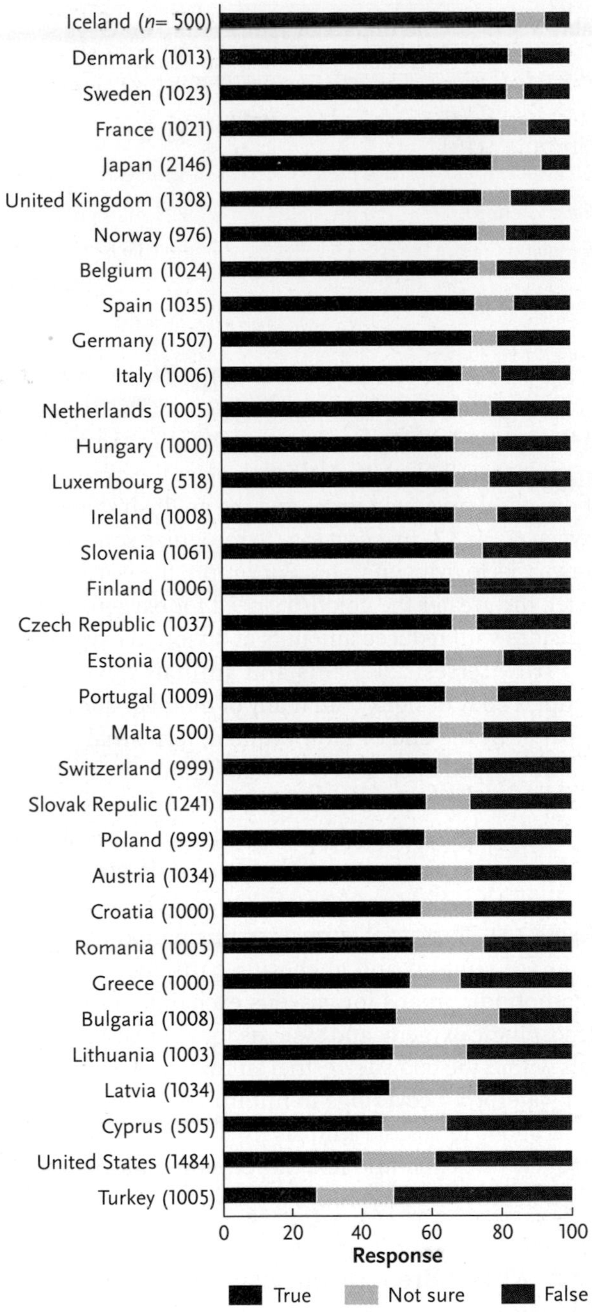

Figure 3.4

Public acceptance of evolution based on surveys of people living in 34 countries. Low acceptance in the United States appears to reflect, in part, the politicization of science and the rise of fundamentalism.

- These organisms pass on favourable traits to their offspring. Over time, the incidence of the trait(s) will change in the population.

Different environments favour different traits. Thus, even though all organisms share a common ancestor, they have diverged over evolutionary time in response to the selection pressures of different environments. The process of **adaptive radiation**, discussed next, is an example of such divergence.

3.3a Adaptive Radiation: Diversification of Lineages of Life

In the history of life on Earth, organisms have had to overcome fundamental barriers that, once crossed, opened many new opportunities for diversification (for example, the cases above under *Selection*). The development of photosynthesis is another example of such a breakthrough. Organisms with the ability to convert solar energy into usable chemical energy survived and thrived as they exploited the "new" energy source. The appearance of oxygenic photosynthesis increased the concentrations of oxygen (a by-product of the process), which led to aerobic respiration and the ozone layer, which allowed organisms to colonize terrestrial environments by blocking harmful ultraviolet (UV) rays. Together, the changes caused by an increase in atmospheric oxygen triggered an extraordinary diversification of life. There is paleontological evidence of the relative timing of some fundamental changes in life (e.g., evolution of whales), and sometimes we know the underlying factors (again, the whales).

An organism may move into a new **adaptive zone** after a chance innovation allows it to use the environment in a unique way. The ability of plants to move onto land opened new opportunities for animals. The dehydration-resistant eggs of early reptiles enabled them to complete their life cycle on land, opening terrestrial habitats to them. The evolution of flowers that attract insect pollinators was a key innovation in the history of flowering plants.

An adaptive zone may open up after the demise of a successful group, for example, the replacement of the mammals Multituberculata by Rodentia (see Chapter 48). We know that a rich diversity of soft-bodied organisms thrived in Precambrian seas. But the beginning of the Cambrian, about 600 million years ago, is marked by the disappearance of many of the soft-bodied organisms and the appearance of an extraordinary diversity of life, including many species with skeletons. The change from soft- to hard-bodied is reflected in the fossil record, but the reasons for the switch in body form are not clear.

3.3b Islands: Showcases of Evolution

Adaptive radiations, therefore, occur when an evolutionary breakthrough allows diversification of life. Adaptive radiations are a recurring theme in the development of biodiversity. At one level, we can see it in the evolution of the fauna and flora of the Hawaiian Islands, arguably the most isolated landmasses in the world. When Captain Cook arrived on the islands in 1778, Hawaii had about 2000 species of higher plants that had arisen from about 275 ancestral stocks. There were also about 6500 species of insects descended from 250 ancestral stocks. There were 600 to 700 species in the genus *Drosophila* alone. Many plants on Hawaii have undergone adaptive radiations. Violets have become shrubs, lobelias are tree-like. These radiatons have occurred in the absence of the plants normally filling the shrub and tree life styles. Biologists suspect that one ancestral insect species and one ancestral plant species gained access to Hawaii in each of the 25 000 to 100 000 years that the islands were "islands," that is, above water. Hawaii is a showcase of evolution and adaptive radiation. Recall that a species may arrive several times, so each arrival is not necessarily a new colonization event.

Islands elsewhere are well known as showcases of evolution and adaptive radiation. One celebrated case is the richness of the Galapagos Islands that so impressed Charles Darwin (see Chapter 20). But whether the setting is New Zealand, Madagascar, or Mauritius, the story repeats itself. As we will see in Chapter 48, island populations of animals and plants can be very vulnerable to extinction. Lamentably, Hawaii is also a showcase of the negative impact of humans on biodiversity.

Adaptive radiation on islands reminds us that species can be adapting to new ways of life at the same time in different parts of the world. The result is a mosaic of life, with many examples of parallel and convergent evolution (see Chapters 19 and 20, respectively).

3.3c Land: Organisms Conquer a New Frontier

The movement of organisms onto land presented many challenges (see Chapters 25, 26, and 27), and many "terrestrial" organisms actually live in films of water, so they have not forsaken an aquatic existence. Included on the list of challenges are matters of support, conservation of water, reproduction, and disposal of wastes. Other facts of life are also different for organisms living on land as opposed to in water.

Some of the differences between water and air include density and viscosity, which, in turn, affect rates of diffusion and availability of oxygen (Table 3.2). Animals operating in water extract dissolved oxygen, although some photoautotrophs actually break water molecules

Table 3.2.	Gases in Water and in Air.		
		Water	Air
Viscosity		100x	x
Density		1000y	y
Diffusion rate		Low	High
O_2 $mL.L^{-1}$		0–10	100–130
CO_2 $mL.L^{-1}$		0–13	>100
O_2 extraction		<80%	25%
% of energy budget to run pump that drives breathing, whether air or water		20%	1–2%

Table 3.3.	The Impact of Temperature on Oxygen Availability for Goldfish (*Carassius Auratus*).	
	5° C	35° C
O_2 available	9 $mL.L^{-1}$	5 $mL.L^{-1}$
Goldfish need	8 $mL.kg.h^{-1}$	225 $mL.kg.h^{-1}$
Ventilation rate	1.3 $L.kg.h^{-1}$	60 $L.kg.h^{-1}$

The amount of oxygen available is further reduced in salt water.

in the process of photosynthesis. Animals that breathe air have more ready access to oxygen and spend less of their overall energy budget acquiring it than aquatic animals (see Table 3.2). A closer look at the availability of dissolved oxygen in water and the goldfish's need for oxygen (Table 3.3) makes it easy to recognize some of the drawbacks to living in water. Put simply, the warmer the water, the greater the goldfish's need for oxygen, which coincides with reduced amounts of dissolved oxygen.

Truly terrestrial plants and animals have more complex body designs than many of their aquatic counterparts. By the end of the Devonian, terrestrial plants had developed specialized sexual organs, stems with mechanisms for fluid transport, structural elements such as wood to provide mechanical support, roots for anchorage, leaves as sites of photosynthesis, stomata in the leaves to allow passage of CO_2 and O_2, and seeds (Figure 3.5). Terrestrial animals of this period had skeletons for support and anchoring muscles (allowing locomotion), organs for gaseous exchange (breathing atmospheric oxygen), and systems for circulating materials within the body. Terrestrial animals and plants also had waterproof coverings to minimize the chances of desiccation. Terrestrial animals used nontoxic excretory products (urea and uric acid), whereas aquatic ones still relied heavily on ammonia.

3.3d Other Breakthroughs Underlying Adaptive Radiations

As you proceed through this book, look for other examples of breakthroughs that appeared to result in a radiation of organisms within a group (e.g., mammals or birds), or where different organisms adopted similar strategies. Examples include the insect traps of carnivorous plants, fungi, and spiders; the wings of bats, birds, insects, and pterosaurs; and the reinvasion of the oceans by reptiles and mammals.

See Chapters 17, 18, 19, and 20 for a more in-depth look at evolution and the ample evidence that has been gathered to support this theory.

Evolution is the idea behind representations of "trees of life" (Figure 3.6). Traditional trees of life are designed to illustrate the relationships between organisms over time and may be presented in the context of a geologic time series (see the geologic time table in *The Chemical and Physical Foundations of Biology* pages).

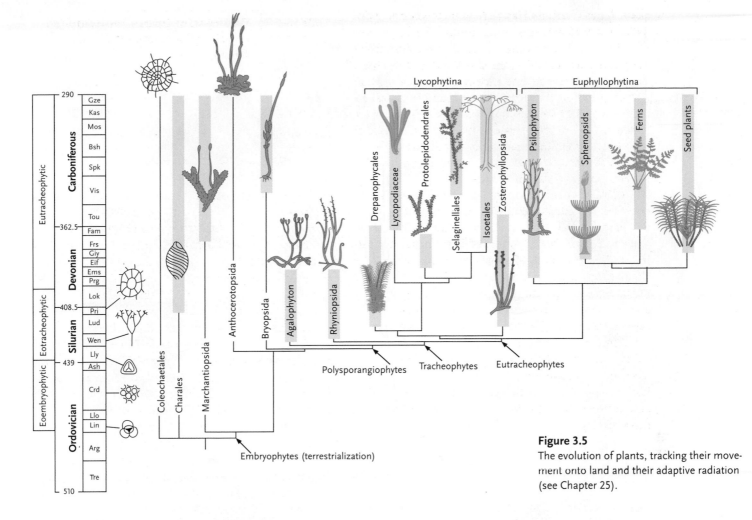

Figure 3.5

The evolution of plants, tracking their movement onto land and their adaptive radiation (see Chapter 25).

With the advent of the tools of molecular genetics (see Chapter 16), biologists have been able to prepare more detailed trees reflecting broader relationships. The example in **Figure 3.7, p. 56** shows that the diversity of life is almost overwhelming because of the broad coverage that can be achieved with genetic data, even though this tree presents only 191 species. One challenge to biologists is putting this diversity in context and appreciating the processes that have produced it.

STUDY BREAK

1. How does the theory of evolution explain the unity and diversity of all life?
2. What are the four central ideas of Darwin's theory of evolution by natural selection?
3. List advantages that oxygenic photosynthesis provided organisms living on Earth.

Figure 3.6

The tree of life. Darwin envisioned the history of life as a tree. Branching points represent the origins of new lineages; branches that do not reach the top represent extinct groups.

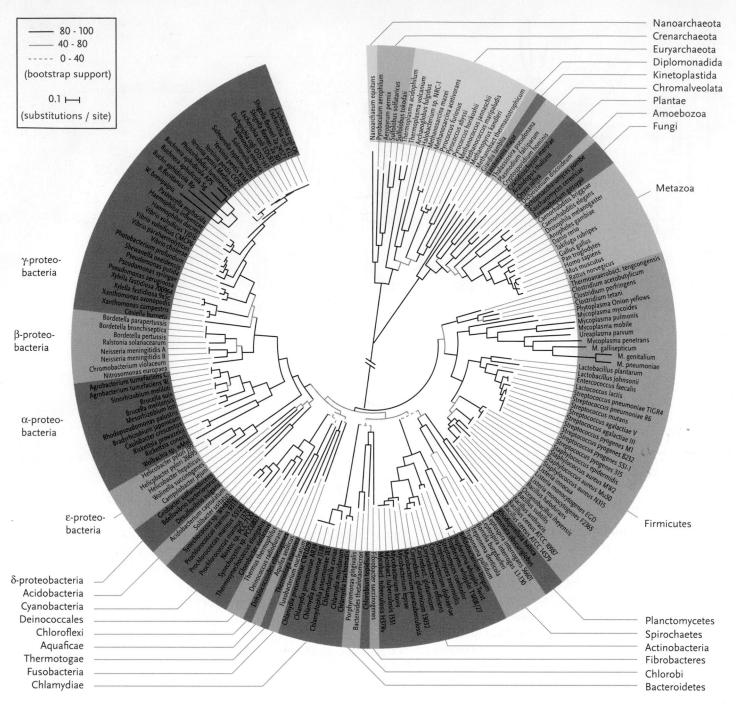

Figure 3.7
Using genetic data, it is possible to generate a global phylogeny or tree of life. This tree is based on 191 species whose genomes have been fully sequenced.

3.4 The Biosphere

The biosphere is the area occupied by life on Earth, from the depths of the ocean to the sky above. The various physical environments of Earth and their different abiotic factors, such as sunlight, temperature, humidity, wind speed, cloud cover, and rainfall, influence the evolution and diversity of organisms. These abiotic factors contribute to a region's **climate**, the weather conditions prevailing over an extended period of time. Climates vary on global, regional, and local scales and undergo seasonal changes almost everywhere.

3.4a Solar Radiation: Energy from the Sun

The global pattern of environmental diversity results from latitudinal variation in incoming solar radiation, Earth's rotation on its axis, and its orbit around the sun **(Figure 3.8)**.

Earth's spherical shape causes the intensity of incoming solar radiation to vary from the equator to

a. Solar radiation

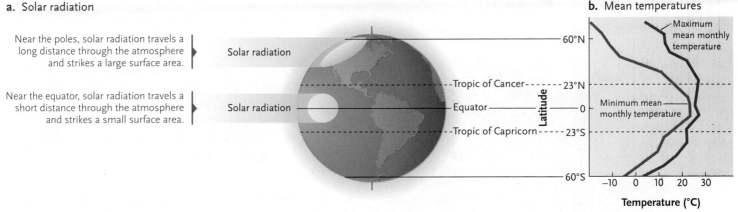

Near the poles, solar radiation travels a long distance through the atmosphere and strikes a large surface area.

Solar radiation

Near the equator, solar radiation travels a short distance through the atmosphere and strikes a small surface area.

Solar radiation

b. Mean temperatures

Figure 3.8
Latitudinal variation of solar radiation.

the poles **(Figure 3.9)**. When sunlight strikes Earth directly at a 90° angle, as it does near the equator, it travels the shortest possible distance through the radiation-absorbing atmosphere and falls on the smallest possible surface area. When sunlight arrives at an oblique angle, as it does near the poles, it travels a longer distance through the atmosphere and shines on a larger area. Thus, solar radiation is more concentrated near the equator than it is at higher latitudes, causing latitudinal variation in Earth's temperature (see Figure 3.9).

3.4b Seasonality: Weather Through the Year

Earth is tilted on its axis at a fixed position of 23.5° from the perpendicular to the plane on which it orbits the sun (see Figure 3.9). This tilt produces seasonal variation in the duration and intensity of incoming solar radiation. The Northern Hemisphere receives its maximum illumination, and the Southern Hemisphere its minimum, on the June solstice (around June 21), when the sun shines directly over the Tropic of Cancer (23.5° N latitude). The reverse is true on the December solstice (around December 21), when

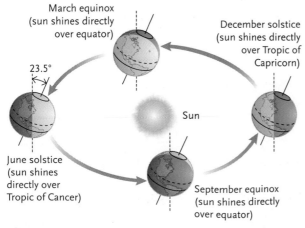

Figure 3.9
Seasonal variation in solar radiation.

the sun shines directly over the Tropic of Capricorn (23.5° S latitude). Twice each year, on the vernal and autumnal equinoxes (around March 21 and September 21, respectively), the sun shines directly over the equator.

The Earth's tilt is permanent, and only the **tropics**, the latitudes between the tropics of Cancer and Capricorn, ever receive intense solar radiation from directly overhead. Moreover, the tropics experience only small seasonal changes in temperature and day length: environmental temperature is high, and day length is approximately 12 hours throughout the year. Tropical seasonality is reflected in the alternation of wet and dry periods rather than warm and cold seasons. Seasonal variation in temperature and day length increases steadily toward the poles. Polar winters are long and cold, with periods of continuous darkness, and polar summers are short, with periods of continuous light.

3.4c Air Circulation: Wind Patterns

Sunlight warms air masses, causing them to expand, lose pressure, and rise in the atmosphere. The unequal heating of air at different latitudes initiates global air movements, producing three circulation cells in each hemisphere **(Figure 3.10, p. 58)**. Warm equatorial air masses rise to high altitude before spreading north and south. They eventually sink back to Earth at about 30° N and S latitude. At low altitude, some air masses flow back toward the equator, completing low-latitude circulation cells. Others flow toward the poles, rise at 60° latitude, and divide at high altitude. Some of this air flows toward the equator, completing the pair of middle-latitude circulation cells. The rest moves toward the poles, where it descends and flows toward the equator, forming the polar circulation cells.

The flow of air masses at low altitude creates winds near the planet's surface. But the planet's surface rotates beneath the atmosphere, moving rapidly near the equator, where Earth's diameter is greatest, and more slowly near the poles. Latitudinal variation in the speed of Earth's rotation deflects the movement of

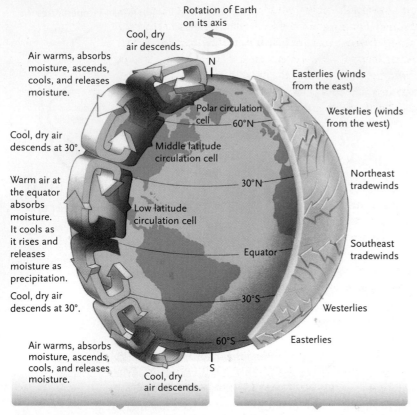

Rotation of Earth on its axis

Cool, dry air descends.

Air warms, absorbs moisture, ascends, cools, and releases moisture.

Cool, dry air descends at 30°.

Warm air at the equator absorbs moisture. It cools as it rises and releases moisture as precipitation.

Cool, dry air descends at 30°.

Air warms, absorbs moisture, ascends, cools, and releases moisture.

Cool, dry air descends.

Polar circulation cell

Middle latitude circulation cell

Low latitude circulation cell

Easterlies (winds from the east)

Westerlies (winds from the west)

60°N

Northeast tradewinds

30°N

Equator

Southeast tradewinds

30°S

Westerlies

60°S

Easterlies

N

S

Idealized pattern of air circulation.

Air flow near Earth's surface is deflected from a strictly north–south direction.

Figure 3.10
Global air circulation.

the rising and sinking air masses from a strictly north–south path into belts of easterly and westerly winds (see Figure 3.10); this deflection is called the Coriolis effect. Winds near the equator are called the trade winds; those further from the equator are the temperate westerlies and easterlies, named for their direction of flow.

3.4d Precipitation: Water

Differences in solar radiation and global air circulation create latitudinal variations in rainfall **(Figure 3.11)**. Warm air holds more water vapour than cool air does. As air near the equator heats up, it absorbs water, primarily from the oceans. However, the warm air masses expand as they rise, and their heat energy is distributed over a larger volume, causing their temperature to drop. A decrease in temperature without the actual *loss* of heat energy is called **adiabatic cooling**. After cooling adiabatically, the rising air masses release moisture as rain. Torrential rainfall is characteristic of warm equatorial regions, where rising, moisture-laden air masses cool as they reach high altitude.

As cool, dry air masses descend at 30° latitude, increased air pressure at low altitude compresses them,

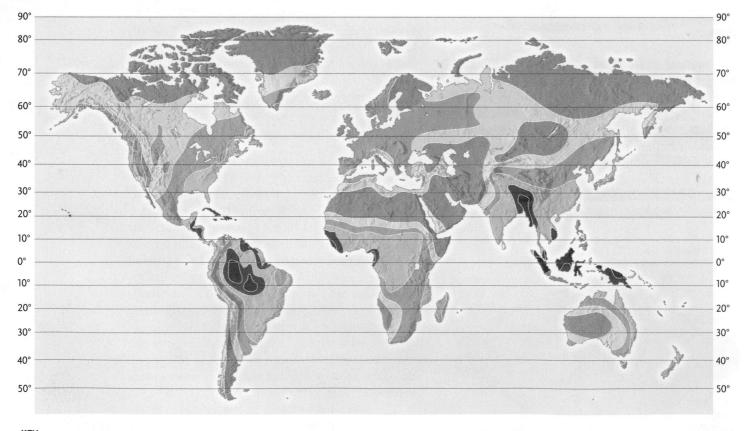

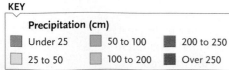

KEY

Precipitation (cm)

Under 25	50 to 100
25 to 50	100 to 200
	200 to 250
	Over 250

Figure 3.11
Global variation in precipitation.

concentrating their heat energy, raising their temperature, and increasing their capacity to hold moisture. Descending air masses absorb water at these latitudes, which are typically dry. Some air masses continue moving poleward in the lower atmosphere. When they rise at 60° latitude, they cool adiabatically and release precipitation (see Figure 3.11), creating moist habitats in the northern and southern temperate zones.

3.4e Ocean Currents: Rivers within the Oceans

Latitudinal variations in solar radiation also warm the oceans' surface water unevenly. Because the volume of water increases as it warms (= decrease in density), sea level is about 8 cm higher at the equator than at the poles. The volume of water associated with this "slope" is enough to cause surface water to move in response to gravity. The trade winds and temperate westerlies also contribute to the mass flow of water at the ocean surface. Thus, surface water flows in the direction of prevailing winds, forming major currents. The Earth's rotation, the positions of landmasses, and the shapes of ocean basins also influence the movements of these currents.

Oceanic circulation is generally clockwise in the Northern Hemisphere and counterclockwise in the Southern Hemisphere (Figure 3.12). The trade winds push surface water toward the equator and westward until it contacts the eastern edge of a continent. Swift, narrow, and deep currents of warm, nutrient-poor water

run toward the poles, parallel to the east coasts of continents. For example, the Gulf Stream flows northward along the east coast of North America, carrying warm water toward northwestern Europe. Cold water returns from the poles toward the equator in slow, broad, and shallow currents, such as the California Current, that parallel the west coasts of continents.

3.4f Regional and Local Effects: Local Conditions for Life

Although global and seasonal patterns determine an area's climate, regional and local effects also influence abiotic conditions.

Currents running along seacoasts exchange heat with air masses flowing above them, moderating the temperature over the nearby land. Breezes often blow from the sea toward the land during the day and in the opposite direction at night (Figure 3.13, p. 60). These local effects sometimes override latitudinal variations in temperature. For example, the climate in London, England, is much milder than that in Winnipeg, Canada, even though Winnipeg is slightly further south. Winnipeg has a **continental climate** that is not moderated by the distant ocean, but London has a **maritime climate,** tempered by winds that cross the nearby North Atlantic Current.

Ocean currents also affect moisture conditions in coastal habitats. For example, the warm Gulf Stream current meets the cold Labrador current off the southeast coast of Newfoundland, in the region known as

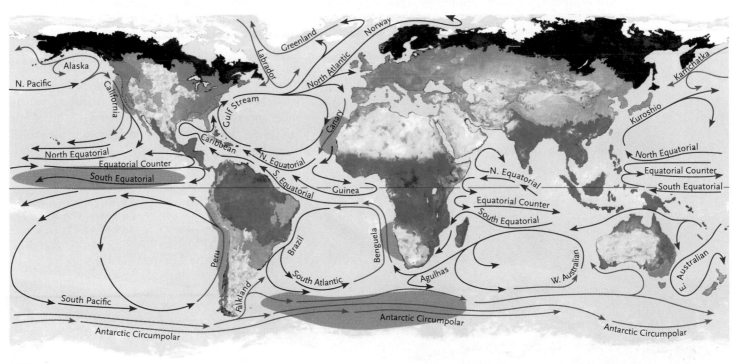

KEY

- Upwelling zone
- → Warm surface current
- → Cold surface current

Figure 3.12
Global ocean currents.

CHAPTER 3 SELECTION, BIODIVERSITY, AND BIOSPHERE

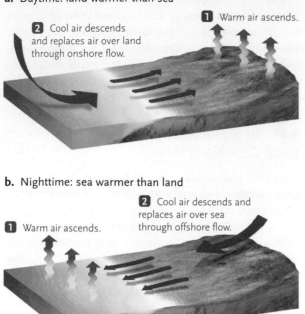

a. Daytime: land warmer than sea

2 Cool air descends and replaces air over land through onshore flow.

1 Warm air ascends.

b. Nighttime: sea warmer than land

2 Cool air descends and replaces air over sea through offshore flow.

1 Warm air ascends.

Figure 3.13
Sea breezes and land breezes—daytime and nighttime.

the Grand Banks. As the air above the water cools, its water vapour condenses into heavy fog and rain, making this region one of the foggiest on Earth.

Some regions experience **monsoon cycles** caused by seasonal reversals in wind direction. In the North American southwest, for example, summer heat causes air masses over land to rise, creating a zone of low pressure. Moist air from the nearby Gulf of California flows inland, where it rises and cools adiabatically, releasing substantial precipitation. Summer monsoon rains deliver one-third to one-half of the annual rainfall in Arizona and New Mexico. During the winter, when land is cooler than the nearby ocean, low-pressure systems form over the ocean and winds blow from the land to the sea; thus, winters in the southwest are generally dry. Seasonal monsoon cycles

also deliver torrential rainfall to parts of Africa, Asia, and South America.

3.4g The Effects of Topography: The Ups and Downs of Weather and Life

Mountains, valleys, and other topographic features also influence regional climates. In the Northern Hemisphere, south-facing slopes are warmer and drier than north-facing slopes because they receive more solar radiation. In addition, adiabatic cooling causes air temperature to decline 3° to 6°C for every 1000 m increase in elevation.

Mountains also establish regional and local rainfall patterns. For example, after a warm air mass picks up moisture from the Pacific Ocean, it moves inland and reaches the Rocky Mountains. As air rises to cross the mountains, it cools adiabatically and loses moisture, releasing heavy rainfall on the windward side **(Figure 3.14)**. After the now-dry air crosses the peaks, it descends and warms, absorbing moisture and forming a **rain shadow**. Habitats on the leeward side of mountains, such as the eastern slopes of the Rockies in Alberta or the Great Basin Desert in western United States, are typically drier than those on the windward side.

3.4h Microclimate: Very Local Changes in Temperature, Humidity, and Air Movements

Although climate influences the overall distributions of organisms, the abiotic conditions that immediately surround them, the **microclimate**, have the greatest effect on survival and reproduction. For example, a fallen log on the forest floor creates a microclimate in the underlying soil that is shadier, cooler, and moister than the surrounding soil that is exposed to sun and wind. Many animals, including some insects, worms, salamanders, and snakes, occupy these sheltered sites and avoid the effects of prolonged exposure to the elements.

1 Winds carry moisture inland from Pacific Ocean.

2 Clouds form and rain falls on windward side of mountain range.

3 Rain shadow forms on leeward side of mountain range.

4000/75
3000/85
1800/125   2000/50
1000/85   1300/30
15/25
Moist habitats

Figure 3.14
Formation of a rain shadow.

STUDY BREAK

1. Abiotic factors contribute to a region's climate. List the abiotic factors that affect the diversity of organisms.
2. List three factors affecting the global pattern of environmental diversity.
3. How does Earth's spherical shape cause the intensity of incoming solar radiation to vary from the equator to the poles?

3.5 Biotic Factors

In addition to the influence of the physical environment, the diversity of living organisms is affected by interactions among organisms. A very important type of interaction is competition among organisms for scarce resources. Organisms also exploit each other by consuming each other (see trophic interactions below) and by parasitism, a symbiotic relationship in which one organism benefits at the expense of another. Parasitism is only one type of symbiotic relationship; in the relationship known as mutualism, both organisms benefit (see Chapter 46).

3.5a Trophic Interactions: Movements of Energy, Biomass, and Numbers

In living, most organisms generate opportunities for other organisms. One way to explore these interrelationships is through the trophic roles that organisms play in the global ecosystem. Remember, however, that interactions between species of organisms can be negative, particularly when more than one species depends on the same limited resources (see Chapter 46).

Organisms can be generally classified into three basic trophic roles: producers, **consumers**, and **decomposers**. Photoautotrophs, the main producers, are organisms that use photosynthesis to capture and harness the sun's energy. They produce most of their own nutritional needs but serve as food for heterotrophs. Heterotrophs that eat autotrophs are called **primary consumers**, whereas those that eat other heterotrophs may be referred to as mesopredators (see Chapter 48). Other heterotrophs, such as fungi, are decomposers, breaking down dead organisms and thus making the nutrients available to themselves and other organisms.

Photosynthesis is considered the domain of plants, but in a few exceptional cases, animals capture chloroplasts and use them to capture solar energy through photosynthesis. In a sense, these animals are continuing life's earlier tradition of capturing other organisms and using them to achieve oxygenic photosynthesis and aerobic respiration (see

Chapter 5). Co-option of other organisms is a recurring theme and brings with it questions of control because chloroplasts and mitochondria have their own DNA. There are many examples of sequestration of chloroplasts by species from the phyla Protista, Platyhelminthes, Porifera, Cnidaria, Mollusca, and Urochordata.

Some sea slugs (e.g., *Elysia chlorotica*) **(Figure 3.15)** use specialized teeth on their radulae to cut into algal cells so that they can suck out (feed by stenophagy) chloroplasts and other cell contents. In the slug's stomach, chloroplasts are engulfed by phagocytosis and then moved to areas below the epidermis. Slugs such as *E. chlorotica* can live for at least five months on the energy generated by chloroplasts they have obtained, their solar panels. This story is an example of how a heterotrophic organism (the slug) acquires the ability to be autotrophic (engage in photosynthesis). How the slugs control the operations of the chloroplasts remains unanswered. Have slugs also taken over some of the chloroplast or algal genome? At least one species, *Elysia crispata*, has nuclear genes from chloroplasts in its genomic DNA. For more about these slugs, see Chapters 25 and 26.

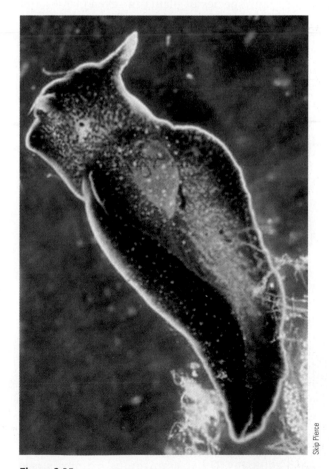

Figure 3.15
The solar-powered sea slug, *Elysia chlorotica*, an animal that extracts chloroplasts from algae and uses them to produce food.

a. *Monotropa unifloris*

b. *Conopholis americana*

M. B. Fenton

M. B. Fenton

Figure 3.16
Two achlorophyllous plants: **(a)** one (*Monotropa unifloris*) obtains nutrients from other plants via fungi, and **(b)** the other (*Conopholis americana*) is parasitic on the roots of other plants.

So, if animals emulate plants, is the reverse also true? Many species of plants in seven classes and 17 families worldwide appear to lack the ability to perform photosynthesis **(Figure 3.16)**. Some of these "achlorophyllous" species are parasitic on the roots of other plants. Other achlorophyllous plants are mycoheterotrophic, obtaining energy and nutrients from mycorrhizal fungi associated with the roots of neighbouring green plants (see Chapters 24 and 25, respectively). Although plants that cannot photosynthesize are called achlorophyllous, many have trace amounts of chlorophyll *a*, and only one is known to have both chlorophyll *a* and chlorophyll *b*. The evidence demonstrates that some plants whose ancestors were capable of photosynthesis have lost that ability.

If you pause for a moment and think of what you have eaten in the last 24 hours, you will realize that if humans are anything to go by, strict categorization of organisms by the trophic role they fill is probably naive. Setting aside people who only eat plant products (vegetarians), most humans eat a variety of food from organisms in different locations in the food web (see Chapter 46). Many organisms are strict autotrophs, and many are just heterotrophs. Can you think of an animal that never eats plant material? Good examples can be found among animals that feed on **blood** (see Chapter 46).

Most people are **omnivores**, and they are in good company. Other omnivorous mammals (see Chapter 27) include bears, pigs, squirrels, and rats. The fact that many animals, as well as fungi and bac-

teria, live on dung suggests that heterotrophs do not remove all of the energy in the food they consume. Heterotrophs expend energy (kilocalories) to obtain food: the energy of mastication and digestion as well as the cost of catching (or buying) what you eat. Food that passes through the digestive tract with much of its energy intact has not been used efficiently. When food is scarce, many heterotrophs make choices suggesting that they are behaving as efficient predators (see Chapter 41).

Other heterotrophs are more efficient at removing energy from food materials. The most efficient primary consumers (herbivores) are those that use other organisms to help in digestion. A familiar example is a cow (*Bos taurus*), which, like other ruminants, uses fermentation aided by symbiotic organisms (bacteria, protozoa). As we shall see in Chapter 41, fermentation also is used by other mammals, some insects (termites, Isoptera), and even some birds (the Hoatzin, *Opisthocomus hoazin*). But the dung of ruminants is eaten by a wide range of animals and saprotrophic fungi, so even they do not extract all the energy available in the food they consume.

Moving up (or down) the food web demonstrates how one species and its activities provide opportunities for others. Parasites are an extension of this reality, whether they live inside the host's body (endoparasites) **(Figure 3.17)**, outside (ectoparasites) **(Figure 3.18)**, or somewhere in between **(Figure 3.19)**. But just the definition of "parasite" is an engaging topic (see Chapter 26).

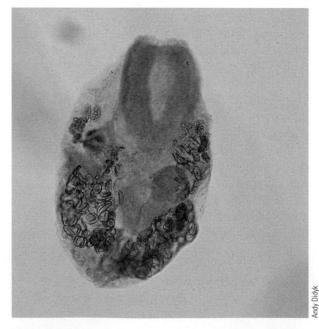

Andy Didyk

Figure 3.17
Paralecithodendrium chilostomum, a 420-micron long endoparasite, was found in the gut of a little brown bat, *Myotis lucifugus*. This species belongs to the class Trematoda, order Plagiorchiida, family Lecithodendriidae.

Beetles, Carbon Cycles, and Climate Change

A live tree is a net carbon sink because during photosynthesis, it takes up more carbon as CO_2 than it releases by respiration. The tree's contribution is expressed as $-x$ grams of carbon per year ($-x$ g C yr^{-1}). Autotrophs, organisms capable of photosynthesis, play a vital role in the carbon cycle (see Chapter 48) of Earth.

In south-central British Columbia, 374 000 km^2 of forest dominated by pine (*Pinus* spp.) and spruce (*Picea* spp.) is changing from being a net carbon sink, -15.8 ± 7.9 MtC yr^{-1} (megatonnes of carbon per year), in 2004 to producing an estimated 17.6 MtC yr^{-1} by 2020. Why is this change happening?

The change from carbon sink to carbon produced results from an outbreak of mountain pine beetles (*Dendroctonus ponderosae*) that killed millions of trees in the area. The outbreak of beetles resulted from climate warming because more beetles survived the winter and thus expanded the geographic range of the species. The magnitude of change in carbon is equivalent to approximately 75% of the average direct forest fire emissions from all of Canada between 1959 and 1999.

Insect pests can have a huge impact on our lives. The destruction of millions of trees has economic effects associated with timber supply. Social impacts include the loss of jobs for the people directly and indirectly employed by the forest industry. We have yet to experience the full impact that climate change associated with the carbon cycle can have on our lives and on Earth's biodiversity. Changes in climate can bring many species to the edge of survival.

Figure 3.18
Common vampire bat (*Desmodus rotundus*) with ectoparasites (streblid flies) with their heads tucked into the bat's fur.

3.6 Cumulative Impact on Biotic and Abiotic Factors

For over 3 billion years, our planet has been the stage for interactions between **biotic** and abiotic factors. Over this time, species have come and gone, reflecting the dynamics of evolution and interactions between species, all under the influence of different climatic conditions. In a sense, the situation in the Hawaiian Islands reflects the richness of the interactions and the products. There the combination of isolation, immigration, and adaptive radiations, in a setting with dramatic climatic variation, produced an impressive diversity of life. One such Hawaiian endemic is a tree in the lily family that grows to a height of 8 metres **(Figure 3.20)**.

Figure 3.19
Schreiber's bent-winged bat (*Miniopterus schreibersii*) with a streblid fly embedded in a tear duct. The adult fly, with wings, entered the tear duct and shed its wings.

Figure 3.20
In a sense, Hala-pepe *(Dracena aurea)* "trees" growing from an old lava flow epitomize the adaptive radiation that has occurred in Hawaii. This member of the lily family is endemic and can reach 8 m in height. Early Hawaiians used the sap in medicines and the wood for carving images to decorate the altar of the goddess Laka. Laka is the patron of the sacred hula.

1. Describe the difference between mutualism and parasitism.
2. Describe three basic trophic roles of organisms and give an example of each.
3. An array of life is shown in **Figure 3.21.** Which organisms or parts of organisms do you recognize?

a.

b.

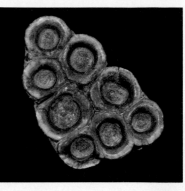

c.

d.

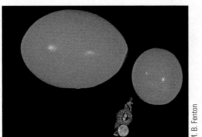

e.

f.

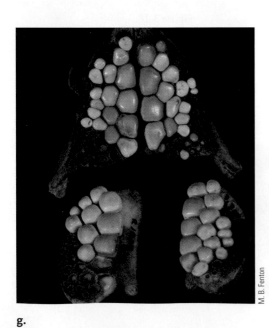

g.

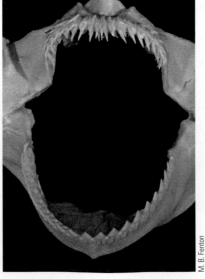

h.

Figure 3.21
(a) Mother scorpion with young;
(b) stinkhorn fungus; **(c)** *Desmostylus* teeth (mammal); **(d)** moss and lichens; **(e)** birds' eggs (elephant bird, ostrich, hummingbird); **(f)** sundew leaf; **(g)** fish teeth, used for crushing; **(h)** cookie-cutter shark teeth.

Ammonia

Smelling salts are used to revive people who have become disoriented or unconscious after an injury. We most often see smelling salts used on the sidelines at sporting events after a player has been hit. Ammonium carbonate is the active ingredient in smelling salts, which are effective because all animals, including humans, are very averse to the smell of ammonia. This aversion is appropriate and adaptive because ammonia can be very toxic.

In its pure form, ammonia (NH_3) is usually a gas. The polarity of ammonia means that it readily dissolves in water. **(Figure 1)** Except for basic (pH > 9) aqueous environments, ammonia is found as the protonated ion NH_4, ammonium.

Directly or indirectly, ammonia is the key building block of almost all nitrogen-containing compounds. In organisms, this includes the amino acids and nucleotides that are the monomers of proteins and nucleic acids, respectively. In the biosphere, ammonia is synthesized through the process of nitrogen fixation by prokaryotes, which converts atmospheric N_2 directly into ammonia using the enzyme nitrogenase. This prokaryotic process makes ammonia available for uptake by microbes and plants that use it to synthesize nitrogen-containing compounds. The enzymes involved in ammonium assimilation are usually abundant within cells. Thus, following import, ammonia is rapidly converted into less toxic forms of nitrogen and does not accumulate within cells.

Ammonia is a major breakdown product of protein and nucleic acid catabolism. Some fungi form fruiting bodies only when ammonia or nitrogenous compounds that release ammonia on breakdown are abundant. These "ammonia" fungi have potential use in forensic science because their fruiting bodies can reveal sites where human remains have been clandestinely buried and can also indicate time since burial.

In aquatic organisms from snails to fish, ammonia is simply excreted across the gills and is rapidly diffused in the surrounding water. Dilution of ammonia by water reduces its danger to the animals that produce it. In land animals, ammonia is converted to uric acid or urea, nontoxic forms that can be excreted without dilution with water. Some amphibious animals, such as snails, excrete ammonia when living in water and urea or uric acid when on land. Some terrestrial animals can live in high concentrations of ammonia. When literally millions of Brazilian free-tailed bats (*Tadarida brasiliensis*) live by day in caves, the levels of ammonia that accumulate are deadly to people. The bats use mucus to protect their respiratory tracts from ammonia.

Several mechanisms are implicated in ammonia toxicity, but all of them relate to the interconversion of ammonia with ammonium. High intracellular concentrations of ammonia may result in a disruption of pH balance within the cell. This is because at physiological pH, ammonia will be converted to ammonium in a process that consumes hydronium ion (H_3O^+), resulting in an increase in pH. Furthermore, high levels of ammonia/ammonium can disrupt the formation of proton gradients across membranes, which are critical for the synthesis of ATP by oxidative phosphorylation and photophosphorylation. Ammonia, despite its toxicity, is vital to life on Earth.

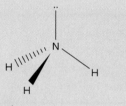

Figure 1
Diagram of ammonia molecule.

Elizabeth Lloyd Clare, Ph.D. Candidate, University of Guelph

Beth Clare and others used the barcode approach to examine the bat fauna at different locations in Guyana, South America **(Figure 1)**. Working with colleagues from the Royal Ontario Museum (ROM) in Toronto, they collected data from 840 specimens representing 87 species of bats. An important element in the work was the connection between the barcode data and specimens (known as "vouchers" in the ROM collections) so that the genetic data could be associated with known individuals.

Clare and her coauthors predicted and found higher levels of divergence in the *CO1* sequence as they moved within species, to within genera, to within family **(Figure 2)**. The tree illustrating their findings **(Figure 3)** demonstrated that whereas 81 species of bats showed one lineage within what is considered to be a species, six others showed larger sequence divergences than expected, suggesting more than one species. The genetic work shows that in some cases, biologists have been correct about the numbers of species, but in other instances, they have underestimated them.

Traditional taxonomic work (see Chapter 19) had suggested that some of the bats currently thought to be one species actually represented several. This use of the barcode approach validated its value to biologists working to document biodiversity and understand the adaptive radiation of bats.

Clare has expanded the use of the barcode approach by looking at the insects eaten by bats. Samples from the mouths of bats that had been feeding produced insect samples that could be analyzed using the barcoding approach. The same was true of insect remains in bat droppings. With a library of barcode data from different insects, bat biologists could use this approach to obtain detailed information about what species of insects bats have eaten.

In 2009, Clare is a Ph.D. student working with Professor Paul Hebert at the Barcode of Life project at the University of Guelph. She completed her honours bachelor of science degree in ecology and evolution at the University of Western Ontario and, as an undergraduate, spent several years studying fish behaviour and genetics.

Clare et al. 2007. Molecular Ecology notes, 7:184–190. Reprinted by permission of Blackwell Publishing.

Figure 1
The general location of Guyana in South America, and specific locations in Guyana from which bat specimens were obtained.

She has a long-standing interest in science and worked as a high school volunteer at a paleontological dig. She also participated in science fairs at both regional and national levels. In addition to her work on bats and barcoding, she is a dedicated photographer.

STUDY BREAK

1. How is ammonia toxic to living organisms? Why is it also necessary for life on Earth?

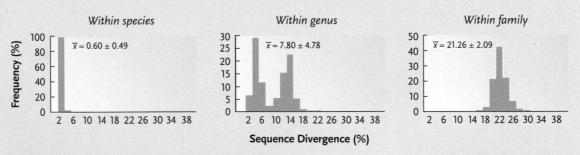

Within species — $\bar{x} = 0.60 \pm 0.49$

Within genus — $\bar{x} = 7.80 \pm 4.78$

Within family — $\bar{x} = 21.26 \pm 2.09$

Frequency (%)

Sequence Divergence (%)

Figure 2
Frequency histograms comparing mean ($\pm$ standard error) COI sequence divergences at different hierarchical levels: within species, within genus, within family. The data are from 87 species of bats (840 individuals) from Guyana.

a.

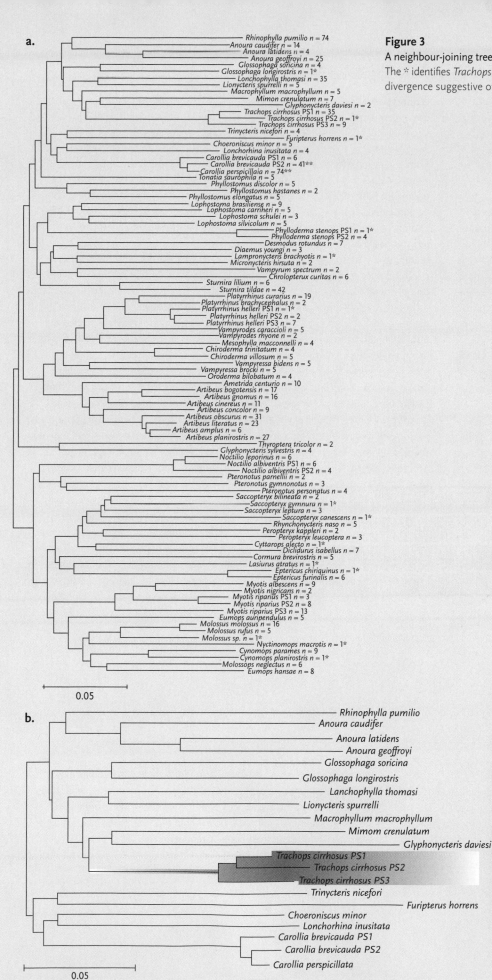

Figure 3

A neighbour-joining tree of COI sequence divergences in 87 species of bats.
The * identifies *Trachops cirrhosus*, one of the species showing high sequence divergence suggestive of several different species.

Rhinophylla pumilio n = 74
Anoura caudifer n = 14
Anoura latidens n = 4
Anoura geoffroyi n = 25
Glossophaga soricina n = 4
*Glossophaga longirostris n = 1**
Lonchophylla thomasi n = 35
Lionycteris spurrelli n = 5
Macrophyllum macrophyllum n = 5
Mimon crenulatum n = 7
Glyphonycteris daviesi n = 2
Trachops cirrhosus PS1 n = 35
*Trachops cirrhosus PS2 n = 1**
Trachops cirrhosus PS3 n = 9
Trinycteris nicefori n = 4
*Furipterus horrens n = 1**
Choeroniscus minor n = 5
Lonchorhina inusitata n = 4
Carollia brevicauda PS1 n = 6
*Carollia brevicauda PS2 n = 41***
*Carollia perspicillaia n = 74***
Tonatia saurophila n = 5
Phyllostomus discolor n = 5
Phyllostomus hastanes n = 2
Phyllostomus elongatus n = 5
Lophostoma brasiliense n = 9
Lophostoma carrheri n = 5
Lophostoma schulei n = 3
Lophostoma silvicolum n = 5
*Phylloderma stenops PS1 n = 1**
Phylloderma stenops PS2 n = 4
Desmodus rotundus n = 7
Diaemus youngi n = 3
*Lampronycteris brachyotis n = 1**
Micronycteris hirsuta n = 2
Vampyrum spectrum n = 2
Chrolopterux curitas n = 6
Sturnira lilium n = 6
Sturnira tildae n = 42
Platyrrhinus curarius n = 19
Platyrrhinus brachycephalus n = 2
*Platyrrhinus helleri PS1 n = 1**
Platyrrhinus helleri PS2 n = 2
Platyrrhinus helleri PS3 n = 7
Vampyrodes caraccioli n = 5
Vampyrodes rhyone n = 2
Mesophylla macconnelli n = 4
Chiroderma trinitatum n = 4
Chiroderma villosum n = 5
Vampyressa bidens n = 5
Vampyressa brocki n = 5
Ororderma bilobatum n = 4
Ametrida centurio n = 10
Artibeus bogotensis n = 17
Artibeus gnomus n = 16
Artibeus cinereus n = 11
Artibeus concolor n = 9
Artibeus obscurus n = 31
Artibeus literatus n = 23
Artibeus amplus n = 6
Artibeus planirostris n = 27
Thyroptera tricolor n = 2
Glyphonycteris sylvestris n = 4
Noctilio leporinus n = 6
Noctilio albiventris PS1 n = 6
Noctilio albiventris PS2 n = 4
Pteronotus parnellii n = 2
Pteronotus gymnonotus n = 3
Pteronotus personatus n = 4
Saccopteryx bilineata n = 2
*Saccopteryx gymnura n = 1**
Saccopteryx leptura n = 3
*Saccopteryx canescens n = 1**
Rhynchonycteris naso n = 5
Peropteryx kappleri n = 2
Peropteryx leucoptera n = 3
*Cyttarops alecto n = 1**
Diclidurus isabellus n = 7
Cormura brevirostris n = 5
*Lasiurus atratus n = 1**
*Eptericus chiriquinus n = 1**
Eptericus furinalis n = 6
Myotis albescens n = 9
Myotis nigricans n = 2
Myotis riparius PS1 n = 3
Myotis riparius PS2 n = 8
Myotis riparius PS3 n = 13
Eumops auripendulus n = 5
Molossus molossus n = 16
Molossus rufus n = 5
*Molossus sp. n = 1**
*Nyctinomops macrotis n = 1**
Cynomops parames n = 9
*Cynomops planirostris n = 1**
Molossops neglectus n = 6
Eumops hansae n = 8

0.05

b.

Rhinophylla pumilio
Anoura caudifer
Anoura latidens
Anoura geoffroyi
Glossophaga soricina
Glossophaga longirostris
Lanchophylla thomasi
Lionycteris spurrelli
Macrophyllum macrophyllum
Mimom crenulatum
Glyphonycteris daviesi
Trachops cirrhosus PS1
Trachops cirrhosus PS2
Trachops cirrhosus PS3
Trinycteris nicefori
Furipterus horrens
Choeroniscus minor
Lonchorhina inusitata
Carollia brevicauda PS1
Carollia brevicauda PS2
Carollia perspicillata

0.05

Alex Borisenko. © 2006, Royal Ontario Museum

Barcodes of Life

Because the diversity of species is overwhelming, it is difficult to provide a confident estimate of how many species remain undescribed (see Chapter 26). For many groups of organisms, few authorities are available to provide descriptions of "new" species, the ones not yet described and therefore nameless. The Barcode of Life Data Systems, based in Guelph, Ontario, Canada, offers one alternative to the challenge of knowing how many species are in the sample you have just acquired or the origin of a mysterious mouse found in a shipment of frozen chickens from Thailand.

The Barcode of Life project depends on variation in the mitochondrial cytochrome c oxidase 1 (CO1) gene, which consists of about 650 nucleotides. This genetic "barcode" is embedded in almost every cell, and it offers biologists a chance to identify a species even if they have only a small sample of feathers or fur, leaf, seed, or caterpillar. Since identification of some species depends on having a whole adult specimen, being able to identify species from an egg, a larva, or a hair offers enormous potential. Identification of organisms with different life stages can be particularly challenging. Using morphology, it can be easy to identify a butterfly or a frog but much more difficult to identify its caterpillar or its tadpole.

The Barcode of Life project is based on polymerase chain reaction (PCR) technology, which allows biologists to process 100 samples every 3 hours. Subsequent advances in genomic technology have increased our capacity for efficient sequencing of DNA. This potential, along with an army of researchers collecting specimens and global positioning technology (GPS) to document locations, means that the Barcode of Life project can deliver accurate (to 97.5%) identifications of specimens in a short time. Further developments could see biologists and naturalists armed with appropriately programmed handheld devices to identify organisms in the field.

One important consequence of this project is that biologists will have a chance to document more fully the diversity of life on Earth. This may mean realizing that the single identified species of a butterfly is actually 10 species, or that what people had thought were several species is, in fact, one. Protecting species through the Convention for Trade in Endangered Species (CITES) means being able to name them so that they can be placed on a protected list. The Barcode of Life project should allow a merchant to be sure that the ivory being sold in her shop is from an extinct mammoth, rather than a living, endangered species (see Chapter 48). The same applies to food species in a market: is that fish really what the label says it is?

But everyone has experience with barcode operations as used in many retail outlets. Scanning barcodes sometimes does not work. These limitations, as well as biological ones associated with genetics of different species, make some organisms more appropriate for Barcode of Life approaches than others.

Barcode of Life

Figure 1
COI barcode of *Trachops cirrhosus*, the frog-eating bat.

UNANSWERED QUESTIONS

Did life on earth evolve just once (i.e., is it monophyletic)? As you've read in this chapter, there is a tremendous diversity of living organisms but there is an underlying unity at the cellular and molecular level (see Ch. 2). This unity suggests that all organisms alive today share a common ancestor. But what if life arose more than once? Is it possible that descendents of this other lineage could still be alive on Earth, hiding in habitats in which DNA-based life forms can't survive? If life is monophyletic, what does this imply about the diversity of systems we see in living organisms? If life did evolve more than once, how would that affect your perception of diversity? Think about membranes and energy transfer systems.

Review

3.1 Biodiversity

- Heterotrophs obtain organic carbon and energy by consuming other organisms. Autotrophs, such as plants, are organisms that synthesize organic carbon molecules using inorganic carbon, CO_2. Plants are also photoautotrophs because they use light as the source of energy for photosynthesis. Chemoautotrophs, such as some bacteria, use reduced chemicals rich in electrons as an energy source.

- Key elements in the selection of individuals and their genetic traits are the presence of a selective force (pressure), genetic variation within a population, and the capacity of individuals with the selected trait to survive and reproduce.

3.3 Evolution

- The theory of evolution states that all organisms alive today descended from a common ancestor, which explains why all organisms share certain features (unity). It also tells us that species change over time as a result of natural selection (diversity).

- All organisms use ATP as their cellular energy source, have DNA as their genetic material, and have plasma membranes composed of lipid bilayers.

- The central ideas of Darwin's theory of evolution by natural selection are as follows:
  - Individual organisms in a population vary in many heritable traits.
  - Any population has the potential to produce far more offspring than the environment can support.
  - This situation results in a struggle for existence, and some individuals have traits giving them an advantage in their local environment.
  - These organisms are more likely to survive and reproduce, and surviving organisms pass on favourable traits to their offspring. In this way, the incidence of trait(s) in the population will change.

- Oxygenic photosynthesis generated oxygen, allowed for aerobic respiration, and created the ozone layer that allowed organisms to colonize more terrestrial environments by blocking harmful UV rays. Together, these changes led to diversification of life.

- An organism can move into a new adaptive zone after the chance evolution of a key morphological innovation that allows it to use the environment in a unique way. Thus, adaptive radiations occur when an evolutionary breakthrough leads to diversification of life.

- The challenges facing organisms that moved onto land included support and locomotion, conservation of water, acquisition of oxygen, reproduction, and disposal of wastes.

- The main differences between water and air are density and viscosity, which affect rates of diffusion and oxygen availability. Animals living in water use gills (or gill-like structures) to extract dissolved oxygen, although some photoautotrophs actually break water molecules in the process of photosynthesis. Animals that breathe air have more ready access to oxygen and spend less of their overall energy budget acquiring it than aquatic animals do. Since water is viscous, it provides organisms with support for locomotion, whereas air does not.

- To cope with a lack of support, terrestrial animals have developed more complex body designs for support (skeletons) and anchoring muscles (for locomotion).

- Temperature and the availability of dissolved oxygen in water are inversely related. As the temperature of water increases, the need for oxygen by aquatic organisms increases, which coincides with reduced amounts of dissolved oxygen available.

- By the end of the Devonian period, terrestrial animals had
  - skeletons for support and anchoring muscles (for locomotion),
  - organs for gaseous exchange (breathing atmospheric oxygen),
  - systems for circulating materials within the body,
  - waterproof coverings to minimize the chances of desiccation, and
  - the use of nontoxic excretory products (urea and uric acid).

3.4 The Biosphere

- Sunlight, temperature, humidity, wind speed, cloud cover, and rainfall are abiotic factors affecting the diversity of organisms.

- A global pattern of environmental diversity results from latitudinal variation in incoming solar radiation, Earth's rotation on its axis, and its orbit around the sun.

- Sunlight strikes Earth directly at a 90° angle near the equator, travelling a short distance through the radiation-absorbing atmosphere and shining on a small concentrated area. At the poles, sunlight arrives at an oblique angle, travelling longer distances through the atmosphere and shining on a larger area. Solar radiation is more concentrated near the equator than it is at higher latitudes, causing latitudinal variation in Earth's temperature.

- Earth's fixed tilt of 23.5° on its axis causes the Northern Hemisphere to receive more sunlight in June and the Southern Hemisphere to receive more in December. These differences are reflected in seasonal variation in day length and temperature, which are more pronounced at the poles than at the equator.

- Latitudinal variation in the speed of Earth's rotation deflects movement of rising and sinking air masses from a strictly north–south path into belts of easterly and westerly winds. This deflection is called the Coriolis effect.

- Adiabatic cooling is a decrease in temperature without the actual loss of heat energy. After cooling adiabatically, rising air masses release moisture as rain.

- Prevailing winds, Earth's rotation, gravity, the shape of ocean basins, and the positions of landmasses establish the direction and intensity of surface currents in the oceans. Generally, warm currents flow away from the equator and cold currents flow toward it.

- Monsoons are brought upon by seasonal reversals of wind direction. Usually, summer heat causes air masses over land to rise, creating a zone of low pressure. Moist air from a nearby body of water flows inland, where it rises and cools adiabatically, releasing substantial precipitation.

- Warm air picks up moisture from a body of water. If the warm air moves inland and reaches a range of mountains, it rises to cross the mountains. The air cools adiabatically and loses moisture, releasing heavy rainfall on the windward side. After the now-dry air crosses the peaks, it descends and warms, absorbing moisture and forming a rain shadow.

3.5 Biotic Factors

- Parasitism is a symbiotic relationship in which one organism benefits at the expense of the other. Mutualism is a symbiotic relationship in which both organisms involved benefit.

- The three basic trophic roles are producers, consumers, and decomposers. Photoautotrophs are the main producers because they use photosynthesis to capture and harness the sun's energy.

Heterotrophs are primary consumers when they eat autotrophs and mesopredators if they eat other heterotrophs. Other heterotrophs, such as fungi, are decomposers, breaking down dead organisms.

3.6 Cumulative Impact on Biotic and Abiotic Factors

- Prokaryotes produce ammonia (NH_3) when they reduce atmospheric nitrogen (N_2 gas). The ammonia that results from this process is directly or indirectly the basis for all nitrogenous molecules such as amino acids and nucleotides, as well as proteins and nucleic acids. The conversion of ammonia to these other nitrogenous compounds inside cells is crucial because ammonia is toxic to cells. At physiological pH, ammonia is converted to ammonium (NH_4); this process not only increases cellular pH but can interfere with formation of the proton gradients necessary for ATP synthesis.

- The Barcode of Life project depends on variation in the mitochondrial cytochrome *c* oxidase 1 (*CO1*) gene. This genetic barcode is embedded in almost every cell, offering biologists a chance to identify a species even if they have only a small sample. The Barcode of Life project uses PCR technology, which permits accurate identifications of specimens in a short time.

Questions

Self-Test Questions

1. *Treponema pallidum* can cause diseases such as
   a. acquired immune deficiency syndrome (AIDS).
   b. black death.
   c. syphilis.
   d. tuberculosis.
   e. small pox.

2. Evolution by natural selection depends on
   a. traits of organisms being inherited.
   b. variation in traits.
   c. traits providing advantages to individuals that have them.
   d. individuals competing for resources.
   e. all of the above.

3. Movement of animals onto land first depended on
   a. development of bones.
   b. availability of atmospheric oxygen.
   c. development of muscles.
   d. excretion of urea or uric acid.
   e. development of internal fertilization.

4. Changes in solar radiation reaching Earth are obvious in the differences between
   a. night and day.
   b. spring equinox and summer solstice.
   c. fall equinox and winter solstice.
   d. cloudy and sunny days.
   e. Both a and b are correct.

5. Adiabatic temperature changes involve
   a. warming of air masses.
   b. cooling of air masses.
   c. changes in water content of air masses.
   d. movement of air from the equator to polar regions.
   e. rainfall.

6. Continental climates tend to be _____ than maritime climates.
   a. warmer
   b. colder
   c. wetter
   d. drier
   e. b and c are correct

7. Solar radiation is captured by
   a. respiration.
   b. photosynthesis.
   c. oxygenic photosynthesis only.
   d. decomposition.
   e. all of the above.

8. Plants can be
   a. primary producers.
   b. carnivorous.
   c. achlorophyllous.
   d. terrestrial
   e. all of the above.

9. The Barcode of Life project depends on
   a. DNA fingerprinting.
   b. the cytochrome *c* oxidase 1 gene.
   c. PCR (polymerase chain reaction) technology.
   d. chromosomal variation.
   e. b and c.

10. Fossil evidence reveals that whales evolved from other mammals such as
    a. hippopotami.
    b. rodents.
    c. raoellids.
    d. seals.
    e. elephants.

Questions for Discussion

1. Find an example of a situation in which selection resulted in an adaptive radiation (going from the premise presented for the evolution of syphilis, whales, or climbing plants).

2. Are all ecosystems directly dependent on photosynthesis? If not, give two examples of systems in which primary productivity does not depend on photosynthesis.

3. Find examples of situations in which the Barcode of Life project might not work or might give false information.

4. How long did it take for life to recolonize the island of Krakatoa? Which organisms arrived there first after the explosion in 1883?

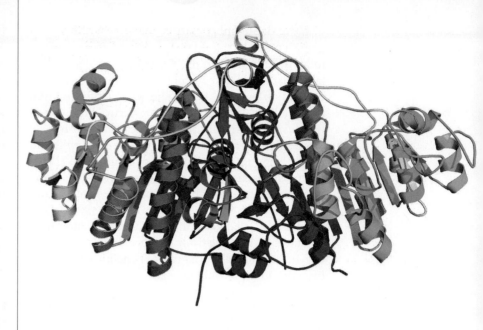

STUDY PLAN

4 Energy and Enzymes

WHY IT MATTERS

Earth is a cold place—at least when it comes to chemical reactions. Life cannot survive at the high temperatures routinely used in most laboratories and industrial plants for chemical synthesis. Instead, life relies on a group of catalysts called enzymes that speed up the rates of reaction without the need for an increase in temperature.

Until recently, however, just how good enzymes are at increasing the rate of a reaction was not fully appreciated. Dr. Richard Wolfenden, professor of Chemistry, Biochemistry and Biophysics at the University of North Carolina and his colleagues estimated the rate of the uncatalyzed versus the enzyme-catalyzed reaction for a range of biologically relevant reactions. The prize for the greatest difference between the uncatalyzed rate and the enzyme-catalyzed rate goes to a reaction that simply removes a phosphate group. In the cell, a group of enzymes called phosphatases catalyze the removal of phosphate groups from a range of molecules, including proteins. The rapid **reversible** phosphorylation of particular proteins is a central mechanism of intracellular communication in almost all cells.

The dephosphorylation reaction within a cell using a phosphatase enzyme is completed in approximately 10 milliseconds. Wolfenden's group calculated that in an aqueous environment such as a cell, without an enzyme, the dephosphorylation reaction would take over 1 trillion years to occur. This exceeds the current estimate for the age of the universe! The difference between the enzyme-catalyzed and uncatalyzed rate is 21 orders of magnitude (10^{21}). For most reactions, the rate difference between the uncatalyzed rate and the catalyzed rate is many millions of times.

It is clear that given the fact that life requires temperatures that are relatively low (below 100°C), without enzymes to speed up the rates of chemical reactions, life as we know it could not exist.

4.1 Energy and the Laws of Thermodynamics

Life, like many chemical and physical activities, is an energy-driven process. Yet, energy cannot be measured or weighed directly. We can detect it only through its ability to do work: to move objects against opposing forces, such as friction, gravity, or pressure, or to push chemical reactions toward completion. Therefore, **energy** is most conveniently defined as the capacity to do work. It takes energy to move a car on a highway, and it takes energy to climb a mountain. It also takes energy to build a protein from a group of amino acids or pump sucrose across a cell membrane.

4.1a Energy Exists in Different Forms and States

Energy can exist in many different forms, including heat, chemical, electrical, and mechanical energy. Electromagnetic radiation, including visible, infrared, and ultraviolet light, is also a type of energy. Although the forms of energy are different, they can be converted readily from one form to another. For example, the chemical energy present in a flashlight battery is converted into electrical energy that passes through the flashlight bulb, where it is transformed into light and heat. Through the process of photosynthesis, the energy of light is converted into chemical energy in the form of complex sugars and other organic molecules.

All forms of energy can be grouped into one of two different states. **Kinetic energy** is the energy possessed by an object because it is in motion. Obvious examples of objects that possess kinetic energy include waves in the ocean, a falling rock, or a kicked football. Less obvious examples include the kinetic energy of electricity, which is a flow of electrons, and heat. Photons of light are also a form of kinetic energy. The movement present in kinetic energy is of use because it can perform work by making other objects move. **Potential energy** is stored energy: the energy an object has because of its location or chemical structure. A boulder at the top of a cliff has potential energy because of its position in the gravitational field of Earth. The arrangement of atoms in a molecule of glucose or gasoline has potential energy stored in the specific arrangement of atoms. This type of energy is often called *chemical potential energy* and is discussed further in Chapter 6.

4.1b The Laws of Thermodynamics Describe the Energy Flow in Natural Systems

The study of energy and its transformations is called **thermodynamics.** When discussing thermodynamics, scientists refer to something called the *system*, which is the object being studied. A system can be anything—a single molecule, one cell, or a planet. Everything outside the system is called the *surroundings*. The *universe*, in this context, is the total of the system and the surroundings. It is important that we distinguish between three different types of systems: isolated, open, and closed. As shown in **Figure 4.1,** an isolated system is one that does not exchange matter or energy with its surroundings. A good example of this would be a perfectly insulated Thermos bottle. A *closed system* can exchange energy but not matter with its surroundings. The Earth can be considered a closed system. It takes in an enormous amount of energy generated by the Sun and releases heat, but, essentially, no matter is exchanged between Earth and the rest of the universe. In an *open system*, both energy and matter can move freely between the system and the surroundings. As we will see later in this chapter, living organisms are open systems.

4.1c The First Law of Thermodynamics

Quantitative research by both physicists and chemists in the nineteenth century regarding energy flow between systems and the surroundings led to the formulation of two fundamental laws of thermodynamics that apply equally to living cells and to stars in galaxies light-years away. According to the **first law of thermodynamics,** *energy can be transformed from one form into another or transferred from one place to another, but it cannot be created or destroyed.* This law is also called the principle of the conservation of energy. The first law of thermodynamics is illustrated by Niagara Falls **(Figure 4.2),** which borders Canada and the United States. Water at the top of the falls has high potential energy because of its location within the Earth's gravitational field. As the water moves over the waterfall, its potential energy is converted into kinetic energy. The higher

a. Isolated system

b. Closed system

c. Open system

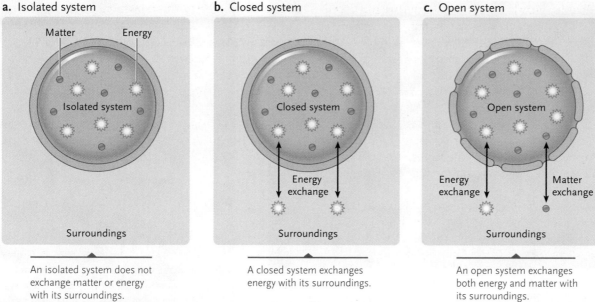

Matter   Energy

Isolated system

Surroundings

An isolated system does not exchange matter or energy with its surroundings.

Energy exchange

Closed system

Surroundings

A closed system exchanges energy with its surroundings.

Open system

Energy exchange   Matter exchange

Surroundings

An open system exchanges both energy and matter with its surroundings.

Figure 4.1
Isolated, closed, and open systems in thermodynamics.

the waterfall, the more kinetic energy the water will possess. When it reaches the bottom of the waterfall, the kinetic energy of the water is dissipated into various forms of potential and kinetic energy, including heat, sound, and mechanical energy (causing weathering of the rocks). For thousands of years, the kinetic energy of waterfalls has been used by humans to do work. At Niagara Falls, the kinetic energy of the moving water is converted into electricity through the use of hydroelectric turbines (see Figure 4.2b) and is used to supply electricity to thousands of homes and businesses.

4.1d The Second Law of Thermodynamics

Another important principle of thermodynamics is that each time energy is transformed from one form into another, some of the energy is lost and unavailable to do work. You can think of this as the reason why machines are never 100% efficient. For example, the engine of a car converts only about 25% of the potential energy in gasoline into the kinetic energy that makes the car move

a.

© Corel

b.

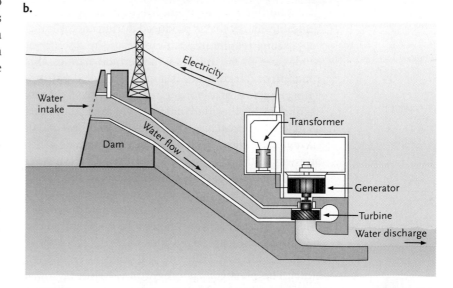

Electricity

Water intake

Transformer

Dam

Water flow

Generator

Turbine

Water discharge

Figure 4.2
Niagara Falls, which borders New York, U.S.A., and Ontario, Canada. **(a)** The potential energy of the water is converted into kinetic energy as it moves over the falls. **(b)** A small portion of this kinetic energy is used to turn hydroelectric turbines, converting the gravitational energy into electrical energy. In accordance with the first law of thermodynamics, energy hasn't been gained or lost but it has changed form. Niagara Falls generates approximately 4.4 gigawatts (a gigawatt is 10^9 watts) of power each year—enough to power thousands of homes and businesses.

a.

b.

Figure 4.3

Two examples of thermodynamic systems that display the second law of thermodynamics. **(a)** A car engine converts only about 30% of the available energy in gasoline into mechanical energy. **(b)** A runner converts only about 40% of the energy in glucose into ATP, which powers his muscles. In both cases, a significant portion of the energy is unused and is given off as heat, which increases the disorder, or entropy, of the surroundings.

(Figure 4.3). Likewise, only a portion of the energy in a notebook computer battery is used to run the computer. If you touch a car engine that has just been switched off or put a notebook computer on your lap for an extended period of time, it is obvious where the remaining energy is going. It is being lost to the surroundings as *heat*, which is the energy associated with random molecular motion. This concept of energy efficiency also applies to living cells. As we will see in Chapter 6, through the process of cellular respiration, cells are able to convert only about 40% of the potential energy in glucose into a form usable for metabolism; the remainder is lost as heat (see Figure 4.3). In most cases, including living cells, heat cannot be harnessed to do work; instead, it is simply lost to the environment.

Whether it is a car engine or a living cell, the unusable energy that is produced during energy transformations results in an increase in the *disorder* or *randomness* of the universe. In thermodynamics, this randomness or disorder is a quantity called **entropy**. This measure of disorder forms the basis of the **second law of thermodynamics**, which can be stated as follows: *the total disorder (entropy) of a system and its surroundings always increases.* There is no single inclusive way to think of entropy, and that is part of what makes it difficult to understand. So let's work through some examples: a cup of hot coffee gets cold. A new car doesn't stay new; first, it loses its "new car smell," and soon you need new brakes and a tune-up, until, eventually, the passenger door falls off. All of these situations are inevitable and will occur given enough time. The physical disintegration of an organized system is the second law in action. Systems will move spontaneously toward arrangements with greater entropy. Your dorm room or apartment will spontaneously move to a more disordered, higher entropy state **(Figure 4.4)**—essentially, it gets messy. You can reverse it, make things more ordered, but this requires work. It takes energy to maintain low entropy.

4.1e Life and the Second Law of Thermodynamics

But what about life: *does it obey the second law of thermodynamics?* One of the qualities of all life is that it is highly ordered. That is, the molecules and

Figure 4.4

An everyday illustration of the spontaneous move toward disorder. Rooms become messy, disorganized. To make the room more ordered requires an input or energy—it requires work.

structures that define life are very precisely arranged, in a nonrandom manner. Living cells have the ability to create ordered structures out of less ordered starting materials. A molecule of DNA, a protein, and a ribosome are all very ordered structures that living things make out of much simpler building blocks. There is nothing random or disordered about a brain or a flower or photosystem II. These examples suggest that life goes against the second law of thermodynamics: things don't become more random in a living cell, they become more ordered. How is this possible? The answer lies in understanding the statement mentioned at the end of the last section: *it takes energy to maintain low entropy.*

That's why.

Living cells are not isolated but rather are open systems, exchanging energy and matter with their surroundings. This energy may be in the form of a falafel sandwich or milkshake for you and me or in the form of photons of light and carbon dioxide for a cyanobacterium. Living things bring in energy and matter and use them to generate order out of disorder. It is understandable why elite athletes need to eat a lot of food, but people who don't exercise at all also need to ingest over a thousand kilocalories every day. Although some of this food supplies us with the energy to use our muscles, much of the food energy we ingest is used simply to maintain our cells in their highly ordered state **(Figure 4.5).**

According to the second law of thermodynamics, things are constantly breaking down. For living organisms this means that cell structures become damaged and need to be constantly replaced, New cells need to be made and old ones maintained by the synthesis of a huge array of proteins, carbohydrates,

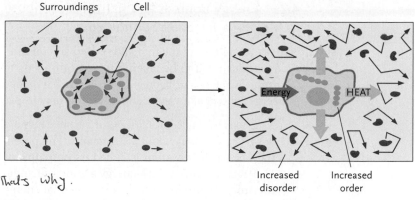

Figure 4.6

A simple thermodynamic example of a living cell. In the diagram on the left, molecules of both the cell and the surroundings are in a relatively disordered state. In the diagram on the right, the cell has taken in energy from the surroundings and used the energy to perform the work required to make molecules more ordered. This energy transformation releases heat, which increases the disorder (or entropy) of the surroundings.

and lipid molecules. In other words, *we eat food to maintain low entropy!*

But according to the second law of thermodynamics, the entropy of a system and the surroundings is always supposed to increase. Absolutely—In the course of the thousands of chemical reactions that take place to generate order, living things give off heat and by-products of metabolism such as carbon dioxide that are much less ordered and increase the disorder, or entropy, of the surroundings **(Figure 4.6).** The entropy of a system such as an organism is allowed to decrease as long as the entropy of the universe as a whole increases. Because of this, living organisms can be thought of as islands of low entropy in a sea (the universe) that is constantly becoming more random and disordered.

STUDY BREAK

1. Distinguish between kinetic and potential energy.
2. In thermodynamics, what is meant by an isolated, an open, and a closed system?

4.2 Free Energy and Spontaneous Reactions

Applying the first and second laws of thermodynamics together allows us to predict whether any particular chemical or physical reaction will occur without an input of energy—what in thermodynamics are called **spontaneous reactions.** In this usage, the word *spontaneous* means only that a reaction will occur—it does not describe the rate of a reaction. Spontaneous reactions may proceed very slowly, such as the formation of rust on a nail, or very quickly, such as a match bursting into flame.

Monkey Business Images/Shutterstock

Figure 4.5

Why do we need to eat? The average person needs to ingest about 1,500 kcal per day. A significant amount of this energy is needed to maintain the order within our cells. We eat food to maintain low entropy.

4.2a Energy Content and Entropy Contribute to Making a Reaction Spontaneous

Two factors related to the first and second laws of thermodynamics need to be taken into account for us to determine whether a reaction is spontaneous: the change in energy content of a system and its change in entropy:

1. *Reactions tend to be spontaneous if the products have less potential energy than the reactants.* The potential energy in a system is called its **enthalpy**, or H. Reactions that absorb energy are termed **endothermic**, the products have more potential energy than the **reactants**. By comparision, those processes that release energy are called **exothermic**. When natural gas burns, methane reacts spontaneously with oxygen to produce carbon dioxide and water:

$$CH_4 + 2\,O_2 \rightarrow CO_2 + H_2O$$

The reaction is exothermic, producing a large amount of heat, as the products have less potential energy than the reactants. We discuss the chemical basis for why molecules such as methane have high potential energy in Chapter 6. As a second example, what about the glass of ice water shown in **Figure 4.7**? Why does the ice spontaneously melt at 25°C? The system (the glass of ice water) is absorbing energy from the surroundings and the potential energy of water is greater than that of ice, not less. The process is endothermic, yet the process of the ice melting is it is spontaneous. Clearly, some other factor besides potential energy is at play here.

2. *Reactions tend to be spontaneous when the products are less ordered than the reactants.* Reactions tend to occur spontaneously if the entropy of the products is greater than the entropy of the reactants, that is, if the products are more random than the reactants. In the glass of ice water (see Figure 4.7), it is an increase in entropy that makes the melting of the ice a spontaneous process at 25°C. Molecules of ice are far more ordered (possess lower entropy) than molecules of water that are moving around randomly. In general, phase changes (solid → liquid → gas) result in an increase in entropy.

Figure 4.7
The melting of ice at room temperature. This is an example of a spontaneous reaction that is endothermic: the energy content of the product (water) is greater than the reactant (ice). The reaction is spontaneous because the entropy of the system, the disorder, increases.

Anna Lyubimtseva/iStockPhoto

4.2b The Change in Free Energy Indicates Whether a Reaction Is Spontaneous

Recall from the second law of thermodynamics that energy transformations are not 100% efficient; some of the energy is lost as an increase in entropy. So how much energy is available? The portion of a system's energy that is available to do work is called **free energy**, which is abbreviated by the letter G in recognition of the physicist Josiah Willard Gibbs, who developed the concept. In living organisms, free energy accomplishes the chemical and physical work involved in activities such as the synthesis of molecules, movement, and reproduction. The change in free energy, ΔG ($\Delta G = G_{final\ state} - G_{initial\ state}$), can be calculated for any specific chemical reaction using the formula

$$\Delta G = \Delta H - T\Delta S$$

where ΔH is the change in enthalpy and ΔS is the change in the entropy of the system over the course of the reaction. T is the absolute temperature in kelvin (K, where K = °C + 273.16). The equation says that *the free energy change as a system goes from initial to final states is the sum of the changes in energy content and entropy.*

For a reaction to be spontaneous, the ΔG must be negative. As the above formula tells us, both the entropy and the enthalpy of a reaction can influence the overall ΔG of a reaction. That is, for all chemical and physical processes, there is an interplay of both entropy and enthalpy to determine whether it will occur spontaneously. In some processes, such as the combustion of methane, the large loss of potential energy, negative enthalpy (ΔH), dominates in making a reaction spontaneous. In other reactions, a decrease in order (ΔS *increases*) dominates, such as the melting of ice at 25°C. Once we know what the ΔG for a reaction is, we can determine if the reaction will proceed spontaneously.

It is important not to forget that the ΔG represents the difference between the free energy of the final state compared with the initial state and that a negative ΔG indicates that the products have less free energy than the reactants. Another way to think about free energy has to do with stability **(Figure 4.8).** Systems that have high free energy are less stable than systems that have less free energy. Furthermore, systems will spontaneously change into a more stable state but cannot spontaneously change into being less stable. For example, a molecule of glucose can be considered as unstable and will spontaneously break down into molecules, including carbon dioxide, that have less free energy but that also are more stable. Likewise, a **concentration gradient** that exists across a membrane is less stable and contains more free energy than after diffusion, when the molecules are equally distributed on both sides of a membrane (see Figure 4.8).

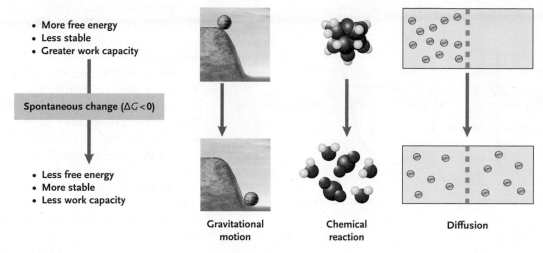

- More free energy
- Less stable
- Greater work capacity

Spontaneous change (ΔG < 0)

- Less free energy
- More stable
- Less work capacity

| Gravitational motion | Chemical reaction | Diffusion |

Figure 4.8

The relationship between free energy, stability, and work capacity. The top diagrams represent unstable systems that have high free energy and are unstable. They can spontaneously change into the bottom diagrams releasing free energy resulting in systems that are more stable. The release in free energy may be harnessed to perform work.

4.2c Life and Equilibrium

Another term for maximum stability is *equilibrium*, which is perhaps best explained in the context of the chemical equilibrium that can be achieved in a chemical reaction. Consider a chemical reaction in which glucose 1-phosphate is converted into glucose 6-phosphate **(Figure 4.9)**. Starting with 0.02 M glucose 1-phosphate, the reaction will proceed spontaneously until there

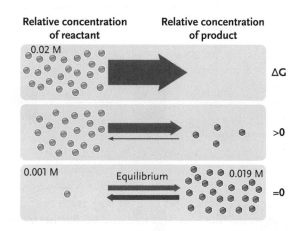

Relative concentration of reactant   Relative concentration of product

0.02 M

ΔG

>0

0.001 M   Equilibrium   0.019 M

=0

Figure 4.9

Chemical reactions run to equilibrium. No matter what quantities of glucose 1-phosphate and glucose 6-phosphate are dissolved in water, when equilibrium is attained, there will always be 95% glucose 6-phosphate and 5% glucose 1-phosphate. At equilibrium, the number of reactant molecules being converted to products equals the number of product molecules being converted back to reactants. The reaction at the equilibrium point is reversible; it may be made to run to the right (forward) by adding more reactants or to the left (backward) by adding more products.

is 0.019 M of glucose 6-phosphate (product) and 0.001 M of glucose 1-phosphate (reactant) in the solution. In fact, regardless of the amounts of each you start with, the reaction will reach a point at which there is 95% glucose 6-phosphate and 5% glucose 1-phosphate. This is called the point of chemical equilibrium, a state in which the reaction does not stop but rather a state in which the rate of the forward reaction equals the rate of the backward reaction. As a system moves toward equilibrium, the free energy of the system becomes progressively lower and reaches its lowest point and maximum stability when the system is at equilibrium (G is zero). You can think of a reaction as an energy valley, with the **equilibrium point** being at the bottom. To move away from the equilibrium point requires free energy and thus will not be spontaneous.

For each reaction, the point of equilibrium is related to the ΔG for the reaction. The more negative the ΔG, the further toward completion the reaction will move before equilibrium is established. If the reaction shown in Figure 4.9 had a positive ΔG, the reaction would run backward toward glucose 1-phosphate. Many reactions have a ΔG that is near zero and are thus readily reversible by adjusting the concentrations of products and reactants slightly.

The reaction shown in Figure 4.9 represents an isolated system, and, over time, equilibrium is reached, the ΔG becoming zero. However, many individual reactions in living organisms never reach an equilibrium point because living systems are open; thus, the supply of reactants is constant, and as products are formed, they do not accumulate but rather become the reactants of another reaction. In fact, overall, the ΔG of life is always negative as organisms

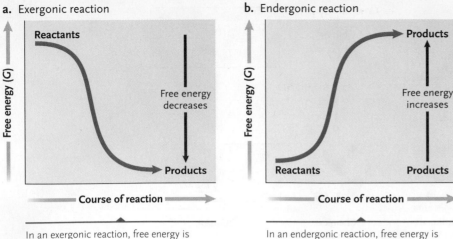

a. Exergonic reaction

Reactants

Free energy (G)

Free energy decreases

Products

Course of reaction

In an exergonic reaction, free energy is released. The products have less free energy than was present in the reactants, and the reaction proceeds spontaneously.

b. Endergonic reaction

Products

Free energy (G)

Free energy increases

Reactants   Products

Course of reaction

In an endergonic reaction, free energy is gained. The products have more free energy than was present in the reactants. An endergonic reaction is not spontaneous: it proceeds only if energy is supplied by an exergonic reaction.

Figure 4.10
Exergonic **(a)** and endergonic **(b)** reactions.

constantly take in energy-rich molecules (or light, if photosynthetic) and use them to do work. Organisms reach equilibrium, $\Delta G = 0$, only when they die.

4.2d Metabolic Pathways Consist of Exergonic and Endergonic Reactions

Based on the free energy of reactants and products, every reaction can be placed into one of two groups. An **exergonic reaction (Figure 4.10a)** is one that releases free energy—the ΔG is negative because the products contain less free energy than the reactants. In an **endergonic reaction (Figure 4.10b)**, the products contain more free energy than the reactants; therefore, the ΔG is positive. The reactants involved in endergonic reactions need to gain free energy from the surroundings to form the products of the reaction.

In metabolism, individual reactions tend to be part of a metabolic pathway, which is a series of sequential reactions in which the products of one reaction are used immediately as the reactants for the next reaction in the series **(Figure 4.11)**. In one type of metabolic pathway called a **catabolic pathway** (see Figure 4.11a), energy is released by the breakdown of complex molecules to simpler compounds. An example of a catabolic pathway that we discuss in detail in

Chapter 6 is cellular respiration, whereby energy is extracted from the breakdown of food such as glucose. In contrast, **anabolic pathways** (see Figure 4.11b) consume energy to build complicated molecules from simpler ones; these are often called biosynthetic pathways. Examples of anabolic pathways include photosynthesis, which is covered in Chapter 7, as well as the synthesis of macromolecules such as proteins and nucleic acids.

As shown in Figure 4.11, the overall ΔG of an anabolic pathway is positive, whereas the overall ΔG of a catabolic pathway is negative. However, any one pathway may be made up of a number of individual chemical reactions, not all of which need to have the same sign (positive or negative) as the overall ΔG. As we will learn in Chapter 6, cellular respiration is a metabolic pathway made up of many individual reactions, some of which release energy ($-\Delta G$), whereas others require energy ($+\Delta G$). However, when you sum the ΔG of all the reactions, the overall free energy is negative, and the pathway of cellular respiration is thus said to be catabolic.

STUDY BREAK

1. What two factors need to be considered to determine if a reaction will proceed spontaneously?
2. Define and distinguish between exergonic and endergonic reactions and anabolic and catabolic pathways.

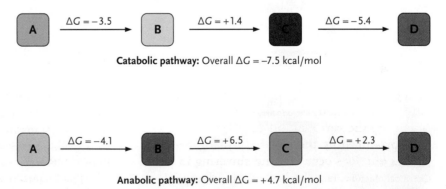

A → $\Delta G = -3.5$ → B → $\Delta G = +1.4$ → C → $\Delta G = -5.4$ → D

Catabolic pathway: Overall $\Delta G = -7.5$ kcal/mol

A → $\Delta G = -4.1$ → B → $\Delta G = +6.5$ → C → $\Delta G = +2.3$ → D

Anabolic pathway: Overall $\Delta G = +4.7$ kcal/mol

Figure 4.11
Hypothetical examples of the two major types of metabolic pathways. The starting molecule A is converted by a series of enzyme-catalyzed reactions to the product D. In catabolic pathways, the starting molecule A has high amounts of free energy, which is released as it gets converted into D. In anabolic pathways, energy must be provided to convert a molecule with low free energy A to one with higher amounts of free energy D. Although each pathway will have either an overall negative or positive ΔG, individual reactions can have the opposite sign.

4.3 The Energy Currency of the Cell: ATP

A huge array of reactions take place within cells that involve the assembly of complex molecules from more simple components. As we discussed in the last section, these reactions have a positive ΔG and are called endergonic, and they may be part of both catabolic and anabolic pathways. How the cell supplies the energy to drive these endergonic reactions is highly conserved among all forms of life and involves the nucleotide adenosine triphosphate (ATP).

4.3a ATP Hydrolysis Releases Free Energy

ATP is the best example of a group of compounds that contain large amounts of free energy because they possess what are called high-energy phosphate bonds. ATP itself consists of a five-carbon sugar, ribose, linked to the **nitrogenous base** adenine and a chain of three phosphate groups **(Figure 4.12).** Much of the potential energy of ATP is associated with the arrangement of the three phosphate groups. As shown in Figure 4.12a, each of the phosphate groups is closely associated with each other and their negative charges strongly repel each other, making the bonding arrangements unstable. Removal of one or two of the three phosphate groups is a spontaneous reaction that relieves the repulsion and releases large amounts of free energy. The breakdown of ATP is a *hydrolysis* reaction (see Figure 4.12b) and results in the formation of adenosine diphosphate (ADP) and a molecule of inorganic phosphate (P_i). ADP can be further hydrolyzed to adenosine monophosphate (AMP); however, this releases somewhat less free energy than the hydrolysis of ATP:

$$ATP + H_2O \rightarrow ADP + P_i$$
$$\Delta G = -7.3 \text{ kcal/mol}$$

4.3b ATP and Energy Coupling

When ATP is dissolved in water in a test tube, the hydrolysis reaction releases free energy that simply warms up the surrounding water. Within cells, the heat produced by the isolated hydrolysis of ATP is rare but does occur during shivering in muscle tissue to maintain body heat. If most ATP was hydrolyzed in this manner, it would be very difficult for the cell to trap the heat produced and use it to do work. In addition, significant heat generation could result in cell death. So, given these two points, how do living cells link or *couple* the hydrolysis of ATP to an endergonic reaction such that energy is not simply wasted as heat?

a. Chemical structure of ATP

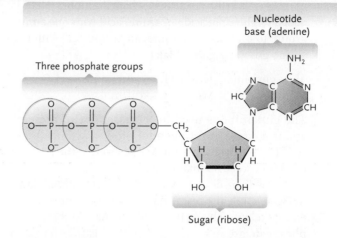

b. Hydrolysis reaction removing a phosphate group from ATP

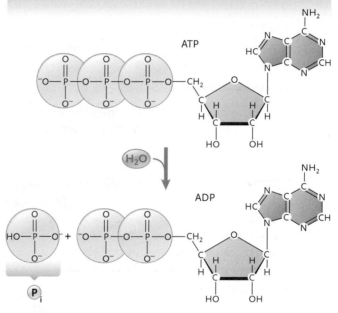

Figure 4.12
ATP, the primary molecule that is used to supply the energy for endergonic reactions. **(a)** Structure of one ATP molecule. **(b)** Reaction of ATP hydrolysis. ATP possesses high free energy because the repulsive forces of the three phosphate groups make the molecule unstable.

In a process called **energy coupling**, ATP is brought in close contact with a reactant molecule involved in an endergonic reaction, and when the ATP is hydrolyzed, the terminal phosphate group is transferred to the reactant molecule. The transfer of the phosphate results in the reactant becoming *phosphorylated*, which makes the molecule less stable (more reactive) than when it was present in the unphosphorylated form. Energy coupling requires the action of an enzyme to bring the ATP and reactant molecule(s) into close association. The enzyme has a specific site on it that binds both the ATP and the reactant molecule, allowing for transfer of the phosphate group.

An example of energy coupling that is very common in most cells is the reaction in which ammonia (NH_3) is added to glutamic acid, an amino acid with one **amino group**, to produce glutamine, an amino acid with two amino groups **(Figure 4.13a):**

$$\text{glutamic acid} + NH_3 \rightarrow \text{glutamine} + H_2O$$
$$\Delta G = +3.4 \text{ kcal/mol}$$

The glutamine is used in the assembly of proteins and is a donor of nitrogen for other reactions in the cell. The positive value for ΔG shows that the reaction cannot proceed spontaneously.

How, then, do cells carry out this reaction? As shown in **Figure 4.13b,** the reaction proceeds by harnessing the energy released by ATP hydrolysis. As a first step, the phosphate group removed from ATP is transferred to glutamic acid, forming glutamyl phosphate:

$$\text{glutamic acid} + ATP \rightarrow \text{glutamyl phosphate} + ADP$$

The ΔG for this reaction is negative, making the reaction spontaneous. In the second step, glutamyl phosphate reacts with NH_3:

$$\text{glutamyl phosphate} + NH_3 \rightarrow \text{glutamine} + P_i$$

This second reaction also has a negative value for ΔG and is spontaneous. Even though the reaction proceeds in two steps, it is usually written for convenience as one reaction, with a combined negative value for ΔG:

$$\text{glutamic acid} + NH_3 + ATP \rightarrow \text{glutamine} + ADP + P_i$$
$$\Delta G = -3.9 \text{ kcal/mol}$$

Because ΔG is negative, the **coupled reaction** is spontaneous and releases energy. The difference between -3.9 kcal/mol and the -7.3 kcal/mol released by hydrolyzing ATP to $ADP + P_i$ represents potential chemical energy transferred to the glutamine molecules produced by the reaction. In effect, the coupling system works by joining an exergonic reaction, the hydrolysis of ATP, to the endergonic biosynthesis reaction, producing an overall reaction that is exergonic. All the endergonic reactions of living organisms, including those of growth, reproduction, movement, and response to stimuli, are made possible by coupling reactions in this way.

4.3c Regeneration of ATP

We have just seen how the breakdown of ATP into ADP and P_i is an exergonic reaction that can be coupled to make otherwise endergonic reactions proceed spontaneously. These coupling reactions occur continuously in living cells, consuming a tremendous amount of ATP. The question we can now ask is *how do cells generate ATP?* ATP is a renewable resource that is synthesized by recombining ADP and P_i. If ATP hydrolysis is an exergonic process, then ATP synthesis from ADP and P_i is an energy-requiring, endergonic process. The energy for ATP synthesis comes from the exergonic breakdown of complex molecules that contain an abundance of free energy. Essentially, what we are referring to is food, carbohydrates, fats, and proteins—all abundant sources of energy.

The continued breakdown and resynthesis of ATP is called the **ATP cycle (Figure 4.14).** Approximately

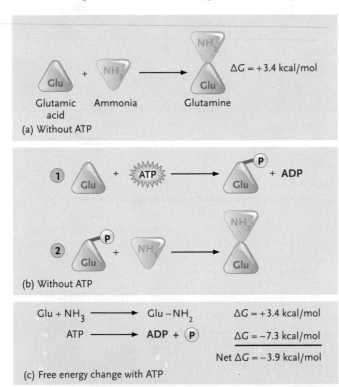

(a) Without ATP

(b) Without ATP

$$\text{Glu} + NH_3 \longrightarrow \text{Glu} - NH_2 \qquad \Delta G = +3.4 \text{ kcal/mol}$$
$$ATP \longrightarrow ADP + \textcircled{P} \qquad \Delta G = -7.3 \text{ kcal/mol}$$
$$\text{Net } \Delta G = -3.9 \text{ kcal/mol}$$

(c) Free energy change with ATP

Figure 4.13
Energy coupling using ATP hydrolysis. **(a)** The synthesis of glutamine from glutamic acid and ammonia is not spontaneous. **(b)** In the presence of ATP hydrolysis, the free energy of the terminal phosphate is transferred to the glutamic acid, making it more unstable. In this form, it spontaneously reacts with ammonia, forming glutamine. **(c)** Adding the ΔG for the amino acid conversion to the ΔG for ATP hydrolysis gives the free energy change for the overall reaction. Because the overall process is exergonic, has a negative ΔG, it occurs spontaneously.

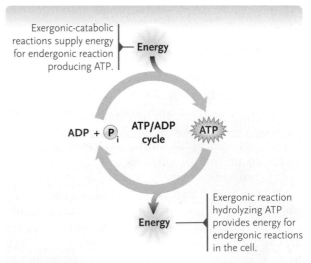

Figure 4.14
The ATP/ADP cycle. This cycle couples reactions that release free energy to reactions that require free energy.

10 million ATP molecules are hydrolyzed and resynthesized each second in a typical cell, illustrating that this cycle operates at an astonishing rate. In fact, if ATP was not regenerated from ADP and P_i, it is estimated that the average human would use an estimated 75 kg of ATP per day. It makes sense that cells should never be limited in their availability of ATP. In fact, a typical cell maintains an ATP concentration that is about 1000 times greater than ADP—very far from equilibrium.

STUDY BREAK

1. Explain, given the structure of ATP, why its hydrolysis releases free energy.
2. What is meant by the term *energy coupling*?

4.4 The Role of Enzymes in Biological Reactions

The laws of thermodynamics are useful because they can tell us if a process will occur without an input of energy, or, said another way, if the process is spontaneous. However, the laws do not tell us anything about the speed of a reaction. For example, even though the breakdown of sucrose into glucose and fructose is a spontaneous process with a ΔG of -7 kcal/mol, a solution of sucrose can sit for years without any detectable fructose or glucose being formed. This is an important point that is worth repeating: *that a reaction is spontaneous does not mean it proceeds rapidly.* In the next few sections, we discuss how the speed of a reaction can be altered through the use of a special group of proteins called enzymes.

4.4a The Activation Energy Represents a Kinetic Barrier

In our example above, what is it that prevents sucrose from being rapidly converted into glucose and fructose? Chemical reactions require bonds to break and new bonds to be formed. For bonds to be broken, they must first be strained or otherwise made less stable so that bond breakage can actually occur. To get reacting molecules into a more unstable state requires a small input of energy. Thus, even though a reaction is spontaneous (negative ΔG), the reaction will not actually start unless a relatively small boost of energy is added **(Figure 4.15a).** This initial energy investment required to start a reaction is called the **activation energy** (E_A). Molecules that gain the necessary activation energy occupy what is called the **transition state,** where bonds are unstable and are ready to be broken.

A rock resting in a depression at the top of a hill provides a physical example of activation energy

(Figure 4.15b). The rock will not roll downhill spontaneously, even though its position represents considerable potential energy and the total "reaction"—the downward movement of the rock—is spontaneous and releases free energy. In this example, the activation energy is the effort required to raise the rock over the rim of the depression and start its downhill roll.

What provides the activation energy for chemical reactions? The molecules taking part in chemical reactions are in constant motion (at temperatures above absolute zero), and, periodically, reacting molecules may gain enough energy to reach the transition state. For a solution of sucrose, the number of molecules that reach the transition state at any one time is very small. However, if a significant number of reactant molecules reach the transition state, then the free energy that is released may be enough to get the remaining reactants to the transition state. A good example of this is illustrated by a propane torch **(Figure 4.16, p. 82).** Propane is a molecule that contains an abundance of free energy and spontaneously decomposes into

a.

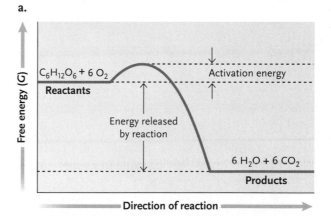

b.

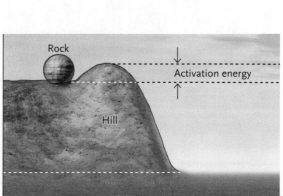

Figure 4.15

The concept of activation energy. (a) The activation energy for the oxidation of glucose is an energy barrier over which glucose molecules must be raised before they can react to form H_2O and CO_2. **(b)** In an analogous physical situation, a rock poised in a depression at the top of a hill will not roll downhill unless activating energy is added to raise it over the rim of the depression.

PEOPLE BEHIND BIOLOGY

Maud Menten

A fundamental topic covered in almost all introductory biochemistry courses is the Michaelis–Menten equation. First stated in 1913, the equation provides a mathematical description of the kinetics of an enzyme-catalyzed reaction. The equation represents one of the fundamental concepts of biochemistry.

The Menten of the equation refers to Maud Menten, who was born on March 20, 1879, in Port Lambton, Ontario. After completing secondary school, Menten attended the University of Toronto and earned a bachelor of arts degree in 1904, followed by a master's degree in physiology in 1907. In the same year, Menten was appointed a fellow at the Rockefeller Institute for Medical Research in New York City, where she studied the effect of radium bromide on cancerous tumours in rats. Menten and two other scientists published the results of their experiment, producing the institute's first monograph. She returned to Canada and began studies at the University

of Toronto a year later. In 1911, she became one of the first Canadian women to receive a doctor of medicine degree.

In 1912, Menten travelled to Germany to work with Leonor Michaelis, a biochemist who shared Menton's interest in understanding enzyme kinetics. After a year of research, the two scientists coauthored a paper that put forward a description of the basis of enzyme-catalyzed chemical kinetics. The paper introduced the Michaelis–Menten equation as a tool for measuring the rates of enzyme reactions. The formula gave scientists a way to record how enzymes worked and is the standard for most enzyme-kinetic measurements. Michaelis and Menten were able to demonstrate that each enzyme, given enough substrate, has its own rate of causing that substrate to undergo chemical change. The Michaelis–Menten equation profoundly changed the study of biochemistry and earned Menten and Michaelis worldwide recognition.

When Menten returned from Berlin, she enrolled at the University of Chicago, where she obtained a Ph.D. in biochemistry in 1916. Unable to find an academic position in her native Canada, in 1918 she joined the medical school faculty at the University of Pittsburgh. While maintaining an active research program, she was also known as an avid mountain climber who went on several expeditions to the Arctic. As well, she spoke numerous languages, loved to paint, and played the clarinet. Over the years, Menten authored more than 70 publications, including discoveries related to blood sugar, hemoglobin, and kidney functions. In so-called retirement, she returned to British Columbia to do research at the British Columbia Medical Research Institute, almost until her death. A plaque commemorating the life and work of Maud Menten is located in the Medical Sciences Building, University of Toronto, Queen's Park.

carbon dioxide and water. However, the reaction proceeds very slowly—the propane in a torch can sit

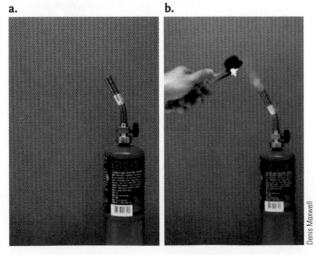

a.   **b.**

Denis Maxwell

Figure 4.16

Combustion of propane. (a) The combustion of propane is a spontaneous reaction; however, the activation energy is a barrier that makes propane kinetically stable. **(b)** By providing a spark, propane obtains the energy required to attain the transition state.

for years and remain unchanged. This is because if left undisturbed, it is a rare event for molecules of propane to acquire the energy needed to reach the transition state. However, if you supply a stream of propane with a spark (see Figure 4.16), then you provide molecules of propane with the energy to reach the transition state, resulting in a tremendous release of free energy into the environment.

If you walk through a typical undergraduate chemistry lab, you will often find at least one Bunsen burner that provides the necessary heat to make a range of chemical reactions proceed rapidly. Chemists routinely use heat to provide the energy needed for reactant molecules to get to the transition state and thus speed up the rate of a reaction. In biology, using heat to speed up a reaction is problematic for two reasons: First, high temperatures destroy the structural components of cells, particularly proteins, and can result in cell death. Second, an increase in temperature would speed up all possible chemical reactions in a cell, not just the specific reactions that are part of metabolism.

4.4b Enzymes Accelerate Reactions by Reducing the Activation Energy

So how can you increase the rate of a reaction without raising the temperature? You can use a **catalyst**, which is a chemical agent that speeds up the rate of a reaction without itself taking part in the reaction. The most common biological catalysts is a group of proteins called **enzymes**.

Recall that the activation energy represents a hurdle that a reaction needs to get over in order to proceed spontaneously. This activation energy represents a real *kinetic* barrier that prevents spontaneous reactions from proceeding quickly. The greater the activation energy barrier, the slower the reaction will proceed. Enzymes increase the rate of a reaction by lowering this barrier—by lowering the activation energy of the reaction **(Figure 4.17)**. Since the rate of a reaction will be proportional to the number of reactant molecules that can acquire the necessary energy to get to the transition state, enzymes make it possible for a greater proportion of reactant molecules to attain the activation energy.

An important point that is shown in Figure 4.17 is that although enzymes lower the activation energy of a reaction, they do not alter the change in free energy (ΔG) of the reaction. The free energy of the reactants and products is the same; the only difference is the path the reaction takes.

Since it is often a point of confusion, it is important at this juncture to review what enzymes do and do not do with regard to biological reactions. By lowering the activation energy, enzymes DO speed up the rate of spontaneous (exergonic) reactions. However, enzymes DO NOT supply free energy to a reaction. Therefore, enzymes CANNOT make an endergonic reaction proceed spontaneously. ATP hydrolysis can be used to make an endergonic reaction proceed spontaneously, but alone, an enzyme cannot. Lastly, enzymes DO NOT change the ΔG of a reaction.

4.4c Enzymes Combine with Reactants and Are Released Unchanged

In enzymatic reactions, an enzyme combines briefly with reacting molecules and is released unchanged when the reaction is complete. For example, the enzyme in **Figure 4.18,** hexokinase, catalyzes the following reaction:

$$\text{glucose} + \text{ATP} \xrightarrow{\text{hexokinase}} \text{glucose 6-phosphate} + \text{ADP}$$

The reactant that an enzyme acts on is called the enzyme's substrate, or substrates if the enzyme binds two or more molecules. Each type of enzyme catalyzes the reaction of only a single type of molecule or a group of closely related molecules. This *enzyme specificity* explains why a typical cell needs about 4000 different enzymes to function properly. Looking at Figure 4.17, notice that the enzyme is much larger than the size of the substrate. As well, the substrate interacts with only a very small region of the enzyme called the **active site**, the place on the enzyme where catalysis occurs. The active site is usually a pocket or groove that is formed when the newly synthesized enzyme (which is a protein) folds into its correct shape.

In the early twentieth century, biochemists proposed the *lock-and-key hypothesis* to explain the

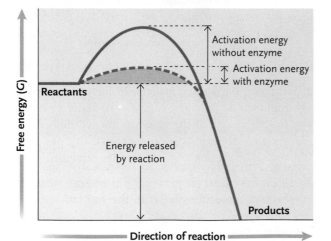

Figure 4.17

Enzymes lower the activation energy of a reaction. The reduction allows biological reactions to proceed rapidly at the relatively low temperatures that can be tolerated by living organisms. As you can see, enzymes do not change the free energy of the reactants or products, and thus do not change the overall ΔG.

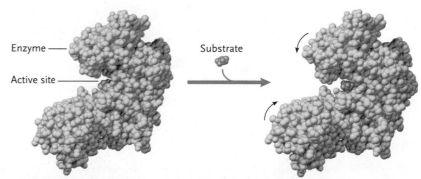

Figure 4.18

Space-filling models showing the combination of an enzyme, hexokinase (in blue), with its substrate, glucose (in yellow). Hexokinase catalyzes the phosphorylation of glucose to form glucose 6-phosphate. The phosphate group that enters the reaction is not shown. Note how the enzyme undergoes a conformational change, closing the active site more tightly as it binds the substrate.

specificity of the substrate–enzyme interaction. The analogy worked well to explain how even somewhat similar substrates (keys) were unable to bind to the same enzyme (lock) to cause catalysis (unlocking of the door). However, more recently, this hypothesis has been superseded by what has become known as the *induced-fit hypothesis*. Research has shown that enzymes are not rigid objects (like locks) but instead are flexible; just prior to substrate binding, the enzyme changes its shape, or what we call its *conformation*, so that the active site becomes even more precise in its ability to bind substrate. This is shown in Figure 4.18 where the conformation of the enzyme changes slightly when it binds to substrate.

As shown in **Figure 4.19,** the enzyme binds to substrate, forming an enzyme–substrate complex. Catalysis occurs when the two are joined, with the action of the enzyme converting the substrate (or substrates) into one or more products. Because enzymes are released unchanged after a reaction, enzyme molecules can rapidly bind to other substrate molecules, catalyzing the same reaction again, repeating what is called the enzyme cycle (see Figure 4.19). The rate at which enzymes catalyze reactions varies depending on the specifics of the

enzyme and substrates involved, but typical rates vary between about 100 and 10 million substrate molecules per second.

Many enzymes require a *cofactor*, a nonprotein group that binds very precisely to the enzyme. Cofactors are often metals such as iron, copper, zinc, and manganese. Although your body often needs very small amounts of some of these metals, they are absolutely essential for the catalytic activity of the enzyme to which they bind. Organic cofactors called *coenzymes* play similar roles and are often derived from vitamins.

4.4d Enzymes Reduce the Activation Energy by Inducing the Transition State

A central question of enzyme function is *how do they actually reduce the activation energy of a reaction?* Recall that substrate molecules need to be in the transition state for catalysis to occur. Enzymes function by increasing the number of reactant molecules that acquire the transition state conformation. Research has shown that enzymes can achieve this through three major mechanisms **(Figure 4.20):**

1. *Bringing the reacting molecules together.* Reacting molecules can assume the transition state only when they collide; binding to an enzyme's active site brings the reactants together in the right orientation for catalysis to occur.

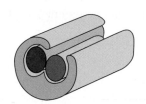

Bring reacting molecules close together

2. *Exposing the reactant molecule to altered charge environments that promote catalysis.* In some systems, the active site of the enzyme may contain ionic groups whose positive or negative charges alter the substrate in a way that favours catalysis.

Charge interactions

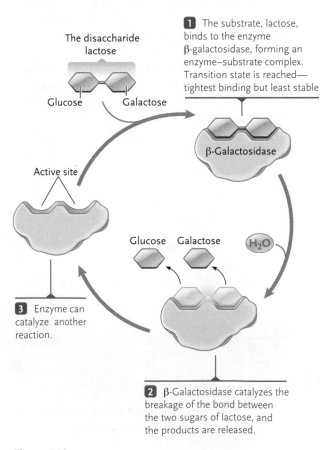

1 The substrate, lactose, binds to the enzyme β-galactosidase, forming an enzyme–substrate complex. Transition state is reached— tightest binding but least stable

The disaccharide lactose

Glucose   Galactose

β-Galactosidase

Active site

Glucose Galactose   H₂O

3 Enzyme can catalyze another reaction.

2 β-Galactosidase catalyzes the breakage of the bond between the two sugars of lactose, and the products are released.

Figure 4.19
The catalytic cycle of an enzyme. Shown is the enzyme β-galactosidase, which cleaves the sugar lactose to produce glucose and galactose.

Figure 4.20
The binding of substrate(s) to an active site results in the substrate acquiring the transition state conformation.

(continued)

3. *Changing the shape of a substrate molecule.* The active site may strain or distort substrate molecules into a conformation that mimics the transition state.

Distort or strain substrate molecules

Regardless of the mechanism, the binding of the substrate to the active site results in the substrate attaining the transition state conformation. Although without the enzyme, substrate molecules do acquire the transition state, this may be a rare event. The inclusion of an enzyme enables many more molecules to reach the transition state more rapidly. This is fundamentally why enzymes speed up the rate of a reaction.

STUDY BREAK

1. How do enzymes increase the rate of a chemical reaction?
2. Can enzymes alter the ΔG of a chemical reaction?

4.5 Conditions and Factors that Affect Enzyme Activity

Several conditions can alter enzyme activity, including changes in the concentration of substrate and other molecules that bind to enzymes. In addition, a number of control mechanisms modify enzyme activity, thereby adjusting reaction rates to meet a cell's requirements for chemical products. As well, changes in temperature and pH can have a significant impact on enzyme activity.

4.5a The Influence of Enzyme and Substrate Concentrations on the Rate of Catalysis

Biochemists use a wide range of approaches to study enzymes. These include molecular tools to study the structure and regulation of the gene that encodes the enzyme to using sophisticated computer programs to model the three-dimensional structure of the enzyme itself. The most fundamental and central approach has been to determine the rate of an enzyme-catalyzed reaction and how it changes in response to altering certain experimental parameters. This usually requires isolating the enzyme from the remainder of the cell, incubating it in an appropriate buffered solution and supplying the reaction mixture with substrate. With these constituents, one can then determine the rate of catalysis by measuring the rate at which the product of the reaction is formed.

As shown in **Figure 4.21a,** in the presence of excess substrate, the rate of catalysis will be proportional to the amount of enzyme. That is, as enzyme concentration increases, the rate of product formation increases. In this system (see Figure 4.21a), what is limiting the rate of the reaction (the rate-limiting component) is the amount of enzyme in the reaction mixture. Now what happens to the rate of the reaction if we keep the amount of enzyme constant at some intermediate concentration and change the substrate concentration from low to high? As shown in **Figure 4.21b,** at very low concentrations, substrate molecules collide so infrequently with enzyme molecules that the reaction proceeds slowly. As the substrate concentration increases, the reaction rate initially increases as enzyme and substrate molecules collide more frequently. But as the enzyme molecules approach the maximum rate at which they can combine with reactants and release products, increasing substrate concentration has a smaller and smaller effect, and the rate of reaction eventually levels off. When the enzymes are cycling as rapidly as possible, further increases in substrate concentration have no effect on the reaction rate. At this point, the enzymes are said to be *saturated* with substrate.

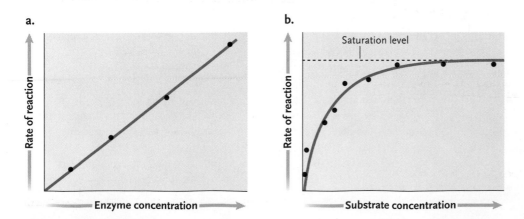

Figure 4.21
Changes in substrate concentration and enzyme concentration alter the rate of reaction. **(a)** The rate of reaction (usually measured as the rate of product formation) as a function of increasing enzyme concentration. The concentration of substrate is kept very high. **(b)** The rate of reaction as a function of increasing substrate concentration. The amount of enzyme is kept constant.

4.5b Enzyme Inhibitors Have Characteristic Effects on Enzyme Activity

The rate at which an enzyme can catalyze a reaction can be lowered by *enzyme inhibitors*, molecules that bind to an enzyme and decrease its activity. Some inhibitors work by binding to the active site of an enzyme, whereas other inhibitors bind to critical sites located elsewhere in the structure of the enzyme.

Inhibitors that combine with the active site have shapes that resemble the normal substrate closely enough to fit into and occupy the active site, thereby blocking access for the normal substrate and slowing the reaction rate. If the concentration of the inhibitor is high enough, the reaction may stop completely. Inhibition of this type is called **competitive inhibition** because the inhibitor *competes* with the normal substrate for access to the active site of the enzyme **(Figure 4.22a).**

In **noncompetitive inhibition**, specific molecules inhibit enzyme activity, but they do not compete with substrate molecules for binding to the active site **(Figure 4.22b).** Instead, noncompetitive inhibitors bind to an enzyme at a location other than the active site. This binding often results in a change to the conformation of the enzyme that reduces the ability of the active site to efficiently bind substrate.

Inhibitors differ with respect to how strongly they bind to enzymes. In reversible inhibition, the binding

a. Competitive inhibition

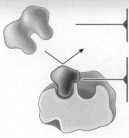

Substrate is unable to bind when inhibitor is bound to active site.

Competitive inhibitor molecule resembles substrate and competes for active site.

b. Noncompetitive inhibition

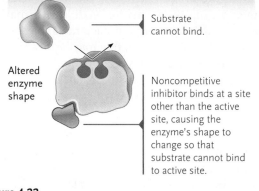

Substrate cannot bind.

Altered enzyme shape

Noncompetitive inhibitor binds at a site other than the active site, causing the enzyme's shape to change so that substrate cannot bind to active site.

Figure 4.22
Actions of **(a)** competitive and **(b)** noncompetitive inhibitors of enzyme activity.

MOLECULE BEHIND BIOLOGY

Penicillin: A Competitive Inhibitor of Enzyme Action

Penicillin is an antibiotic that is used in the treatment of bacterial infections. It was first discovered by Alexander Fleming, who isolated it from the mould *Penicillium* after he accidently found that the presence of the mould inhibited the growth of bacteria on a Petri plate. Following the development of methods for its mass production, penicillin was a true wonder drug as it was effective in treating a wide range of bacterial infections that in the past often led to death.

Penicillin acts by inhibiting the synthesis of peptidoglycan, a key component of the bacterial cell wall. Peptidoglycan is a complex polymer consisting of sugars and amino acids

that forms a meshlike structure outside the plasma membrane. As such, peptidoglycan provides structural strength and protects the bacterial cell from osmotic changes that would otherwise cause the cell to burst. If a bacterium is unable to synthesize components necessary for its cell wall, it is unable to grow and divide.

A key factor that is required for the synthesis of peptidoglycan is the enzyme transpeptidase, which catalyzes the formation of a peptide bond between two amino acids, which effectively links two portions of the peptidoglycan together. Penicillin inhibits peptidoglycan synthesis because it is a competitive inhibitor of transpeptidase

activity. The structure of penicillin mimics that of the two amino acids, which normally are brought together by the active site. Penicillin binds irreversibly to the active site of transpeptidase, effectively destroying the molecule. Given the concentrations of penicillin usually administered to a patient, this leads to total inhibition of all transpeptidase activity.

Although penicillin was widely employed in the 1950s and 1960s, most infections today involve bacteria that have acquired resistance to the drug. New antibiotics are constantly being developed to try to stop the growing problem of antibiotic-resistant bacteria.

of inhibitors to the enzyme is weak and readily reversible, with the enzyme activity returning to normal following inhibitor release. By contrast, some inhibitors bind so strongly to the enzyme through the formation of **covalent bonds** that the enzyme is completely disabled. This is called irreversible inhibition. Not surprisingly, many irreversible inhibitors that act on critical enzymes are highly toxic to the cell. This includes a wide variety of drugs and pesticides. Cyanide is a potent poison because it binds strongly to and inhibits **cytochrome** oxidase, the enzyme that catalyzes the last step of respiratory electron transport. In addition, many antibiotics are toxins that inhibit enzyme activity in bacteria (see *Molecule Behind Biology*). Irreversible inhibition can be overcome only by the cell synthesizing more of the enzyme.

4.5c Allosteric Control of Enzyme Activity

Many cellular metabolites act as reversible inhibitors of enzyme activity and should not be considered detrimental to cell function but rather as an important mechanism of metabolic regulation. A typical cell contains thousands of enzymes, and for many enzymes that synthesize a specific molecule, usually another enzyme exists that catalyzes its breakdown. If both enzymes were active in the same cell compartment at the same time, the result would be what is called futile cycling. A **futile cycle** occurs when two metabolic pathways run simultaneously in opposite directions and have no overall effect other than wasting energy. To prevent this, the cell is able to regulate enzyme activity in such a way that not all enzymes are active at the same time. Many enzymes are regulated by natural inhibitors, including inhibitors that work either competitively or noncompetitively. Typically, the combination between these inhibitors and the enzyme is fully reversible. If the concentration of the inhibitor increases, it combines with the enzymes in greater numbers, thereby interfering with enzyme activity and decreasing the rate of the reaction. If the concentration of the inhibitor decreases, its combination with enzymes decreases proportionately, and the rate of the reaction increases. Control by the inhibitors changes enzyme activity precisely to meet the needs of the cell for the products of the reaction catalyzed by the enzyme.

In the mechanism of **allosteric regulation (Figure 4.23),** enzyme activity is controlled by the reversible

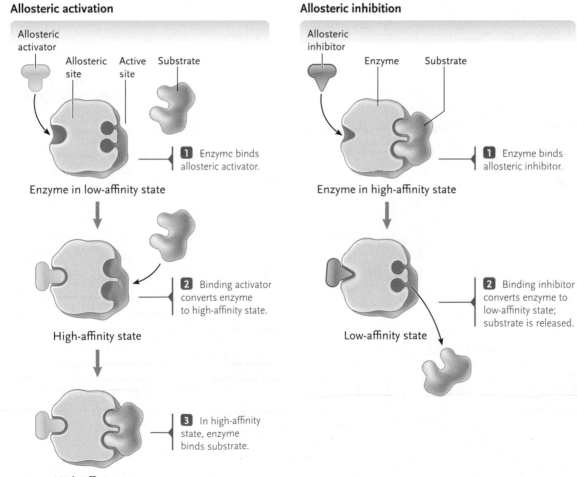

Figure 4.23
Allosteric regulation.

binding of a regulatory molecule to the *allosteric site*, a location on the enzyme outside the active site. The mechanism of control may either increase or decrease enzyme activity. Because allosteric inhibitors work by binding to sites separate from the active site, their action is *noncompetitive*. Enzymes controlled by allosteric regulation typically have two alternate conformations controlled from the **allosteric site**. In one conformation, called the high-affinity state (the active form), the enzyme binds strongly to its substrate; in the other conformation, the low-affinity state (the inactive form), the enzyme binds the substrate weakly or not at all. Binding with regulatory substances may induce either state: binding an allosteric inhibitor converts an allosteric enzyme from the high- to the low-affinity state, and binding an **allosteric activator** converts it from the low- to the high-affinity state (see Figure 4.23).

Frequently, **allosteric inhibitors** are a product of the metabolic pathway that they regulate. If the product accumulates in excess, its effect as an inhibitor automatically slows or stops the enzymatic reaction producing it, typically by inhibiting the enzyme catalyzing the first reaction of the pathway. If the product becomes too scarce, the inhibition is reduced, and its production increases. Regulation of this type, in which the product of a reaction acts as a regulator of the reaction, is termed **feedback inhibition**. Feedback inhibition prevents cellular resources from being wasted in the synthesis of molecules made at intermediate steps of the pathway.

The biochemical pathway that makes the amino acid isoleucine from threonine is an excellent example of feedback inhibition. The pathway proceeds in five steps, each catalyzed by an enzyme (**Figure 4.24**). The end product of the pathway, isoleucine, is an allosteric inhibitor of the first enzyme of the pathway, threonine deaminase. If the cell makes more isoleucine than it needs, isoleucine combines reversibly with threonine deaminase at the allosteric site, converting the enzyme to the low-affinity state and inhibiting its ability to combine with threonine, the substrate for the first reaction in the pathway. If isoleucine levels drop too low, the allosteric site of threonine deaminase is vacated, the enzyme is converted to the high-affinity state, and isoleucine production increases.

4.5d Temperature and pH Are Key Factors Affecting Enzyme Activity

The activity of most enzymes is strongly altered by changes in pH and temperature. Characteristically, enzymes reach maximal activity within a narrow range of temperature or pH; at levels outside this range, enzyme activity drops off. These effects produce a typically peaked curve when enzyme activity is plotted, with the peak where temperature or pH produces maximal activity.

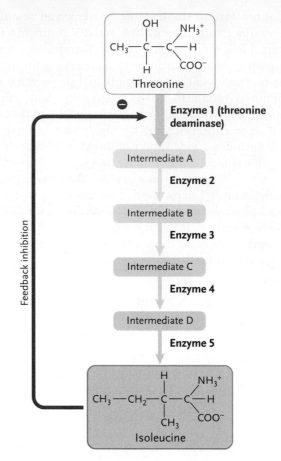

Figure 4.24

Feedback inhibition in the pathway that produces isoleucine from threonine. If the product of the pathway, isoleucine, accumulates in excess, it slows or stops the pathway by acting as an allosteric inhibitor of the enzyme that catalyzes the first step in the pathway.

Effects of pH Changes. Typically, each enzyme has an optimal pH where it operates at peak efficiency in speeding the rate of its biochemical reaction (**Figure 4.25**). On either side of this pH optimum, the rate of the catalyzed reaction decreases because of the resulting alterations in charged groups. The effects on the structure and function of the active site become more extreme at pH values farther from the optimum, until the rate drops to zero. Most enzymes have a pH optimum near the pH of the cellular contents, about pH 7. Enzymes that are secreted from cells may have pH optima farther from neutrality. An example is pepsin, a protein-digesting enzyme secreted into the stomach. This enzyme's pH optimum is 1.5, close to the acidity of stomach contents. Similarly, trypsin, also a protein-digesting enzyme, has a pH optimum at about pH 8, allowing it to function well in the somewhat alkaline contents of the intestine, where it is secreted.

Effects of Temperature Changes. The effects of temperature changes on enzyme activity reflect two

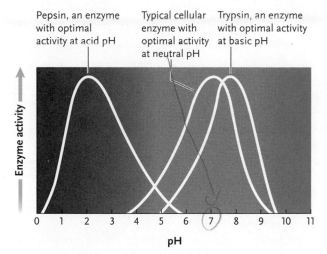

Pepsin, an enzyme with optimal activity at acid pH

Typical cellular enzyme with optimal activity at neutral pH

Trypsin, an enzyme with optimal activity at basic pH

Figure 4.25

Effects of pH on enzyme activity. An enzyme typically has an optimal pH at which it is most active; at pH values above or below the optimum, the rate of enzyme activity drops off. At extreme pH values, the rate drops to zero.

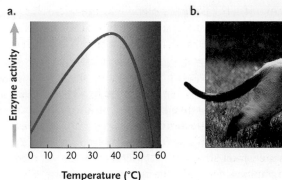

Figure 4.26

Effect of temperature on enzyme activity. **(a)** As the temperature rises, the rate of the catalyzed reaction increases proportionally until the temperature reaches the point at which the enzyme begins to denature. The rate drops off steeply as denaturation progresses and becomes complete. **(b)** Visible effects of environmental temperature on enzyme activity in Siamese cats. The fur on the extremities—ears, nose, paws, and tail—contains more dark brown pigment (melanin) than the rest of the body. A heat-sensitive enzyme controlling melanin production is denatured in warmer body regions, so dark pigment is not produced, but fur colour is.

distinct processes. First, temperature has a general effect on chemical reactions of all kinds. As the temperature rises, the rate of chemical reactions typically increases. This effect reflects increases in the kinetic motion of all molecules, with more frequent and stronger collisions as the temperature rises. Second, temperature has an effect on all proteins, including enzymes. As the temperature rises, the kinetic motions of the amino acid chains of an enzyme increase, along with the strength and frequency of collisions between enzymes and surrounding molecules. At some point, these disturbances become strong enough to denature the enzyme: the hydrogen bonds and other forces that maintain its three-dimensional structure break, making the enzyme unfold and lose its function. The two effects of temperature act in opposition to each other to produce characteristic changes in the rate of enzymatic catalysis **(Figure 4.26)**. In the range of 0° to about 40°C, the reaction rate doubles for every 10°C increase in temperature. Above 40°C, the increasing kinetic motion begins to denature the enzyme, reducing the rate of increase in enzyme activity. At some point, as the temperature rises, the denaturation of the enzyme causes the reaction rate to level off at a peak. Further increases cause such extensive unfolding that the reaction rate decreases rapidly to zero.

For most enzymes, the peak in activity lies between 40° and 50°C; the dropoff becomes steep at

55°C and falls to zero at about 60°C. Thus, the rate of an enzyme-catalyzed reaction peaks at a temperature at which kinetic motion is greatest, but no significant unfolding of the enzyme has occurred. Although most enzymes have a temperature optimum between 40° and 50°C, some have activity peaks below or above this range. For example, the enzymes of maize (corn) pollen function best near 30°C and undergo steep reductions in activity above 32°C. As a result, environmental temperatures above 32°C can seriously inhibit the growth of corn crops. Many animals living in frigid regions have enzymes with much lower temperature optima than average. For example, the enzymes of arctic snow fleas are most active at 10°C. At the other extreme are the enzymes of archaeans that live in hot springs, which are so resistant to denaturation that they remain active at temperatures of 85°C or more.

STUDY BREAK

1. Why do enzyme-catalyzed reactions reach a saturation level when substrate concentration is increased?
2. Distinguish between competitive and noncompetitive inhibition.
3. Explain why the activity of an enzyme will eventually decrease to zero as the temperature rises.

Many biological processes rely on enzymes to catalyze key reactions. A complete understanding of those processes requires knowledge about the structure and function of the enzymes involved. Much research continues to be done to elucidate enzyme structure and function.

How does protein structure relate to enzyme function?

Many researchers are studying protein structure and its relation to protein function. For example, Janet Smith at the University of Michigan uses X-ray crystallography to determine the structures of proteins. The patterns of diffraction of X-rays shone at a protein crystal give information about how the protein's atoms are organized. The crystal structure is "solved" once a model for the protein's structure is achieved in this way.

Smith's group uses information about the structure of solved proteins to predict the functions of other proteins. Even though it is possible to solve protein structures rapidly, it is not practical to solve the structures of all proteins involved in important biological processes. Instead, Smith, as well as other researchers, draws on the current understanding of the evolution of proteins. In particular, genes for useful proteins often have been duplicated during evolution and the duplicate copy adapted to a new function. Therefore, proteins can be related in an evolutionary sense. An understanding of the molecular mechanisms of particular enzymes may then be transferrable to other proteins, which is an underlying theme of Smith's research.

How does ribozyme structure relate to function, and how might ribozymes be used as therapeutic agents?

Ribozymes are catalytic ribonucleic acid (RNA) molecules. Various types of ribozymes exist, each type differing in its three-dimensional structure and mechanism of catalysis.

Researcher John Burke at the University of Vermont and his group are studying hairpin ribozymes and hammerhead ribozymes, which are catalytically active once they fold into those two shapes (the hammerhead shape is similar to that of the head of a hammerhead shark). Their research has four directions: determining the molecular structure of ribozymes, characterizing RNA conformational changes during catalysis, elucidating the mechanisms of catalysis, and exploring ways to use ribozymes as therapeutic agents.

For example, Burke's group has shown that the hairpin ribozyme undergoes a dramatic conformational change when the substrate binds to the active site. Furthermore, they have engineered hairpin ribozymes that can inhibit viral replication in mammalian cells. The particular viruses targeted have RNA genomes and include human immunodeficiency virus 1 (HIV-1, the causative agent of acquired immune deficiency syndrome [AIDS]) and hepatitis B virus. To achieve their goal, they had to identify appropriate target sites within the viral RNA molecules and to express the engineered ribozymes efficiently within the cell. Current research focuses on optimizing the inhibition of viral replication by the ribozymes, determining the mechanism of antiviral activity, and extending this technology to develop therapeutic approaches for significant infectious diseases such as AIDS and hepatitis B.

Review

Go to CENGAGENOW™ at http://hed.nelson.com/ to access quizzing, animations, exercises, articles, and personalized homework help.

4.1 Energy and the Laws of Thermodynamics

- Energy is the capacity to do work. Kinetic energy is the energy of motion; potential energy is the energy stored in an object because of its location or chemical structure.

- Thermodynamics is the study of energy flow between a system and its surroundings during chemical and physical reactions. A system that exchanges energy but not matter with its surroundings is a closed system. A system that exchanges both energy and matter with its surroundings is an open system (see Figure 4.1). A system that does not exchange energy or matter with its surroundings is said to be an isolated system.

- The first law of thermodynamics states that the total amount of energy in a system and its surroundings remains constant (see Figure 4.2). The second law states that in any process involving a spontaneous (possible) change from an initial to a final state, the total entropy (disorder) of the system and its surroundings always increases (see Figure 4.3).

- Life is highly ordered, which suggests that it goes against the second law of thermodynamics. However, the high order of living things comes about because organisms are open systems and take in energy from their surroundings. In the process of living, organisms release heat and more simple molecules that increase the disorder of the surroundings (see Figures 4.4 and 4.5).

4.2 Free Energy and Spontaneous Reactions

- A spontaneous reaction is one that will occur without an input of energy from the surroundings. A spontaneous reaction releases free energy—energy that is available to do work.

- The free energy equation, $\Delta G = \Delta H - T\Delta S$, states that the free energy change, ΔG, is influenced by two factors: the changes in energy content and entropy of the system as a reaction goes to completion.

- Systems with high free energy are unstable and will spontaneously move to a more stable state (see Figure 4.8).

- Factors that oppose the completion of spontaneous reactions, such as the relative concentrations of reactants and products, produce an equilibrium point at which reactants are converted to products and products are converted back to reactants, at equal rates (see Figure 4.9).

- Organisms reach equilibrium ($\Delta G = 0$) only when they die.

- Reactions with a negative ΔG are spontaneous; they release free energy and are known as exergonic reactions. Reactions with a positive ΔG require free energy and are known as endergonic reactions (see Figure 4.10).

4.3 The Energy Currency of the Cell: ATP

- The hydrolysis of ATP releases free energy that can be used as a source of energy for the cell (see Figure 4.12).

- A cell can couple the exergonic reaction of ATP hydrolysis to make an otherwise endergonic (anabolic) reaction proceed spontaneously. These coupling reactions require enzymes (see Figure 4.13).
- The ATP used in coupling reactions is replenished by reactions that link ATP synthesis to catabolic reactions. ATP thus cycles between reactions that release free energy and reactions that require free energy (see Figure 4.14).

4.4 The Role of Enzymes in Biological Reactions

- What prevents many exergonic reactions from proceeding rapidly is that they need to overcome an energy barrier (the activation energy) to get to the transition state (see Figure 4.15).
- Enzymes are catalysts that greatly speed the rate at which spontaneous reactions occur because they lower the activation energy (see Figure 4.17).
- Catalysis occurs at the site of substrate binding, which is referred to as the active site of the enzyme (see Figure 4.18). Enzymes usually are specific: they catalyze reactions of only a single type of molecule or a group of closely related molecules.
- The active site of an enzyme combines briefly with the reactants (the substrates); the enzyme is released unchanged when the reaction is complete (see Figure 4.19)
- Many enzymes include a cofactor, which is an inorganic ion or an organic nonprotein group called a coenzyme that is necessary for catalysis to occur.

- Enzymes reduce the activation energy by inducing the transition state of the reaction, from which the reaction can move easily in the direction of either products or reactants.
- Several mechanisms contribute to enzymatic catalysis by helping to induce the transition state. They include bringing the reactant molecules into close proximity, orienting the reactants in positions that favour the transition state, and exposing the reactants to altered environments that promote their interaction (see Figure 4.20).

4.5 Conditions and Factors that Affect Enzyme Activity

- At high substrate concentrations, enzymes become saturated with reactants, and further increases in substrate concentration do not increase the rate of the reaction (see Figure 4.21).
- Enzymes may be inhibited by nonsubstrate molecules. Competitive inhibitors interfere with reaction rates by combining with the active site of an enzyme; noncompetitive inhibitors combine with sites elsewhere on the enzyme (see Figure 4.22).
- Many cellular enzymes are regulated by inhibitors. A special type of regulation, allosteric regulation, resembles noncompetitive inhibition, except that regulatory molecules may either increase or decrease enzyme activity (see Figure 4.23). Allosteric regulation often carries out feedback inhibition, in which a product of an enzyme-catalyzed pathway acts as an allosteric inhibitor of the first enzyme in the pathway (see Figure 4.24).
- Typically, enzymes have optimal activity at a certain temperature and a certain pH; at temperature and pH values above and below the optimum, reaction rates fall off (see Figures 4.25 and 4.26).

Questions

Self-Test Questions

1. Which of the following statements about energy and thermo-dynamics is correct?
   a. Energy conversions can never be 100% efficient.
   b. All living organisms are open systems.
   c. Earth can be considered a closed system.
   d. The total amount of energy in the universe is constant.
   e. All of the above are correct.

2. Which of the following statements about entropy is NOT correct?
   a. Entropy is a thermodynamic measure of disorder or randomness.
   b. The entropy of a system plus the surroundings always increases.
   c. By consuming food, humans can maintain low entropy.
   d. Entropy increases as a substance changes from a liquid into a solid.
   e. An increase in entropy is the reason why energy transformations are never 100% efficient.

3. For a reaction to be exergonic,
   a. it must also be exothermic.
   b. the entropy of the products must be greater than the reactants.
   c. the products must have less enthalpy than the reactants.
   d. the free energy of the products must be less than the reactants.
   e. the reaction required an input of energy to proceed.

4. Which of the following statements is correct?
   a. Molecules that have high free energy are very stable.
   b. An isolated system will never reach equilibrium.
   c. At equilibrium, the ΔG is negative.
   d. Living organisms are never at equilibrium.
   e. Most biochemical reactions have a ΔG far from zero.

5. Within a cell, the hydrolysis of ATP in a biochemical reaction
   a. produces more heat than if ATP is simply hydrolyzed in a beaker of water.
   b. can occur only in the absence of an enzyme.
   c. is required only for exergonic reactions, which do not proceed spontaneously.
   d. results in transfer of a phosphate group to a substrate, making it unstable.
   e. None of the above are correct.

6. Although propane is thermodynamically unstable, the reason that it is kinetically stable is because
   a. it contains an abundance of oxygen and little hydrogen.
   b. its breakdown is exergonic $(-\Delta G)$.
   c. it has a high activation energy (E_A).
   d. it is highly electronegative.
   e. All of the above are correct.

7. An enzyme
   a. is a protein and therefore is encoded by a gene.
   b. can make an endergonic reaction proceed spontaneously.
   c. lowers the ΔG of an endergonic reaction.
   d. increases the probability that reactant molecules will reach the transition state.
   e. Only a and d are correct.

8. Unlike competitive inhibition, the noncompetitive inhibition of an enzyme-catalzyed reaction
   a. inhibits substrate binding to the active site.
   b. is due to molecules that are structurally very similar to molecules of substrate
   c. changes the conformation of the enzyme.
   d. results in the enzyme becoming permanently inactive.
   e. requires the hydrolysis of ATP.

9. Which of the following statements about allosteric enzymes is correct?
   a. The allosteric site of the enzyme binds additional substrate molecules.
   b. An allosteric activator prevents binding at the active site.
   c. An enzyme that possesses allosteric sites does not possess an active site.
   d. Their activity can be finely controlled by metabolites within the cell.
   e. None of the above are correct.

10. What explains the shape of a curve that plots the enzyme activity as a function of temperature?
    a. At high temperatures, the rate of catalysis stays high and constant—it saturates.
    b. As the temperature is low but increasing, the rate of collisions between substrate and enzyme molecules increases.
    c. At high temperatures, the structural integrity of the enzyme breaks down.
    d. As the temperature increases, the rate of all reactions slows down.
    e. Both b and c are correct.

Questions for Discussion

1. Trees become more complex as they develop spontaneously from seeds to adults. Does this process violate the second law of thermodynamics? Why or why not?

2. Trace the flow of energy through your body. What products increase the entropy of you and your surroundings?

3. You have found a molecular substance that accelerates the rate of a particular reaction. What kind of information would you need to demonstrate that this molecular substance is an enzyme?

4. The addition or removal of phosphate groups from ATP is a fully reversible reaction. In what way does this reversibility facilitate the use of ATP as a coupling agent for cellular reactions?

5. Researchers once hypothesized that an enzyme and its substrate fit together like a lock and key but that the products do not fit the enzyme. Criticize this idea with respect to reversible reactions.

The cystic fibrosis transmembrane conductance regulator is a chloride pump. Mutations to the CFTR gene result in the pump being defective, causing cystic fibrosis.

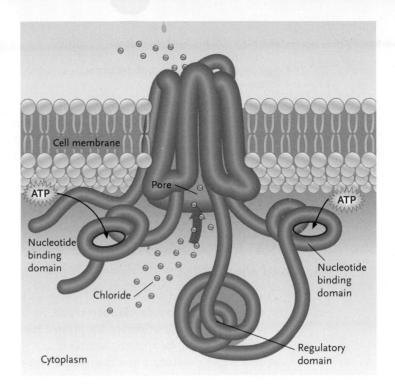

5 Membranes and Transport

WHY IT MATTERS

Cystic fibrosis (CF) is one of the most common genetic diseases. It affects approximately 1 in 3900 children born in Canada. People with CF suffer from a progressive impairment of lung and gastrointestinal function. Although the treatment of CF patients is slowly improving, their average life span remains under 40 years.

CF is caused by mutations to a single gene that codes for a protein called the cystic fibrosis transmembrane conductance regulator (CFTR). In normal cells, CFTR acts as a membrane transport protein that pumps chloride (Cl^-, negatively charged) out of the cells that line the lungs and intestinal tract into the covering mucus lining. This results in an electrical gradient across the membrane and leads to the movement of (positively charged) sodium ions in the same direction as the chloride. Because of the high ion concentration (Na^+ and Cl^-), water moves, by osmosis, out into the mucus lining keeping it moist. Keeping the lining of the lungs and intestinal tract wet is critical to their proper functioning. In individuals with CF, the Cl^- channel CFTR does not function properly, which results in water being retained within cells, resulting in a buildup of thick mucus that cannot effectively be removed by coughing. Besides obstructing airways and preventing normal **breathing**, the buildup of mucus in the lungs makes CF patients very susceptible to bacterial infections.

Currently, there is no cure for CF, with lung transplantation being a common procedure as the disease progresses. Since CF is caused by a defect to a single gene, the greatest hope is in gene therapy (see Chapter 10) that would attempt to insert normal copies of the CFTR gene into affected cells. However, many technical hurdles need to be overcome before gene therapy becomes a viable treatment option.

5.1 An Overview of the Structure of Membranes

One of the keys to the evolution of life was the development of the cell or **plasma membrane.** By acting as a selectively permeable barrier, the plasma membrane allowed for the uptake of key nutrients and elimination of waste products while maintaining a protected environment in which metabolic processes can occur. The subsequent development of internal membranes allowed for compartmentalization of processes and increased complexity. A good example of this is the nuclear envelope, which defines the hallmark of the eukaryotic cell, the nucleus.

5.1a The Fluid Mosaic Model of Membranes

Our current view of membrane structure is based on the **fluid mosaic model (Figure 5.1).** The model proposes that membranes are not rigid with molecules locked into place but rather consist of fluid lipid molecules in which proteins are embedded and float freely.

The lipid molecules of all biological membranes exist in a double layer, called a bilayer that is less than 10 nanometres (nm) thick. By comparison, this page is approximately 100 000 nm thick. The lipid molecules of the bilayer vibrate, flex back and forth, spin around their long axis, move sideways, and exchange places within the same bilayer half. Only rarely does a lipid molecule flip-flop between the two layers. Exchanging places within a layer occurs millions of times a second, making the lipid molecules in the membrane highly dynamic. As we discuss later, maintaining the membrane in a fluid state is critical to overall membrane function.

The mosaic part of the fluid mosaic model refers to the fact that membranes contain a wide assortment of different types of proteins, each with a specific function. As we discuss in detail later, this includes proteins involved in transport and

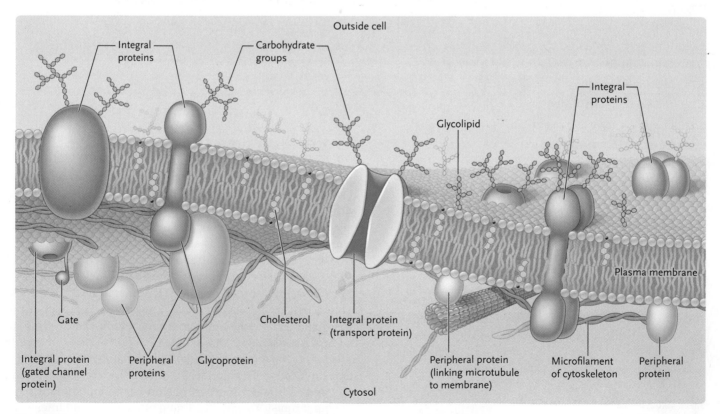

Figure 5.1

Membrane structure according to the fluid mosaic model, in which integral membrane proteins are suspended individually in a fluid lipid bilayer. Peripheral proteins are attached to integral proteins or membrane lipids mostly on the cytoplasmic side of the membrane (shown only on the inner surface in the figure). In the plasma membrane, carbohydrate groups of membrane glycoproteins and glycolipids face the cell exterior.

attachment, as well as a variety of enzymes involved in such processes as electron transport. Because they are larger than lipid molecules, the proteins move more slowly in the fluid environment of the membrane. As well, a small number of membrane proteins anchor cytoskeleton filaments to the membrane and thus do not move (Figure 5.1). As also shown in Figure 5.1, a number of the lipid and protein components of some membranes have carbohydrate groups linked to them, forming glycolipids and glycoproteins.

The relative proportions of lipid and protein within a membrane vary considerably depending on the type of membrane. For example, membranes that contain protein complexes involved in electron transport, such as the inner mitochondrial membrane, contain large amounts of protein (76% protein and only 24% lipid), whereas the plasma membrane contains nearly equal amounts of protein and lipid (49% and 51%, respectively). Myelin, which is a membrane that functions to insulate nerve fibres, is composed mostly of lipids (18% protein and 82% lipid).

An important characteristic of membranes, illustrated in Figure 5.1, is that the proteins and other components of one half of the lipid bilayer are different from those that make up the other half of the bilayer. This is referred to as membrane asymmetry, and it reflects differences in the functions performed by each side of the membrane. For example, a range of glycolipids and carbohydrate groups are attached to proteins on the external side of the membrane, whereas components of the cytoskeleton bind to proteins on the internal side of the membrane. In addition, hormones and growth factors bind to **receptor proteins** that are found only on the external surface of the plasma membrane. Their binding triggers changes to distinctly different protein components found on the inner surface of the membrane, which lead to signal transduction within the cell (see Chapter 15).

5.1b Experimental Evidence in Support of the Fluid Mosaic Model

The fluid mosaic model of membrane structure is supported by two major pieces of experimental evidence.

Membranes Are Fluid. In a now classic study carried out in 1970, David Frye and Michael A. Edidin grew human cells and mouse cells separately in tissue culture. They were able to tag the human or mouse membrane proteins **(Figure 5.2)** with dye molecules: the human proteins were linked to red dye molecules and the mouse proteins were linked to green. Frye and Edidin then fused the human and mouse cells. Within minutes, they found that the two distinctly coloured proteins began to mix. In less than an hour, the two

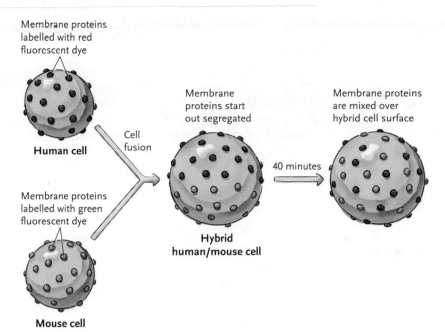

Figure 5.2
The Frye-Edidin experiment provided evidence that the membrane bilayer is fluid. In the experiment, membrane proteins were found to rapidly migrate over the surface of the hybrid cell.

colours had completely intermixed on the fused cells, indicating that the mouse and human proteins had moved around in the fused membranes.

Based on the measured rates at which molecules mix in biological membranes, the membrane bilayer appears to be about as fluid as a light machine oil, like the lubricants you might use around the house to oil a door hinge, the wheels of a skateboard, or a bicycle chain.

Membrane Asymmetry. One of the key experiments revealing membrane asymmetry utilizes the freeze-fracture technique in combination with electron microscopy **(Figure 5.3, p. 96).** In this technique, a block of cells is rapidly frozen by dipping it in liquid nitrogen (−196°C). Then the block is fractured by hitting it with a microscopically sharp knife edge. Often the fracture splits bilayers into inner and outer halves, exposing the membrane interior. In the **electron microscope**, the split membranes appear as smooth layers in which individual particles the size of proteins are embedded (shown in Figure 5.3c). From these images, it is clear that the particles on either side of the membrane differ in size, number, and shape, providing evidence that the two sides are distinctly different.

STUDY BREAK

1. Describe the fluid mosaic model of membrane structure.
2. What is meant by the term *membrane asymmetry*?

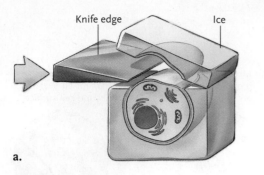

Knife edge   Ice

a.

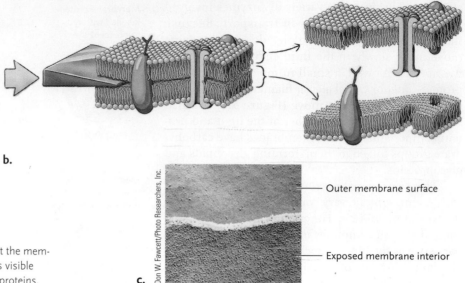

b.

Outer membrane surface

Exposed membrane interior

Don W. Fawcett/Photo Researchers, Inc.

c.

Figure 5.3

(a) The freeze-fracture technique. **(b)** The fracture may split the membrane bilayers into inner and outer halves. **(c)** The particles visible in the exposed membrane interior are integral membrane proteins.

5.2 The Lipid Fabric of a Membrane

The foundation or underlying fabric of all biological membranes is the lipid molecules. As we discuss in this section, keeping membranes in a fluid state is important to membrane function. Many organisms can adjust the types of lipids in the membranes such that membranes do not become too stiff (viscous) or too fluid (liquid). To review the basics of lipid structure, see *The Chemical and Physical Foundations of Biology* pages.

5.2a Phospholipids Are the Dominant Lipids in Membranes

The dominant lipids found in membranes are **phospholipids**, which consist of two fatty acid "tails" linked to one of several types of **alcohols** or amino acids by a phosphate group **(Figure 5.4a)**. A property that all phospholipids possess, which is critical to the structure and function of membranes, is that they are **amphipathic**. That is, each phospholipid molecule contains a region that is *hydrophobic* and a region that is *hydrophilic*. Whereas the fatty acid chains of a lipid are very hydrophobic (nonpolar), the phosphate-containing head group is charged and hydrophilic (polar). Detergents are excellent at removing oil stains from clothing because they are also amphipathic molecules.

When added to an aqueous solution, phospholipids associate with each other and assemble into a **bilayer**, which is a sheet two lipid molecules thick **(Figure 5.4b)**.

What is required for a bilayer to form? The answer is, absolutely nothing. Both micelles and bilayers form spontaneously in an aqueous environment because of the tendency of the hydrophobic fatty acids to aggregate together while the polar head groups associate with water. These arrangement are favoured because they represent the lowest energy state and are more likely to occur over any other arrangement.

5.2b Membrane Fluidity

The fluidity of the lipid bilayer is dependent on how densely the individual lipid molecules can pack together. This is influenced by two major factors: the composition of the lipid molecules that make up the membrane and the temperature. Fatty acids composed of saturated hydrocarbons, in which each carbon is bound to a maximum number of hydrogen atoms, tend to have a straight shape, which allows the lipids to pack more tightly together **(Figure 5.5a)**. Alternatively, lipid molecules with unsaturated fatty acids are less straight as the double bonds in an unsaturated fatty acid introduce kinks or bends in its structure. This results in lipid molecules packing together less closely **(Figure 5.5b)**.

Membranes remain in a fluid state over a relatively wide range of temperatures. However, if the temperature drops low enough, the phospholipid molecules become closely packed, and the membrane forms a highly viscous semisolid gel. This is exactly what happens when melted butter cools. At any given temperature, the fluidity of a membrane is related to the degree to which the membrane lipids are unsaturated. The more unsaturated a membrane, the lower its gelling temperature is. For most membrane systems, the normal fluid state is achieved by a mixed population of saturated and **unsaturated** fatty acids. The more carbon–carbon double bonds within the fatty acid tails, the more space will exist between neighbouring lipids, and the more fluid the resulting membrane will be.

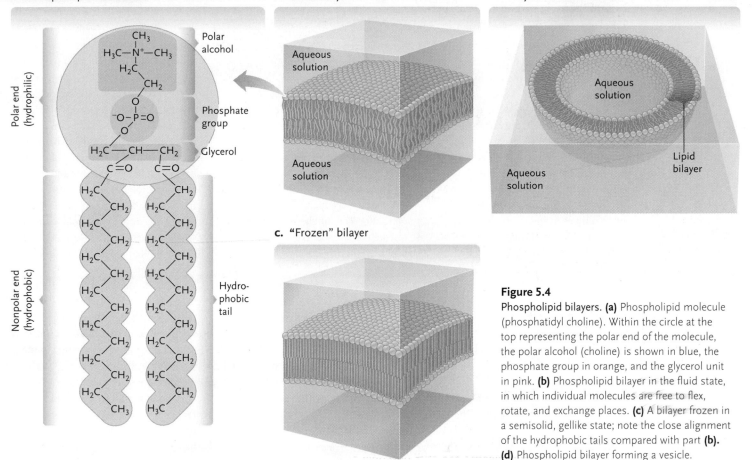

a. Phospholipid molecule

Polar end (hydrophilic)

Polar alcohol

Phosphate group

Glycerol

Nonpolar end (hydrophobic)

Hydrophobic tail

b. Fluid bilayer

Aqueous solution

Aqueous solution

c. "Frozen" bilayer

d. Bilayer vesicle

Aqueous solution

Aqueous solution

Lipid bilayer

Figure 5.4

Phospholipid bilayers. **(a)** Phospholipid molecule (phosphatidyl choline). Within the circle at the top representing the polar end of the molecule, the polar alcohol (choline) is shown in blue, the phosphate group in orange, and the glycerol unit in pink. **(b)** Phospholipid bilayer in the fluid state, in which individual molecules are free to flex, rotate, and exchange places. **(c)** A bilayer frozen in a semisolid, gellike state; note the close alignment of the hydrophobic tails compared with part **(b)**. **(d)** Phospholipid bilayer forming a vesicle.

5.2c Organisms Can Adjust Fatty Acid Composition

The maintenance of membranes in a fluid state is absolutely essential to cell function. Exposure to low temperatures may result in membrane viscosity increasing to the point where normal membrane permeability is inhibited, as well as causing enzymes and other proteins in the membrane to stop functioning. Electron transport chains, for example, require components to move very rapidly within the membrane bilayer. If the membrane solidifies, electron transport ceases to operate. Problems also arise at high tempera-

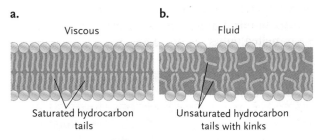

a.
Viscous

b.
Fluid

Saturated hydrocarbon tails

Unsaturated hydrocarbon tails with kinks

Figure 5.5

Lipid molecules that contain saturated hydrocarbon tails are closely packed, whereas unsaturated hydrocarbon tails have kinks that prevent lipid molecules from packing closely together.

ture. Membranes may become too fluid and liquid due to the increase in molecular motion, which can result in membrane leakage. Ions such as K^+, Na^+, and Ca^{2+} begin to freely diffuse across the membrane, resulting in an irreversible disruption of cellular ion balance that can rapidly lead to cell death.

Given this, it is not surprising that most organisms can adjust the fatty acid composition of their membranes such that proper fluidity is maintained over a relatively broad range of temperatures. For example, many prokaryotes, protists, and plants can thrive at temperatures that are far below the temperature at which a typical animal membrane would solidify. Such organisms are able to survive at low temperatures, in part because they are able to increase the relative proportion of unsaturated fatty acids in their membranes.

Unsaturated fatty acids are produced during fatty acid synthesis through the action of a group of enzymes called **desaturases**. All fatty acids are initially synthesized as fully saturated molecules without any double bonds. Desaturases act on these saturated fatty acids by catalyzing a reaction that removes two hydrogen atoms from neighbouring carbon atoms and introduces a double bond **(Figure 5.6a, p. 99)**. There are a wide range of desaturase enzymes, each one introducing a double bond at a specific point along the fatty acid. Whereas

Trans Fats

In the food industry, the use of fats containing **saturated fatty acids** is more desirable than the use of oils that contain unsaturated fatty acids. The lack of double bonds means that lipids containing saturated fatty acids are more stable and less prone to oxidation that can decrease shelf life as well as affect the texture and taste of the final product. Moreover, hard fats have a higher melting temperature, which makes them useful in many applications, such as in baking and in the process of deep-frying.

Because animal-based saturated fats such as butter or lard are expensive and susceptible to spoilage, the food industry has, for many decades, used saturated fats produced through the industrial process of hydrogenation. This process removes *cis* double bonds from fatty acids by heating vegetable oil in the presence of hydrogen gas and a catalyst. In the food industry, partial hydrogenation is practised, which results in a product that is still malleable and not too hard. One of the unintended consequences of partial hydrogenation is that the *cis* double bonds that do not become

hydrogenated tend to be reconfigured into the *trans* orientation. Although small amounts of *trans* fats are found naturally in the milk and meat of **ruminant** animals such as cows and sheep, through partial hydrogenation, human consumption of *trans* fats has increased tremendously over the last 70 years.

There is now clear medical evidence that the consumption of *trans* fats is unhealthy. A comprehensive review of research on *trans* fat consumption and health by the *New England Journal of Medicine* in 2006 clearly demonstrated the existence of a strong connection between *trans* fat consumption and elevated risk of coronary heart disease, a leading cause of death in North America. *Trans* fats have also been linked to increased incidence of other health problems as well. The physiological basis for the increased risk to health by increased *trans* fat consumption is not fully understood and remains a very active area of research. The increased risk may be due, in part, to the fact that a major group of enzymes called lipases, which aid in the breakdown of many types of lipids, including *cis*

unsaturated fats, do not recognize the *trans* configuration. This leads to *trans* fats staying in the bloodstream longer, which may lead to increased incidence of arterial deposition, which may lead to coronary heart disease.

In response to the overwhelming medical evidence that *trans* fats are harmful, governments around the world are implementing restrictions on the amount of *trans* fats foods can contain. In Canada, the *trans* fat content of vegetable oils and soft margarines is now limited to 2% of the total fat content, whereas the *trans* fat content for all other foods is 5% of the total fat content, including ingredients sold to restaurants. Similar guidelines are in place in many European countries, as well as being implemented in the United States.

In response to these new guidelines, food manufacturers and restaurant chains have reformulated their products to be "*trans* fat free." This has primarily been achieved by simply replacing hydrogenated fats with naturally saturated fats. Many nutritionists argue that these fully saturated alternatives may not offer any health benefit.

some unsaturated fatty acids contain only one carbon–carbon double bond, others may contain two or more.

Changes in the transcription of a gene often result in changes in the abundance of its transcript (mRNA) and resulting protein abundance. **Figure 5.6b** shows that transcript abundance of a desaturase gene increases as the temperature is lowered. This results in an increase in synthesis and overall abundance of the desaturase enzyme. Higher amounts of desaturates would, in turn, result in an increase in the abundance of unsaturated fatty acids. By regulating the amount of desaturase enzyme that is synthesized, a wide range of organisms can closely regulate the amount of unsaturated fatty acids that get incorporated into membranes and thereby maintain membrane fluidity within the optimum range. It is important to realize that *high temperature* and *low temperature* are relative terms. For a typical cyanobacterium, room temperature (20–25°C) is low temperature since its optimum growth temperature is above 35°C.

Besides lipids, a group of compounds called **sterols** also influence membrane fluidity. The best example of a sterol is cholesterol **(Figure 5.7),** which is found in the membranes of animal cells but not in those of plants or prokaryotes. Sterols act as membrane buffers: at high temperatures, they help restrain the movement of lipid molecules, thus reducing the fluidity of the membrane. However, at lower temperatures, sterols disrupt fatty acids from associating by occupying space between lipid molecules, thus slowing the transition to the nonfluid gel state.

STUDY BREAK

1. Why is maintaining proper membrane fluidity important for membrane function?
2. What is the relationship between temperature and desaturase expression?

a. Stearic acid, $CH_3(CH_2)_{16}COOH$

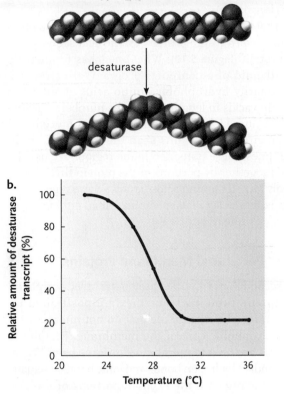

Figure 5.6
Fatty acids become unsaturated **(a)** through the action of a group of enzymes called desaturases that introduce double bonds.
(b) In organisms whose temperature changes with the environment, the expression of desaturase enzymes usually increases as the temperature is lowered.

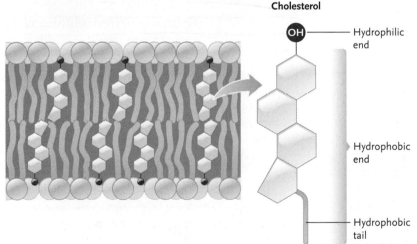

Figure 5.7
The position taken by cholesterol in bilayers. The hydrophilic ↓OH group at one end of the molecule extends into the polar regions of the bilayer; the ring structure extends into the nonpolar membrane interior.

5.3 Membrane Proteins

Although lipid molecules constitute the backbone of a membrane, the unique set of proteins that are associated with the membrane determines its function and makes each membrane unique.

5.3a The Key Functions of Membrane Proteins

Membrane proteins can be separated into four major functional categories as shown in **Figure 5.8, p. 100.** It should be noted that all of these functions may exist in a single membrane and that one protein or protein complex may serve more than one of these functions:

1. *Transport.* Many substances cannot freely diffuse through the membrane. Instead, a protein may provide a hydrophilic channel that allows movement of a specific compound. Alternatively, a membrane protein may change its shape and in so doing shuttle specific molecules from one side of a membrane to the other.

2. *Enzymatic activity.* A number of enzymes are membrane proteins. The best example of this is the enzymes associated with the respiratory and photosynthetic electron transport chains.

3. *Signal transduction.* Membranes often contain receptor proteins on their outer surface that bind to specific chemicals such as hormones. On binding, these receptors trigger changes on the inside surface of the membrane that lead to transduction of the signal through the cell.

4. *Attachment/recognition.* Proteins exposed to both the internal and external membrane surfaces act as attachment points for a range of cytoskeleton elements, as well as components involved in cell–cell recognition.

All membrane proteins can be classified into one of two distinct categories, integral and peripheral membrane proteins.

5.3b Integral Membrane Proteins

Membrane proteins that are embedded in the phospholipid bilayer are called **integral membrane proteins.** Although all integral membrane proteins possess at least one region that interacts with the hydrophobic core of the membrane, most integral proteins are *transmembrane proteins,* which span the entire membrane bilayer and therefore have regions that are exposed to the aqueous environment on both sides of the membrane. To be able to interact with the hydrophobic core of a membrane, integral proteins are composed of regions (or domains) that consist of predominantly nonpolar amino acids that are usually coiled into alpha helices

a. Transport

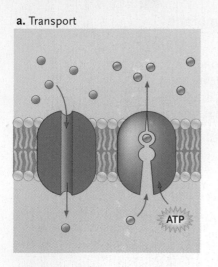

b. Enzymatic activity

Enzymes

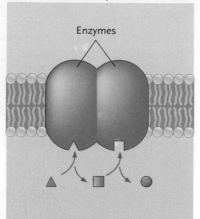

ATP

c. Signal transduction

Signal

Receptor

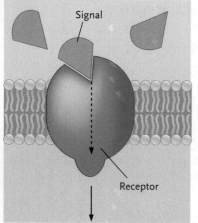

d. Attachment/recognition

Figure 5.8
The major functions of membrane proteins: **(a)** transport, **(b)** enzymatic activity, **(c)** signal transduction, and **(d)** attachment/recognition.

(Figure 5.9) (see *The Chemical and Physical Foundations of Biology* pages).

That a protein is a transmembrane protein can often be inferred from the primary amino acid sequence of the protein **(Figure 5.10)**. What one looks for, usually with the aid of a computer program, are stretches of primarily hydrophobic amino acids about 17 to 20 amino acids in length. This is the number of amino acids required to span a membrane once. Since many transmembrane proteins span the membrane multiple times, these transmembrane regions are usually linked together by portions of the protein that consist mainly of polar amino acids because these regions are exposed to the aqueous environment on either side of the membrane (Figure 5.10).

5.3c Peripheral Membrane Proteins

The second major group of proteins is called **peripheral membrane proteins** since they are positioned on the surface of a membrane and do not interact with the hydrophobic core of the membrane. Peripheral proteins are held to membrane surfaces by noncovalent bonds—hydrogen bonds and ionic bonds—usually by interacting with the exposed portions of integral proteins as well as directly with membrane lipid molecules. Most peripheral proteins are on the cytoplasmic side of the membrane. Some peripheral proteins are parts of the cytoskeleton, such as microtubules, microfilaments, or intermediate filaments, or proteins

Figure 5.9
The structure of membrane proteins. A typical membrane protein showing the membrane-spanning alpha-helical segments (green cylinders), connected by flexible loops of the amino acid chain at the membrane surfaces.

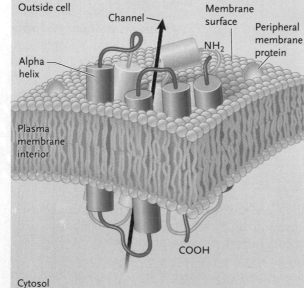

Outside cell

Channel

Membrane surface

Peripheral membrane protein

NH₂

Alpha helix

Plasma membrane interior

COOH

Cytosol

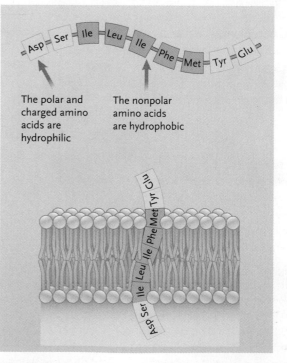

The polar and charged amino acids are hydrophilic

The nonpolar amino acids are hydrophobic

Figure 5.10
Transmembrane proteins can be identified because of the presence of stretches of amino acids that are primarily nonpolar. These regions of the protein interact with the hydrophobic regions of the membrane. Unlike this model that shows five amino acids, usually between 17–20 amino acids are needed to span the membrane once.

that link the cytoskeleton together. These structures hold some integral membrane proteins in place. For example, this anchoring constrains many types of receptors to the sides of cells facing body surfaces, cavities, or tubes. Because peripheral membrane proteins do not interact with the hydrophobic core of the membrane, they are made up of a mixture of polar and nonpolar amino acids like the majority of proteins.

STUDY BREAK

1. What are the two major classes of membrane proteins?
2. Give two examples each of integral proteins and peripheral proteins.

5.4 Passive Membrane Transport

Membranes can be considered the cell's "gatekeepers"— they control what gets in and what gets out. The hydrophobic nature of a membrane severely restricts the free movement of many molecules and substances essential for life.

Molecules such as O_2 diffuse very rapidly across membranes, which is important considering the vital role O_2 plays in cellular respiration. However, a range of other molecules, including a huge array of ions and charged molecules, as well as macromolecules such as sugars and proteins, are needed to move between cellular compartments and yet cannot diffuse rapidly across membranes. In the following sections, we address, first, what controls the movement of molecules such as O_2 and CO_2 that can freely move from one side of a membrane to the other and, second, how a cell transports molecules that cannot freely move across a membrane.

5.4a Passive Transport Is Based on Diffusion

Passive transport is defined as the movement of a substance across a membrane without the need to expend chemical energy such as ATP. What drives passive transport is **diffusion**, the net movement of a substance from a region of higher concentration to a region of lower concentration. Diffusion is based on the fact that above absolute zero ($-273°C$), molecules are in constant motion, and this results in them becoming uniformly distributed in space. Diffusion is the primary mechanism of solute movement within a cell and between cellular compartments separated by a membrane.

The driving force behind diffusion is an increase in entropy. In the initial state, when molecules are more concentrated in one region of a solution or on one side of a membrane, the molecules are highly ordered and in a state of low entropy. As diffusion occurs, the entropy, or disorder, increases

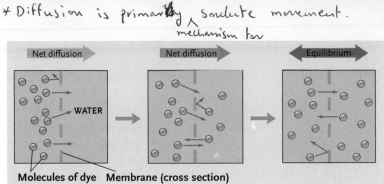

Net diffusion Net diffusion Equilibrium

WATER

Molecules of dye Membrane (cross section)

Diffusion is primarily ⟨mechanism for⟩ solute movement.

until, when the molecules are evenly distributed, entropy reaches its maximum **(Figure 5.11).** As the distribution proceeds to the state of maximum disorder, the molecules release free energy that can accomplish work (see Section 4.1 for a discussion of entropy and free energy).

The rate of diffusion depends on the concentration difference or concentration gradient that exists between two areas or across a membrane. The bigger the gradient the faster the rate of diffusion. Even after their concentration is the same in all regions, there is still constant movement of molecules or ions from one space to another, but there is no net change in concentration. This condition is an example of a dynamic equilibrium (see Figure 5.11).

5.4b The Two Types of Passive Transport: Simple and Facilitated

There are two types of passive transport: simple diffusion and facilitated diffusion.

Simple Diffusion. As shown in **Figure 5.12,** membranes display selective permeability; whereas some molecules diffuse very rapidly across the membrane, other molecules are essentially unable to transit the membrane. Overall, the interplay of two factors, size and

Figure 5.11
Diffusion is an entropy-driven process as molecules move from regions of high concentration to areas of low concentration. Entropy is at its maximum when equilibrium is reached.

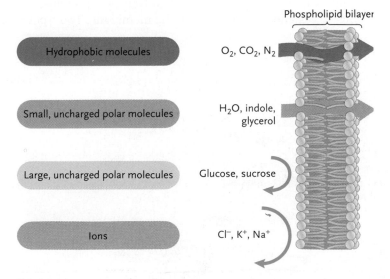

Phospholipid bilayer

Hydrophobic molecules — O_2, CO_2, N_2

Small, uncharged polar molecules — H_2O, indole, glycerol

Large, uncharged polar molecules — Glucose, sucrose

Ions — Cl^-, K^+, Na^+

Figure 5.12
The size and charge of a molecule affect the rate of diffusion across a membrane.

charge, determines the ease with which a molecule can move across a membrane.

Very small nonpolar molecules such as O_2 and CO_2 are readily soluble in the hydrophobic interior of a membrane and move rapidly from one side to the other. As well steroid hormones and most drugs both of which tend to be nonpolar can readily transit a membrane. Small uncharged molecules such as water or glycerol, even though they are polar, are still able to move quite rapidly across the membrane (see Figure 5.12). In contrast, however, the membrane is practically impermeable to charged molecules, including ions such as Cl^-, Na^+, and phosphate (PO^{4-}). Compared with the rate of transport of water, transport of small ions is about 10^9 times slower. The presence of a charge and a hydration shell of water surrounding the ion (see *The Chemical and Physical Foundations of Biology* pages) contribute to ions being prevented from entering the hydrophobic core of the membrane.

Facilitated Diffusion. Metabolic processes often have a demand for many polar and charged molecules, such as water, amino acids, sugars, and ions, that cannot be met by the relatively slow rate at which these molecules can diffuse passively across a membrane. To speed up the movement of these compounds, transport can be helped or *facilitated* by protein complexes that span the membrane **(Table 5.1)**. Although facilitated diffusion involves specific transporters, what drives the movement of the molecules is still diffusion based on a concentration gradient across the membrane. When the gradient falls to zero, transport stops.

5.4c Two Groups of Transport Proteins Carry Out Facilitated Diffusion

Facilitated diffusion is carried out by integral membrane proteins, called transport proteins, that extend entirely through the membrane. Two types of transport proteins are involved in facilitated diffusion. One type, called **channel proteins**, forms hydrophilic pathways in the membrane through which water and ions can pass **(Figure 5.13a)**. The channel aids the diffusion of molecules through the membrane by providing an avenue such that hydrophilic molecules do not have to interact with the hydrophobic portions of the membrane. Other channels facilitate the transport of ions such as Na^+, K^+, Ca^{2+}, and Cl^-. Most of these ion transporters, which occur in all eukaryotes, are **gated channels**; that is, they switch between open, closed, or intermediate states. The gates may be opened or closed by changes in voltage across the membrane, for instance, or by binding signal molecules. In animals, voltage-gated ion channels are used in nerve conduction and the control of muscle contraction.

The second type of transport proteins, called **carrier proteins**, also forms passageways through the lipid bilayer **(Figure 5.13b)**. Each carrier protein binds a specific single solute, such as a sugar molecule or an amino acid, and transports it across the lipid bilayer. Because a single solute is transferred in this carrier-mediated fashion, the transfer is called *uniport transport*. In performing the transport step, the carrier protein undergoes **conformational changes** that progressively move the solute binding site from one side of the membrane to the other, thereby transporting the solute. This property distinguishes carrier protein function from channel protein function.

Many transport proteins display a high degree of substrate specificity, in a way similar to an enzyme. For example, transporters that carry glucose are unable to transport fructose, which is structurally very similar. This specificity allows various cells and cellular compartments to tightly control what gets in and out. The kinds of transport proteins present in the plasma membrane or, for example, on the outer membrane of the mitochondria depend ultimately on the type of cell and growth conditions.

Table 5.1	Characteristics of Transport Mechanisms		
	Passive Transport		**Active Transport**
Characteristic	**Simple Diffusion**	**Facilitated Diffusion**	
Membrane component responsible for transport	Lipids	Proteins	Proteins
Binding of transported substance	No	Yes	Yes
Energy source	Concentration gradients	Concentration gradients	ATP hydrolysis or concentration gradients
Direction of transport	With gradient of transported substance	With gradient of transported substance	Against gradient of transported substance
Specificity for molecules or molecular classes	Nonspecific	Specific	Specific
Saturation at high concentrations of transported molecules	No	Yes	Yes

a. Channel protein

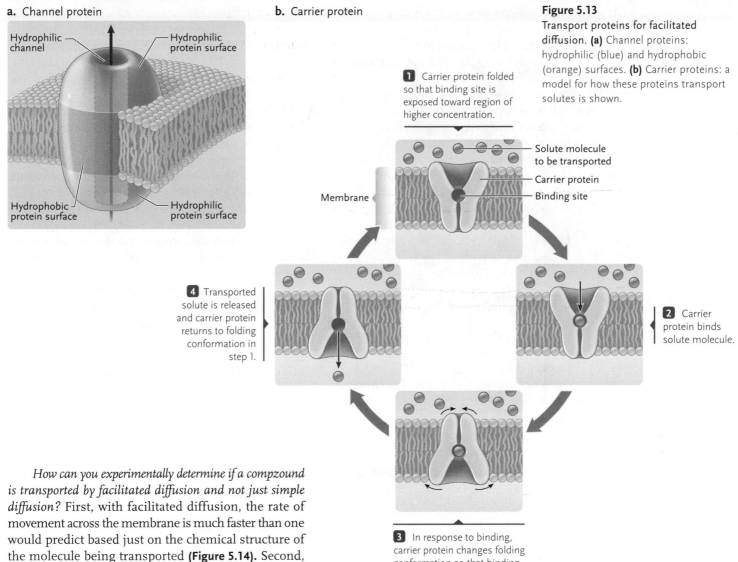

Hydrophilic channel

Hydrophilic protein surface

Hydrophobic protein surface

Hydrophilic protein surface

b. Carrier protein

1 Carrier protein folded so that binding site is exposed toward region of higher concentration.

Solute molecule to be transported

Membrane

Carrier protein

Binding site

2 Carrier protein binds solute molecule.

4 Transported solute is released and carrier protein returns to folding conformation in step 1.

3 In response to binding, carrier protein changes folding conformation so that binding site is exposed to region of lower concentration.

How can you experimentally determine if a compzound is transported by facilitated diffusion and not just simple diffusion? First, with facilitated diffusion, the rate of movement across the membrane is much faster than one would predict based just on the chemical structure of the molecule being transported **(Figure 5.14)**. Second, facilitated diffusion can be *saturated* in a way analogous

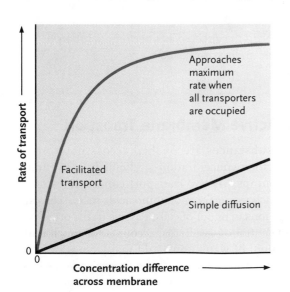

Rate of transport

Approaches maximum rate when all transporters are occupied

Facilitated transport

Simple diffusion

0

Concentration difference across membrane

Figure 5.14
The rate of transport as a function of concentration across the membrane. Compared with simple diffusion, facilitated diffusion leads to higher rates of transport and displays saturation kinetics.

to an enzyme. A membrane has a limited number of transporters for a particular molecule. If you measure the rate of transport at increasing concentration differences across a membrane, the rate of transport of a particular molecule (the substrate) reaches a plateau that represents a state when all the transporters are occupied. Increasing the concentration further has no effect (see Figure 5.14). By comparison, in simple diffusion, the whole membrane surface is effectively the transporter; thus, the rate of transport, although slower, never reaches a plateau but keeps increasing with increasing concentration gradient.

5.4d Osmosis: The Passive Diffusion of Water

Like solutes, water can also move passively across membranes in a process called **osmosis**. The passive transport of water occurs constantly in living cells. Inward or outward movement of water by osmosis

Movement of water by osmosis is dictated by solute concentration.

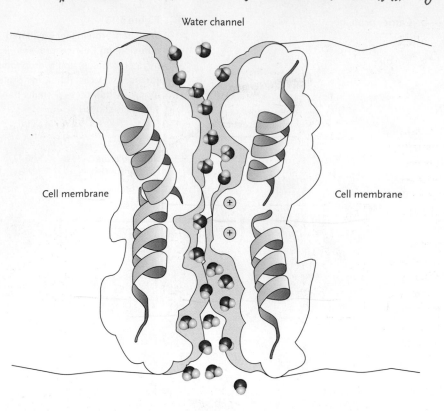

Water channel

Cell membrane

Cell membrane

Figure 5.15

A model of aquaporin, a water-specific channel. Positive charges in the centre of the channel prevent the diffusion of protons.

tone). When a cell is in a hypotonic solution, water enters by osmosis, and the cell tends to swell **(Figure 5.16a)**. Animal cells in a hypotonic solution may actually swell to the point of bursting. Organisms that live in surroundings that contain salts or other molecules at higher concentrations than their bodies must constantly expend energy to replace water lost by osmosis. In this situation, the outside solution is said to be hypertonic to the cells (*hyper* = over or above), as shown in **Figure 5.16b.** The concentration of water inside and outside cells is usually equal or isotonic (*iso* = the same), as shown in **Figure 5.16c.** To keep the fluids on either side of the plasma membrane isotonic, animal cells must constantly use energy to pump Na^+ ions from inside to outside by active transport (see Section 5.6); otherwise, water would move inward by osmosis and cause the cells to burst.

develops forces that can cause cells to swell or shrink. In formal terms, osmosis is *the net movement of water molecules across a selectively permeable membrane by diffusion, from a solution of lesser solute concentration to a solution of greater solute concentration.* For osmosis to take place, the selectively permeable membrane must allow water molecules to pass but not molecules of the solute. Osmosis occurs in cells because they contain a solution of proteins and other molecules that are retained in the cytoplasm by a membrane impermeable to them but freely permeable to water.

Osmosis can occur either by simple diffusion or it can be facilitated by water-specific transport proteins called aquaporins. This group of transporters has been found in organisms as diverse as prokaryotes, plants, and humans. The aquaporin channel is very narrow and allows for the single-file movement of about a billion water molecules every second **(Figure 5.15)**. The channel is also very specific for water and does not allow for the diffusion of ions such as protons. The structural basis of this is explained by recent three-dimensional models of aquaporin-1, which show the presence of positive charges in the centre of the channel that are thought to repel the transport of protons through the channel. For his discovery of aquaporins, Peter Agre was awarded the Nobel Prize for chemistry in 2003.

The movement of water by osmosis is dictated by solute concentration. If the solution surrounding a cell contains dissolved substances at lower concentrations than in the cell, the solution is said to be hypotonic to the cell (*hypo* = under or below; *tonos* = tension or

STUDY BREAK

1. How do the size and charge of a molecule influence its transport across a membrane?
2. What is the difference between passive transport and active transport?
3. Explain how aquaporin functions to transport water.
4. Explain the effect of a hypertonic solution surrounding animal cells.

5.5 Active Membrane Transport

Many substances are pushed across membranes against their concentration gradients by active transport "pumps." Active transport concentrates molecules such as sugars and amino acids inside cells and pushes ions in or out of cells. Passive transport, driven by concentration gradients, accounts for much of the movement of water, ions, and many types of molecules into or out of cells. Often, however, substances need to be moved against a concentration gradient—that is, from a region of low concentration to a region of higher concentration. For example, in muscle cells, a difference in calcium ion concentration between two compartments can be as high as 30 000. Such a huge concentration difference, which is required for normal muscle function, is established and maintained through an energy-dependent mechanism called **active transport.**

5.5a Active Transport Requires Energy

The term "active" in the term active transport means that the cell has to expend energy, which is usually ATP, to pump molecules across a membrane. It is estimated that about 25% of a cell's ATP requirements are for active transport. Active transport concentrates molecules such as sugars and amino acids inside cells and pushes ions in or out of cells.

There are two kinds of active transport. In **primary active transport,** the same protein that transports a substance also hydrolyzes ATP to power the transport directly. In **secondary active transport,** the transport is indirectly driven by ATP hydrolysis. That is, the transport proteins do not break down ATP; instead, the transporters use a favourable concentration gradient of ions, built up by primary active transport, as their energy source for active transport of a different ion or molecule.

Other features of active transport resemble facilitated diffusion (listed in Table 5.1). Both processes depend on membrane transport proteins, both are specific, and both can be saturated. The transport proteins are carrier proteins that change their conformation as they function.

5.5b Primary Active Transport Moves Positively Charged Ions

All primary active transport pumps move positively charged ions—H^+, Ca^{2+}, Na^+, and K^+—across membranes **(Figure 5.17, p. 106).** The gradients of positive ions established by primary active transport pumps underlie functions that are absolutely essential for cellular life.

For example, **H^+ pumps** (also called **proton pumps**) in plasma membranes push hydrogen ions from the cytoplasm to the cell exterior. These pumps (as in Figure 5.17) temporarily bind a phosphate group removed from ATP during the pumping cycle. Proton pumps are not common in animals; although one pump of this type moves H^+ from cells lining the stomach into the gastric juice, making the stomach contents highly acidic.

The **Ca^{2+} pump** (or **calcium pump**) is widely distributed among eukaryotes. It pushes Ca^{2+} from the cytoplasm to the cell exterior and from the cytosol into the vesicles of the endoplasmic reticulum (ER). As a result, Ca^{2+} concentration is typically high outside cells and inside ER vesicles and low in the cytoplasmic solution. This Ca^{2+} gradient is used universally among eukaryotes as a regulatory control of cellular activities as diverse as secretion, microtubule assembly, and muscle contraction. The latter is discussed further in Chapter 41.

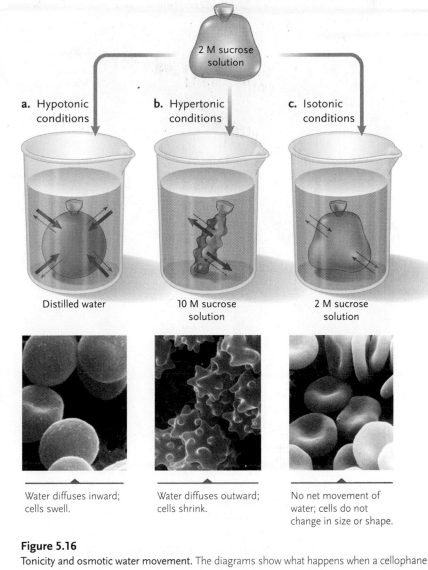

Figure 5.16

Tonicity and osmotic water movement. The diagrams show what happens when a cellophane bag filled with a 2 M sucrose solution is placed in a **(a)** hypotonic, **(b)** hypertonic, or **(c)** isotonic solution. The cellophane is permeable to water but not to sucrose molecules. The width of the arrows shows the amount of water movement. In the first beaker, the distilled water is hypotonic to the solution in the bag; net movement of water is into the bag. In the second beaker, the 10 M solution is hypertonic to the solution in the bag; net movement of water is out of the bag. In the third beaker, the solutions inside and outside the bag are isotonic; there is no net movement of water into or out of the bag. The animal cell micrographs show the corresponding effects on red blood cells placed in hypotonic, hypertonic, or isotonic solutions. (Micrographs, M. Sheetz, R. Painter, and S. Singer. Journal of Cell Biology, 70:493, 1976. By permission of Rockefeller University Press.)

The **Na^+/K^+ pump** (or **sodium–potassium pump**), located in the plasma membrane, pushes 3 Na^+ ions out of the cell and 2 K^+ ions into the cell in the same pumping cycle. As a result, positive charges accumulate in excess outside the membrane, and the inside of the cell becomes negatively charged with respect to the outside. Voltage—an electrical potential difference—across the plasma membrane results from this difference in charge as well as from the unequal distribution of ions across the membrane created by passive transport. The voltage across a membrane, called a **membrane potential,** measures

Figure 5.17

Model for how a primary active transport pump operates.

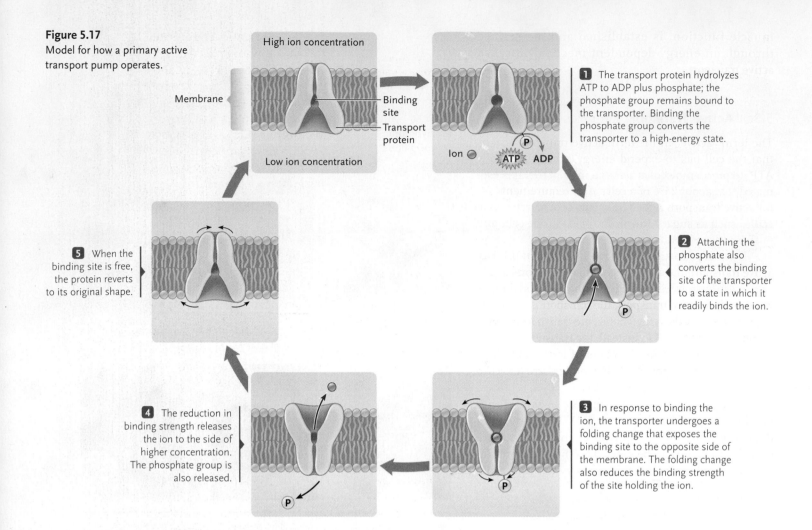

High ion concentration

Membrane

Binding site

Transport protein

Low ion concentration

Ion

ATP ADP

P

1 The transport protein hydrolyzes ATP to ADP plus phosphate; the phosphate group remains bound to the transporter. Binding the phosphate group converts the transporter to a high-energy state.

2 Attaching the phosphate also converts the binding site of the transporter to a state in which it readily binds the ion.

5 When the binding site is free, the protein reverts to its original shape.

4 The reduction in binding strength releases the ion to the side of higher concentration. The phosphate group is also released.

3 In response to binding the ion, the transporter undergoes a folding change that exposes the binding site to the opposite side of the membrane. The folding change also reduces the binding strength of the site holding the ion.

---

from about −50 to −200 millivolts, with the minus sign indicating that the charge inside the cell is negative versus the outside. In sum, we have both a concentration difference (of the ions) and an electrical charge difference on the two sides of the membrane, constituting what is called an **electrochemical gradient.** Electrochemical gradients store energy that is used for other transport mechanisms. For instance, the electrochemical gradient across the membrane is involved with the movement of ions associated with nerve impulse transmission (described in Chapter 33).

5.5c Secondary Active Transport Moves Both Ions and Organic Molecules

As already noted, secondary active transport pumps use the concentration gradient of an ion established by a primary pump as their energy source. For example, the driving force for most secondary active transport in animal cells is the high outside/low inside Na$^+$ gradient set up by the sodium–potassium pump. In secondary active transport, the transfer of the solute across the membrane is always coupled with the transfer of the ion supplying the driving force.

Secondary active transport occurs by two mechanisms known as *symport* and *antiport* **(Figure 5.18).** In **symport,** the cotransported solute moves through the membrane channel in the same direction as the driving ion, a phenomenon known as **cotransport.** Sugars such as glucose and amino acids are examples of molecules actively transported into cells by symport. In **antiport,** the driving ion moves through the membrane channel in one direction, providing the energy for the active transport of another molecule in the opposite direction, a phenomenon known as **exchange diffusion.** In many cases, ions are exchanged by antiport. For example, antiport is the mechanism used in red blood cells for the coupled movement of chloride ions and bicarbonate ions through a membrane channel.

Active transport and passive transport move ions and smaller hydrophilic molecules across cellular membranes. Cells can also move much larger molecules or aggregates of molecules from inside to outside, or in the reverse direction, by including them in the cell's inward or outward vesicle traffic. The mechanisms carrying out this movement— exocytosis and endocytosis—are discussed in the next section.

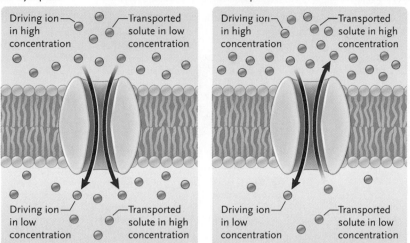

a. Symport

Driving ion in high concentration — Transported solute in low concentration

Driving ion in low concentration — Transported solute in high concentration

b. Antiport

Driving ion in high concentration — Transported solute in high concentration

Driving ion in low concentration — Transported solute in low concentration

Figure 5.18

Secondary active transport, in which a concentration gradient of an ion is used as the energy source for active transport of a solute. **(a)** In symport, the transported solute moves in the same direction as the gradient of the driving ion. **(b)** In antiport, the transported solute moves in the direction opposite to the gradient of the driving ion.

STUDY BREAK

1. What is active transport?
2. What is the difference between primary active transport and secondary active transport?
3. How is a membrane potential generated?

5.6 Exocytosis and Endocytosis

The largest molecules transported through cellular membranes by passive and active transport are about the size of amino acids or monosaccharides such as glucose. Eukaryotic cells import and export larger molecules by endocytosis and exocytosis. The export of materials by exocytosis primarily carries secretory proteins and some waste materials from the cytoplasm to the cell exterior. Import by endocytosis may carry proteins, larger aggregates of molecules, or even whole cells from the outside into the cytoplasm. Exocytosis and endocytosis also contribute to the back-and-forth flow of membranes between the endomembrane system and the plasma membrane. Both exocytosis and endocytosis require energy; thus, both processes stop if a cell's ability to make ATP is inhibited.

5.6a Exocytosis Releases Molecules to the Outside by Means of Secretory Vesicles

In exocytosis, secretory vesicles move through the cytoplasm and contact the plasma membrane **(Figure 5.19, p. 108)**. The vesicle membrane fuses with the plasma membrane, releasing the vesicle's contents to the cell exterior.

All eukaryotic cells secrete materials to the outside through exocytosis. For example, in animals, glandular cells secrete peptide hormones or milk proteins, and cells lining the digestive tract secrete mucus and digestive enzymes. Plant cells secrete carbohydrates by exocytosis to build a strong cell wall.

5.6b Endocytosis Brings Materials into Cells in Endocytic Vesicles

In endocytosis, proteins and other substances are trapped in pitlike depressions that bulge inward from the plasma membrane. The depression then pinches off as an endocytic vesicle. Endocytosis takes place in most eukaryotic cells by one of two distinct but related pathways. In the simplest of these mechanisms, **bulk-phase endocytosis** (sometimes called **pinocytosis**, meaning "cell drinking"), extracellular water is taken in along with any molecules that happen to be in solution in the water **(Figure 5.19b, p. 108)**. No binding by surface receptors takes place.

In the second endocytic pathway, **receptor-mediated endocytosis**, the molecules to be taken in are bound to the outer cell surface by receptor proteins **(Figure 5.19c, d, p. 108)**. The receptors, which are integral proteins of the plasma membrane, recognize and bind only certain molecules—primarily proteins, or other molecules carried by proteins—from the solution surrounding the cell. After binding their target molecules, the receptors collect into a depression in the plasma membrane called a **coated pit** because of the network of proteins (called **clathrin**) that coat and reinforce the cytoplasmic side. With the target molecules attached, the pits deepen and pinch free of the plasma membrane to form endocytic vesicles. Once in the cytoplasm, an endocytic vesicle rapidly loses its clathrin coat and may fuse with a lysosome. The enzymes within the lysosome then digest the contents of the vesicle, breaking them down into smaller molecules useful to the cell. These molecular products—for example, amino acids and monosaccharides—enter the cytoplasm by crossing the vesicle membrane via transport proteins. The membrane proteins are recycled to the plasma membrane.

Mammalian cells take in many substances by receptor-mediated endocytosis, including peptide hormones, antibodies, and blood proteins. The receptors binding these substances to the plasma membrane are present in thousands to hundreds of thousands of copies. For example, a mammalian cell plasma membrane has about 20 000 receptors for low-density lipoprotein

Figure 5.19

Exocytosis and endocytosis.
(a) Exocytosis. **(b)** Bulk-phase endocytosis. **(c)** Receptor-mediated endocytosis. **(d)** Electron micrographs of receptor-mediated endocytosis.

a. Exocytosis

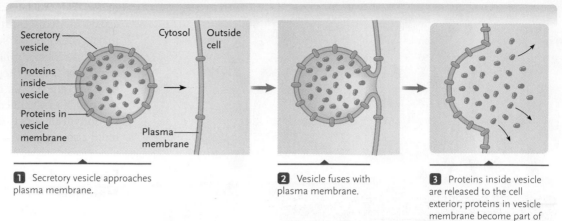

Secretory vesicle
Proteins inside vesicle
Proteins in vesicle membrane
Cytosol
Outside cell
Plasma membrane

1 Secretory vesicle approaches plasma membrane.

2 Vesicle fuses with plasma membrane.

3 Proteins inside vesicle are released to the cell exterior; proteins in vesicle membrane become part of plasma membrane.

b. Bulk-phase endocytosis (pinocytosis)

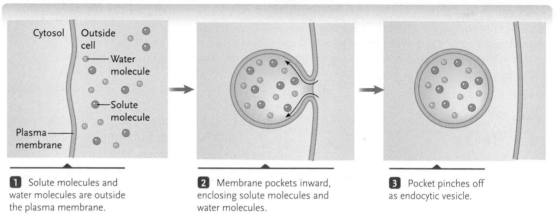

Cytosol
Outside cell
Water molecule
Solute molecule
Plasma membrane

1 Solute molecules and water molecules are outside the plasma membrane.

2 Membrane pockets inward, enclosing solute molecules and water molecules.

3 Pocket pinches off as endocytic vesicle.

c. Receptor-mediated endocytosis

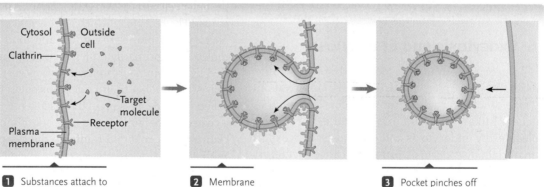

Cytosol
Clathrin
Outside cell
Target molecule
Receptor
Plasma membrane

1 Substances attach to membrane receptors.

2 Membrane pockets inward.

3 Pocket pinches off as endocytic vesicle.

d. Electron micrographs of receptor-mediated endocytosis shown in 5.19c.

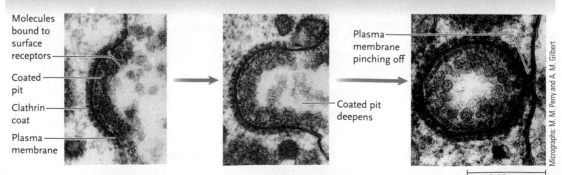

Molecules bound to surface receptors
Coated pit
Clathrin coat
Plasma membrane

Coated pit deepens

Plasma membrane pinching off

0.25 μm

Micrographs: M. M. Perry and A. M. Gilbert

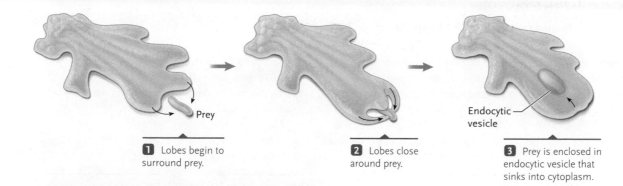

1 Lobes begin to surround prey.

2 Lobes close around prey.

3 Prey is enclosed in endocytic vesicle that sinks into cytoplasm.

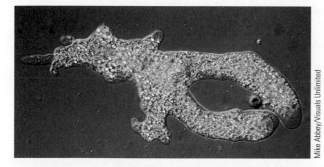

Phagocytosis = white blood cells take in molecules like receptor-mediated endocytosis

Figure 5.20

Phagocytosis, in which lobes of the cytoplasm extend outward and surround a cell targeted as prey. The micrograph shows the protistan *Chaos carolinense* preparing to engulf a single-celled alga (*Pandorina*) by phagocytosis; white blood cells called phagocytes carry out a similar process in mammals.

(LDL). LDL, a complex of lipids and proteins, is the way cholesterol moves through the bloodstream. When LDL binds to its receptor on the membrane, it is taken into the cell by receptor-mediated endocytosis. Then, by the steps just described, the LDL is broken down within the cell and cholesterol is released into the cytoplasm.

Some cells, such as certain white blood cells (*phagocytes*) in the bloodstream or protists such as *Amoeba proteus*, can take in large aggregates of molecules, cell parts, or even whole cells by a process related to receptor-mediated endocytosis. The process, called **phagocytosis** (meaning "cell eating"), begins when surface receptors bind molecules on the substances to be taken in **(Figure 5.20)**. Cytoplasmic lobes then extend, surround, and engulf the materials, forming a pit that pinches off and sinks into the cytoplasm as a large endocytic vesicle. The materials are then digested within the cell as in receptor-mediated endocytosis, and any remaining residues are sequestered permanently into storage vesicles or are expelled from cells as waste by exocytosis.

The combined workings of exocytosis and endocytosis constantly cycle membrane segments between the internal cytoplasm and the cell surface. The balance of the two mechanisms maintains the surface area of the plasma membrane at controlled levels.

Thus, through the combined mechanisms of passive transport, active transport, exocytosis, and endocytosis, cells maintain their internal concentrations of ions and molecules and exchange larger molecules such as proteins with their surroundings. The next two chapters on respiration and photosynthesis show another vital role of membranes in cells of all kinds—their participation in the fundamentally important reactions of energy metabolism.

STUDY BREAK

1. What is the mechanism of exocytosis?
2. What is the difference between bulk-phase endocytosis and receptor-mediated endocytosis?

Lap-Chee Tsui, University of Hong Kong

Identification of the gene that is defective in patients with cystic fibrosus (CF) (see *Why It Matters*) was a breakthrough in human genetics and was achieved by a research team headed by Lap-Chee Tsui (1950–) of the Department of Genetics at The Hospital for Sick Children in Toronto.

Born in Shanghai, Tsui studied biology at the Chinese University of Hong Kong and was awarded a bachelor of science degree in 1972, which was followed by a master of philosophy degree in 1974. He undertook doctoral research in the United States, completing his Ph.D. at the University of Pittsburgh in 1979. He followed this with postdoctoral training at Oak Ridge National Laboratory in Tennessee before moving in 1981 to the Department of Genetics at The Hospital for Sick Children, where soon after he became a staff member investigating the underlying genetic cause of CF.

Although today reports of gene discovery are commonplace, in the 1980s, the discovery of the gene that is mutated in patients with CF was particularly noteworthy for two major reasons. First, researchers relied on DNA isolated from people with CF to identify genetic markers of the disease. Using these, researchers used the novel method of positional cloning to identify the CF gene without any knowledge of the gene itself or what it did. Second, CF is the most common single-gene disease among Caucasians; thus, much anticipation awaited this particular discovery, with many research teams worldwide trying to be the first to identify the gene.

In 1985, Tsui and his team identified the first DNA marker linked to CF, on chromosome 7. Four years later, Dr. Tsui's team, along with collaborators at the University of Michigan, finally identified the defective gene responsible for CF, defining the principal mutation (Δ*F508). This mutation is the result of a three-nucleotide deletion that results in the loss of the amino acid phenylalanine (F) at the 508th position of the protein. As a result, the protein does not fold normally and is more quickly degraded.

The research was described in three seminal papers in the September 8, 1989, issue of *Science*. The gene was called the cystic fibrosis transmembrane regulator (CFTR). *Science* named Dr. Tsui's achievement "the most refreshing scientific development of 1989," and *Maclean*'s Honour Roll hailed it as one of the "discoveries of hope at the heart of human life" in the same year.

Dr. Tsui has received many honours, including fellow of the Royal Society of Canada, several honorary doctoral degrees, and the Order of Canada. Dr. Tsui is currently the vice-chancellor of the University of Hong Kong, but he remains an active researcher and is still affiliated with The Hospital for Sick Children's Program in Genetics and Genomic Biology.

In this chapter, we have discussed the structure of membranes and the transport of substances across membranes by various mechanisms, and research continues in all of those areas to obtain a more detailed understanding. For instance, research is being done to determine how the assembly of phospholipids and proteins into new membranes occurs. Also, as we will learn later in the book, cells contain a number of signalling pathways in which a signal received at the cell surface is relayed through the cell to the site at which the signal is targeted. How this signalling occurs at the molecular level is an important area of research. And exocytosis is responsible for the secretion of neurotransmitters (chemical messengers that communicate between neurons and between neurons and other cells), hormones, and enzymes. One important area of research is determining the molecular mechanisms for the membrane fusion event of exocytosis. Another is examining how cell-surface receptors control exocytosis.

Let us consider two specific examples of current research, one involving aquaporins and the other endocytosis.

Molecular and Cellular Analysis of Aquaporin Channels

As we discussed in the chapter, aquaporins are specific channels for water transport across cell membranes. Interestingly, problems with aquaporin function are associated with various human diseases, such as congenital cataracts, a form of diabetes, congestive heart failure, and brain edema (fluid-caused swelling). Therefore, having a better understanding of aquaporin function could help facilitate the development of drugs to treat those diseases.

Peter Agre at Johns Hopkins University School of Medicine in Baltimore, Maryland, received a Nobel Prize in 2003 for his discovery of aquaporins. In the chapter, we gave a simple overview of aquaporin channels, but the bigger picture is much more complicated. We know, for instance, that the ability to absorb or release water varies considerably among the cells and tissues of an organism and between organisms. Since Agre's discovery, over 200 different aquaporins have been identified in tissues from mammals, nonmammalian vertebrates, invertebrates, plants, and various microorganisms. Variation in aquaporin structure among these forms is likely responsible for their differences in function. Agre's research group is pursuing this issue by characterizing the structures of various aquaporins from humans, yeast, and bacteria to produce high-resolution models. Such models will be informative for designing experiments to further our understanding of the function of these channel molecules. Agre's group is also studying the regulation of the aquaporin genes to characterize tissue-specific production of aquaporins. The results of this line of investigation will provide a valuable piece of the puzzle concerning the variation in water uptake among tissues mentioned earlier.

Many other research groups are working on aquaporins, so we can expect great strides to be made in this area in the future.

Entry of Nanotubes into Cells by Endocytosis

We learned in this chapter that substances can enter cells by endocytosis. In either bulk-phase endocytosis or receptor-mediated endocytosis, the result is an endocytic vesicle that may then fuse with a lysosome. Using endocytosis to deliver therapeutic agents to diseased cells, such as cancer cells, has been the goal of many research groups. One such group is that of Hongjie Dai, a physical chemist at Stanford University.

There are many possible ways to deliver therapeutic agents to cells. Dai's group has been working with carbon nanotubes, which are cylindrical carbon molecules with a diameter of just a few nanometres (about 50 000 times smaller than the width of a human hair) and up to several centimetres long. In one experiment, Dai's group tagged carbon nanotubes so that they would bind specifically to cancer cells. The carbon nanotubes absorb near-infrared light, whereas normal tissue does not. Therefore, by shining a near-infrared laser on the tagged cells, the researchers could kill just cancer cells without harming normal tissue.

Dai's research team also showed that carbon nanotubes could carry proteins and DNA into cells. This property would be extremely valuable for delivering drugs or therapeutic genes into diseased cells. How were the carbon nanotubes taken into the cells? Knowing the route is important for determining what kinds of chemical bonds will be needed to attach the therapeutic agents to the carbon nanotubes. For example, as described in this chapter, endocytosis produces vesicles that can fuse with lysosomes. Therefore, if carbon nanotubes were taken up by endocytosis, then the drug or DNA being delivered could be attached to the nanotubes by disulfide bonds because those bonds would readily be broken by the acidic environment of the lysosome, thereby releasing the agent.

Dai and his colleagues have obtained evidence that carbon nanotubes are taken into cells by endocytosis. Endocytosis, as opposed to passive mechanisms, requires energy in the form of either ATP or heat. When cell cultures were cooled, or treated with an inhibitor that stopped ATP production, the cells could no longer take in carbon nanotubes. Experiments using specific inhibitors against clathrin provided support for a receptor-mediated endocytosis uptake mechanism.

Future research will turn to using carbon nanotubes to deliver anticancer agents specifically to cancer cells in tissue culture. Undoubtedly, a lot of work will be needed to produce an efficient method for that delivery, as well as an effective way to release and activate the anticancer agent within the cell. If success is forthcoming with tissue culture systems, the protocols would be moved to model organisms for cancer and eventually to humans for clinical trials.

Review

Go to CENGAGENOW™ at http://hed.nelson.com/ to access quizzing, animations, exercises, articles, and personalized homework help.

5.1 An Overview of the Structure of Membranes

- The fluid mosaic model proposes that the membrane consists of a fluid lipid bilayer in which proteins are embedded and float freely.

- Membranes are asymmetrical. The two halves of a membrane are not the same. The membrane proteins found on one half of the bilayer are structurally and functionally distinct from those of the other half.

5.2 The Lipid Fabric of a Membrane

- The lipid bilayer forms the structural framework of membranes and serves as a barrier preventing the passage of most water-soluble molecules.

- The basic part of a membrane is a fluid phospholipid bilayer, in which the polar regions of phospholipid molecules lie at the surfaces of the bilayer and their nonpolar tails associate together in the interior.

- Organisms can adjust the fatty acid composition of membrane lipids to maintain proper fluidity.

5.3 Membrane Proteins

- Proteins embedded in the phospholipid bilayer carry out most membrane functions, including transport of selected hydrophilic substances, enzymatic activity, recognition, and signal reception.

- Integral membrane proteins are embedded deeply in the bilayer and cannot be removed without dispersing the bilayer. Peripheral membrane proteins associate with membrane surfaces.

5.4 Passive Membrane Transport

- Passive transport depends on diffusion, the net movement of molecules from a region of higher concentration to a region of lower concentration. Passive transport does not require cells to expend energy.

- Simple diffusion is the passive transport of substances across the lipid portion of cellular membranes with their concentration gradients.

- Small uncharged molecules can move rapidly across membranes, whereas large or charged molecules may be strongly impeded from transiting a membrane.

- Facilitated diffusion is the passive transport of substances at rates higher than predicted from their lipid solubility. It depends on membrane proteins, follows concentration gradients, is specific for certain substances, and becomes saturated at high concentrations of the transported substance.

- Osmosis is the net diffusion of water molecules across a selectively permeable membrane in response to differences in the concentration of solute molecules.

- Aquaporins are membrane transport proteins that facilitate the diffusion of water.

- Water moves from hypotonic solutions (lower concentrations of solute molecules) to hypertonic solutions (higher concentrations of solute molecules). When the solutions on each side are isotonic, there is no osmotic movement of water in either direction.

5.5 Active Membrane Transport

- Active transport moves substances against their concentration gradients and requires cells to expend energy. Active transport depends on membrane proteins, is specific for certain substances, and becomes saturated at high concentrations of the transported substance.

- Active transport proteins are either primary transport pumps, which directly use ATP as their energy source, or secondary transport pumps, which use favourable concentration gradients of positively charged ions, set up by primary transport pumps, as their energy source for transport.

- Secondary active transport may occur by symport, in which the transported substance moves in the same direction as the concentration gradient used as the energy source, or by antiport, in which the transported substance moves in the direction opposite to the concentration gradient used as the energy source.

5.6 Exocytosis and Endocytosis

- Large molecules and particles are moved out of and into cells by exocytosis and endocytosis. The mechanisms allow substances to leave and enter cells without directly passing through the plasma membrane.

- In exocytosis, a vesicle carrying secreted materials contacts and fuses with the plasma membrane on its cytoplasmic side. The fusion introduces the vesicle membrane into the plasma membrane and releases the vesicle contents to the cell exterior.

- In endocytosis, materials on the cell exterior are enclosed in a segment of the plasma membrane that pockets inward and pinches off on the cytoplasmic side as an endocytic vesicle. Endocytosis occurs in two overall forms, bulk-phase endocytosis (pinocytosis) and receptor-mediated endocytosis. Most of the materials entering cells are digested into molecular subunits small enough to be transported across the vesicle membranes.

Questions

Self-Test Questions

1. In the fluid mosaic model,
   a. the plasma membrane is a rigid association of proteins and lipid molecules.
   b. phospholipids often flip-flop between the inner and outer layers.
   c. the mosaic refers to proteins attached to the underlying cytoskeleton.
   d. the fluid refers to the phospholipid bilayer.
   e. the mosaic refers to the symmetry of the internal membrane proteins and sterols.

2. The freeze-fracture technique demonstrates
   a. that the plasma membrane is a bilayer with individual proteins suspended in it.
   b. that the plasma membrane is fluid.
   c. the different functions of membrane proteins.
   d. that proteins are bound to the cytoplasmic side but not embedded in the lipid bilayer.
   e. the direction of movement of solutes through the membrane.

3. Which of the following statements about desaturase enzymes is correct?
   a. They are expressed specifically in bacteria grown at high temperatures.
   b. They increase the degree of unsaturation of membrane fatty acids.
   c. They increase the number of hydrogens in a fatty acid.
   d. They are essential to keep membranes fluid at low temperatures.
   e. Both b and d are correct.

4. Which of the following statements is correct?
   a. Membrane lipids are polar molecules.
   b. A lipid bilayer requires energy in the form of ATP to form.
   c. The higher the proportion of saturated lipids, the more fluid a membrane will be.
   d. Molecules of cholesterol are found integrated into membranes.
   e. Both a and d are correct.

5. Compared with integral membrane proteins, peripheral membrane proteins
   a. are composed of a greater total number of amino acids.
   b. are involved in the transport of ions across membranes.
   c. tend to be hydrophobic.
   d. are usually composed of a mixture of polar and nonpolar amino acids.
   e. None of the above statements are correct.

6. Which one of the following molecules shows the slowest rate of membrane diffusion?
   a. CO_2
   b. water
   c. O_2
   d. glucose
   e. K^+

7. Unlike simple diffusion, facilitated diffusion
   a. requires a source of chemical energy, such as ATP.
   b. can transport molecules against a concentration gradient.
   c. can be saturated by high substrate concentrations.
   d. is an entropy-driven process.
   e. Both b and c are correct.

8. An ion moving through a membrane channel in one direction gives energy to actively transport another molecule in the opposite direction. This describes
   a. facilitated diffusion.
   b. exchange diffusion.
   c. symport transport.
   d. primary active transport pump.
   e. cotransport.

9. Phagocytosis illustrates the phenomenon of
   a. receptor-mediated endocytosis.
   b. bulk-phase endocytosis.
   c. exocytosis.
   d. pinocytosis.
   e. cotransport.

10. Place in order the events of receptor-mediated endocytosis.
    (1) Clathrin coat disappears.
    (2) Receptors collect in a coated pit covered with clathrin on the cytoplasmic side.
    (3) Receptors recognize and bind specific molecules.
    (4) Endocytic vesicle may fuse with lysosome while receptors are recycled to the cell surface.
    (5) Pits deepen and pinch free of plasma membrane to form endocytic vesicles.
    a. 41253
    b. 21354
    c. 32514
    d. 41523
    e. 31245

Questions for Discussion

1. The bacterium *Vibrio cholerae* causes cholera, a disease characterized by severe diarrhea that may cause infected people to lose up to 20 L of fluid in a day. The bacterium enters the body when someone drinks contaminated water. It adheres to the intestinal lining, where it causes the cells of the lining to release sodium and chloride ions. Explain how this release is related to the massive fluid loss.

2. In hospitals, solutions of glucose with a concentration of 0.3 M can be introduced directly into the bloodstream of patients without tissue damage by osmotic water movement. The same is true of NaCl solutions, but these must be adjusted to 0.15 M to be introduced without damage. Can you explain why one is introduced at 0.3 M and the other at 0.15 M?

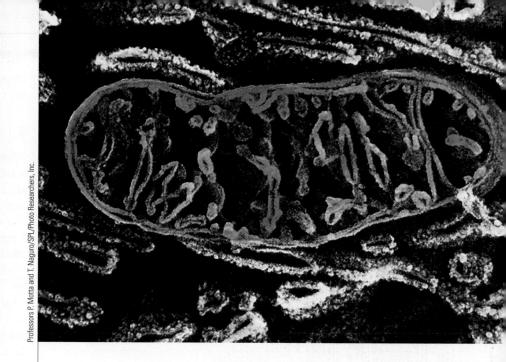

Mitochondrion (colorized SEM). Mitochondria are the sites of cellular respiration.

Professors P. Motta and T. Naguro/SPL/Photo Researchers, Inc.

6 Cellular Respiration

WHY IT MATTERS

In the early 1960s, Swedish physician Rolf Luft mulled over some odd symptoms of a patient. The young woman was hot all the time. Even on the coldest winter days, she never stopped perspiring and her skin was always flushed. She also felt weak and was thin, despite a huge appetite.

Luft inferred that his patient's symptoms pointed to a metabolic disorder. Her cells seemed to be active, but much of their activity was being dissipated as metabolic heat. He decided to order tests to measure her metabolic rates. The patient's oxygen consumption was the highest ever recorded!

Luft also examined a tissue sample from the patient's skeletal muscles. Using a microscope, he found that her muscle cells contained many more mitochondria—the adenosine triphosphate (ATP)-producing organelles of the cell—than are normal; also, her mitochondria were abnormally shaped. Other studies showed that the mitochondria were engaged in cellular respiration—their prime function—but little ATP was being generated.

The disorder, now called *Luft syndrome,* was the first disorder to be linked directly to a defective cellular organelle. This syndrome is extremely rare and has now been shown to be due to a defect in one of the complexes of cellular respiration that links electron transport to proton pumping and subsequent ATP generation. With such a disorder, skeletal and heart muscles and the brain, the tissues with the highest energy demands, are affected the most.

More than 100 mitochondrial disorders are now known. Defective mitochondria also contribute to many age-related problems, including type 1 diabetes, atherosclerosis, and amyotrophic lateral sclerosis (ALS, also called Lou Gehrig disease), as well as Parkinson, Alzheimer, and Huntington diseases.

Clearly, human health depends on mitochondria that are structurally sound and functioning properly. More broadly, every animal, plant, and fungus and most protists depend on mitochondria that are functioning correctly to grow and survive.

6.1 The Chemical Basis of Cellular Respiration

The vast majority of energy enters the biosphere through the process of photosynthesis, which we describe in detail in the next chapter. The reactions of photosynthesis trap light energy and use it to convert CO_2 and water into organic molecules such as sugars, which contain an abundance of free energy **(Figure 6.1)**. The focus of this chapter is another fundamental biological process that enables organisms to efficiently extract the energy present in molecules such as sugar: cellular respiration. By slowly oxidizing energy-rich molecules, the reactions of cellular respiration extract the potential energy and convert it into ATP, a form of chemical energy that can readily be

use light energy ← to convert CO_2 to carbohydrate.

 # Convert molecule's energy to ATP.

used by the cell for the majority of energy-requiring reactions. The complete oxidation of food molecules results in the formation of CO_2, which is released into the environment (see Figure 6.1).

6.1a Food as Fuel → C–H bonds → their similarities.

What is it about the structure of glucose that makes it a source of energy that organisms can use to live? A similar question could be asked about gasoline: what is it about the chemical makeup of gasoline that provides energy to run a car? What glucose and gasoline have in common **(Figure 6.2)** that makes them both good fuel molecules is an abundance of hydrogen in the form of carbon–hydrogen (C–H) bonds.

The chemical basis for why C–H bonds are a source of energy can be explained by **Figure 6.3.** For any atom, an electron that is farther away from the nucleus contains more energy than an electron that is more closely held by the nucleus. As a result, an electron loses energy as it moves closer to the parent nucleus and gains energy as it moves away. The electrons associated with a C–H bond are equidistant from both nuclei. Because of this, they contain high energy and can be easily removed. In contrast, molecules that have an abundance of oxygen contain less potential energy because oxygen is strongly electronegative. The more electronegative an atom is, the greater the force that holds the electrons to that atom, and, therefore, the greater the energy required to remove these electrons. These fundamental principles of chemistry have an everyday relevance; they explain why, for example, compared to proteins (polymers of amino acids) and carbohydrates (groups of sugars), fats contain more calories per unit of weight. A fat is almost entirely C–H bonds (to review the structure of these molecules, see the *The Chemical and Physical Foundations of Biology* pages).

6.1b The Principle of Redox

The potential energy that is contained within fuel molecules is released by their oxidation. The term **oxidation** refers to the loss of electrons (e^-),

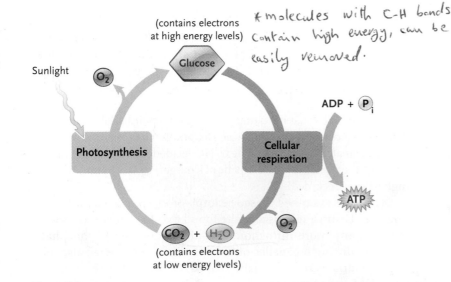

Sunlight

(contains electrons at high energy levels)

 # molecules with C–H bonds contain high energy, can be easily removed.

Glucose

O_2

ADP + P_i

Photosynthesis

Cellular respiration

ATP

CO_2 + H_2O O_2

(contains electrons at low energy levels)

Figure 6.1
Flow of energy from sunlight to ATP. Photosynthesis occurs in plants, many protists, and some prokaryotes. Cellular respiration occurs in all eukaryotes and many prokaryotes.

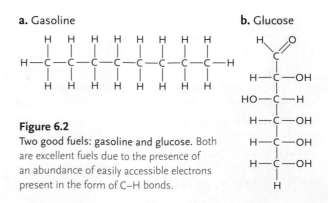

a. Gasoline

b. Glucose

Figure 6.2
Two good fuels: gasoline and glucose. Both are excellent fuels due to the presence of an abundance of easily accessible electrons present in the form of C–H bonds.

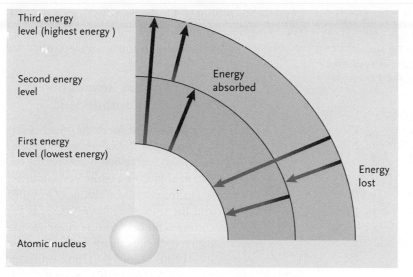

Figure 6.3

Energy levels of electrons of an atom. Electrons can exist only in discrete energy states. Electrons that gain energy move to a higher energy level that is farther away from the nucleus. Electrons that lose energy move closer to the nucleus.

Third energy level (highest energy)

Second energy level

First energy level (lowest energy)

Atomic nucleus

Energy absorbed

Energy lost

and the molecule afterward is said to be **oxidized**. The oxidation of a molecule is linked to a **reduction** reaction in which another molecule gains the electrons, or becomes **reduced**. Oxidation and reduction reactions are coupled processes; you never have one without the other. A simple mnemonic to remember the direction of electron transfer is OIL RIG—Oxidation Is Loss (of electrons), Reduction Is Gain (of electrons). For short, oxidation–reduction reactions are called **redox reactions**. A generalized redox reaction can be written like this:

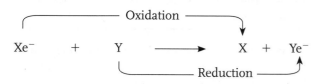

$$Xe^- \quad + \quad Y \quad \longrightarrow \quad X \quad + \quad Ye^-$$

The redox reaction describing the respiratory breakdown of glucose is as follows:

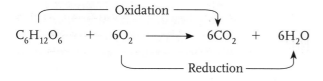

$$C_6H_{12}O_6 \quad + \quad 6O_2 \quad \longrightarrow \quad 6CO_2 \quad + \quad 6H_2O$$

The term *oxidation* comes from that fact that many reactions in which electrons are removed from fuel molecules involve oxygen as the atom that accepts the electrons (or, stated in another way, the molecule that gets reduced, or the electron acceptor). The involvement of oxygen is essential for many commonplace oxidation reactions: a car engine requires large amounts of air to be delivered to each piston for combustion to take place; an oil fire on a stove can be rapidly put out by putting a lid on the pot, restricting its supply of air. As we

will see later in this chapter, the high affinity of O_2 for electrons, its high **electronegativity**, makes it ideal as the terminal electron acceptor of cellular respiration.

The concept of redox reactions is made a little more challenging to understand by two points of fact. First, although many oxidation reactions involve oxygen, many others, including many involved in cellular respiration, do not. Second, the gain or loss of an electron in a redox reaction is not always complete. That is, whereas in some redox reactions, electrons are transferred completely from one atom to another, in other redox reactions, what changes is the degree to which electrons are shared between the two atoms.

As an example, the reaction between methane and oxygen (the burning of natural gas in air) illustrates a redox reaction in which only the degree of electron sharing changes. The dots in **Figure 6.4** indicate the positions of the electrons involved in the covalent bonds of the reactants and products. Compare the reactant methane with the product CO_2. In methane, the covalent electrons are shared essentially equally between bonded C and H atoms because C and H are almost equally electronegative. In CO_2, electrons are closer to the O atoms than to the C atom because O atoms are highly electronegative. Overall, this means that the C atom has partially "lost" its shared electrons in the reaction. In short, methane has

*many reactions in cellular respiration do not involve O_2.

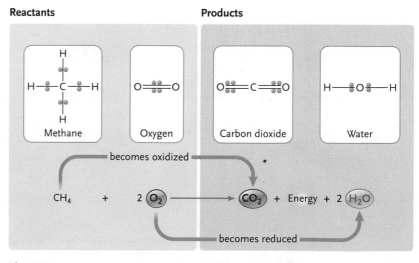

Figure 6.4

Relative loss and gain of electrons in a redox reaction, the burning of methane (natural gas) in oxygen. Compare the positions of the electrons in the covalent bonds of reactants and products. In this redox reaction, methane is oxidized and oxygen is reduced.

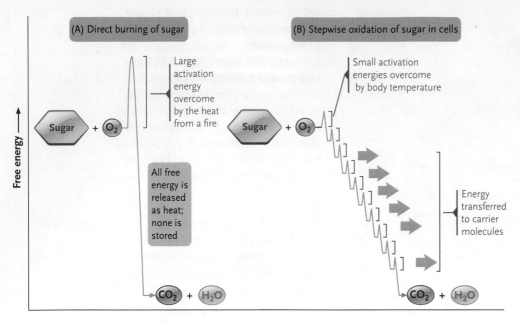

Figure 6.5

A comparison of the oxidation of glucose by direct burning (combustion) with cellular respiration.

holds the electrons to that atom, and, therefore, the greater the energy required to remove an electron.

6.1c Cellular Respiration Is Controlled Combustion

Like gasoline or methane, glucose can also undergo combustion and burn, and like most combustion reactions, the oxidation of glucose results in the transfer of electrons to O_2, yielding CO_2, water, and the release of energy. CO_2 is the common product for the complete oxidation of all organic molecules. Because it is a fully oxidized carbon molecule CO_2 contains no usable energy.

A good way to think of cellular respiration is *controlled* combustion, in which the energy of the C–H bonds is not liberated, suddenly producing heat, but is slowly released in a stepwise fashion, with the energy being transferred to other molecules. If we simply burn some glucose **(Figure 6.5a)**, energy would be released as heat, with the initial large energy of activation (see Section 4.4) being overcome by using a spark or flame. In the cell, the oxidation of glucose occurs via a series of enzyme-catalyzed reactions **(Figure 6.5b)**, each with a small activation energy. The energy released is transferred to energy-carrying molecules. Thermodynamically speaking, the two processes are identical: they are both exergonic, having the same change in free energy (686 kcal/mol). The difference is that if the energy released by the oxidation of glucose is released as heat, it cannot be harnessed to drive metabolic reactions.

In cellular respiration, the oxidation of food molecules occurs in the presence of a group of enzymes called *dehydrogenases* that facilitate the transfer of electrons from food to a molecule that acts as an energy carrier or shuttle. The most common energy carrier is the coenzyme *nicotinamide adenine dinucleotide* **(Figure 6.6)**. During respiration, the dehydrogenases remove two hydrogen atoms from a substrate molecule and transfer the two electrons—but only one of the protons—to NAD$^+$, resulting in its complete reduction to NADH. The other proton is simply released. The efficiency of energy transfer between food molecules and NAD$^+$ is high, with very little energy lost as heat. As we will see later, the potential energy carried in NADH is used to synthesize ATP.

been oxidized. Now compare the oxygen reactant with the product water. In the oxygen molecule, the two O atoms share their electrons equally. The oxygen reacts with the hydrogen from methane, producing water, in which the electrons are closer to the O atom than to the H atoms. This means that each O atom has partially "gained" electrons; in short, oxygen has been reduced. Because of this, the reaction between methane and O_2 releases much heat. The energy is released as the electrons in the C–H bonds of methane move closer to the electronegative oxygen atoms that form CO_2. The more electronegative an atom is, the greater the force that

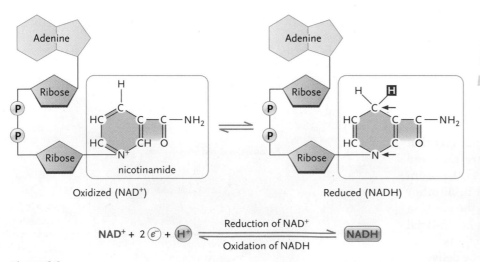

Figure 6.6

Electron carrier NAD$^+$. As the carrier is reduced to NADH, an electron is added at each of the two positions marked by a red arrow; a proton is also added at the position boxed in red. The nitrogenous base (blue) that adds and releases electrons and protons is nicotinamide, which is derived from the vitamin niacin (nicotinic acid).

6.2 Cellular Respiration: An Overview

At this point, let's step back and remind ourselves of the primary goal of cellular respiration: it is to transform the potential energy found in food molecules into a form that can be used for metabolic processes, adenosine triphosphate (ATP). We will see later in the chapter that both proteins and lipids can also be oxidized by cellular respiration and their potential energy harnessed. However, because the oxidation of glucose utilizes the entire respiratory pathway, it is the main focus of our discussion.

6.2a The Three Parts of Cellular Respiration

Cellular respiration can be divided into three parts or stages **(Figure 6.7):**

1. *Glycolysis.* Enzymes break down a molecule of glucose into two molecules of pyruvate. Some ATP and NADH is synthesized.
2. *Citric acid cycle.* Acetyl coenzyme A (acetyl-CoA), which is formed from the oxidation of pyruvate, enters a metabolic cycle, where it is completely oxidized to CO_2. Some ATP and NADH is synthesized.
3. *Electron transport and chemiosmosis.* The NADH synthesized by both glycolysis and the citric acid cycle is oxidized, with the liberated electrons being passed along an electron transport chain until they are transferred to O_2, producing water. The free energy released during electron transport is used to establish a proton gradient across a membrane, and this, in turn, is what synthesizes the remaining ATP.

Although all three stages are required to extract the maximum amount of energy that is biologically possible from a molecule of glucose, not all organisms, and, in fact, not all tissues, possess all three stages.

6.2b The Mitochondrion

In prokaryotes, glycolysis and the citric acid cycle occur in the cytosol of the cell, whereas electron transport occurs on internal membranes that are derived from the plasma membrane. By comparison, in eukaryotic cells, the citric acid cycle and electron transport occur in a specialized organelle called the mitochondrion (plural, mitochondria) **(Figure 6.8).** This membrane-bound organelle is often referred to as the powerhouse of the cell because as the location of both the citric acid cycle and electron transport, it is the largest generator of ATP in the cell.

Handwritten margin notes:
2 ATP
2 NADH

2 ATP
10 NADH
2 FADH

3# ATP

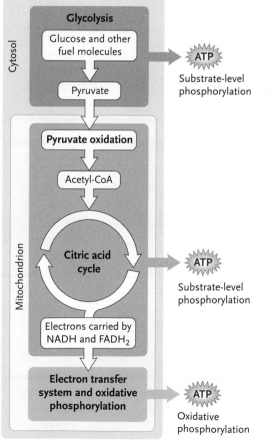

Figure 6.7
The three stages of cellular respiration, glycolysis, pyruvate oxidation, and the citric acid cycle, and the electron transport chain and oxidative phosphorylation.

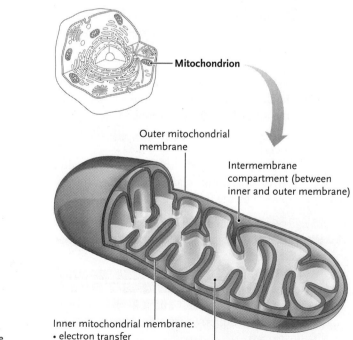

Figure 6.8
Membranes and compartments of mitochondria. Label lines that end in a dot indicate a compartment enclosed by the membranes.

The mitochondrion is composed of two membranes, the outer membrane and the inner membrane, which together define two compartments (see Figure 6.8): the intermembrane space, which is found between the outer and inner membranes, and the matrix, which is the interior aqueous environment of the organelle.

In the description of cellular respiration that follows, we often refer specifically to mitochondria and its various compartments, but it is important to remember that there is nothing uniquely eukaryotic about cellular respiration. Prokaryotes do not have mitochondria, but many do possess the complete complement of reactions that comprise cellular respiration—from glycolysis through electron transport and oxidative phosphorylation.

STUDY BREAK

In eukaryotes, what stages of respiration take place in the mitochondrion?

6.3 Glycolysis

Glycolysis is the first set of reactions that extracts energy from sugar molecules. Glycolysis (*glykys* = sweet; *lysis* = breakdown) consists of 10 sequential enzyme-catalyzed reactions that lead to the oxidation of the six-carbon sugar glucose, producing two molecules of the three-carbon compound pyruvate. The potential energy released in the oxidation leads to the overall synthesis of both NADH and ATP.

6.3a Glycolysis Is an Ancient Pathway

Glycolysis was one of the first metabolic pathways studied and is one of the best understood, in terms of the enzymes involved, their mechanisms of action, and how the pathway is regulated to meet the energy needs of the organism. The first experiments investigating glycolysis took place over 100 years ago and were some of the first to show, using the extracts from yeast cells, that one could study biological reactions in an isolated, cell-free system. These experiments became the foundation of modern biochemistry.

Glycolysis is considered the most fundamental and probably most ancient of all metabolic pathways. This is supported by the following facts:

1. Glycolysis is universal, being found in almost all organisms, both prokaryotes and eukaryotes, from all branches of the tree of life.

2. Unlike other stages of cellular respiration, glycolysis does not require O_2, which became abundant in Earth's atmosphere only about 2.5 billion years ago—about 1.5 billion years after scientists think life developed.

3. Glycolysis occurs in the cytosol of all cells requiring soluble enzymes and therefore does not require

more sophisticated electron transport chains or subcellular compartments in order to operate.

6.3b The Reactions of Glycolysis

Figure 6.9 summarizes the major aspects of the glycolytic pathway, whereas **Figure 6.10** provides the details of each step. Looking at both, there are three key points to keep in mind:

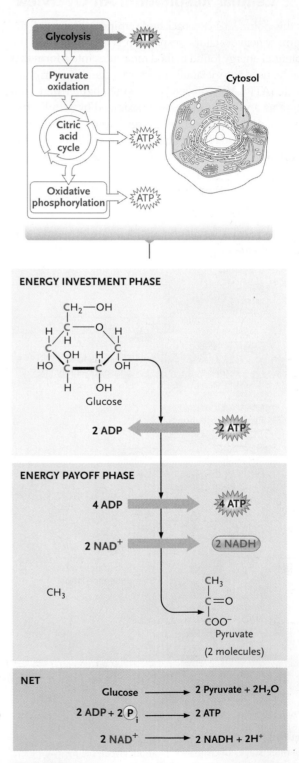

Figure 6.9
Summary of glycolysis showing the energy inputs and outputs.

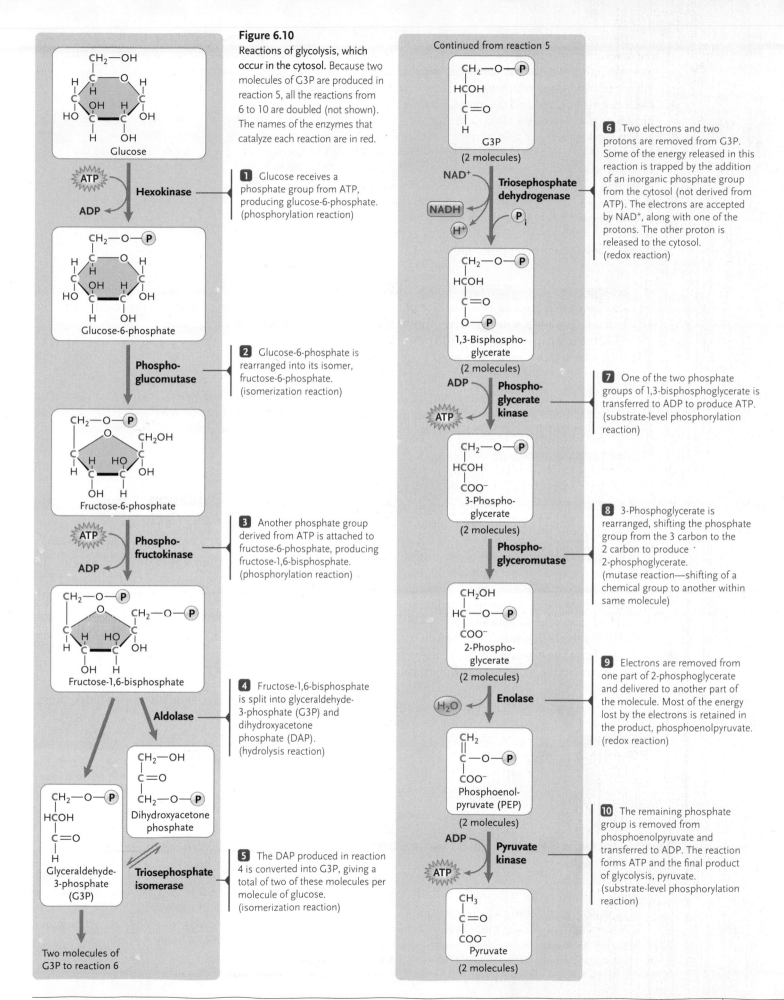

Figure 6.10
Reactions of glycolysis, which occur in the cytosol. Because two molecules of G3P are produced in reaction 5, all the reactions from 6 to 10 are doubled (not shown). The names of the enzymes that catalyze each reaction are in red.

Glucose

Hexokinase

1 Glucose receives a phosphate group from ATP, producing glucose-6-phosphate. (phosphorylation reaction)

Glucose-6-phosphate

Phospho-glucomutase

2 Glucose-6-phosphate is rearranged into its isomer, fructose-6-phosphate. (isomerization reaction)

Fructose-6-phosphate

Phospho-fructokinase

3 Another phosphate group derived from ATP is attached to fructose-6-phosphate, producing fructose-1,6-bisphosphate. (phosphorylation reaction)

Fructose-1,6-bisphosphate

Aldolase

4 Fructose-1,6-bisphosphate is split into glyceraldehyde-3-phosphate (G3P) and dihydroxyacetone phosphate (DAP). (hydrolysis reaction)

Dihydroxyacetone phosphate

Glyceraldehyde-3-phosphate (G3P)

Triosephosphate isomerase

5 The DAP produced in reaction 4 is converted into G3P, giving a total of two of these molecules per molecule of glucose. (isomerization reaction)

Two molecules of G3P to reaction 6

Continued from reaction 5

G3P
(2 molecules)

NAD^+

Triosephosphate dehydrogenase

NADH

H^+ P_i

6 Two electrons and two protons are removed from G3P. Some of the energy released in this reaction is trapped by the addition of an inorganic phosphate group from the cytosol (not derived from ATP). The electrons are accepted by NAD^+, along with one of the protons. The other proton is released to the cytosol. (redox reaction)

1,3-Bisphospho-glycerate
(2 molecules)

ADP

Phospho-glycerate kinase

ATP

7 One of the two phosphate groups of 1,3-bisphosphoglycerate is transferred to ADP to produce ATP. (substrate-level phosphorylation reaction)

3-Phospho-glycerate
(2 molecules)

Phospho-glyceromutase

8 3-Phosphoglycerate is rearranged, shifting the phosphate group from the 3 carbon to the 2 carbon to produce 2-phosphoglycerate. (mutase reaction—shifting of a chemical group to another within same molecule)

2-Phospho-glycerate
(2 molecules)

H_2O **Enolase**

9 Electrons are removed from one part of 2-phosphoglycerate and delivered to another part of the molecule. Most of the energy lost by the electrons is retained in the product, phosphoenolpyruvate. (redox reaction)

Phosphoenol-pyruvate (PEP)
(2 molecules)

ADP

Pyruvate kinase

ATP

10 The remaining phosphate group is removed from phosphoenolpyruvate and transferred to ADP. The reaction forms ATP and the final product of glycolysis, pyruvate. (substrate-level phosphorylation reaction)

Pyruvate
(2 molecules)

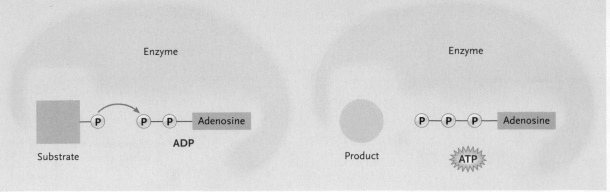

1. *Energy investment followed by payoff.* Glycolysis can be considered as two distinct phases: an initial five-step energy investment phase followed by a five-step energy payoff phase. Initially in glycolysis, two molecules of ATP are actually consumed as glucose and fructose-6-phosphate become phosphorylated. The investment of two ATP for each glucose molecule leads to an energy reward as four ATP and two NADH molecules are produced during the energy payoff phase.

2. *No carbon is lost.* Besides yielding a net of two ATP and two NADH, for each molecule of glucose oxidized, you should note that no carbon has been lost. All six carbons present in glucose are accounted for in the two molecules of pyruvate. However, since glucose has been oxidized, the potential energy in two molecules of pyruvate is less than that of one molecule of glucose.

3. *ATP is generated by substrate-level phosphorylation.* During glycolysis, ATP is produced using a process called *substrate-level phosphorylation.* This mode of ATP synthesis **(Figure 6.11)** requires an enzyme that transfers a phosphate group from a high-energy substrate molecule to adenosine diphosphate (ADP),

producing ATP. Substrate-level phosphorylation is also the mode of ATP synthesis used during the citric acid cycle.

STUDY BREAK

1. What evidence suggests that glycolysis is an ancient metabolic pathway?
2. What are the products of glycolysis?

6.4 Pyruvate Oxidation and the Citric Acid Cycle

The two molecules of pyruvate synthesized by glycolysis still contain approximately 75% of the energy found in one molecule of glucose. The extraction of the remaining free energy in pyruvate and trapping this energy in the form of ATP and electron carriers such as NADH are the overarching goals of the series of reactions described in this section.

6.4a Bridging Glycolysis and the Citric Acid Cycle

Because the reactions of the citric acid cycle are localized to the **mitochondrial matrix**, the product of glycolysis, pyruvate, must pass through both the outer and inner mitochondrial membranes **(Figure 6.12)**. Large pores in the outer membrane allow pyruvate to simply diffuse through, but to cross the inner membrane requires a pyruvate-specific membrane carrier.

Once it gets into the matrix, pyruvate is converted into a molecule called acetyl-CoA through a multistep process that is referred to as **pyruvate oxidation** (also known as **pyruvic acid oxidation**) (see Figure 6.12). The conversion of pyruvate to acetyl-CoA starts with *a decarboxylation reaction* whereby the carboxyl ($-COO^-$) group of pyruvate is lost as CO_2. This reaction is understandable given that the **carboxyl group** itself

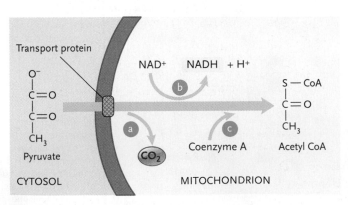

Figure 6.12
Reactions of pyruvate oxidation. After transport into the mitochondrion pyruvate is oxidized to an acetyl group, which is carried to the citric acid cycle by CoA. The reactions which are catalyzed by the *pyruvate dehydrogenase complex* include **(a)** decarboxylation, followed by **(b)** a dehydrogenation and finally **(c)** reaction with coenzyme A producing acetyl CoA.

contains little potential energy (no C–H bonds and a lot of oxygen). The decarboxylation reaction is followed by oxidation of the remaining two carbon molecules, producing acetate. This *dehydrogenation* reaction leads to transfer of two electrons and a proton to NAD^+, forming NADH. Lastly, the acetyl group reacts with coenzyme A, forming the high-energy intermediate acetyl-CoA.

If you look at the molecule of acetyl-CoA formed in Figure 6.12, you should notice that it still contains three C–H bonds and can be further oxidized to release even more free energy. Extracting this energy is the purpose of the reactions that make up the citric acid cycle.

6.4b The Citric Acid Cycle

The citric acid cycle consists of eight enzyme-catalyzed reactions: seven are soluble enzymes located in the mitochondrial matrix, and one enzyme is bound to the matrix side of the inner mitochondrial membrane. Combined, the reactions result in the oxidization of acetyl groups to CO_2 accompanied by the synthesis of ATP, NADH, and another nucleotide-based molecule, flavin adenine dinucleotide (FAD; the reduced form is $FADH_2$). A summary of the inputs and outputs of the citric acid cycle is shown in **Figure 6.13,** which, to put the cycle in context, also includes the pyruvate to acetyl-CoA step. Looking at the stoichiometry, for each acetyl-CoA that enters the citric acid cycle, three NADH, one $FADH_2$, and a single molecule of ATP, generated by substrate-level phosphorylation, are synthesized. In a complete turn of the cycle, one two-carbon acetyl unit is consumed and two molecules of CO_2 are released, thereby completing the conversion of all the C atoms originally in glucose to CO_2. The CoA molecule that carried the acetyl group to the cycle is released and participates again in pyruvate oxidation to pick up another acetyl group. The net reactants and products of one turn of the citric acid cycle are

1 acetyl-CoA + 3 NAD^+ + 1 FAD +
$$1 ADP + 1 P_i + 2 H_2O \rightarrow$$
2 CO_2 + 3 NADH + 1 $FADH_2$ + 1 ATP +
$$3 H^+ + 1 CoA$$

Because one molecule of glucose is converted to two molecules of pyruvate by glycolysis and each molecule of pyruvate is converted to one acetyl group, all the reactants and products in this equation are doubled when the citric acid cycle is considered as a continuation of glycolysis and pyruvate oxidation. **Figure 6.14 (p. 124)** shows the individual steps of the citric acid cycle.

STUDY BREAK

1. What are the steps involved in converting pyruvate into acetyl-CoA?
2. What purpose is served by the citric acid cycle?

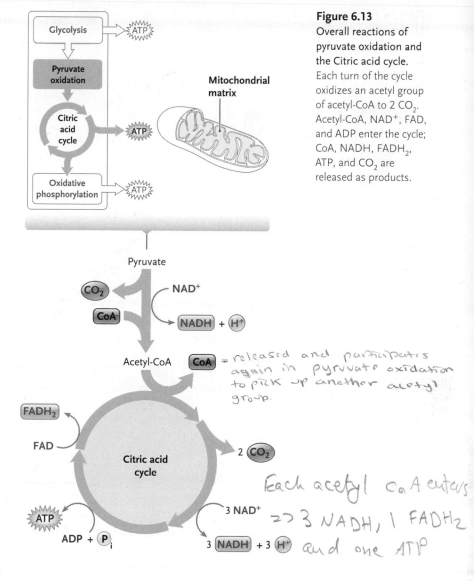

Figure 6.13
Overall reactions of pyruvate oxidation and the Citric acid cycle. Each turn of the cycle oxidizes an acetyl group of acetyl-CoA to 2 CO_2. Acetyl-CoA, NAD^+, FAD, and ADP enter the cycle; CoA, NADH, $FADH_2$, ATP, and CO_2 are released as products.

[handwritten note: = released and participates again in pyruvate oxidation to pick up another acetyl group.]

[handwritten note: Each acetyl CoA enters ⇒ 3 NADH, 1 $FADH_2$ and one ATP]

6.5 Electron Transport and Chemiosmosis

Following the citric acid cycle, all the carbon present in glucose has been completely oxidized and released as CO_2. As well, besides the formation of ATP by substrate-level phosphorylation, the potential energy originally present in glucose now exists in the form of NADH and $FADH_2$. It is the purpose of the electron transport chain coupled with the process of chemiosmosis to extract the potential energy in these molecules and synthesize additional ATP.

6.5a The Respiratory Electron Transport Chain

The respiratory electron transport chain **(Figure 6.15, p. 125)** comprises a system of components that in eukaryotes is found on the inner mitochondrial membrane. The chain facilitates the transfer of electrons from $NADH_2$ and $FADH_2$ to O_2. The chain consists of four protein complexes: complex I, NADH dehydrogenase; complex II, succinate dehydrogenase; complex III,

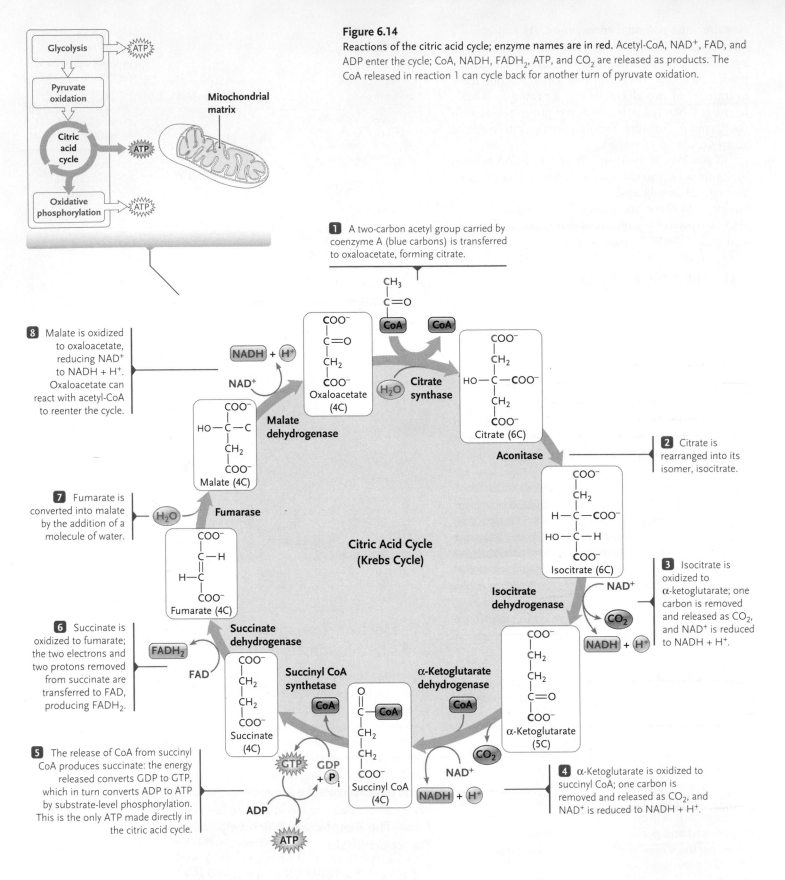

Figure 6.14

Reactions of the citric acid cycle; enzyme names are in red. Acetyl-CoA, NAD^+, FAD, and ADP enter the cycle; CoA, NADH, $FADH_2$, ATP, and CO_2 are released as products. The CoA released in reaction 1 can cycle back for another turn of pyruvate oxidation.

Mitochondrial matrix

1 A two-carbon acetyl group carried by coenzyme A (blue carbons) is transferred to oxaloacetate, forming citrate.

8 Malate is oxidized to oxaloacetate, reducing NAD^+ to $NADH + H^+$. Oxaloacetate can react with acetyl-CoA to reenter the cycle.

7 Fumarate is converted into malate by the addition of a molecule of water.

6 Succinate is oxidized to fumarate; the two electrons and two protons removed from succinate are transferred to FAD, producing $FADH_2$.

5 The release of CoA from succinyl CoA produces succinate: the energy released converts GDP to GTP, which in turn converts ADP to ATP by substrate-level phosphorylation. This is the only ATP made directly in the citric acid cycle.

Citric Acid Cycle (Krebs Cycle)

Citrate synthase
Aconitase
Isocitrate dehydrogenase
α-Ketoglutarate dehydrogenase
Succinyl CoA synthetase
Succinate dehydrogenase
Fumarase
Malate dehydrogenase

Oxaloacetate (4C)
Citrate (6C)
Isocitrate (6C)
α-Ketoglutarate (5C)
Succinyl CoA (4C)
Succinate (4C)
Fumarate (4C)
Malate (4C)

2 Citrate is rearranged into its isomer, isocitrate.

3 Isocitrate is oxidized to α-ketoglutarate; one carbon is removed and released as CO_2, and NAD^+ is reduced to $NADH + H^+$.

4 α-Ketoglutarate is oxidized to succinyl CoA; one carbon is removed and released as CO_2, and NAD^+ is reduced to $NADH + H^+$.

cytochrome complex; and complex IV, cytochrome oxidase. Whereas complex II is a single peripheral membrane protein, the remaining complexes are composed of multiple proteins. For example, about 40 protein subunits are needed to assemble together to make complex I.

Electron flow from one complex to another is facilitated by two mobile electron shuttles. Ubiquinone, which is a hydrophobic molecule found in the core of the membrane, shuttles electrons from complexes I and II to complex III. A second shuttle, cytochrome *c*, is located on the intermembrane space side of the

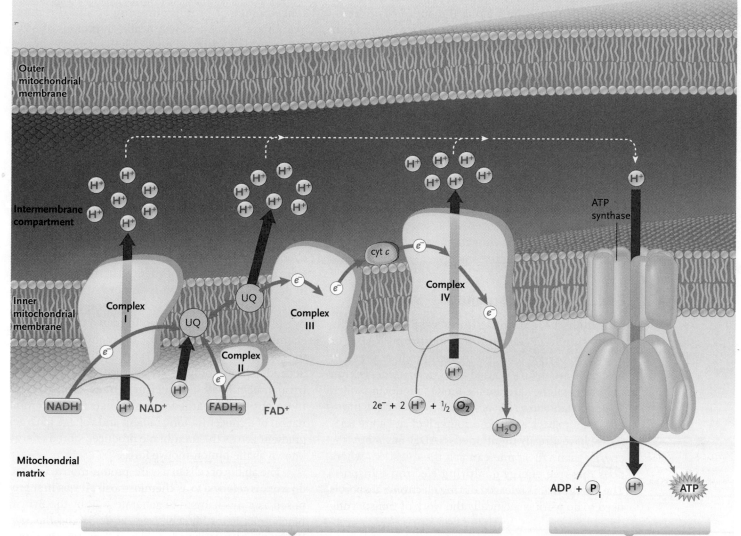

Figure 6.15

Mitochondrial electron transfer system and oxidative phosphorylation. The electron transfer system includes three major complexes, I, III, and IV. Two smaller electron carriers, ubiquinone (UQ) and cytochrome *c* (cyt *c*), act as shuttles between the major complexes, and succinate dehydrogenase (complex II) passes electrons to ubiquinone, bypassing complex I. Blue arrows indicate electron flow; red arrows indicate H^+ movement. H^+ is pumped from the matrix to the intermembrane compartment as electrons pass through complexes I and IV. H^+ are also moved into the matrix by the cyclic reduction/oxidation of ubiquinone. Oxidative phosphorylation involves the ATP synthase–catalyzed synthesis of ATP using the energy of the H^+ gradient across the inner mitochondrial membrane that is, by chemiosmosis.

membrane and transfers electrons from complex III to complex IV, cytochrome oxidase.

6.5b What Is the Driving Force behind Electron Transport?

Each of complexes I, III, and IV has bound to it specific *prosthetic groups* (see **Figure 6.16, p. 126**). These are redox active cofactors that alternate between reduced and oxidized states as they accept electrons from upstream molecules and subsequently donate electrons to downstream molecules. Thus, it is not the proteins themselves

that transfer electrons but rather nonprotein groups bound to the proteins of each complex. A common prosthetic group is the molecule heme, which is a component of the cytochromes. Heme is a widely used molecule and is vital to the oxygen-carrying capacity of hemoglobin. The heme group contains a central redox-active iron atom that alternates from Fe^{2+} and Fe^{3+}.

During electron transport, the prosthetic group of complex I, flavin mononucleotide (FMN), is reduced by electron donation from NADH on the matrix side of the inner membrane. FMN then donates an electron to another complex I prosthetic group, the

Fe/S (iron–sulphur) group, which, in turn, donates electrons to ubiquinone. This process of reduction followed by oxidation continues along the entire chain until, finally, the electrons are donated to oxygen, resulting in its reduction to water with the addition of protons, which are abundant in the aqueous environment of the cell.

Why do electrons move down the chain at all? Figure 6.16 shows that the individual electron carriers of the chain are, in fact, organized in a very specific way—from high to low free energy. Any single component is more electronegative (higher affinity for electrons) than the preceding carrier in the chain. Overall, molecules such as NADH contain an abundance of free energy and can be readily oxidized, whereas O_2, the terminal electron acceptor of the chain, is strongly electronegative and can be easily reduced. As a consequence of this organization, electron movement along the chain is spontaneous, releasing free energy.

6.5c Chemiosmosis and ATP Synthesis

Although the goal of cellular respiration is the synthesis of ATP, electron transport from NADH or $FADH_2$ to oxygen does not in itself produce any ATP. Electrons are simply passed along a chain of electron carriers until they are donated to O_2, producing water. To understand how ATP is formed from electron transport, let's go back and take another look at Figure 6.15. As we have already mentioned, NADH has more free energy than O_2, so one can ask the question, where does this free energy go during electron transport? The energy that is released during electron transport is used to do work, specifically the work of transporting

protons across the inner mitochondrial membrane from the matrix to the intermembrane space. As a consequence of proton pumping across the inner membrane, which is impermeable to protons, the H^+ concentration becomes much higher (the pH lower) in the intermembrane space compared to the matrix.

Proton translocation occurs at distinct sites along the electron transport chain (see Figure 6.15). Within complexes I and IV, specific protein components use the energy released from electron transport for proton pumping. In addition, as ubiquinone molecules accept electrons from complexes I and II, they pick up protons from the matrix. After migrating through the membrane and donating electrons to complex III, ubiquinone retains a neutral charge by releasing protons into the intermembrane space.

The situation in which one side of the inner mitochondrial membrane has more protons than the other side represents a source of energy that can be harnessed to do work. The situation is somewhat analogous to water behind a dam. The potential energy possessed by a proton gradient is derived from two factors: first, a chemical gradient exists across the membrane because the concentration of protons is not equal on both sides. Second, because protons are charged, there is an electrical gradient with the intermembrane compartment more positively charged than the matrix. The combination of a concentration gradient and voltage (charge) gradient across the membrane produces stored energy known as the **proton-motive force.**

The ability of cells to use the proton-motive force to do work is referred to as **chemiosmosis.** It was first proposed as a mechanism to generate ATP by the British biochemist Peter Mitchell (see *People Behind Biology*). Whereas in mitochondria, the energy for chemiosmosis comes from the oxidation of energy-rich molecules such as NADPH by the electron transport chain, chemiosmosis also applies to the generation of ATP in chloroplasts, where electron transport is driven by light energy. Chemiosmosis, however, does not only apply to the synthesis of ATP as the proton-motive force is also used to pump substances across membranes. It is also used to drive the rotation of flagella in prokaryotes.

The mode of ATP synthesis that is linked to the oxidation of energy-rich molecules by an electron transport chain is called **oxidative phosphorylation.** Compared with substrate-level phosphorylation that occurs during glycolysis and the citric acid cycle, oxidative phosphorylation relies on the action of a large multiprotein complex that spans the inner mitochondrial membrane called **ATP synthase (Figure 6.17).**

6.5d ATP Synthase Is a Molecular Motor

ATP synthase is a lollipop-shaped structure consisting of a *basal unit,* which is embedded in the inner mitochondrial membrane, connected to a *headpiece* by a *stalk* (see Figure 6.17). The headpiece extends into the

Figure 6.16
Redox components of the electron transport chain are organized from high to low free energy. Electron flow is spontaneous from high to low potential energy as electrons are passed from one redox molecule to the next.

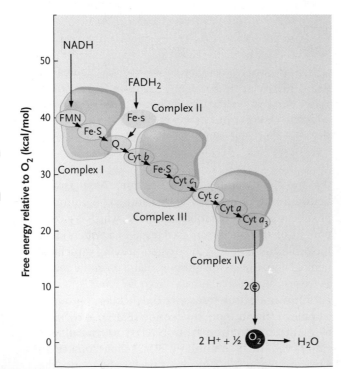

Peter Mitchell, Glynn Research Institute

Peter Mitchell was a British biochemist who in 1978 was awarded the Nobel Prize in Chemistry for what the Royal Swedish Academy of Sciences committee stated was "his contribution to the understanding of biological energy transfer through the formulation of the chemiosmotic theory."

Mitchell completed an undergraduate degree and a Ph.D. at Cambridge University, graduating with the latter in 1951. In 1955, he was invited to set up and direct a biochemical research unit in the Department of Zoology, Edinburgh University, where he was a faculty member until 1964. From 1964 onward, he was director of the Glynn Research Institute. Glynn is a mansion that Mitchell renovated and turned into a personal research institute, located near Bodmin in Cornwall, England.

By the 1950s, it was known that both the chloroplast and the mitochondrion contained electron transport chains and made ATP, but a solid theory on how the two were linked was elusive. The dominant theories were based on substrate-level phosphorylation, which was already well understood. It was thought that electron transport chains passed energy to a high-energy chemical intermediate, which, in turn, passed it on to ATP through an ATP synthase that was known to exist in both the chloroplast and the mitochondrion. But, of course, the problem was that no one could find this chemical intermediate. Moreover, the substrate-level phosphorylation idea could not explain troubling findings: Why did so many different reagents act as uncouplers? Why were the enzymes of oxidative phosphorylation associated with the mitochondrial membrane? Why did coupling seem so dependent on the maintenance of membrane structure?

Mitchell proposed the chemiosmotic theory in 1961 in an elegant paper published in *Nature*. It is hard to imagine now how revolutionary the paper was at the time. It contained very little experimental evidence and was opposed by almost the entire biochemical community, which was stuck believing in the high-energy intermediate concept. The paper was based on Mitchell's realization that the movement of ions across an electrochemical membrane potential could provide the energy needed to produce ATP. The basis of chemiosmosis is that the components of the electron transport chain are inserted into a membrane in only one way, which allows for protons to be transported in one direction during electron transport. The protons would flow back through the ATP synthase, causing synthesis of ATP. In Mitchell's model, the proton gradient across the membrane served as the high-energy intermediate and the elusive chemical intermediate could not be found because, of course, it did not exist.

---

mitochondrial matrix. The basal unit forms a channel through which H$^+$ can pass freely. The proton-motive force moves protons in the intermembrane space through the channel in the enzyme's basal unit, down their concentration gradient, and into the matrix. The flow of protons powers ATP synthesis by the headpiece. Evidence indicates that the binding of individual protons to sites in the headpiece causes it to rotate in a way that catalyzes the formation of ATP from ADP and P$_i$. The spinning of the headpiece of ATP synthase represents the smallest molecular rotary motor known in nature.

In Chapter 5, we described active transport pumps that use the energy created by hydrolysis of ATP to ADP and P$_i$ to transport ions across membranes against their concentration gradients (see Figure 5.6). An active transport pump is, in fact, an ATP synthase that is simply operating in reverse. It doesn't synthesize ATP but rather uses the free energy from the hydrolysis of ATP to provide the energy necessary to pump ions (such as protons) across a membrane.

Harnessing the potential energy that is present in a proton gradient to synthesize ATP is fundamental to almost all forms of life and developed early in the evolution of life. This is shown, in part, by the fact that the structure and function of the ATP synthase complex found in mitochondria are essentially identical to those of the ATP synthase complexes found

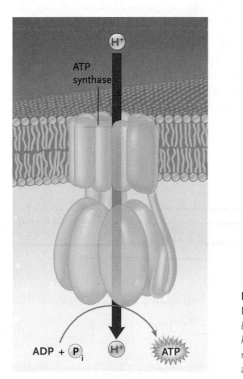

Figure 6.17
Detailed structure of ATP synthase—a molecular motor. The enzyme consists of a *basal unit*, which is embedded in the inner mitochondrial membrane, connected to a *headpiece* by a *stalk*, and with the *stator* bridging the basal unit and headpiece. Protons move through a channel between the basal unit and the stator which makes the stalk and headpiece spin. This results in ATP synthesis.

in the thylakoid membrane of the chloroplast and the plasma membrane of prokaryotic cells.

6.5e Uncoupling Electron Transport and Chemiosmosis

The synthesis of ATP by ATP synthase is linked, or *coupled*, to electron transport by the proton gradient that is established across the inner mitochondrial membrane. A fundamental concept that is important to grasp is that electron transport and the activity of ATP synthase are distinct processes and are not always coupled **(Figure 6.18)**. For example, it is possible to have high rates of electron transport without the synthesis of ATP. This *uncoupling* of the two processes can occur by mechanisms that prevent the formation of the proton-motive force by making the inner mitochondrial membrane permeable to protons. A number of chemical compounds called ionophores act as uncouplers because they form channels across membranes through which ions, including protons, can leak. Because these compounds allow for high rates of electron transport but inhibit ATP synthesis, they are all highly toxic. As well, a group of proteins called uncoupling proteins are transmembrane proteins that form channels through which protons can freely flow.

STUDY BREAK

1. Why do electrons flow down an electron transport chain?
2. What is the distinction among the terms *proton-motive force, chemiosmosis,* and *oxidative phosphorylation?*
3. What does it mean that electron transport and oxidative phosphorylation are "coupled processes"?

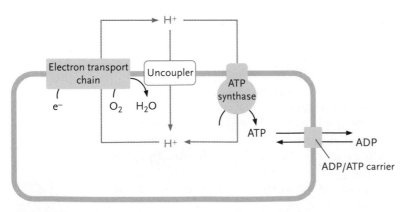

Figure 6.18

Uncoupling of electron transport and ATP synthesis. The respiratory electron transport chain results in the establishment of a proton gradient across the membrane. Usually, this gradient is dissipated by the ATP synthase in the formation of ATP. Uncouplers, which may be specific chemicals or proteins, provide an alternative route for protons to flow back across the membrane. By circumventing the ATP synthase, no ATP is generated.

6.6 The Efficiency and Regulation of Cellular Respiration

In this section, we calculate the efficiency with which cellular respiration extracts the energy from a molecule of glucose. As well, we discuss how this entire multienzyme pathway is regulated such that it remains flexible in the face of changing cellular demands for ATP and changes in food supply.

6.6a How Efficient Is Cellular Respiration?

Determining the total number of ATP molecules synthesized for each molecule of glucose oxidized is an important exercise that forces one to integrate all parts of the respiratory pathway. Before we look at the whole pathway, we oxidative phosphorylation. *How many ATP molecules are produced by oxidative phosphorylation as electrons flow through the mitochondrial electron transport chain?* This is not a straightforward question to answer because electron transport and oxidative phosphorylation, as we have seen, are distinct processes that are not always completely coupled to each other. But research suggests that for each NADH that is oxidized, and thus for each pair of electrons that travels down the electron transport chain, 10 H^+ are pumped into the inner membrane space. (Don't try to figure out how you get 10 protons from 2 electrons—it is not straightforward. Wait to take an advanced biochemistry course.) We also know that somewhere between 3 and 4 H^+ are needed to flow back through the ATP synthase for the synthesis of one molecule of ATP. So that gives about 3 ATP made for every NADH oxidized by the electron transport chain. Because the oxidation of $FADH_2$ bypasses the proton-pumping complex I (look back at Figure 6.15), it does not lead to as many protons being pumped across the membrane. Thus, for each $FADH_2$ oxidized, only about two molecules of ATP are synthesized.

Now we can act as accountants and work out the ATP yield for the entire cellular respiratory pathway given the complete oxidation of glucose to CO_2 and H_2O and assuming that the entire H^+ gradient produced by electron transfer is used for ATP synthesis **(Figure 6.19)**.

During glycolysis, substrate-level phosphorylation produces 2 ATP directly and produces 2 molecules of NADH that are transported into the mitochondrion. During the oxidation of pyruvate, 2 NADH are produced. During the citric acid cycle, the 2 molecules of acetyl-CoA that are oxidized result in the synthesis of 2 ATP, along with 6 NADH and 2 $FADH_2$. That gives a total of 10 NADH and 2 $FADH_2$ that need to be oxidized by the electron transport chain. Given that 3 ATP are produced by the oxidation of each NADH, that gives (10 × 3) = 30 ATP synthesized by electron transport and (2 × 2) = 4 ATP from the

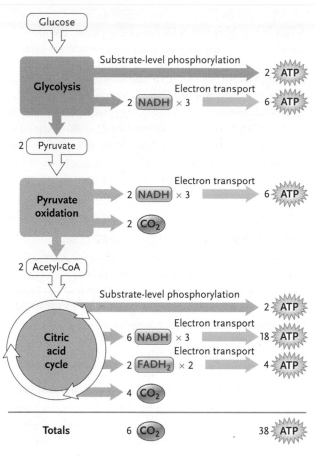

Figure 6.19
Total ATP yield by cellular respiration from the oxidation of one molecule of glucose.

So how efficient is cellular respiration at extracting the energy from glucose and converting it into ATP? The hydrolysis of ATP to ADP yields about 7.0 kilocalories per mole (kcal/mol). Assuming that complete glucose oxidation produces 32 ATP, the total energy conserved in ATP production would be about 224 kcal/mol. By contrast, glucose contains exactly 686 kcal/mol of energy. On this basis, the efficiency of cellular glucose oxidation would be $(224/686 \times 100) =$ about 32%. In other words, 32% of the energy in glucose is converted into ATP. This may not seem amazingly high, but this value is considerably better than that of most devices designed by human engineers—for example, an automobile extracts only about 25% of the energy in the fuel it burns. Recall from Chapter 4 that because of entropy, energy transformations are never 100% efficient.

6.6b The Regulation of Cellular Respiration

Cellular respiration includes a large number of enzymes and transport systems, as well as, in eukaryotes, numerous cellular compartments. The overall rate of cellular respiration, which is often measured as the rate of oxygen consumption, is tightly controlled so that ATP synthesis matches the requirements of the cell for chemical energy. This is often referred to in general terms as the concept of "supply and demand"—the cell does not waste valuable resources, making more of a substance than it needs. Most metabolic pathways are regulated by supply and demand through the process of feedback inhibition: the end products of the pathway inhibit an enzyme early in the pathway (see Section 4.5).

Not surprisingly, the rate of cellular respiration is controlled by key metabolic intermediates. The rate of sugar oxidation by glycolysis is closely regulated by

oxidation of the 2 $FADH_2$ molecules. So adding up, 2 ATP from glycolysis, 2 ATP directly from the citric acid cycle, and 34 ATP from electron transport gives a total ATP yield of 38 molecules made from each glucose oxidized.

The physiological importance of uncoupling

During oxidative phosphorylation, the potential energy released by the oxidation of NADH is used to do the work of pumping protons into the intermembrane space and building up the proton-motive force. When electron transport and ATP synthesis are uncoupled, the energy released during electron transport is not conserved but is simply lost as heat. This source of heat is important in mammals and birds in regulating body temperature. One way this is achieved is through regulating the expression of a number of uncoupling proteins. In addition, certain tissues, including brown adipose fat, contain mitochondria in which the expression of uncoupling proteins is particularly high. The heat generated by these tissues is important for the maintenance of body temperature in both hibernating mammals and in very young offspring, including human infants.

several mechanisms to match the cell's need for ATP **(Figure 6.20).** For example, if excess ATP is present in the cytosol, it binds to *phosphofructokinase,* the enzyme that catalyzes reaction 3 in Figure 6.20, inhibiting its action. The resulting decrease in the concentration of fructose-1,6-bisphosphate slows or stops the subsequent reactions of glycolysis and, as a consequence, the remainder of cellular respiration. Thus, glycolysis does not oxidize fuel substances needlessly when ATP is in adequate supply.

If energy-requiring activities then take place in the cell, ATP concentration would decrease and ADP concentration would rise in the cytosol. As a result, ATP is released from phosphofructokinase, relieving inhibition of the enzyme. In addition, ADP activates the enzyme stimulating cellular respiration. Therefore, the rates of glycolysis and ATP production increase proportionately as cellular activities convert ATP to ADP.

Like glycolysis, the citric acid cycle is regulated at several steps to match its rate to the cell's requirements

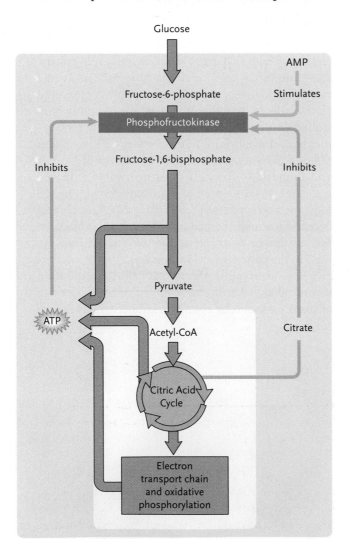

Figure 6.20

The control of cellular respiration. A major mechanism is allosteric control of the activity of the enzyme Phosphofructokinase which is found early in glycolysis. High levels of ATP and the citric acid cycle intermediate citrate allosterically inhibit phosphofructokinase. Alternatively, when ATP concentrations are low the levels of ADP and AMP increase. AMP is an allosteric activator of the enzyme.

for ATP. For example, some enzymes of the cycle are inhibited by elevated ATP concentrations. The inhibitions automatically slow or stop the cycle when ATP production exceeds the demands of the cell and, by doing so, conserve cellular fuels. Phosphofructokinase is also inhibited by NADH and citrate, which is an intermediate of the citric acid cycle. The accumulation of either NADH or citrate is an indication that downstream reactions are moving slowly. This may occur, for example, under conditions of limited oxygen when the rate of oxidative phosphorylation is restricted.

6.6c Catabolism of Carbohydrates, Fats, and Proteins

In addition to glucose and other six-carbon sugars, reactions leading from glycolysis through pyruvate oxidation also oxidize a range of other carbohydrates, as well as lipids and proteins, which enter the cellular respiratory pathway at various points **(Figure 6.21).**

Carbohydrates such as sucrose and other disaccharides are easily broken into monosaccharides such as glucose and fructose, which enter glycolysis at early steps. Starch is hydrolyzed by digestive enzymes into individual glucose molecules, whereas glycogen, a more complex carbohydrate, is broken down and converted by enzymes into glucose-6-phosphate, an early substrate molecule in glycolysis.

Among the fats, the **triglycerides** are major sources of electrons for ATP synthesis. Before entering the oxidative reactions, they are hydrolyzed into glycerol and individual fatty acids. The glycerol is converted to glyceraldehyde-3-phosphate before entering glycolysis. The fatty acids—and many other types of lipids—are split into two-carbon fragments, which enter the citric acid cycle as acetyl-CoA.

Proteins are hydrolyzed to amino acids before oxidation. The amino group ($-NH_2$) is removed, and the remainder of the molecule enters the respiratory pathway as either pyruvate, acetyl units carried by coenzyme A, or intermediates of the citric acid cycle (see Figure 6.21). For example, the amino acid alanine is converted into pyruvate; leucine, into acetyl units; and phenylalanine, into fumarate, which enters the citric acid cycle.

6.6d Respiratory Intermediates Are Utilized for Anabolic Reactions

The organic molecules of food are oxidized by cellular respiration to provide ATP for growth and metabolism. In addition, they also supply cells with the carbon skeletons required to synthesize a range of essential molecules that food does not directly provide. The intermediates of glycolysis and the citric acid cycle are routinely diverted and used as the starting substrate for the anabolic pathways required for the synthesis of certain amino acids as well as the pyrimidine and purine bases needed for nucleic acid synthesis. As well, respiratory intermediates supply the carbon backbones for the array of hormones, growth factors, prosthetic groups, and cofactors that are essential to cell function. The huge degree of metabolic flexibility is illustrated by the fact that many reactions illustrated in Figure 6.21 are reversible. For example, whereas fatty acids can be used as a source of energy by being oxidized to acetyl-CoA, excess acetyl-CoA can be removed from the respiration and used to synthesize fatty acids needed for a range of cellular processes.

STUDY BREAK

1. What is the maximum yield of ATP from the breakdown of a molecule of ATP? Give an accounting of how each molecule is generated.
2. Explain the various ways cellular respiration can regulate the activity of the enzyme phosphofructokinase.
3. How is cellular respiration used to extract energy from proteins and fats?

6.7 Oxygen and Cellular Respiration

A constant supply of oxygen is required to maintain the high rates of oxidative phosphorylation necessary to supply cells with sufficient ATP. Although humans have an almost constant requirement of oxygen, other organisms and certain tissues can survive in the absence of oxygen. There are two general mechanisms by which certain cells can oxidize fuel molecules and generate ATP in the absence of oxygen: fermentation and anaerobic respiration. The distinction between these two processes is that fermentation does not utilize an electron transport chain, whereas anaerobic respiration uses an electron transport chain that employs a molecule other than oxygen as the terminal electron acceptor.

6.7a Fermentation

Following glycolysis, cellular respiration can continue along one of two distinct pathways depending on whether or not oxygen is present **(Figure 6.22, p. 132)**. When oxygen is plentiful, the pyruvate and two NADH produced by glycolysis are transported into the mitochondrion, where they are oxidized using the citric acid cycle and electron transport chain. If, instead, oxygen is absent or in short supply, the pyruvate remains in the cytosol, where it is reduced, consuming the NADH generated by glycolysis by a series of reactions that are called **fermentation**.

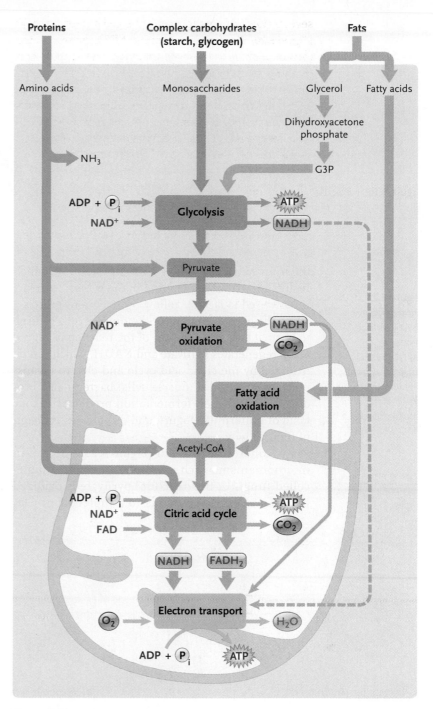

Figure 6.21

Major pathways that oxidize carbohydrates, fats, and proteins. Reactions that occur in the cytosol are shown against a tan background; reactions that occur in mitochondria are shown inside the organelle. CoA funnels the products of many oxidative pathways into the citric acid cycle.

Two types of fermentation reactions exist: lactate fermentation and alcohol fermentation. In **lactate fermentation**, pyruvate is converted into lactate **(Figure 6.23a, p. 132)**. This reaction commonly occurs in the cytosol of muscle cells in animals whenever strenuous activity results in a demand for ATP that exceeds the rate at which O_2 can be supplied to the electron transport chain for oxidative phosphorylation. For example, significant quantities of lactate accumulate in the leg muscles of a sprinter during a 100-metre race. The high rates of O_2 consumption in

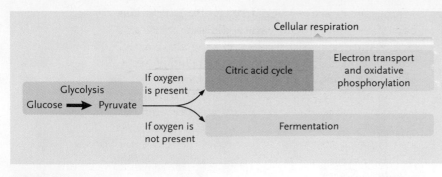

Figure 6.22
The metabolic path of pyruvate oxidation is dependent upon the presence of oxygen.

Figure 6.23
Fermentation reactions that produce
(a) lactate and
(b) ethyl alcohol.
The fermentations, which occur in the cytosol, convert NADH to NAD$^+$, allowing the electron carrier to cycle back to glycolysis. This process keeps glycolysis running, with continued production of ATP.

the mitochondria keep the concentration low, which results in pyruvate remaining in the cytosol, where it is converted to lactate. Following strenuous exercise, when the oxygen content of the muscle cells returns to normal levels, the reverse of the reaction in Figure 6.23a regenerates pyruvate and NADH, which can be oxidized by the citric acid cycle and electron transport chain. Besides muscle cells, bacteria also produce lactate as their fermentation product; the sour taste of buttermilk, yogurt, and dill pickles is a sign of their activity.

Alcohol fermentation (Figure 6.23b) occurs in microorganisms such as yeasts, which are single-celled fungi. In this reaction, pyruvate is oxidized in two successive reactions to a molecule of CO_2

and a molecule of ethyl alcohol as NADH is converted to NAD$^+$. Alcoholic fermentation by yeasts has widespread commercial applications. Bakers use the yeast *Saccharomyces cerevisiae* to make bread dough rise. They mix the yeast with a small amount of sugar and blend the mixture into the dough, where oxygen levels are low. As the yeast cells convert the sugar into ethyl alcohol and CO_2, the gaseous CO_2 expands and creates bubbles that cause the dough to rise. Oven heat evaporates the alcohol and causes further expansion of the bubbles, producing a light-textured product. Alcoholic fermentation is also the mainstay of beer and wine brewing. Fruits are a natural home to wild yeasts **(Figure 6.24)**; for example, winemakers rely on a mixture of wild and cultivated yeasts to produce wine. Alcoholic fermentation also occurs naturally in the environment; for example, overripe or rotting fruit frequently will start to ferment, and birds that eat the fruit may become too drunk to fly.

Overall, the reactions of fermentation play a critical role whenever organisms are exposed to conditions in which the oxygen concentration is too low to support oxidative phosphorylation. By consuming the NADH generated by glycolysis, fermentation reactions keep cytosolic NAD$^+$ levels high, which allows for glycolysis to continue to operate and thereby produce ATP by substrate phosphorylation.

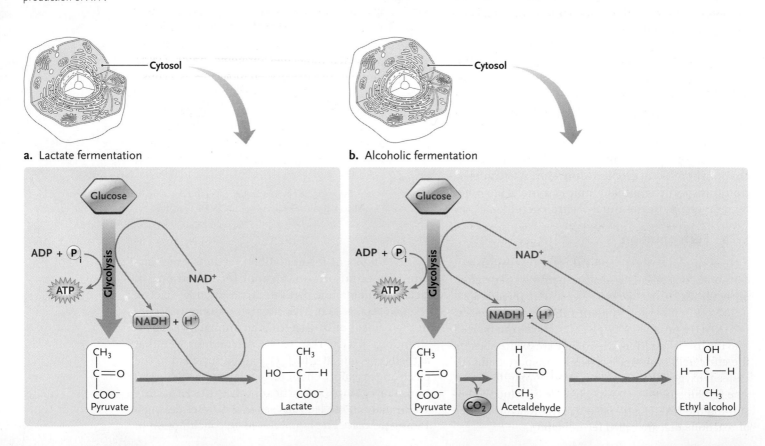

a. Lactate fermentation

b. Alcoholic fermentation

Figure 6.24
Alcoholic fermentation in nature: wild yeast cells, visible as a dustlike coating on grapes.

David M. Phillips/Visuals Unlimited

6.7b Anaerobic Respiration

Although they lack mitochondria, many prokaryotes have respiratory electron transport chains, which are located on internal membrane systems derived from the plasma membrane. Some of these electron transport systems are very similar to those found in the mitochondria of eukaryotes and use O_2 and the terminal electron acceptor. Other prokaryotes, however, have respiratory chains that use a molecule other than O_2 as the terminal electron acceptor and are said to possess anaerobic (An = without; $aero$ = air) respiration. For example, sulphate (SO_4^{2-}), nitrate (NO_3^-), and the ferric ion (Fe^{3+}) are common electron acceptors used by many groups of prokaryotes that do not use O_2 as the terminal electron acceptor.

Generally, there is a huge diversity of molecules with relatively low potential energy used as electron acceptors; likewise, there are a range of molecules besides glucose that contain high amounts of chemical potential energy that can be used as substrates for cellular respiration. Even though the starting and ending points of cellular respiration may be different, cells are still able to use electron transport chains to create a proton-motive force that drives the synthesis of ATP.

6.7c Lifestyles Dictated by Oxygen

We can differentiate three different lifestyles depending on the ability of an organism to utilize oxygen in cellular respiration. A number of prokaryotes and a few fungi are classified as **strict anaerobes** because they require an oxygen-free environment to survive. Strict anaerobes gain ATP either from fermentation or anaerobic respiration. Among these organisms are the bacteria that cause botulism, tetanus, and some other serious diseases. For example, the bacterium that causes botulism thrives in the oxygen-free environment of canned foods that prevents the growth of most other microorganisms.

Other organisms, called **facultative anaerobes**, can switch between fermentation and full oxidative pathways, depending on the oxygen supply. Facultative anaerobes include *Escherichia coli,* the bacterium that

inhabits the digestive tract of humans; the *Lactobacillus* bacteria used to produce buttermilk and yogurt; and *S. cerevisiae,* the yeast used in brewing and baking. Many cell types in higher organisms, including vertebrate muscle cells, are also facultatively anaerobic.

Some prokaryotic and eukaryotic cells are **strict aerobes**—that is, they have an absolute requirement for oxygen to survive and are unable to live solely by fermentation. Vertebrate brain cells are key examples of strictly aerobic cells that need a constant supply of oxygen to function.

6.7d The Paradox of Aerobic Life

Strict anaerobes cannot live in an oxygen environment. But why can't they? Lacking the ability to use O_2 as an electron acceptor is one thing, but actually dying in the presence of O_2? The reason that strict anaerobes die is related to what is often called the *paradox of aerobic life:* although many organisms cannot exist without oxygen because it is required for electron transport, oxygen itself is inherently dangerous to all forms of life.

It takes four electrons to completely reduce a molecule of oxygen to water **(Figure 6.25)**. However, partially reduced forms of O_2 are readily formed when O_2 accepts a fewer number of electrons, producing what are called *reactive oxygen species* (ROS). These molecules, which include the compounds superoxide and hydrogen peroxide (see Figure 6.25), are particularly strong oxidizing agents and can readily remove electrons from proteins, lipids, and DNA, resulting in damage. If ROS levels within a cell are excessive, their strong oxidizing nature can result in destruction of many biological molecules and can lead to cell death. Because most cells contain an abundance of both O_2 and electron-rich molecules (proteins, lipids, DNA), the formation of reactive oxygen molecules is a consequence of aerobic life that cannot be avoided.

To survive in such an unfriendly oxygen environment, all known aerobic organisms have an antioxidant defence system that includes both enzymes and nonenzyme molecules that have the

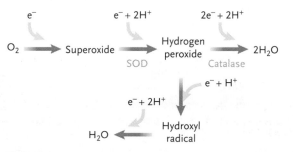

Figure 6.25
The reduction of O_2 to water is a four-electron reduction. If this occurs stepwise, it results in the formation of intermediates called reactive oxygen species (ROS), which are potentially harmful. Aerobic cells contain the enzymes superoxide dismutase (SOD) and catalase, which together quickly convert superoxide and hydrogen peroxide to water.

role of intercepting and inactivating reactive oxygen molecules as they accumulate within cells. Two of the major reactive oxygen scavenging enzymes are superoxide dismutase and catalase (see Figure 6.25). The absence of one or both of these enzymes results in anaerobic cells being unable to live in the presence of oxygen. They die because of high intracellular reactive oxygen levels. In addition to enzymes, many cells have a range of *antioxidants,* including vitamin C and vitamin E, which act as reducing agents, safely and rapidly reducing reactive oxygen compounds to water. Although they are extremely important, the antioxidant enzymes and compounds are not completely effective in preventing oxidative damage. To deal with the damage that does still occur, cells have an elaborate system of damage removal/repair enzymes for proteins, lipids, and DNA.

In recent years, excessive reactive oxygen formation has been implicated in a wide variety of degenerative processes, diseases, and syndromes, including Parkinson disease and Alzheimer dementia, and a wide variety of age-related disorders. It is thought that the buildup of oxidative damage may underlie the aging process itself. This, in part, explains the huge interest in the possible protective value of a wide variety of antioxidant compounds, particularly those from fruits and vegetables.

The huge advantage gained by using oxygen as the terminal electron acceptor is that cells can extract more energy from food molecules. However, the evolution of the aerobic lifestyle required the development of antioxidants and enzymes such as catalase and superoxide dismutase to combat the inevitable formation of ROS. In addition, it required that cytochrome oxidase, the last enzyme of the mitochondrial electron transport chain, develop a remarkable mode of catalysis. Recall that this enzyme complex donates electrons from the electron carrier cytochrome c to O_2 (see Figure 6.15). However, it does so in a way that, remarkably, leads to essentially no ROS generation. The enzyme is structurally quite complex, containing four redox centres (two hemes and two copper ions), each of which can store a single electron. When all centres are reduced, the enzyme simultaneously transfers all four electrons to an oxygen molecule, producing two molecules of water. That cytochrome oxidase is the only enzyme that aerobic organisms, from bacterial to human, use as the terminal complex of electron transport indicates the chemical difficulty of carrying out the transfer of electrons to O_2 in a safe and controlled manner. Given that approximately 98% of the oxygen we metabolize is handled by this single enzyme, if the reaction resulted in significant ROS formation, aerobic life as we know it would never have been able to develop.

MOLECULE BEHIND BIOLOGY

Cyanide

Cyanide is an ion that consists of a carbon atom triple-bonded to an atom of nitrogen ($C≡N^-$). It is a very toxic metabolic poison acting as an irreversible inhibitor of the terminal enzyme of respiratory electron transport, cytochrome oxidase. By binding to the iron atom of the heme prosthetic groups in the enzyme, cyanide prevents electron flow to O_2, essentially inhibiting electron transport and subsequent chemiosmosis. Acute cyanide poisoning can result in death within minutes of exposure.

Cyanide is produced in small amounts by a range of microorganisms and is found in small amounts in apple seeds, almonds, and the pits of fruits such as peaches. In some plants, the production of cyanide in a form bound to sugars is thought to be a deterrent to herbivory. The presence of cyanide in the potato-like root of the cassava plant is of concern because it is a staple food in a number of tropical countries. The presence of cyanide glycosides is diminished by extensive soaking and cooking of the cassava root, but health problems associated with chronic cyanide poisoning remain quite common.

Cyanide has clear applications in a range of industries but especially in electroplating, metallurgy, and mining owing to the high solubility of gold $[Au(CN)_2]^-$ and silver $[Ag(CN)_2]^-$ cyanides in water. For these purposes, approximately 500 000 tons of highly toxic sodium cyanide are produced each year. In gold mining, the addition of a solution of sodium cyanide to ore containing low amounts of gold is effective at extracting the gold by bringing the gold into solution. The resulting formation of huge amounts of cyanide-contaminated water makes this form of gold mining highly controversial, yet it remains a highly effective and cheap method of extraction.

In addition to a respiratory electron transport chain that is inhibited by cyanide, plants contain a pathway of electron transport that is resistant to cyanide. Instead of using cytochrome oxidase, this second pathway of respiration uses a terminal oxidase called the alternative oxidase. This alternative pathway of respiration is not linked to proton pumping like the normal respiratory chain; instead, electron flow simply generates heat. Intestinally, high levels of alternative oxidase in the flowers of some plant species are used to volatilize attractants for pollinators. This includes the aptly named skunk cabbage, which tells you that the attractants for pollinators are not necessarily pleasant.

In addition to being found in all plants, the alternative oxidase has been found in algae, some fungi, and, recently, some animal phyla. The physiological role of cyanide-resistant respiration in these species is being actively investigated by a number of research groups.

Glycolysis and energy metabolism are crucial for the normal functioning of an animal. Research of many kinds is being conducted in this area, such as characterizing the molecular components in detail and determining how the reactions are regulated. The goal is to generate comprehensive models of cellular respiration and its regulation. Following are two specific examples of ongoing research related to human disease caused by defects in cellular respiration.

How do mitochondrial proteins change in patients with Alzheimer disease (AD)?

AD is an age-dependent, irreversible, neurodegenerative disorder in humans. Symptoms include a progressive deterioration of cognitive functions and, in particular, a significant loss of memory. Reduced brain metabolism occurs early in the onset of AD. One of the mechanisms for this physiological change appears to be damage to or reduction of key mitochondrial components, including enzymes of the citric acid cycle and the oxidative phosphorylation system. However, the complete scope of mitochondrial protein changes has not been established, nor have detailed comparisons been made in mitochondrial protein changes among AD patients. Currently, Gail Breen at the University of Texas, Dallas, is performing research to detail qualitatively and quantitatively all mitochondrial proteins and their levels in healthy and AD brains. A mouse model of AD is being used for this research. Breen's group hopes that the information they obtain will provide a better understanding of how mitochondrial dysfunction contributes to AD. With such information in hand, it may be possible to develop interventions to slow or halt the progression of AD in humans.

How are the oxidative phosphorylation complexes in the mitochondrion assembled?

Defects in oxidative phosphorylation may cause disorders in which several systems of the human body are adversely affected. Often these disorders involve the nervous system and the skeletal and cardiac muscles. The enzyme complexes of the oxidative phosphorylation system consist of about 80 different protein subunits, some of which are encoded by nuclear genes and some by mitochondrial genes. The protein subunits are assembled into complexes in the mitochondria. This assembly process requires a large number of accessory proteins, and many important mitochondrial diseases are caused by defects in the assembly protein genes.

Eric Shoubridge of McGill University in Montreal is studying the molecular genetics of assembly of oxidative phosphorylation complexes. His focus is identifying and characterizing the assembly genes, with the long-term goals of understanding how the complexes are assembled and how defects in complex assembly lead to disease. Shoubridge's group has identified mutations in four different assembly genes in infants with a fatal disease caused by cytochrome c deficiency (a defect in the assembly of complex IV). They have also identified complex I assembly proteins, and they were the first to show an association between a defect in one of the proteins and a human disease. Unexpectedly, the biochemical deficiencies caused by the mutant assembly proteins tend to be tissue specific, even though the assembly protein genes are expressed in all tissues. As a result, clinical symptoms caused by defective assembly proteins vary based on the extent of the enzyme deficiencies in different tissues. Understanding how the tissue-specific differences occur and how they are regulated will be important in developing therapies for patients with the diseases.

Review

Go to CENGAGENOW™ at http://hed.nelson.com/ to access quizzing, animations, exercises, articles, and personalized homework help.

6.1 The Chemical Basis of Cellular Respiration

- Oxidation–reduction reactions, called redox reactions, partially or completely transfer electrons from donor to acceptor atoms; the donor is oxidized as it releases electrons, and the acceptor is reduced.

- Almost all organisms obtain energy for cellular activities through cellular respiration, the process of transferring electrons from donor organic molecules to a final acceptor molecule such as oxygen; the energy that is released drives ATP synthesis.

6.2 Cellular Respiration: An Overview

- Cellular respiration occurs in three stages: (1) in glycolysis, glucose is converted to two molecules of pyruvate through a series of enzyme-catalyzed reactions; (2) in pyruvate oxidation and the citric acid cycle, pyruvate is converted to an acetyl compound that is oxidized completely to CO_2; and (3) in the electron transfer system and oxidative phosphorylation, high-energy electrons produced from the first two stages pass through the transfer system, with much of their energy being used to establish an H^+ gradient across the membrane that drives the synthesis of ATP.

- Both eukaryotes and prokaryotes may undergo cellular respiration. In eukaryotes, however, most of the reactions of cellular respiration occur in mitochondria.

6.3 Glycolysis

- In glycolysis, which occurs in the cytosol, glucose (six carbons) is oxidized into two molecules of pyruvate (three carbons each). Electrons removed in the oxidation are delivered to NAD^+, producing NADH. The reaction sequence produces a net gain of two ATP, two NADH, and two pyruvate molecules for each molecule of glucose oxidized.

- ATP molecules produced in the energy-releasing steps of glycolysis result from substrate-level phosphorylation, an enzyme-catalyzed reaction that transfers a phosphate group from a substrate to ADP.

6.4 Pyruvate Oxidation and the Citric Acid Cycle

- In pyruvate oxidation, which occurs inside mitochondria, one pyruvate (three carbons) is oxidized to one acetyl group (two carbons) and one CO_2. Electrons removed in the oxidation are accepted by 1 NAD^+ to produce one NADH. The acetyl group is transferred to coenzyme A, which carries it to the citric acid cycle.

- In the citric acid cycle, acetyl groups are oxidized completely to CO_2. Electrons removed in the oxidation are accepted by NAD^+ or FAD, and substrate-level phosphorylation produces ATP. For each acetyl group oxidized by the cycle, two CO_2, one ATP, three NADH, and one $FADH_2$ are produced.

6.5 Electron Transport and Chemiosmosis

- Electrons are passed from NADH and $FADH_2$ to the electron transfer system, which consists of four major protein complexes and two smaller shuttle carriers. As the electrons flow from one carrier to the next through the system, some of their energy is used by the complexes to pump protons across the inner mitochondrial membrane.

- Two major protein complexes (I and IV) and the reduction/oxidation of ubiquinone result in the pumping of protons from the matrix to the intermembrane compartment, generating an H^+ gradient with a high concentration in the intermembrane compartment and a low concentration in the matrix.

- The H^+ gradient produced by the electron transfer system is used by ATP synthase as an energy source for synthesis of ATP from ADP and P_i. The ATP synthase is embedded in the inner mitochondrial membrane together with the electron transfer system.

6.6 The Efficiency and Regulation of Cellular Respiration

- An estimated three ATP are synthesized as each electron pair travels from NADH to oxygen through the mitochondrial electron transfer system; about two ATP are synthesized as each electron pair travels through the system from $FADH_2$ to oxygen.

- In glycolysis, 2 ATP and 2 NADH are synthesized; during the oxidation of pyruvate and the citric acid cycle, 2 ATP, 8 NADH, and 2 $FADH_2$ are produced. That gives a total of 10 NADH and 2 $FADH_2$ that are oxidized by the electron transport chain. This gives a total ATP yield for each glucose oxidized of 38.

- Using these totals gives an efficiency of more than 30% for the utilization of energy released by glucose oxidation if the H^+ gradient is used only for ATP production.

6.7 Oxygen and Cellular Respiration

- Organisms differ in regard to their oxygen requirements.

- Fermentations are reaction pathways that reduce pyruvate in the cytosol by the consumption of NADH. In so doing, NAD^+ is produced, which is required as a substrate for glycolysis. This allows glycolysis to continue to run, producing ATP by substrate-level phosphorylation. The NAD^+ can accept electrons generated by glycolysis, allowing glycolysis to supply ATP by substrate-level phosphorylation.

- Strict anaerobes cannot grow in the presence of oxygen, whereas strict aerobes require oxygen. Facultative aerobes can grow in the presence of oxygen and can grow using fermentative pathways.

- Although oxygen is required for aerobic life, paradoxically, O_2 is toxic to cells. Cells are protected by the toxicity of O_2 by both enzymatic and nonenzymatic antioxidants that detoxify ROS.

Questions

Self-Test Questions

1. What is a common feature of organic molecules that are good fuels?
   a. Easily reduced.
   b. An abundance of oxygen.
   c. Presence of C–H bonds.
   d. High molecular weight.
   e. Low solubility in water.

2. Which of the following general statements about respiration is correct?
   a. The CO_2 produced can be used as an energy source for metabolism.
   b. O_2 is used as an electron donor for the process.
   c. Since bacteria are prokaryotic, they do not respire.
   d. It represents a series of reactions in which a carbon substrate is oxidized.
   e. It is able to extract more energy from glucose than direct burning can.

3. In glycolysis,
   a. all the reactions occur in the mitochondrion.
   b. the carbon products are oxidized further by the electron transport chain.
   c. ATP is generated by substrate-level phosphorylation.
   d. oxygen is required as an electron acceptor.
   e. the two molecules of pyruvate made contain the same amount of potential energy as one molecule of glucose.

4. The proton-motive force associated with chemiosmosis
   a. is only important for ATP synthesis in mitochondria.
   b. needs to be high to synthesize ATP during the citric acid cycle.
   c. requires that membranes are freely permeable to protons.
   d. has an electrical and a concentration component.
   e. Both c and d are correct.

5. You are reading this text while breathing in O_2 and breathing out CO_2. The CO_2 arises from the
   a. oxidation of acetyl-CoA by the citric acid cycle.
   b. conversion of glucose to pyruvate during glycolysis.
   c. conversion of pyruvate to acetyl-CoA.
   d. oxidative phosphorylation.
   e. Both a and c are correct.

6. A key role of fermentation in overall metabolism is to
   a. synthesize extra ATP.
   b. regenerate NAD^+ in the cytosol.
   c. increase O_2 concentration for electron transport.
   d. increase NADH synthesis for oxidative phosphorylation.
   e. produce acetyl-CoA.

7. In cellular respiration, the term *uncoupling* refers to when
   a. the two parts of glycolysis are running independently of each other.
   b. the citric acid cycle is operating but is not generating any ATP.
   c. respiratory electron transport is operating, but chemiosmosis is not.
   d. Substrate-level phosphorylation is inhibited.
   e. None of the above statements are correct.

8. Which of the following statements about phosphofructokinase is *false*?
   a. It is an enzyme found in the cytosol.
   b. It catalyzes a phosphorylation reaction.
   c. It is an enzyme of glycolysis.
   d. It is inhibited by high cytosolic ADP levels.
   e. It is activated by high cytosolic citrate levels.

9. The breakdown of fats release fatty acids which enter the respiratory pathway at the level of
   a. NADH
   b. Glucose
   c. Pyruvate
   d. Acetyl-CoA
   e. Citrate

10. Which of the following statements is correct?
   a. Strict anaerobes can grow either by fermentation, or they can use O_2 in aerobic respiration.
   b. It takes two electrons to fully reduce a molecule of O_2 to water.
   c. Partially reduced forms of O_2 are formed by the action of cytochrome oxidase.
   d. The enzymes superoxide dismutase and catalase are not essential to aerobic life.
   e. Some forms of O_2 can damage macromolecules.

Questions for Discussion

1. Respond to this statement: Respiration occurs in animals but not in plants.

2. In your opinion, are fermentations part of cellular respiration? Why or why not?

3. Why do you think nucleic acids are not oxidized extensively as a cellular energy source?

4. Migrating birds, which fly for long distances without stopping, oxidize fatty acids as an energy source in their flight muscles. Why do you think this would be an advantage to the birds? In the fields below a flock of migrating geese, a rabbit accelerates rapidly to escape a coyote. Which oxidative pathway predominates in the rabbit's leg muscles? Why wouldn't the pathway being used in the flight muscles of the geese benefit the rabbit very much?

5. Recently, a hospital patient was regularly found to be intoxicated. He denied that he was drinking alcoholic beverages. The doctors and nurses made a special point to eliminate the possibility that the patient or his friends were smuggling alcohol into his room, but he was still regularly intoxicated. Then one of the doctors had an idea that turned out to be correct and cured the patient of his intoxication. The idea involved the patient's digestive system and one of the oxidative reactions covered in this chapter. What was the doctor's idea?

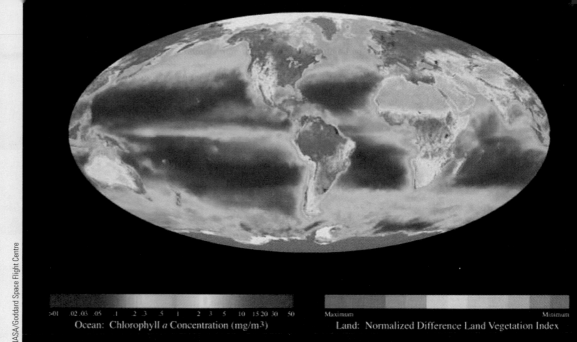

False-colour image estimating global marine and terrestrial photoautotroph abundance. Estimates of surface chlorophyll were achieved using data collected by the GeoEye Orb View-2 satellite (SeaWiFS project) and NASA/Goddard Space Flight Centre.

NASA/Goddard Space Flight Centre

Ocean: Chlorophyll *a* Concentration (mg/m³)

Maximum   Minimum

Land: Normalized Difference Land Vegetation Index

7 Photosynthesis

WHY IT MATTERS

The Earth can be considered a giant photoreceptor—a massive harvester of light energy from the sun. Life on Earth is dependent entirely on energy from the Sun, not only to keep the planet at a suitable temperature but also to provide the energy required to sustain life. The energy of the sun is actively captured by chlorophyll and related pigments present in photosynthetic organisms found in both terrestrial and aquatic habitats. The vast majority of energy enters the biosphere through the process of photosynthesis by which the energy of photons is captured by chlorophyll and other pigments founds in photoautotrophs that live in both terrestrial and aquatic habitats. This captured energy is used to convert carbon dioxide into complex energy-rich molecules.

The amount of carbon dioxide that is incorporated into organic form by photosynthetic organisms is staggering—approximately 11×10^{13} kg of carbon per year. And although we often think about photosynthesis in terms of plants and trees, about half of this carbon is fixed by the photosynthetic microorganisms that inhabit marine environments: phytoplankton.

Looking at photosynthesis on a global scale (see opening figure), you may notice that surprisingly, the abundance of phytoplankton (as estimated by chlorophyll concentration) is very low in the temperate regions of the Pacific and Atlantic oceans and higher as you move nearer the poles, especially the Arctic. The reason for this is that, although the waters near the equator are warmer, they are very nutrient poor (being especially deficient in iron) and unable to support phytoplankton growth.

7.1 Photosynthesis: An Overview

Photosynthetic organisms are photoautotrophs and are classified as the *primary producers* of Earth **(Figure 7.1)**. They convert the energy of sunlight into chemical energy and use it to assemble simple inorganic raw materials into complex organic molecules. Primary producers use some of the organic molecules they make as energy sources for their own activities. But they also serve—directly or indirectly—as food sources for *consumers*, the animals that live by eating plants or other animals. Eventually, the bodies of both primary producers and consumers provide chemical energy for bacteria, fungi, and other *decomposers*.

7.1a The Two Parts of Photosynthesis

Photosynthesis can be conceptually divided into two distinct stages **(Figure 7.2)**: the **light-dependent reactions** (sometimes called the light reactions) and the light-independent reactions (called the **Calvin cycle**). The light reactions involve the capture of light energy by pigment molecules and the utilization of that energy to synthesize both NADPH and ATP. This involves an electron transport chain that in plants, algae, and cyanobacteria utilizes electrons donated from water. Oxygen generated from the splitting of water is released to the environment as a by-product:

$$2H_2O + \text{light energy} \rightarrow 4H^+ + 4e^- + O_2$$

In the Calvin cycle, the electrons carried by NADPH and the energy of ATP are used to convert CO_2 from inorganic to organic form, a process called CO_2 fixation. The conversion is a reduction, in which electrons (and protons) are added to CO_2 (reduction and oxidation are discussed in Chapter 6). With the added electrons and protons (H^+), CO_2 is converted to a carbohydrate, with carbon, hydrogen, and oxygen atoms in the ratio 1C:2H:1O. Carbohydrate units are often symbolized as $(CH_2O)n$, with the "n" indicating that different carbohydrates are formed from different multiples of the carbohydrate unit.

$$CO_2 + H^+ + e^- \rightarrow (CH_2O)_n$$

Three-carbon sugars are the major direct product of the Calvin cycle. These can be readily combined to form six-carbon monosaccharides, including glucose.

Figure 7.1
Examples of photoautotrophs.

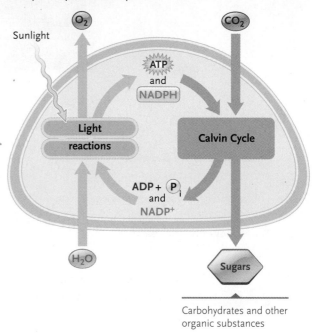

Carbohydrates and other organic substances

Figure 7.2
Photosynthesis can be conceptually divided into two processes: The light reactions and The Calvin cycle which are linked together by reactants and products. Both processes occur in the chloroplasts of photoautotrophic eukaryotes (plants and algae) as well as in photosynthetic prokaryotes.

Combining the two reactions above, the overall balanced equation for photosynthesis is

$$6CO_2 + 12 H_2O \rightarrow C_6H_{12}O_6 + 6O_2 + 6H_2O.$$

While sugar (glucose) is the major product of photosynthesis it is important to realize that the reduced carbon produced by photosynthesis is also the source of the carbon back-bone for a huge range of other molecules, including lipids and proteins. In fact, all the organic molecules of plants are assembled as direct or indirect products of photosynthesis.

7.1b In Eukaryotes, Photosynthesis Takes Place in Chloroplasts

In photosynthetic eukaryotes, both the light reactions and the Calvin cycle take place within the chloroplast **(Figure 7.3)**, an organelle that is formed from

Figure 7.3
The membranes and compartments of chloroplasts.

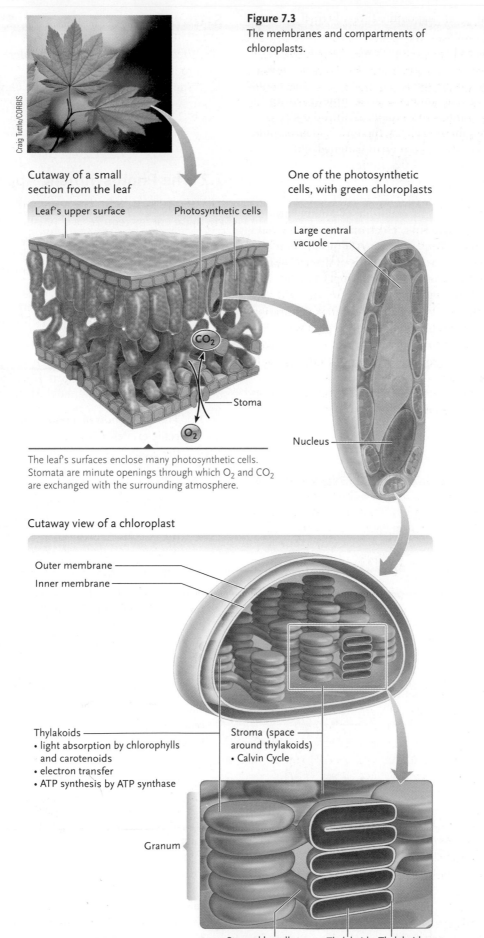

Cutaway of a small section from the leaf

Leaf's upper surface

Photosynthetic cells

CO₂

Stoma

O₂

The leaf's surfaces enclose many photosynthetic cells. Stomata are minute openings through which O_2 and CO_2 are exchanged with the surrounding atmosphere.

One of the photosynthetic cells, with green chloroplasts

Large central vacuole

Nucleus

Cutaway view of a chloroplast

Outer membrane
Inner membrane

Thylakoids
• light absorption by chlorophylls and carotenoids
• electron transfer
• ATP synthesis by ATP synthase

Stroma (space around thylakoids)
• Calvin Cycle

Granum

Stromal lamellae   Thylakoid lumen   Thylakoid membrane

Craig Tuttle/CORBIS

three membranes that define three distinct compartments (see Figure 7.3). An *outer membrane* covers the entire surface of the organelle, whereas an *inner membrane* lies just inside the outer membrane. Between the outer and inner membranes is the *intermembrane compartment*. The aqueous environment within the inner membrane is the *stroma*. Within the stroma is the third membrane system, the *thylakoid membranes*, or thylakoids, which often form flattened, closed sacs. The space enclosed by a thylakoid is called the *thylakoid lumen*.

The thylakoid membrane houses the molecules that carry out the light reactions of photosynthesis, including the pigments, electron transfer carriers, and ATP synthase enzymes for ATP production. The enzymes that catalyze the reactions of the Calvin cycle are found in the stroma of the chloroplast.

In the same way that organisms without mitochondria may still undergo cellular respiration, cells lacking chloroplasts may still be photosynthetic. Many photosynthetic prokaryotes also have thylakoid membranes that are formed from infoldings of the plasma membrane.

STUDY BREAK

1. Why are photoautotrophs considered primary producers?
2. What is CO_2 converted to in the Calvin cycle?

7.2 The Photosynthetic Apparatus

The ability to trap light energy and convert it into chemical energy requires a sophisticated photochemical apparatus that is unique in biology. In this section, we describe the components of the light reactions that are located on the thylakoid membranes.

7.2a Electrons in Pigment Molecules Absorb Light Energy

From our discussion of light in Chapter 1, recall two important points about light and pigment molecules:

1. The absorption of a photon by a pigment molecule excites a single electron, moving it from the ground state to an excited state.
2. The difference in energy level between the ground state and the excited state is equivalent to the energy of the photon of light that was absorbed. If the energies do not match, the photon is not absorbed by the pigment.

As shown in **Figure 7.4**, following light absorption, there are three possible fates of the energy possessed by an excited-state electron within a pigment molecule. The relative probabilities of each event taking place depends on the environment surrounding the pigment molecules, including the presence of other molecules.

In the first mechanism (see Figure 7.4, left), the excited electron may simply return to its ground state, releasing its energy either as heat or as *fluorescence*, which is emission of light of a longer wavelength (lower energy) than the absorbed light. The fluorescence will be of lower energy because a small amount of energy of the photon initially absorbed is always lost as heat (recall from Chapter 4 that energy transformations are never 100% efficient). In the second option (see Figure 7.4, centre), the energy of the excited electron can be transferred to a neighbouring pigment molecule, a process called *inductive resonance*. This transfer of energy excites the pigment molecule, whereas the first molecule returns to its ground state. This requires the two molecules to be very closely and precisely aligned with one another. In the third option (see Figure 7.4, right), the excited-state electron may

Figure 7.4
Three possible fates of an excited-state electron within a pigment molecule.

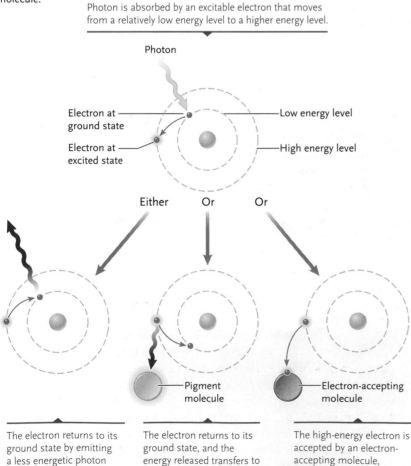

Photon is absorbed by an excitable electron that moves from a relatively low energy level to a higher energy level.

Photon

Electron at ground state — Low energy level

Electron at excited state — High energy level

Either   Or   Or

Pigment molecule

Electron-accepting molecule

The electron returns to its ground state by emitting a less energetic photon (fluorescence) or releasing energy as heat.

The electron returns to its ground state, and the energy released transfers to a neighbouring pigment molecule, a process called inductive resonance.

The high-energy electron is accepted by an electron-accepting molecule, the primary acceptor.

a. Chlorophyll structure

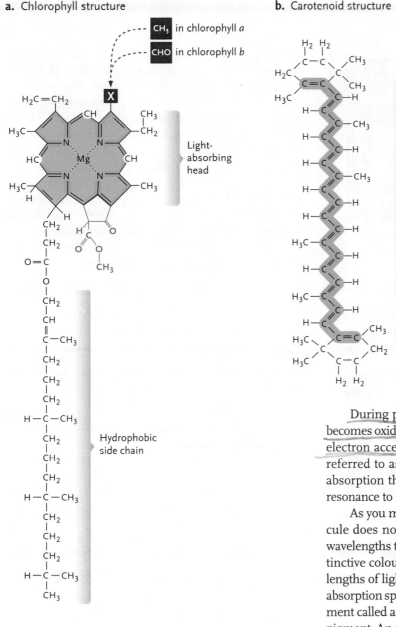

CH₃ in chlorophyll *a*
CHO in chlorophyll *b*

X

Light-absorbing head

Hydrophobic side chain

b. Carotenoid structure

Light-absorbing region

Figure 7.5
Pigment molecules used in photosynthesis.
(a) Chlorophylls *a* and *b*, which differ only in the side group attached at the X. Light-absorbing electrons are distributed among the bonds shaded in red.
(b) Carotenoids. The electrons absorbing light are distributed in a series of alternating double and single bonds in the backbone of these pigments.

During photosynthesis it is only chlorophyll a that becomes oxidized and donates an electron to the primary electron acceptor. Carotenoids and chlorophyll b are referred to as accessory pigments because after light absorption they donate excitation energy by inductae resonance to molecules of chlorophyll a.

As you may recall from Chapter 1, a pigment molecule does not absorb all wavelengths of light—those wavelengths that are not absorbed give a pigment its distinctive colour. One can precisely determine the wavelengths of light absorbed by a pigment by producing an absorption spectrum for that pigment by using an instrument called a spectrophotometer and a pure sample of a pigment. An **absorption spectrum** is a plot of the absorption of light as a function of wavelength. **Figure 7.6a (p. 144)** shows that chlorophyll *a* absorbs strongly blue and red light but does not absorb green or yellow light. The absorption spectra of the accessory pigments (chlorophyll *b* and carotenoids; see Figure 7.6 a) illustrate that these pigments expand the wavelengths of light that can be effectively captured and used for photosynthesis.

Photosynthesis is dependent on the absorption of light by chlorophylls and carotenoids, acting in combination. This is supported by the **action spectrum** for photosynthesis, which is a plot of the effectiveness of light of particular wavelengths in driving photosynthesis **(Figure 7.6b, p. 144)**. The action spectrum is usually determined by using a suspension of chloroplasts or algal cells and measuring the amount of O_2 released by photosynthesis at different wavelengths of visible light. Whenever an action spectrum for a physiological phenomenon matches the absorption

itself be transferred to a nearby electron-accepting molecule. In photosynthesis, this molecule is called the primary acceptor.

7.2b Chlorophylls and Carotenoids Cooperate in Light Absorption

Chlorophylls are the major photosynthetic pigments in plants, green algae, and cyanobacteria. Of the chlorophylls, the most dominant types are chlorophyll a and b which are structurally only slightly different **(Figure 7.5)**. Besides the chlorophylls, the closely related molecules, the bacteriochlorophylls, carry out the same functions in groups of photosynthetic prokaryotes other than the cyanobacteria. The second major group of pigments involved in photosynthesis is the carotenoids.

a. The absorption spectra of chlorophylls *a* and *b* and carotenoids

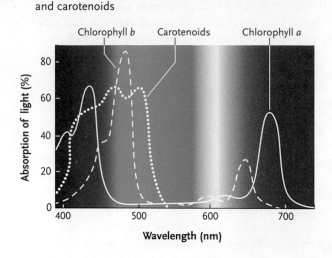

b. The action spectrum in higher plants, representing the combined effects of chlorophylls and carotenoids

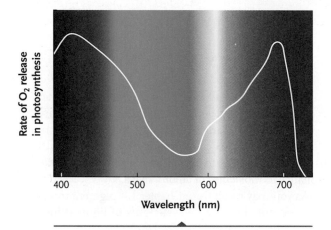

The peaks in the action spectrum are typically broader than those for the individual pigments, reflecting both their combined effects and changes in the absorption spectra of individual pigments by their combination with proteins in chloroplasts.

Figure 7.6

The absorption spectra of the photosynthetic pigments **(a)** and the action spectrum of photosynthesis **(b)**.

spectrum of a pigment, it is highly suggestive that the two are linked.

One of the earliest action spectra was produced in 1883 by Theodor Engelmann, who used only a **light microscope** and a glass prism to determine which wavelengths of light were most effective for photosynthesis **(Figure 7.7)**. Engelmann placed a strand of a green alga, *Spirogyra*, on a glass microscope slide, along with water containing bacteria that require oxygen to survive. He adjusted the prism so that it split a beam of light into its separate colours, which spread like a rainbow across the strand (see Figure 7.7). After a short time, he noticed that the bacteria had begun to cluster around the algal strand in different locations. The largest clusters were under the blue and violet light at one end of the strand and the red light at the other end. Very few bacteria were found in the green light.

7.2c Photosynthetic Pigments Are Organized into Photosystems

Pigment molecules are not freely floating within the thylakoid membranes but rather are bound very precisely to a number of different proteins. These pigment-proteins are organized into what are called photosystems. Each photosystem is composed of a large *antenna complex* (also called a *light-harvesting complex*) of pigment-proteins that surrounds a central *reaction centre*. The reaction centre of a photosystem comprises a small number of proteins that bind a pair of specialized chlorophyll *a* molecules as well as the primary electron acceptor **(Figure 7.8)**.

There are two distinctly different kinds of photosystems: photosystem I and photosystem II (also called PSI and PSII). The specialized chlorophyll *a* at the reaction centre of photosystem I is called P700 (P = pigment) because it absorbs light optimally at a wavelength of 700 nm, whereas the reaction centre of photosystem II contains a specialized chlorophyll *a*, P680, which absorbs light optimally at a wavelength

Figure 7.7

Engelmann's 1882 experiment revealed the action spectrum of light used in photosynthesis by *Spirogyra*, a green alga. The aerobic bacteria clustered along the algal strand in the regions where oxygen was released in greatest quantity—the regions in which photosynthesis proceeded at the greatest rate. Those regions corresponded to the colours (wavelengths) of light being absorbed most effectively by the alga—in this case, violet and red.

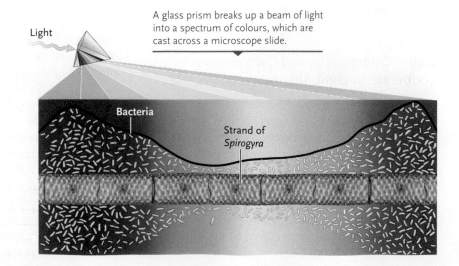

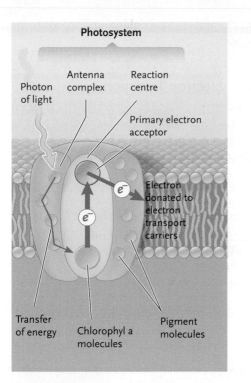

Figure 7.8

A Photosystem: comprised of a light-harvesting antenna complex and a reaction centre. Light energy absorbed by the antenna complex is transferred to specialized chlorophyll molecules in the reaction centre. Light energy is converted to chemical energy as a reaction centre chlorophyll donates an electron to the primary electron acceptor. This electron in turn is passed along an electron transport chain.

of 680 nm. P700 and P680 are structurally identical to other chlorophyll *a* molecules; their specific light absorption patterns result from interactions with particular proteins in the photosystems.

The function of a photosystem is to trap photons of light and use the energy to oxidize a reaction centre chlorophyll, with the electron being transferred to the primary electron acceptor. High rates of oxidation–reduction within the reaction centre are achieved by the large antenna complex of pigments absorbing light of a range of wavelengths and efficiently funnelling the energy to the reaction, through inductive resonance.

STUDY BREAK

1. What are the components of a photosystem?
2. What is the difference between an absorption spectrum and an action spectrum?

7.3 Photosynthetic Electron Transport

Photosystem I and photosystem II are the two major light-trapping components involved in photosynthetic electron transport in most photoautotrophs. In this section, we look in detail at how this particular electron

transport chain operates and draw some analogies with respiratory electron transport. As in all electron transport systems, the electron carriers of the photosynthetic system consist of nonprotein organic groups that alternate between being oxidized and reduced as electrons move through the system. The carriers include the same types that act in mitochondrial electron transfer—cytochromes, quinones, and iron-sulphur centres.

7.3a The Structure and Function of Photosystem II

In Chapter 2, we discussed the evolutionary significance of the development of oxygenic photosynthesis and how it allowed organisms to use the most abundant substance on Earth—water—as a source of electrons. By splitting water, these organisms released O_2, as a by-product which slowly accumulated in the atmosphere. Oxygenic photosynthesis is the result of the development of photosystem II. The sequence of light harvesting and photochemical events within this very important photosystem **(Figure 7.9)** is as follows:

1. The absorption of photons by the antenna complex and funnelling of energy to the reaction centre results in an electron within P680 being raised from the ground state to an excited state. The excited state is denoted with an asterisk (P680*).
2. Once in the excited state, P680* can be easily oxidized to P680$^+$ by the primary electron acceptor of photosystem II, a molecule called pheophytin

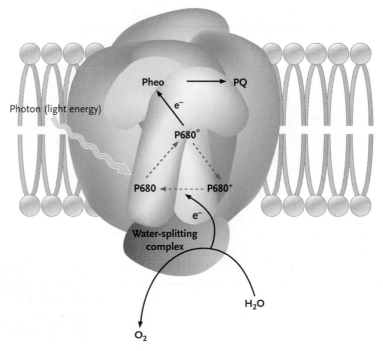

Figure 7.9

A structural model of photosystem II showing the major protein components and pathway of electron flow from water to plastoquinone (PQ). The chlorophyll molecule (P680) remains bound to a reaction centre protein but cycles through three different forms as shown by dashed arrows. See text for full explantation.

(pheo), which initiates electron transport by donation to plastoquinone (PQ) which is analogous to ubiquinone of respiratory electron transport.

3. P680 is re-formed by P680$^+$ gaining an electron by oxidizing water.

P680$^+$ is the strongest oxidant known in biology, and its ability to oxidize water, a very stable molecule, is remarkable. The reduction of P680$^+$ to P680 by electrons from water is facilitated by an enzyme subunit of photosystem II, called the water-splitting complex which is exposed to the thylakoid lumen.

The absorption of energetic photons of light in combination with the formation of such strong oxidants as P680$^+$ and O$_2$ makes the reaction centre of photosystem II particularly susceptible to damage by reactive oxygen species (see Figure 6.7). In fact, the proteins of the photosystem II reaction centre are constantly being irreversibly damaged. This damage is countered by a very efficient and elaborate system

of repair that is described in more detail in *Molecule Behind Biology*.

7.3b Linear Electron Transport

Figure 7.10 shows how the electron transport and ATP synthesis systems for the light reactions are organized in the thylakoid membrane. Let us follow the **noncyclic electron pathway** using this figure. Don't worry about the stoichiometry of electrons and photons yet.

1. **Oxidation of P680.** Absorption of light energy by photosystem II results in the formation of excited state P680 (P680*). This molecule is rapidly oxidized by the primary electron acceptor pheophytin.

2. **Oxidation–reduction of the plastoquinone pool.** From the primary acceptor, the electrons transfer to *plastoquinone* (PQ), which migrates through the lipid bilayer and acts as an electron transfer

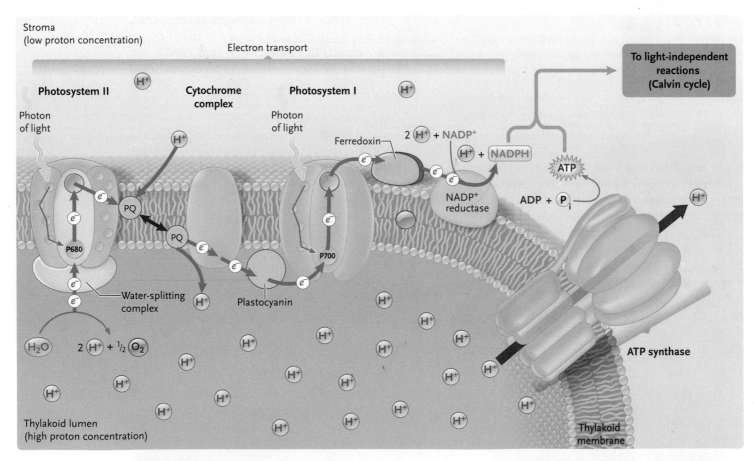

Figure 7.10

A model of the eukaryotic thylakoid membrane illustrating the major protein and redox cofactors required for photosynthetic electron transport and ATP synthesis by chemiosmosis. The four major protein complexes are photosystem II, the cytochrome complex, photosystem I, and ATP synthase. The blue arrow illustrates the pathway of noncyclic (linear) electron transport. As a consequence of electron transport, protons are transported from the stroma into the thylakoid lumen. This occurs during the movement of plastoquinone (PQ) as it alternates from being reduced by photosystem II and then oxidized by the cytochrome complex. The proton gradient is enhanced by the splitting of water on the luminal side of photosystem II and the formation of NADPH on the stromal side of the thylakoid. ATP synthesis occurs by chemiosmosis as protons flow back across the thylakoid membrane through the ATP synthase.

The D1 Protein Keeps Photosystem II Operating

Photosystem II can be considered the most important development in the evolution of life on Earth. Unlike anything that came before it, organisms that had photosystem II could harvest the energy of the Sun and use it to extract electrons from water. These electrons were used to convert CO_2 from the atmosphere into the organic building blocks of the cell. This ability to use water meant that life could thrive almost anywhere on the planet and led to an explosion in the conversion of CO_2 into organic molecules. By splitting water, photosystem II also produced O_2, which gradually accumulated in the atmosphere and led to the development of aerobic respiration. The process of aerobic respiration extracts 18 times more energy from sugar than the anaerobic pathway that came before it, resulting in an energy bounty that allowed the emergence of complex, multicellular eukaryotic organisms. Because of this, photosystem II is known as "the engine of life."

The splitting of water by photosystem II is the most energetically demanding reaction in all of biology. The reaction is carried out by a molecule, P680, which is found in the core of photosystem II, bound to a protein called D1. When photosystem II absorbs light, P680 is converted into the strongest known biological oxidant, $P680^+$, and this molecule is able to break apart H_2O, releasing electrons, protons, and O_2.

As a consequence of absorbing the energy of about 10 000 photons every second and generating powerful oxidants, photosystem II is constantly being damaged, which results in its inactivation. The major site of damage is the D1 protein, which is found in the core of the complex and binds P680. Over the course of two billion years of evolution, organisms that have photosystem II have been unable to prevent the damage from occurring—but they have developed a highly specialized mechanism to repair it.

It takes only 20 minutes for a newly synthesized photosystem II complex to stop working because of damage to D1. However, damaged complexes are rapidly disassembled, the damaged D1 protein is removed and degraded, a newly synthesized D1 protein is inserted, and a functional photosystem is reassembled. This repair cycle is very efficient and is dependent on a high rate of D1 protein synthesis. It has been estimated that in the absence of this repair system, damage to photosystem II would lower the photosynthetic productivity of the planet by 95%. Thus, life on Earth could not have evolved to present-day levels of both abundance and complexity in the absence of a D1 repair mechanism.

---

link between PSII and the cytochrome complex. Plastoquinone is analogous in structure and function to ubiquinone of the mitochondrial electron system and exists as a pool within the thylakoid membrane. As plastoquinone accepts electrons from photosystem II, it also gains protons from the lumen. This reduced form migrates through the membrane. When it donates electrons to the cytochrome complex, it also releases protons into the stroma.

3. **Electron transfer from the cytochrome complex and shuttling by plastocyanin.** From the cytochrome complex, electrons pass to the mobile carrier *plastocyanin*, which shuttles electrons between the cytochrome complex and photosystem I.

4. **Oxidation–reduction of P700.** Absorption of a photon of light by photosystem I results in the formation of P700*. This is oxidized to $P700^+$ by the primary electron acceptor of photosystem I. $P700^+$ is reduced back to P700 by electron donation from plastocyanin.

5. **Electron transfer to $NADP^+$ by ferredoxin.** After passage through a short sequence of carriers within photosystem I, the electron from P700 is transferred to *ferredoxin*, an iron–sulphur protein. The ferredoxin transfers the electrons to $NADP^+$, the final acceptor of the noncyclic pathway. $NADP^+$ is reduced to NADPH by the enzyme $NADP^+$ reductase.

7.3c Chemiosmotic Synthesis of ATP

In a way analogous to respiratory electron transport, the flow of electrons along the photosynthetic electron transport chain is coupled to ATP synthesis by the buildup of a proton gradient across the thylakoid membrane. In photosynthetic electron transport, the proton gradient across the thylakoid membrane is derived from three processes. First, protons are translocated into the lumen by the cyclic reduction and oxidation of plastoquinone as it migrates from photosystem II to the cytochrome complex (see Figure 7.10) and back again. Second, the gradient is enhanced by the addition of two protons for each water molecule oxidized on the luminal side of PSII. Third, the removal of one proton from the stroma for each NADPH molecule synthesized further enhances the gradient across the membrane. Recall from Section 6.5 that the proton gradient is a source of energy. The *proton-motive force* (see Section 6.5) established across the thylakoid membrane is utilized to synthesize ATP by chemiosmosis using the chloroplast ATP synthase. This multiprotein complex is identical to the ATP synthase used in oxidative phosphorylation in cellular respiration (see Section 6.5).

7.3d What Light Is Actually Used For

All electron transport chains operate by electrons flowing spontaneously "downhill" from molecules with high-energy electrons (and are thus easily oxidized) to molecules that are progressively more easily reduced (more electronegative). In the case of mitochondrial respiration, flow is "downhill" from NADH to O_2. In photosynthesis, electron transport occurs by the same principle. However, unlike NADH in respiration, the chlorophyll molecules in the reaction centres of PSII and PSI are not readily oxidized. So how does photosynthesis get chlorophyll molecules into a state where they readily give up electrons? By absorbing light! The absorption of light energy and funnelling of this high energy to the reaction centres boost the energy level of the electrons within the reaction centre chlorophylls **(Figure 7.11)**.

By converting P680 into P680*, the absorption of light energy produces a molecule that is easily oxidized by the electron transport chain, and electron flow is downhill from P680* to photosystem I. A second photon of light must be absorbed by photosystem I to form P700*. Only P700* and not P700 can donate electrons to ferredoxin and eventually on to $NADP^+$ (see Figure 7.11).

In respiratory electron transport, electron flow is spontaneous from NADH to O_2, producing water. By comparison, in photosynthetic electron transport, electron flow is essentially opposite, from water to $NADP^+$. Electron flow is made spontaneous through the absorption of light energy. A mechanical analogy of the role of light absorption and the flow of electrons through the electron transport chain is shown in **Figure 7.12**.

7.3e The Stoichiometry of Linear Electron Transport

We have described in detail the structure and function of the photosynthetic apparatus. Now it's time to go over the stoichiometry of the light reactions.

To get a single electron down the electron transport chain from photosystem II (or water; it doesn't matter) to $NADP^+$ takes two photons of light, one photon absorbed by photosystem II and a second by photosystem I. *How many photons need to be absorbed by the photosynthetic apparatus to produce a single molecule of O_2?* First, write out a balanced equation,

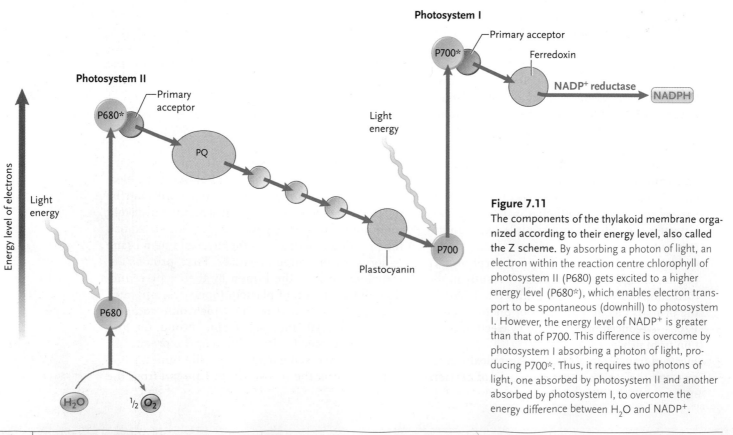

Figure 7.11

The components of the thylakoid membrane organized according to their energy level, also called the Z scheme. By absorbing a photon of light, an electron within the reaction centre chlorophyll of photosystem II (P680) gets excited to a higher energy level (P680*), which enables electron transport to be spontaneous (downhill) to photosystem I. However, the energy level of $NADP^+$ is greater than that of P700. This difference is overcome by photosystem I absorbing a photon of light, producing P700*. Thus, it requires two photons of light, one absorbed by photosystem II and another absorbed by photosystem I, to overcome the energy difference between H_2O and $NADP^+$.

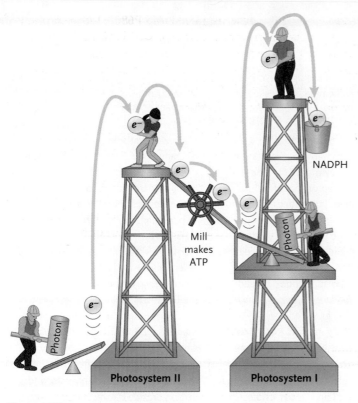

Figure 7.12
A mechanical analogy of the light reactions of photosynthesis.

which shows you need to oxidize two molecules of H_2O which releases 4 electrons.

$$2H_2O \rightarrow 4H^+ + 4e^- + O_2$$

2 photon for each electron.

To move a single electron down the chain requires the absorption of two photons, thus to get four electrons, the photosynthetic apparatus needs to absorb a total of eight photons of light, four by each photosystem.

7.3f Cyclic Electron Transport → *more ATP produced*

Photosystem I can function independently of photosystem II in what is called **cyclic electron transport (Figure 7.13).** In this process, electron transport from photosystem I to ferredoxin is not followed by electron donation to the $NADP^+$ reductase complex. Instead, reduced ferredoxin donates electrons back to the plastoquinone pool. In this manner, the plastoquinone pool gets continually reduced and oxidized and keeps moving protons across the thylakoid membrane without the involvement of photosystem II. The net result of cyclic electron transport is that the energy absorbed from

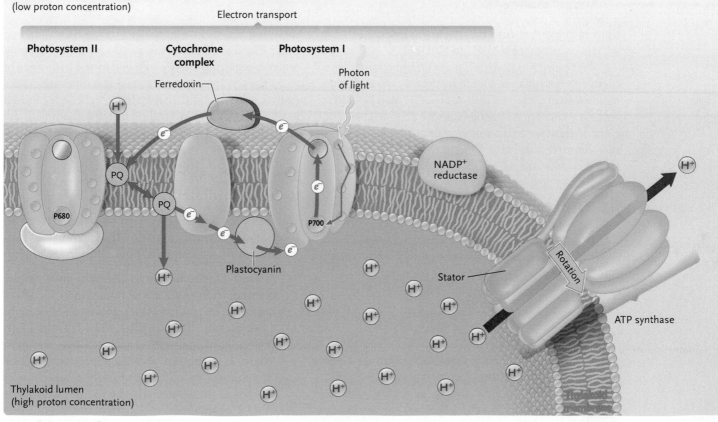

Figure 7.13
Cyclic electron transport. Electrons move in a circular pathway from photosystem I through ferredoxin back to the plastoquinone pool, through the cytochrome complex and plastocyanin and then back to photosystem I. In cyclic electron transport Photosystem II does not operate. The pathway generates proton pumping and thus leads to ATP production but does not result in the synthesis of NADPH.

Norm Hüner, University of Western Ontario

A number of advances into our understanding of the regulation of photosynthesis have been elucidated by the research group of Dr. Norm Hüner, who presently holds a Tier 1 Canada Research Chair in Environmental Stress Biology at the University of Western Ontario in London.

Hüner's research has established that the photosynthetic apparatus has a dual role: not only does it function as the primary energy transformer of the biosphere, it also acts as a sensor of environmental change in all photoautotrophs. Using a range of organisms, including plants, green algae, and cyanobacteria, Hüner's group has discovered that the relative redox state of photosynthetic electron transport acts as a natural sensor of the balance between energy input from the Sun and the demands for that energy by the metabolic processes of the organism.

The redox state of the photosynthetic apparatus can be readily assessed by measuring the "excitation pressure" on photosystem II using a fluorescence-based technique. Hüner's group has shown that changes in excitation pressure are a key trigger that initiates changes to a number of cellular processes, including gene expression, which enable photoautotrophs to readily acclimate to changes in light, temperature, and nutrient availability.

Hüner is the coauthor of an internationally acclaimed textbook entitled *Introduction to Plant Physiology*, which is presently in its fourth edition. As well, he has received more than 25 national and international awards and honours for his research, which include election as a fellow of the Academy of Science, Royal Society of Canada, and as president of the Canadian Society of Plant Physiologists; an honorary degree from the University of Umea, Sweden; and an honorary professorship from Xinjiang University, China.

In recent years, Hüner has been the lead investigator in the establishment of The Biotron Experimental Climate Change Research Centre, an international research facility on the campus of the University of Western Ontario. The research focus of this $30 million facility is the elucidation of the mechanisms by which plants, microbes, and insects sense and adjust to climate change. One of the unique aspects of the Biotron is that it gives researchers the ability to conduct control experiments on a much larger scale than possible in a conventional laboratory. This allows for the study of how changes to temperature, light, nutrients, and carbon dioxide concentrations may impact not only the growth of individual species, but also entire ecosystems.

---

more ATP Produced.

light is converted into the chemical energy of ATP *without* reduction of $NADP^+$ to NADPH.

Cyclic electron transport plays an important role in overall photosynthesis. The reduction of carbon dioxide by the Calvin cycle requires more ATP than NADPH, and the additional ATP molecules are provided by cyclic electron transport. Other energy-requiring reactions in the chloroplast are also depend on ATP produced by the cyclic pathway.

STUDY BREAK

To get one electron down the photosynthetic electron transport chain, how many photons need to be absorbed?

7.4 The Calvin Cycle

Recall from the last chapter that CO_2 is a fully oxidized carbon molecule and thus contains no usable energy. On the other hand, sugar molecules such as glucose and sucrose are highly reduced. They contain many C–H bonds and thus are an abundant source of energy. In the cytosol of prokaryotic photoautotrophs and in the stroma of the chloroplast, a series of 11 enzyme-catalyzed reactions use NADPH to reduce CO_2 into sugar. The overall process is, as you would expect, endergonic, requiring energy supplied by the hydrolysis of ATP. These 11 enzyme-catalyzed reactions are collectively known as the Calvin cycle (or light-independent reactions), which is by far the most dominant pathway on Earth by which CO_2 is *fixed* into carbohydrates.

7.4a The Calvin Cycle Reduces CO_2 to a Carbohydrate

The Calvin cycle is illustrated in **Figure 7.14**. It can be conceptually divided into three distinct phases: fixation, reduction, and regeneration.

Phase 1: carbon fixation. This phase involves the incorporation of a carbon atom from CO_2 into a molecule of ribulose 1,5-bisphosphate (RuBP), a five-carbon sugar, to produce two three-carbon molecules of 3-phosphoglycerate.

Phase 2: reduction. In this phase, each of the two molecules of 3-phosphoglycerate gets an additional phosphate added from the hydrolysis of ATP, producing 1,3-bisphosphoglycerate. This molecule is subsequently reduced by electrons from NADPH, producing glyceraldehyde-3-phosphate (G3P).

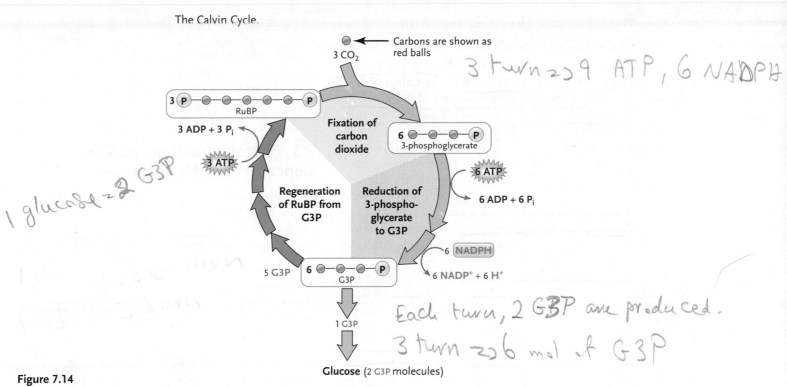

The Calvin Cycle.

3 turn = 9 ATP, 6 NADPH

1 glucose = 2 G3P

Each turn, 2 G3P are produced.
3 turn = 6 mol of G3P

Figure 7.14

Reactions of the Calvin cycle tracking carbon atoms through the cycle. What is shown is the sum of three turns of the cycle (three CO_2 molecules), which produces one extra molecule of a three-carbon sugar G3P.

Phase 3: regeneration. For each turn of the Calvin cycle, two molecules of G3P are produced—a total of six carbon atoms. In a multienzyme-step process, five of these carbons are rearranged to regenerate the single molecule of RuBP required to start the cycle over again.

What we have just described is what takes place during a *single* turn of the Calvin cycle. For each turn, one molecule of CO_2 is converted into one reduced carbon—essentially one (CH_2O) unit of carbohydrate. However, it takes three turns of the cycle to actually produce something the cell can use— one extra molecule of the three-carbon sugar G3P. Because of this, Figure 7.14 actually is a summary of three turns of the cycle as it tracks the fate of three carbon atoms.

Let's work through Figure 7.14—the key is to keep track of the carbons. In three turns of the Calvin cycle, 3 CO_2 (3 carbons) are incorporated into 3 molecules of RuBP (15 carbons), which produces 6 molecules of 3-phosphoglycerate (18 carbons). Three turns of the Calvin cycle produce 6 molecules of G3P (totalling 18 carbons). Of these, 5 molecules of G3P (totalling 15 carbons) are used to regenerate the 3 RuBP molecules (15 carbons) required for three turns of the cycle. Thus, the cycle generate one surplus molecule of G3P (three carbons) after three turns. For the synthesis of this one extra G3P, the Calvin cycle requires a total of nine molecules of ATP and six molecules of NADPH. Both ATP and NADPH are regenerated from ADP and $NADP^+$, respectively, by the light reactions.

7.4b   G3P Is the Starting Point for Synthesis of Many Other Organic Molecules

The G3P molecule formed by three turns of the Calvin cycle is the starting point for the production of a wide variety of organic molecules. More complex carbohydrates, such as glucose and other monosaccharides, are made from G3P by reactions that, in effect, reverse the first half of glycolysis. Once produced, the monosaccharides may enter biochemical pathways that make disaccharides such as sucrose, polysaccharides such as starches and cellulose, and other complex carbohydrates. Other pathways manufacture amino acids, fatty acids and lipids, proteins, and nucleic acids. The reactions forming these products occur both within chloroplasts and in the surrounding cytosol and nucleus.

Sucrose, a disaccharide consisting of glucose linked to fructose, is the main form in which the products of photosynthesis circulate from cell to cell in higher plants. Organic nutrients are stored in most higher plants as sucrose, starch, or a combination of the two in proportions that depend on the plant species. Sugar cane and sugar beets, which contain stored sucrose in high concentrations, are the main sources of the sucrose we use as table sugar.

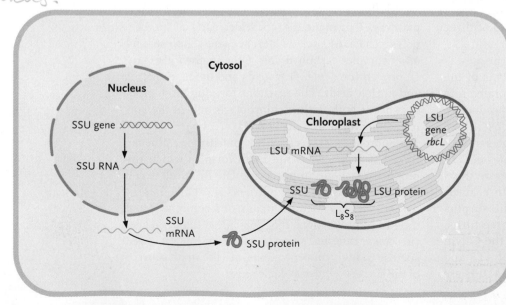

Handwritten margin notes:

Rubisco:
① catalyze first reaction of calvin cycle
② catalyze CO_2 fixation in all photoautotrophs
③ world's most abundant protein
④ cube shaped
⑤ 8 small sub unit 8 large " "
⑥ Each large sub.u. have active site for CO_2 and $RuBP$
⑦ large sub.u. is encoded by gene of chloroplast genome
⑧ small sub.u. is encoded by gene in nucleus.

7.4c Rubisco: The Most Abundant Protein on Earth

Rubulose-1,5-bisphosphate or rubisco, the enzyme that catalyzes the first reaction of the Calvin cycle, is arguably the most important enzyme of the biosphere. By catalyzing CO_2 fixation in all photoautotrophs, it provides the source of organic carbon molecules for most of the world's organisms. The enzyme converts about 100 billion tons of CO_2 into carbohydrates annually. There are so many rubisco molecules in chloroplasts that the enzyme makes up 50% or more of the total protein of plant leaves. As such, it is also the world's most abundant protein, estimated to total some 40 million tons worldwide—equivalent to about 10 kg per person on Earth.

Isolation and purification of rubisco from the chloroplast stroma have led to the elucidation of its three-dimensional structure. The molecule is cube shaped and contains eight small subunits and eight large subunits. Each of the large subunits contains an active site, which has defined binding sites for both CO_2 and RuBP. The small subunits do not have a role in catalysis but do serve an important regulatory role, although their exact function remains unknown.

The synthesis of rubisco is quite remarkable as it requires the coordinated expression of genes in two different genomes **(Figure 7.15)**. Whereas the large subunit is encoded by a gene of the chloroplast genome, the small subunit is encoded by a gene that is found in the nucleus. After the small subunit **polypeptide** is synthesized in the cytosol, it is imported into the chloroplast, where it associates with large subunit monomers to make the functional enzyme.

The vast majority of the proteins found in chloroplasts (and mitochondria) are, in fact, encoded by the nuclear genome and thus are synthesized on ribosomes in the cytosol. They are then imported into the organelle using specific transport complexes that span the membranes. Many of the protein complexes of the electron transport chains of both mitochondria and chloroplasts are the products of both nuclear and organellar genes.

7.5 Photorespiration and CO_2-Concentrating Mechanisms

Besides argulably being the most important enzyme of the biosphere, rubisco has some rather unique properties. First, it is a very slow enzyme catalzying the fixation of only about three molecules of CO_2 per second. Its slow rate of catalysis is countered by it very high abundance within the cell. Second, rubisco is remarkably inefficient at fixing CO_2. This inefficiency is because a Rubsico can also catalyze the incorporation of a molecule of O_2 into RuBP. The product of this so-called oxygenation reaction results in the formation of a molecule that is actually toxic, and its metabolism results in the loss of carbon from the cell and the consumption of ATP (in the form of CO_2). Because O_2 is consumed in this process and CO_2 released at later steps, the entire process is somewhat similar to respiration and is termed **photorespiration.**

Recall from Chapter 4 (Section 4.5b) that a molecule that can compete with the normal substrate for the active site of an enzyme is termed a competitive inhibitor. In this case, O_2 can compete with CO_2 for the active site of rubsico, and is therefore a competitive inhibitor of rubisco. This is surprising because most enzymes have active sites that are very specific for their substrates. Given the importance of rubisco to life on Earth, why would rubisco have evolved an active site that could bind both CO_2 and O_2? The most likely explanation is related to the fact that rubisco is a very ancient enzyme and is found in a range of prokaryotes. Because of this, rubisco developed at a time before oxygenic photosynthesis and, thus, at a time when there was very little O_2 in the atmosphere. Under such conditions of low atmospheric O_2 natural selection would not have favoured an enzyme that had specificity only for CO_2.

In the next few sections, we discuss some of the remarkable adaptations

Figure 7.15

Rubisco synthesis. Rubisco is an enzyme that is composed of a total of 16 subunits: 8 large subunits (LSU) and 8 small subunits (SSU). Each LSU is synthesized in the stroma of the chloroplast following the transcription of a gene coded by the chloroplast genome. The gene that encodes the SSU is found in the nucleus with SSU monomers being synthesized by cytosolic ribosomes before being imported into the chloroplast.

plants and algae have made to minimize the competition of O_2 for the active site of rubisco.

7.5a The Oxygenase Activity of Rubisco

When oxygen binds to the active site of rubisco, the enzyme acts as an *oxygenase* instead of a *carboxylase*. A comparison of the products of the carboxylation reaction and the oxygenation reaction of rubisco is shown in **Figure 7.16**. The incorporation of a CO_2 molecule into RuBP leads to a net increase in the carbon of the plant by producing two molecules of 3-phosphoglycerate. As described in the last section, this molecule gets reduced in the Calvin cycle to the three-carbon sugar G3P.

Alternatively, in the oxygenation reaction, the incorporation of O_2 into RuBP produces a single molecule of 3-phosphoglycerate and one molecule of phosphoglycolate. There is no carbon gain—five carbons in and five carbons out. But photoautotrophs cannot use phosphoglycolate. In the process of breaking it down to salvage the carbon, a toxic compound called *glycolate* is produced. The elimination of glycolate results in its oxidation that results in the release of CO_2. Thus, whereas the carboxylation reaction leads to carbon gain, the oxygenation reaction actually results in the cell losing carbon. It is worth remembering that to grow, all organisms must gain carbon.

If one compares the carboxylation and oxygenation reactions of rubisco under laboratory conditions, where we can keep the concentrations of both O_2 and CO_2 equal, then the carboxylation reaction will dominate since the active site of rubisco has a greater affinity for CO_2 than O_2. In fact, the carboxylation reaction will occur about 80 times faster than the oxygenation reaction. However, unlike in the laboratory, the atmosphere does not contain equal amounts of the two gases—it contains approximately 21% O_2 and only about 0.04% CO_2. Under normal atmospheric concentrations and at moderate temperatures, the carboxylation of rubisco will occur about 75% of the time. This means that 25% of the time, the wasteful oxygenation reaction occurs, which is a significant drain on cell resources. It should not come as a surprise that many species have evolved mechanisms to try to decrease the prevalence of the oxygenation reaction. The strategies that we discuss below involve decreasing the extent of photorespiration and the oxygenation reaction using mechanisms that increase the CO_2/O_2 ratio at the site where the Calvin cycle takes place.

7.5b Carbon-Concentrating Mechanisms in Algae

In aquatic environments, the concentration of CO_2 dissolved in the water is usually well below that needed to saturate the active site of rubisco. Yet experimentally, the addition of CO_2 to a culture of phytoplankton does not usually lead to an increase in the rate of photosynthesis.

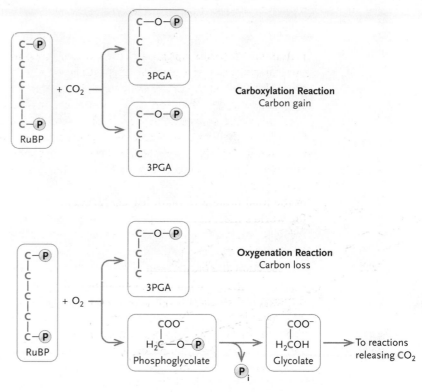

Figure 7.16

The enzyme rubisco possesses both a carboxylase and an oxygenase activity. Compared with the usual carboxylase activity of the Calvin cycle, the oxygenase activity results in a net loss of carbon by the plant. Because oxygenase activity consumes O_2 and releases CO_2, it is also called photorespiration.

These data suggest that aquatic photoautotrophs, including cyanobacteria, phytoplankton, and various other algae, possess a *carbon-concentrating mechanism* whereby inorganic carbon is actively pumped into their cells such that the concentration of CO_2 at the site of rubisco is higher than would otherwise be possible through simple diffusion.

A model for one type of carbon-concentrating mechanism is presented in **Figure 7.17**. In aqueous

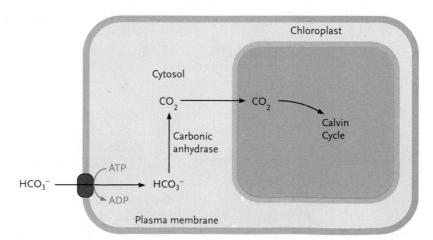

Figure 7.17

Many aquatic photoautotrophs have a CO_2-concentrating mechanism that involves an ATP-dependent bicarbonate (HCO_3) pump on the plasma membrane. The bicarbonate is rapidly converted in the cytosol to CO_2 by the enzyme carbonic anhydrase.

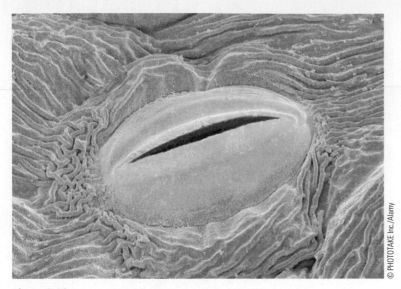

Figure 7.18
Gas exchange and water loss by a plant are controlled by the presence of stomata. Each stoma is formed from two guard cells that control the opening and closing of the pore.

© PHOTOTAKE Inc./Alamy

fully closed to fully open to balance the demands for gas exchange with the need to minimize water loss. As you may suspect, plants that are adapted to hot dry climates are faced with a constant dilemma: they need to open their stomata to let CO_2 in for the Calvin cycle, but to conserve water, they need to keep the stomata closed.

The dilemma is even harder to reconcile because photorespiration becomes a bigger problem the warmer the climate. The reason for this relates to the effect of temperature on the solubility of gases in solution (the stroma is an aqueous environment). As shown in **Table 7.1**, the solubility of O_2 and CO_2 decreases as the temperature increases. However, the solubility of CO_2 decreases more rapidly than O_2 as the temperature increases, resulting in a decrease in the CO_2/O_2 ratio. As this ratio decreases, the extent of photorespiration (oxygenation reaction) becomes greater. Under conditions of high temperature, as much as 50% of the plant's energy could be wasted by photorespiration.

environments of near-neutral pH, the dominant form of inorganic carbon is not CO_2 but rather the bicarbonate anion (HCO_3^-). In the system shown in **Figure 7.18,** an ATP-dependent pump on the plasma membrane transports HCO_3^- into the cell, resulting in a concentration that is higher inside the cell than outside. Within the cytosol, the bicarbonate is rapidly converted into CO_2 by the enzyme carbonic anhydrase. The CO_2 then rapidly diffuses into the chloroplast to the site of rubisco. This system results in a concentration of CO_2 at the site of rubisco that is sufficiently high to essentially outcompete any O_2 that is present for the active site of rubisco.

7.5c Photorespiration and the Problem of Temperature

Unlike aquatic photoautotrophs, many terrestrial plants, especially those living in hot dry climates, face not only the problem of photorespiration but also the problem of water loss. Interestingly, in many plant species, these two problems are inextricably linked.

The major photosynthetic organ of a plant is the leaf, and because of its high surface area, you would think that this would result in high rates of water loss due to evaporation. However, the surface of leaves is covered by a waxy cuticle that prevents water loss. The problem is that the cuticle also prevents the rapid diffusion of gases such as CO_2 into the leaf. To enable high rates of gas exchange (CO_2 in and O_2 out) between the air and the cells within the leaf, the surface of a leaf has small pores, called stomata (singular, stoma) (Figure 7.18). The plant can regulate the size of the stomata from

7.5d The C_4 Pathway Circumvents Photorespiration

Some plant species that are adapted to hot dry climates have evolved a mode of carbon fixation that minimizes photorespiration. Besides having the Calvin cycle, these plants have a second carbon fixation pathway, called the C_4 cycle **(Figure 7.19)**. In this cycle, CO_2 initially combines with a three-carbon molecule, *phosphoenolpyruvate* (PEP), producing the four-carbon intermediate oxaloacetate. Oxaloacetate is then reduced to *malate* by electrons transferred from NADPH. After being transported to the site of the Calvin cycle, the malate gets oxidized to pyruvate, releasing CO_2. To complete the cycle, pyruvate is converted back into PEP in a reaction that consumes ATP. The oxygenation reaction of rubisco is inhibited by the C_4 cycle because the conversion of malate to pyruvate actually generates CO_2, resulting in much higher concentrations at the site of rubisco (see Figure 7.19).

The C_4 cycle gets its name because its first product, oxaloacetate, is a four-carbon molecule rather than the

Table 7.1	Effect of Temperature on the Solubility of O_2 and CO_2		
Temperature (°C)	[CO_2] (μ M in solution)	[CO_2] (μ M in solution)	$\dfrac{[CO_2]}{[O_2]}$
5	21.93	401.2	0.0515
15	15.69	319.8	0.0462
25	11.68	264.6	0.0416
35	9.11	228.2	0.0376

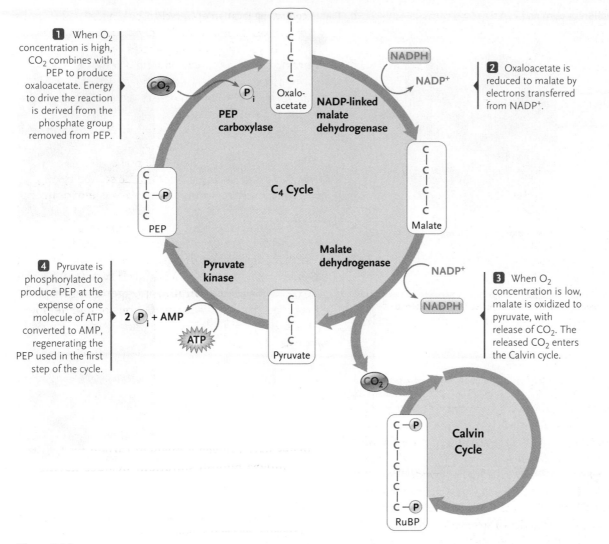

Figure 7.19

The C_4 cycle and its integration with the Calvin cycle. Enzymes are printed in rust. Each turn of the cycle, which delivers one molecule of CO_2 to the Calvin cycle, proceeds at the expense of two phosphate groups removed from ATP.

1 When O_2 concentration is high, CO_2 combines with PEP to produce oxaloacetate. Energy to drive the reaction is derived from the phosphate group removed from PEP.

2 Oxaloacetate is reduced to malate by electrons transferred from NADP+.

3 When O_2 concentration is low, malate is oxidized to pyruvate, with release of CO_2. The released CO_2 enters the Calvin cycle.

4 Pyruvate is phosphorylated to produce PEP at the expense of one molecule of ATP converted to AMP, regenerating the PEP used in the first step of the cycle.

three-carbon phosphoglycerate, the first product of the Calvin cycle. One often talks in terms of the C_4 versus the C_3 pathways when distinguishing between plants that have the C_4 cycle and those that possess only the Calvin cycle. A key distinction between C_4 and C_3 metabolism concerns the carboxylation reactions. In the C_4 cycle, the initial carboxylation reaction that incorporates CO_2 into phosphoenolpyruvate is catalyzed by the enzyme *PEP carboxylase*. Unlike rubisco, PEP carboxylase has much greater affinity for CO_2 and does not possess any oxygenase activity. It can efficiently catalyze the carboxylation of PEP regardless of the O_2 concentration near the enzyme.

7.5e C_4 Plants

Plants that possess C_4 metabolism include many tropical and several temperate crop species, including corn and sugar cane. In these species, the C_4 cycle occurs in *mesophyll* cells, which lie close to the surface of leaves and stems, where O_2 is abundant **(Figure 7.20a, b, p. 156)**. The malate intermediate of the C_4 cycle diffuses from the mesophyll cells to *bundle sheath cells*, located in deeper tissues, where O_2 is less abundant. In these cells, in which the Calvin cycle operates, the malate enters chloroplasts and is converted to pyruvate and CO_2. Because O_2 concentration is low and CO_2 concentration is high because of its release by malate breakdown, the oxygenase activity of rubisco is inhibited, and the carboxylation reaction runs highly efficiently. The pyruvate produced by malate oxidation returns to the mesophyll cells to enter another turn of the C_4 cycle.

You may ask, *if C_4 metabolism is so good at preventing photorespiration, why don't all plants use it?* Looking back at Figure 7.19, notice that the C_4 pathway has an additional energy requirement. For each turn of the C_4 cycle, the hydrolysis of ATP to AMP is required to regenerate PEP from pyruvate.

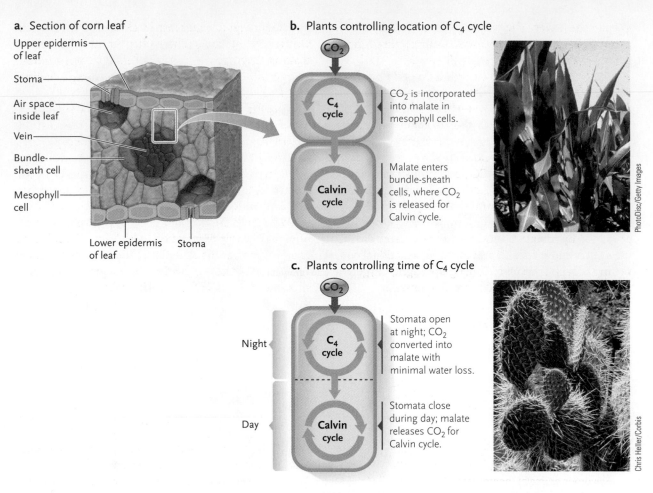

a. Section of corn leaf

Upper epidermis of leaf
Stoma
Air space inside leaf
Vein
Bundle-sheath cell
Mesophyll cell
Lower epidermis of leaf
Stoma

b. Plants controlling location of C_4 cycle

CO_2

C_4 cycle — CO_2 is incorporated into malate in mesophyll cells.

Calvin cycle — Malate enters bundle-sheath cells, where CO_2 is released for Calvin cycle.

c. Plants controlling time of C_4 cycle

CO_2

Night — C_4 cycle — Stomata open at night; CO_2 converted into malate with minimal water loss.

Day — Calvin cycle — Stomata close during day; malate releases CO_2 for Calvin cycle.

PhotoDisc/Getty Images

Chris Heller/Corbis

Figure 7.20

Coordination of the C_4 and Calvin cycles to minimize photorespiration. **(a)** and **(b)** Some C_4 plants separate the two cycles into different locations internally, as in the corn leaf shown in this diagram. The mesophyll cells (lighter green), which are closer to the leaf surfaces, carry out the C_4 cycle in a relatively O_2-rich environment. The bundle sheath cells (darker green), which are cut off from O_2 by the surrounding layer of mesophyll cells, carry out the Calvin cycle. **(c)** Other C_4 plants carry out the two cycles at different times, as in the beavertail cactus (*Opuntia basilaris*) in the photo.

This puts an additional energy requirement equivalent to six ATP molecules for each G3P produced by the Calvin cycle. However, in hot climates, photorespiration can decrease carbon fixation efficiency by over 50%, so the additional ATP requirement is worthwhile. As well, hot climates tend to receive a lot of sunshine; thus, the additional ATP requirement is easily met by increasing the output of the light reactions. In temperate climates, the lower temperatures mean that photorespiration is not as big of a problem (look back at Table 7.1), and the additional ATP requirement is harder to meet given less sunshine. As an example, in Florida, 70% of all native species are C_4 plants compared with 0% in Manitoba.

C_4 plants not only perform better where it is hot, they also perform better where it is dryer. Because PEP carboxylase has a very high affinity only for CO_2, C_4 plants are more efficient at fixing CO_2 than C_3 plants are. As a consequence, they don't have to keep their stomata open for as long as a C_3 plant does under the same conditions. Because this reduces water loss, C_4 plants are much better suited to arid conditions.

7.5f CAM Plants

Instead of running the Calvin and C_4 cycles simultaneously in different locations, some plants, such as pineapple, run the cycles at different times. These plants are known as **CAM plants**, named for **crassulacean acid metabolism**, from the Crassulaceae family in which the adaptation was first observed. The plants in this group include many with thick, succulent leaves or stems, such as the cactus shown in **Figure 7.20c.**

CAM plants typically live in regions that are hot and dry during the day and cool at night. Their fleshy leaves or stems have a low surface-to-volume ratio, and their stomata are reduced in number. Further, the stomata open only at night, when they release O_2 that accumulates from photosynthesis during the day and allow CO_2

to enter the leaves. The entering CO_2 is fixed by the C_4 pathway into malate, which accumulates throughout the night and is stored in large cell vacuoles.

Daylight initiates the second phase of the strategy. As the sun comes up and the temperature rises, the stomata close, reducing water loss and cutting off the exchange of gases with the atmosphere. Malate diffuses from cell vacuoles into the cytosol, where it is oxidized to pyruvate, and CO_2 is released in high concentration. The high CO_2 concentration favours the carboxylase activity of rubisco, allowing the Calvin cycle to proceed at maximum efficiency with little loss of organic carbon from photorespiration. The pyruvate produced by malate breakdown accumulates during the day; as night falls, it enters the C_4 reactions, converting it back to malate. During the night, oxygen is released by the plants, and more CO_2 enters.

Reduction of water loss by closure of the stomata during the hot daylight hours has the added benefit of making CAM plants highly resistant to dehydration. As a result, CAM species can tolerate extreme daytime heat and dryness.

In this chapter, you have seen how photosynthesis supplies the organic molecules used as fuels by almost all the organisms of the world. Photosynthesis is a story of capturing photons of light and using the energy to oxidize water and using the liberated electrons to fix CO_2 into carbohydrates and other fuel molecules. The high-energy electrons are then removed from the fuel molecules by the oxidative reactions of cellular respiration, which use the released energy to power the activities of life. Among the most significant of these activities are cell growth and division, the subjects of the next chapter.

Unanswered Questions

Photosynthesis is considered by many to be the most important biological process on Earth. In particular, directly or indirectly (through herbivorous animals), photosynthesis provides all of our food requirements. Research on photosynthesis therefore is of high importance and is likely to have significant benefit for humankind. For example, a complete understanding of the chemistry of photosynthesis, the regulation of the process, and the genes that encode the components of the process could be applicable to other endeavours of human interest, such as solar energy conversion and the development of therapeutic drugs.

From research on agricultural crops, we have learned that photosynthesis is not a very efficient process. Estimates are that only 1 to 2% of the solar energy that strikes the planet's surface is converted to new photosynthetic products. Research is being done to learn enough about photosynthesis so that crop plants can be engineered to be more efficient. An area of particular relevance here is photorespiration, which reduces the efficiency of energy use in photosynthesis. It is hoped that research will give us a better understanding of the biochemical control of photorespiration and provide clues about breeding new, more energy-efficient plants.

Let us consider two specific avenues of research.

How is the efficiency of photosynthesis regulated?

The laboratory of David Kramer at Washington State University is interested in the energetics and control of photosynthesis, the electron transfer reactions, the coupling of electron transfer reactions to ATP synthesis, and photosynthesis in extreme environments. As you have learned, energy conversion by the chloroplast involves the capture of light energy and the channelling of that energy through an electron transfer system with the eventual synthesis of NADPH and ATP.

At high concentrations, many of the intermediates produced in this energy conversion can potentially destroy the photosynthetic apparatus, a phenomenon called photoinhibition. To prevent such damage, the efficiency of some of the photosystem components is reduced by the release of some of the energy as heat. Increased heat lowers the efficiency of photosynthesis, however. Evidence from a range of studies indicates that the balance between protection against photoinhibition and photosynthetic efficiency is important in enabling plants to acclimate to environmental changes. Kramer's group is doing research to develop an understanding of the structure and function of ATP synthase and the cytochrome complex and the effects of these components on the proton-motive force, which is known to play a pivotal role in balancing photoinhibition and photosynthetic efficiency. The results will illuminate how the specific mechanisms of photosynthesis determine plant growth and survival. In addition, the technology developed as part of the research may lead to applications in plant breeding and farming, providing farmers with a means to assess the physiological states of the plants they are growing and, therefore, to modify the conditions for optimal growth.

How are chloroplast thylakoid membrane–protein complexes assembled?

Research by Andrew Webber's group at Arizona State University is directed at understanding the formation of chloroplast thylakoid membrane–protein complexes. Those complexes are key to the process of photosynthesis, but their assembly is not understood. Using molecular biology and biochemistry techniques, Webber's group is studying how the synthesis of chloroplast proteins, some of which are encoded by genes in the chloroplast and others of which are encoded by genes in the nucleus, is coordinated and regulated. The researchers are also using molecular techniques to change specific amino acids in the chloroplast proteins with the aim of elucidating how those amino acids are involved in the assembly and functioning of the complexes. The results will add more detailed knowledge about the structure and function of components that are key to the process of photosynthesis.

Review

Go to CENGAGENOW™ at http://hed.nelson.com/ to access quizzing, animations, exercises, articles, and personalized homework help.

7.1 Photosynthesis: An Overview

- Photoautotrophs are the primary producers of the planet as they use the energy of sunlight to drive synthesis of organic molecules from simple inorganic raw materials. The organic molecules are used by the photosynthesizers themselves as fuels; they also form the primary energy source for animals, fungi, and other heterotrophs.

- Photosynthesis takes place in two overall stages called the light reactions and the Calvin cycle. In eukaryotes, both stages take place inside chloroplasts.

- Absorption of light energy is used to synthesize NADPH and ATP through photosynthetic electron transport and chemiosmosis, respectively.

7.2 The Photosynthetic Apparatus

- Pigment molecules absorb light of specific wavelengths that result in electrons being raised to an excited state.

- Pigments including chlorophylls and carotenoids are organized into two types of photosystems: photosystem I and photosystem II. Each contains a reaction centre surrounded by an antenna complex.

- Energy trapped by the antenna complex is funnelled to the reaction centre, where it is used to oxidize a chlorophyll and donate an electron to a primary acceptor molecule.

7.3 Photosynthetic Electron Transport

- Photosystem II absorbs light energy that oxidizes the reaction centre chlorophyll P680, producing the powerful oxidant P680$^+$. This molecule oxidizes water, releasing electrons and O_2. The O_2 escapes into the atmosphere.

- Electrons from photosystem II are passed through an electron transfer system. In the first part of the pathway, called non-cyclic electron transport, electrons removed from water are excited in photosystem II. The electrons become excited again in photosystem I, and then they are delivered to NADP$^+$ as the final electron acceptor. NADP$^+$ is reduced to NADPH by NADP$^+$ reductase.

- ATP is generated through chemiosmosis by the establishment of a proton gradient across the thylakoid membrane. An ATP synthase in the thylakoid membrane operates in a fashion identical to that seen in cellular respiration.

- Electrons can also flow cyclically around photosystem I, building the H$^+$ concentration and allowing extra ATP to be produced, but no NADPH.

7.4 The Calvin Cycle

- In the Calvin cycle, CO_2 is reduced and converted into organic substances by the addition of electrons and hydrogen carried by the NADPH produced in the light reactions. ATP, also derived from the light reactions, provides additional energy. The key enzyme of the Calvin cycle is rubisco (RuBP carboxylase/oxygenase), which catalyzes the reaction that combines CO_2 into organic compounds.

- For every three turns of the Calvin cycle, a single molecule of the three-carbon molecule G3P is produced. G3P is the starting point for synthesis of glucose, sucrose, starches, and other organic molecules.

- The Calvin cycle reactions take place in the chloroplast stroma in eukaryotes and in the cytoplasm of photosynthetic bacteria.

7.5 Photorespiration and CO_2-Concentrating Mechanisms

- Oxygen can compete with CO_2 for the active site of rubisco.

- As an oxygenase, rubisco catalyzes the combination of RuBP with O_2 rather than with CO_2, forming toxic products that cannot be used in photosynthesis. The toxic products are eliminated by reactions that release carbon in inorganic form as CO_2, greatly reducing the efficiency of photosynthesis. The entire process is called photorespiration because it uses oxygen and releases CO_2.

- Some plants have evolved the C_4 pathway, a supplemental system that bypasses the oxygenase activity of rubisco. In the pathway, initial fixation of CO_2 is catalyzed by a carboxylase that has no oxygenase activity, in specific locations or at times within the plant when oxygen is overabundant. In later steps, the CO_2 is released at relatively oxygen-free regions or times for final fixation in the reactions using RuBP in the Calvin cycle.

Questions

Self-Test Questions

1. Photosynthesis
   a. results in the breakdown of food molecules releasing energy.
   b. uses the energy of light to oxidize CO_2.
   c. occurs only in eukaryotic cells.
   d. generates ATP by substrate-level phosphorylation.
   e. results in the reduction of CO_2 to energy-rich organic molecules.

2. The light reactions of photosynthesis resemble aerobic respiration as both
   a. synthesize NADPH.
   b. synthesize NADH.
   c. synthesize ATP by chemiosmosis.
   d. require oxygen as the final electron acceptor.
   e. have the same initial energy source.

3. Which one of the following statements is correct?
   a. It takes four photons of light to reduce one molecule of NADP$^+$ to NADPH.
   b. It takes two photons of light to split one molecule of H_2O.
   c. The reaction centre of PSII contains P700.
   d. P680 is easier to oxidize than P680*.
   e. Both a and d are correct.

4. The role of cyclic electron transport is to
   a. produce both ATP and NADPH.
   b. increase the amount of ATP generated by the light reactions.
   c. produce NADH rather than NADPH.
   d. increase the rate of O_2 evolution by the light reactions.
   e. Both b and d are correct.

5. Rubisco
   a. is a catalytically very fast enzyme.
   b. is not very abundant.
   c. is assembled into a functional enzyme in the cytosol.
   d. is encoded by a single gene found in the nucleus.
   e. contains a total of 16 subunits.

6. With regard to rubisco, oxygen
   a. is an allosteric activator of the enzyme.
   b. is a competitive inhibitor.
   c. helps prevent photorespiration.
   d. increases the catalytic efficiency of the carboxylation reaction.
   e. is produced when rubisco "splits" water.

7. In three turns of the Calvin cycle,
   a. one molecule of glucose is synthesized.
   b. six molecules of ATP are hydrolyzed.
   c. six NADPH molecules are oxidized.
   d. one (CH_2O) unit of carbohydrate is formed.
   e. two molecules of phosphoenolpyruvate (PEP) are synthesized.

8. Photorespiration does not occur in C_4 plants because
   a. during the daytime, C_4 plants do not respire.
   b. the active site of rubisco in C_4 plants can only bind CO_2.
   c. C_4 plants lack rubisco.
   d. PEP carboxylase binds O_2.
   e. O_2 concentration in bundle sheath cells is kept very low.

9. Which of the following statements about the C_4 cycle is NOT correct?
   a. CO_2 initially combines with phosphoenolpyruvate.
   b. PEP carboxylase catalyzes a reaction to produce oxaloacetate.
   c. Oxaloacetate transfers electrons from $NADP^+$ and is reduced to malate.
   d. Less ATP is used to run the C_4 cycle than the C_3 cycle.
   e. The cycle runs when O_2 concentration is high.

10. At high temperatures, C_4 plants use less water than C_3 plants because
    a. their leaves are not covered by a waxy cuticle.
    b. they don't have to keep their stomata open as long.
    c. they have a larger root system.
    d. they have smaller leaves.
    e. they can keep their stomata closed at all times.

Questions for Discussion

1. What would be the absorption spectrum of a plant that is purple in colour?

2. Exposing plants to light at low temperatures increases the damage to photosystem II. Why do you think this is the case?

3. If global warming raises the temperature of our climate significantly, will C_3 plants or C_4 plants be favoured by natural selection? How will global warming change the geographic distributions of plants?

A B cell and a T cell communicating by direct contact in the human immune system (computer image). Cell communication coordinates the cellular defence against disease.

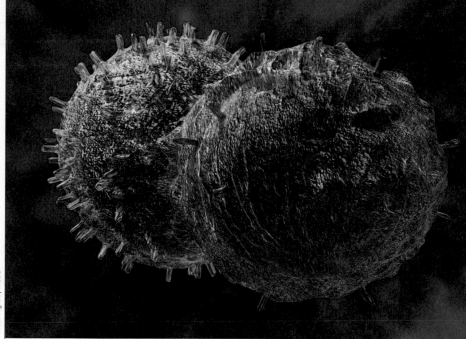

Russell Kightley Media

8 Cell Communication

WHY IT MATTERS

Hundreds of aircraft, ranging from small private planes to huge passenger jets, approach and leave airports in Southern California. In addition to the large terminals in Los Angeles and San Diego, dozens of smaller airports are located in the vicinity. The aircraft that approach these airports are travelling at various speeds, entering from all points of the compass, and flying at different altitudes. Airplanes are also leaving the same airports with routes distributed over the same directions, speeds, and altitudes. A wrong turn, ascent, or descent by any one of the hundreds of planes could lead to disaster. Yet disasters are extremely rare. How are all these aircraft kept separate and routed to and from their airports safely and efficiently? The answer lies in a highly organized system of controllers, signals, and receivers.

As the aircraft thread their way along the various approach and departure routes, they follow directions arriving on a radio frequency unique to each aircraft. Instructions arriving on the frequency assigned to Piper 4879Z, a slow-moving two-seater headed for Montgomery Field near San Diego, keep this plane's path separate from that of "five-two heavy," a passenger jet, leaving the main San Diego air terminal. The flow of directing signals, followed individually by each aircraft in the vicinity, keeps the traffic unscrambled and moving safely.

The principle of the air control system is nothing new. An equivalent system of signals and tuned receivers evolved hundreds of millions of years ago as one of the developments that made multicellular life possible. Within a multicellular organism, the activities of individual cells are directed by molecular signals, such as hormones, that are released by controlling cells. Although the controlling cells release many signals, each receiving cell has receptors that are "tuned" to recognize only one or a few of the many signal molecules that circulate in its vicinity; other signals pass by without effect because the cell has no receptors for them.

When a cell binds a signal molecule via a receptor, it modifies its internal activities in accordance with the signal, coordinating its functions with the activities of other cells of the organism. The responses of the receiving cell may include changes in gene activity, protein synthesis, transport of molecules across the plasma membrane, metabolic reactions, secretion, movement, and division. In some cases, the response to a signal may be "suicide" or programmed death of the receiving cell **(Figure 8.1)**. As part of its response, a cell may itself become a signaller and thus contribute to the organizational network by releasing signal molecules that modify the activity of other cell types. The total network of signals and responses allows multicellular organisms to grow, develop, reproduce, and compensate for environmental changes in an internally coordinated fashion.

This chapter describes the major pathways that form parts of the cell communication system based on both surface and internal receptors, including the links that tie the different response pathways into fully integrated networks. (Nerve communication in animals is discussed in Chapter 33.) This chapter concentrates primarily on the systems working in animals, particularly in mammals, from which most of our knowledge of cell communication has been developed. Nonetheless, the principles of cell communication illustrated by these pathways apply to most eukaryotic organisms, including plants, protists and fungi. (The plant communication and control systems are described in more detail in Chapter 31.) This discussion begins with a few fundamental principles that underlie the often complex networks of cell communication.

8.1 Cell Communication: An Overview

Communication is critical for the function and survival of cells that compose a multicellular animal. For example, the ability of cells to communicate with one another in a regulated way is responsible for the controlled growth and development of an animal, as well as the integrated activities of its tissues and organs.

Cells communicate with one another in three ways. Adjacent cells use direct channels of communication. In this rapid means of communication, small molecules and ions exchange directly between the two cytoplasms. In animal cells, the direct channels of communication are *gap junctions,* the specialized connections between the cytoplasms of adjacent cells (Chapter 32). The main role of gap junctions is to synchronize metabolic activities or electronic signals between cells in a tissue. For example, gap junctions play a key role in the spread of electrical signals from one cell to the next in cardiac muscle. In plant cells, the direct channels of communication are plasmodesmata (see Chapter 28). Small molecules moving between adjacent cells in plants include plant hormones that regulate growth. In this way, responses triggered by plant hormones are spread to other cells.

Cells also communicate through *specific contact between cells.* Certain cells have molecules on their surfaces that allow them to interact directly with other cells. Some cells use their surface molecules to recognize particular molecules on the surfaces of invading pathogens or parasites that signal them as foreign. The host cell then engulfs the invader. Cells also have on their surfaces *cell adhesion molecules,* integral membrane proteins that allow the cells to bind to other cells or to the extracellular matrix. There are many important functions of cell adhesion molecules, including roles in cell movement and coordinating tissue and organ formation as an embryo develops.

Finally, cells communicate through *intercellular* ("between cell") *chemical messengers.* This method is the most common means of cell communication. Here, one cell, the *controlling cell,* synthesizes a specific molecule that acts as a *signalling molecule* to affect the activity of another cell, the *target cell.* The target cell is not in contact with the cell that synthesizes the signalling molecule; rather, it is either nearby or at a distance away in the organism. For example, in response to stress, cells of the adrenal glands (located on top of the kidneys) secrete the hormone epinephrine into the bloodstream. Among its actions, epinephrine acts on target cells so that the amount of glucose in the blood increases.

Cell communication through intercellular chemical messengers is the focus of this chapter, and the

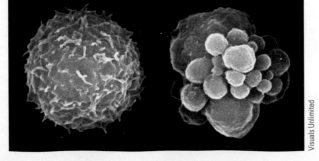

Figure 8.1
A normal cell (left) and a cell undergoing apoptosis (programmed cell death) (right).

Visuals Unlimited

epinephrine example is used to illustrate the principles involved. In the 1950s, Earl Sutherland and his research team at Case Western Reserve University, Cleveland, Ohio, began investigating this cell communication system. Sutherland discovered that the hormone epinephrine acts by activating an enzyme, glycogen phosphorylase, which catalyzes the production of glucose from glycogen. That is, the result of the secretion of epinephrine into the blood by adrenal gland cells is an increase in the amount of glucose in the blood. Sutherland's experiments showed that enzyme activation did not involve epinephrine directly but did require an unknown (at the time) cellular substance. Sutherland called the hormone the *first messenger* in the system and the unknown cellular substance the *second messenger*. He proposed that the following chain of reactions was involved: epinephrine (the first messenger) leads to the formation of the second messenger, which activates the enzyme for conversion of glycogen to glucose.

Sutherland's work was the foundation for research that developed our current understanding of this type of cell communication. In brief, a controlling cell releases a signal molecule that causes a response (affects the function) of target cells. Target cells

process the signal in the following three sequential steps **(Figure 8.2):**

1. **Reception.** Reception is the binding of a signal molecule with a specific receptor of target cells. Target cells have receptors that are specific for the signal molecule, which distinguishes them from cells that do not respond to the signal molecule. The signal molecules are often peptides or steroids, but many other types of molecules, such as amines, can act as chemical signals between cells. Each molecule will have a cellular receptor that is shaped to recognize and bind that molecule specifically **(Figure 8.3).** Membrane receptors are normally embedded in the plasma membrane with a binding site for the signal molecule on the cell surface (see Figures 8.2 and 8.3a). Epinephrine, the first messenger in Sutherland's research, is an

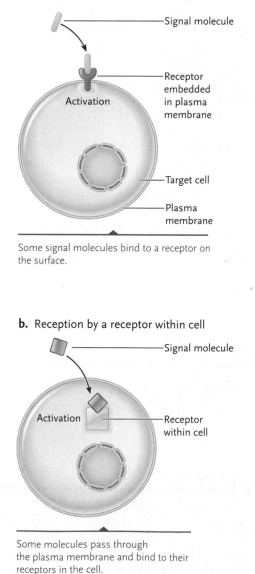

a. Reception by a cell-surface receptor

Some signal molecules bind to a receptor on the surface.

b. Reception by a receptor within cell

Some molecules pass through the plasma membrane and bind to their receptors in the cell.

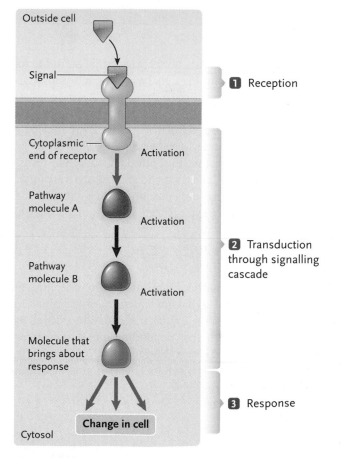

Figure 8.2
The three stages of signal transduction: reception, transduction, and response (shown for a system using a surface receptor).

Figure 8.3
Reception **(a)** of a signal molecule by a receptor on the cell surface and **(b)** of a signal molecule by a receptor in the cell.

Douglas Storey, University of Calgary

Bacterial cells are also able to communicate with each other via chemical signals, a communication system known as **quorum sensing** (see Chapter 21). In this method of communication, a growing population of bacteria produces signalling molecules (either peptides or lactones, depending on the type of bacterium) that accumulate in the environment around the cells. When the concentration of these signalling molecules reaches a critical threshold, they bind to protein receptors inside the bacterial cells. The complex formed by the signal molecule and the protein receptor then binds to specific regions of the cell's genome, activating certain genes. In this way, cells "know" that their population is large enough to perform some coordinated function and synthesize the proteins necessary to carry out that function. Behaviours that are regulated by quorum sensing include bioluminescence (see Chapter 1) and biofilm formation (see Chapter 21). In addition, quorum sensing also regulates pathogenesis as the bacteria begin to produce virulence factors (molecules that cause disease or create conditions needed for the pathogen to thrive inside the host). This last aspect of quorum sensing has important implications for our understanding of pathogenic bacteria—does quorum sensing occur in pathogenic bacteria infecting humans?

This is a question of great interest to Doug Storey, a microbiologist at the University of Calgary. Storey studies *Pseudomonas aeruginosa*, a bacterium that causes serious lung infections in people with cystic fibrosis (See chapter 5 for a discussion of this disease). Storey's research goal is to understand how *P. aeruginosa* is able to infect the lungs of CF patients and to look for new ways of fighting these infections. Of particular interest to Storey are the virulence factors produced by *P. aeruginosa*—what regulates the production of these factors? Does *P. aeruginosa* use quorum sensing to regulate levels of virulence factors when infecting host lungs? Recent research carried out by Storey and his collaborators indicates that the quorum-sensing system of *P. aeruginosa* does function in the lungs of CF patients and coordinates gene expression. This finding offers the potential for a new way to fight these lung infections: perhaps we can interfere with the bacterium's communication system and so prevent it from synthesizing virulence factors. We need to have a better understanding of the details of quorum sensing, but this is an exciting new tool in the fight against pathogenic infections.

---

amine that is recognized by a surface receptor on target cells. Receptors for some molecules are located within the cell (see Figure 8.3b). In this case, the signal molecule passes freely through the plasma membrane and interacts with its receptor within the cell. Steroid hormones such as testosterone and estrogen are examples of signal molecules that act on receptors within the cell. Many steroids also have separate actions via membrane receptors. Receptors at the cell surface, *membrane receptors,* usually involve rapid, short-lived events. Internal receptors often act directly on the genome (*nuclear receptors*), activating specific genes. These responses and reactions occur over a longer time.

Although the focus of this chapter is on eukaryotes, bacteria also engage in chemical communication (see *People Behind Biology*).

2. **Transduction.** Transduction is the process of changing the signal into the form necessary to cause the cellular response (see Figure 8.2). In other words, the binding of a signal molecule to its receptor is not directly responsible for the response. Transduction may occur in a single step, although more often it involves a cascade of reactions that include several different molecules, often referred to as a *signalling cascade.* For example, in Sutherland's work, after epinephrine bound to its surface receptor, the signal was transmitted through the plasma membrane into the cell, where transduction by a signalling cascade activated a molecule that triggered a cellular response. This molecule was Sutherland's *second messenger.*

3. **Response.** In the third and last stage, the transduced signal causes a specific cellular response. That response depends on the signal and the receptors on the target cell. In Sutherland's work, the response was the activation of the enzyme glycogen phosphorylase; the active enzyme catalyzed the conversion of stored glycogen to glucose.

The whole series of events from reception to response is called **signal transduction.** As explained in subsequent sections, signal transduction occurs by different mechanisms, depending on the receptor type. Earl Sutherland was awarded a Nobel Prize in 1971 for his research on the mechanisms of action of hormones.

STUDY BREAK

What accounts for the specificity of a cellular response in signal transduction?

8.2 Characteristics of Cell Communication Systems with Surface Receptors

Cell communication systems based on surface receptors have three components: (1) the extracellular signal molecules released by controlling cells, (2) the surface receptors on target cells that receive the signals, and (3) the internal response pathways triggered when receptors bind a signal.

8.2a Hormones and Neurotransmitters Are Extracellular Signal Molecules Recognized by Surface Receptors in Animals

Surface receptors in mammals and other vertebrates recognize and bind two major types of extracellular signal molecules: *hormones* and *neurotransmitters*. These signal molecules are released by control cells and enter the fluids that surround cells, including the blood circulation in animals with a circulatory system.

Hormones (see Chapter 35) are molecules, usually peptides or steroids, that are released by specialized gland cells such as the adrenal glands, by specialized nerve cells such as the pituitary, or by cells distributed in organs such as the liver or intestines. A special class of peptides, the growth factors, affects cell growth, division, and differentiation.

Neurotransmitters are molecules released by neurons that trigger activity in other neurons or other cells in the body; they include small peptides, individual amino acids or their derivatives, and other chemical substances. Some neurotransmitters affect only one or a few cells in the immediate vicinity of the neuron that releases the signal molecule, whereas others are released into the body circulation and act essentially as hormones, affecting many types of tissues. (Neurotransmitters are discussed in further detail in Chapter 33.)

Once signal molecules are released into the body's circulation, they remain for only a certain time. They are either broken down at a steady rate by enzymes in their target cells or in organs such as the liver, or they are excreted by the kidneys. The removal process ensures that the signal molecules are active only as long as controlling cells are secreting them.

8.2b Surface Receptors Are Integral Membrane Glycoproteins

The surface receptors that recognize and bind signal molecules are all glycoproteins—proteins with attached carbohydrate chains. They are integral membrane proteins that extend entirely through the plasma membrane **(Figure 8.4)**. The signal-binding site of the receptor, which extends from the outer membrane surface, is folded in a way that closely fits the signal molecule. The fit, similar to the fit of an enzyme to its substrate, is specific, so a particular receptor binds only one type of signal molecule or a closely related group of signal molecules.

A signal molecule brings about specific changes to the receptor and therefore to the cells to which it binds. When a signal molecule binds to a surface receptor, the molecular structure of that receptor is changed so that it transmits the signal through the plasma membrane, activating the cytoplasmic end of the receptor. The activated receptor then initiates the first step in a cascade of molecular events—the signal transduction pathway—that triggers the cellular response (see Figure 8.2).

Animal cells typically have hundreds to thousands of surface receptors that represent many receptor types. Membrane receptors for a specific hormone may number from 500 to as many as 100 000 or more per cell. Different cell types contain distinct combinations of receptors, allowing them to react individually to the hormones and growth factors circulating in the extracellular fluids. The combination of surface receptors on particular cell types is not fixed but rather changes as cells develop. Changes also occur as normal cells are transformed into cancer cells.

a. Surface receptor

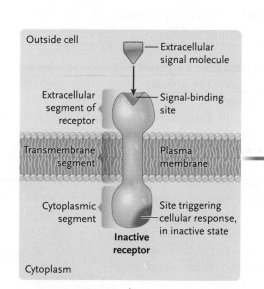

A surface receptor has an extracellular segment with a site that recognizes and binds a particular signal molecule.

b. Activation of receptor by binding of a specific signal molecule

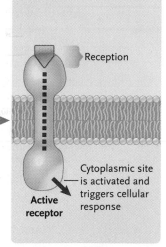

When the signal molecule is bound, a conformational change is transmitted through the transmembrane segment that activates a site on the cytoplasmic segment of receptor. The activation triggers a reaction pathway that results in the cellular response.

Figure 8.4
The mechanism by which a surface receptor responds when it binds a signal molecule.

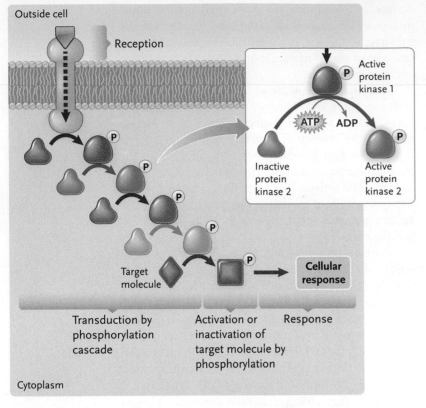

Figure 8.5
Phosphorylation, a key reaction in many signalling pathways.

8.2c The Signalling Molecule Bound by a Surface Receptor Triggers Response Pathways within the Cell

Signal transduction pathways triggered by surface receptors are common to all animal cells. At least parts of the pathways are also found in protists, fungi, and plants.

In all cases, binding of a signal molecule to a surface receptor triggers the cellular response without entering the cell. Experiments have shown that (1) a signal molecule produces no response if it is injected directly into the cytoplasm, and (2) unrelated molecules that mimic the structure of the normal extracellular signal molecule can trigger a full cellular response as long as they can bind to the recognition site of the receptor.

A second typical characteristic of signal transduction is that the signal is relayed inside the cell by **protein kinases**, enzymes that transfer a phosphate group from ATP to one or more sites on particular proteins (**Figure 8.5**). These phosphorylated proteins are

known as *target proteins* because they are the proteins modified by signalling pathways. The added phosphate groups either stimulate or inhibit the activity of the target proteins; the change in the target proteins' activity leads directly or indirectly to the cellular response. Often protein kinases act in a chain, called a *protein kinase cascade,* to pass along a signal. The first kinase catalyzes phosphorylation of the second, which then becomes active and phosphorylates the third kinase, and so on. The proteins that bring about the cellular response may be parts of the reaction pathways, enzymes of other cellular reactions, end targets of the signal transduction pathways (such as transport proteins), or, at the most fundamental level, proteins that regulate gene transcription.

The effects of protein kinases in the signal transduction pathways are balanced or reversed by another group of enzymes called **protein phosphatases**, which remove phosphate groups from target proteins. Unlike the protein kinases, which are active only when a surface receptor binds a signal molecule, most of the protein phosphatases are continuously active in cells. By continually removing phosphate groups from target proteins, the protein phosphatases quickly shut off a signal transduction pathway if its signal molecule is no longer bound at the cell surface.

A third characteristic of signal transduction pathways involving surface receptors is **amplification**—an increase in the magnitude of each step as a signal transduction pathway proceeds (**Figure 8.6**). Amplification occurs because many of the proteins that carry out individual steps in the pathways, including the protein kinases, are enzymes. Once activated, each enzyme can activate hundreds of proteins, including other enzymes, that enter the next step in the pathway. Generally, the more enzyme-catalyzed steps in a

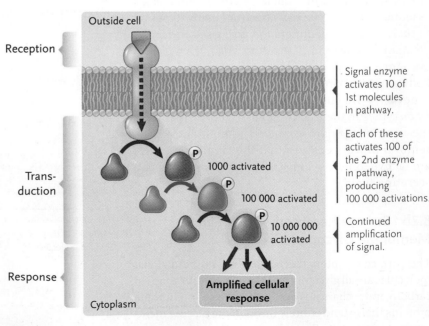

Figure 8.6
Amplification in signal transduction.

response pathway, the greater the amplification. As a result, just a few extracellular signal molecules binding to their receptors can produce a full internal response. For similar reasons, amplification also occurs for signal transduction pathways that involve internal receptors.

As signal transduction runs its course, the receptors and their bound signal molecules are removed from the cell surface by endocytosis. Both the receptor and its bound signal molecule may be degraded in lysosomes after entering the cell. Alternatively, the receptors may be separated from the signal molecules and recycled to the cell surface, whereas only the signal molecules are degraded. Thus, surface receptors participate in an extremely lively cellular "conversation" with moment-to-moment shifts in the information.

The next two sections discuss two large families of surface receptors: the receptor tyrosine kinases and the G protein–coupled receptors.

STUDY BREAK

1. What are protein kinases, and how are they involved in signal transduction pathways?
2. How is amplification accomplished in a signal transduction pathway?

8.3 Surface Receptors with Built-in Protein Kinase Activity: Receptor Tyrosine Kinases

In the simplest form of signal transduction, the receptor itself has a protein kinase site at its cytoplasmic end. For this type of receptor, initiation of transduction occurs when two receptor molecules each bind a signal molecule in the reception step, move together in the membrane, and assemble into a pair called a *dimer* **(Figure 8.7)**. Dimer assembly

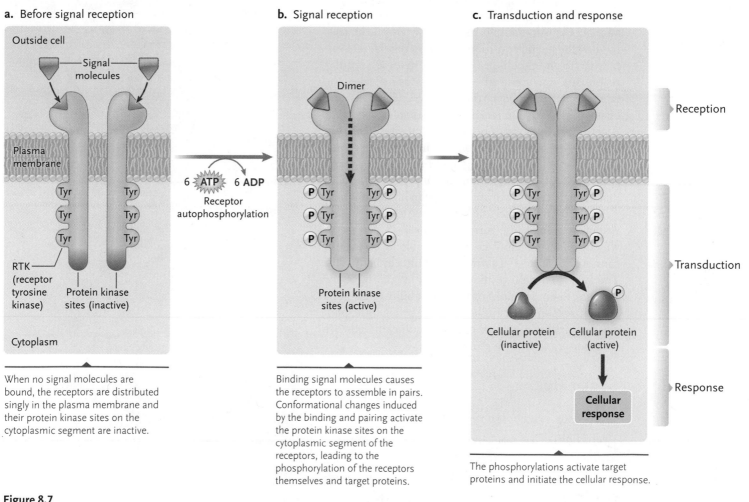

a. Before signal reception

Outside cell

Signal molecules

Plasma membrane

Tyr Tyr
Tyr Tyr
Tyr Tyr

RTK (receptor tyrosine kinase)   Protein kinase sites (inactive)

Cytoplasm

When no signal molecules are bound, the receptors are distributed singly in the plasma membrane and their protein kinase sites on the cytoplasmic segment are inactive.

6 ATP   6 ADP
Receptor autophosphorylation

b. Signal reception

Dimer

P Tyr   Tyr P
P Tyr   Tyr P
P Tyr   Tyr P

Protein kinase sites (active)

Binding signal molecules causes the receptors to assemble in pairs. Conformational changes induced by the binding and pairing activate the protein kinase sites on the cytoplasmic segment of the receptors, leading to the phosphorylation of the receptors themselves and target proteins.

c. Transduction and response

P Tyr   Tyr P
P Tyr   Tyr P
P Tyr   Tyr P

Cellular protein (inactive)   Cellular protein (active) P

Cellular response

Reception

Transduction

Response

The phosphorylations activate target proteins and initiate the cellular response.

Figure 8.7
The action of receptors with built-in protein kinase activity leading to the phosphorylation of the receptors themselves and the subsequent phosphorylation of target proteins. These receptors are called receptor tyrosine kinases because they add phosphate groups to tyrosines in target proteins. These receptors combine into pairs (dimers) when they bind signal molecules; the assembly into a dimer transmits the signal that activates the cytoplasmic end of the receptors.

activates the receptor's protein kinase, which adds phosphate groups to sites on the receptor itself, a process known as *autophosphorylation*. Target proteins recognize and bind to the phosphorylated sites on the receptor and are then activated by being phosphorylated themselves. The total effect of the phosphorylations is to initiate the signal transduction pathway controlled by the receptor.

In autophosphorylation, the phosphate groups are added to tyrosine amino acids on the receptor. The protein kinase activity of the activated receptors also adds phosphate groups to tyrosines in the amino acid chains of target proteins. Because of this specificity of phosphorylation, the receptors in this group are called **receptor tyrosine kinases**. More than 50 receptor tyrosine kinases are known. In mammals, receptor tyrosine kinases fall into 14 different families, all related to one another in structure and amino acid sequence. Relatives of the mammalian receptors have been discovered in yeasts, *Drosophila,* and higher plants, indicating that the origin of the receptor tyrosine kinases is a single ancestral type that must have appeared before the evolutionary splits that led to the fungi, plants, and animals.

The cellular responses triggered by receptor tyrosine kinases are among the most important processes of animal cells. For example, the receptor tyrosine kinases binding the peptide hormone *insulin,* a regulator of carbohydrate metabolism, triggers diverse cellular responses, including effects on glucose uptake, the rates of many metabolic reactions, and cell growth and division. (The insulin receptor is exceptional because it is permanently in the dimer form.) Other receptor tyrosine kinases bind growth factors, including *epidermal growth factor, platelet-derived growth factor,* and *nerve growth factor,* which are all important peptide hormones that regulate cell growth and division in higher animals.

Hereditary defects in the insulin receptor are responsible for some forms of *diabetes,* a disease in which glucose accumulates in the blood because it cannot be absorbed in sufficient quantity by body cells. The inherited defects may impair the ability of the receptor to bind insulin or block its ability to trigger a cellular response. In either case, the cell is unresponsive to insulin and does not add sufficient glucose transporters to take up glucose.

STUDY BREAK

How does a receptor tyrosine kinase become activated?

8.4 G Protein–Coupled Receptors

A second large family of surface receptors, known as the **G protein–coupled receptors**, respond to a signal by activating an inner membrane protein called a G protein, which is closely associated with the cytoplasmic end of the receptor. About 1000 different G protein–coupled receptors have been identified; several hundred types are involved in recognizing and binding odour molecules as part of the sense of smell. Almost all of the receptors of this group are large glycoproteins built up from a single polypeptide chain anchored in the plasma membrane by seven segments of the amino acid chain that zigzag back and forth across the membrane seven times **(Figure 8.8)**.

Unlike receptor tyrosine kinases, these receptors lack built-in protein kinase activity.

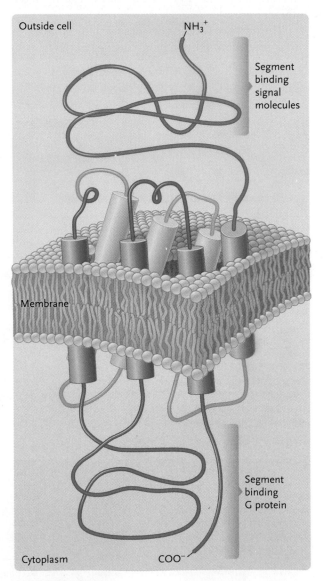

Figure 8.8

Structure of the G protein–coupled receptors, which activate separate protein kinases. These receptors have seven transmembrane α-helical segments (shown as cylinders) that zigzag across the plasma membrane. Binding of a signal molecule at the cell surface, by inducing changes in the positions of some of the helices, activates the cytoplasmic end of the receptor.

8.4a G Proteins Are Key Molecular Switches in Second-Messenger Pathways

The extracellular signal molecule in signal transduction pathways controlled by G protein–coupled receptors is termed the **first messenger**. Binding the first messenger by the receptor activates a site on the cytoplasmic end of the receptor (**Figure 8.9**, step 1). The active site of the receptor then activates the G protein associated with the cytoplasmic tail of the receptor by inducing the G protein to bind GTP, replacing the GDP that was bound to it (step 2). The G protein is an example of a *molecular switch* protein because it changes between inactive and active states. If GDP is bound to the G protein, the G protein is inactive, whereas if GTP is bound, it is active. In fact, G proteins are named because they use GDP and GTP to control their activities. The role of a switched-on G protein is to activate a plasma membrane–associated enzyme called the **effector** (step 3). In turn, the effector generates one or more internal, nonprotein signal molecules called **second messengers** (step 4). The second messengers directly or indirectly activate protein kinases, which elicit the cellular response by adding phosphate groups to specific target proteins (step 5). Thus, the entire control pathway operates through the following sequence:

first messenger → receptor → G proteins → effector → second messenger → protein kinases → target proteins effector

The separate protein kinases of these pathways all add phosphate groups to serine or threonine amino acids in their target proteins, which are typically

- enzymes catalyzing steps in metabolic pathways
- ion channels in the plasma and other membranes
- regulatory proteins that control gene activity and cell division

Cells can make a variety of G proteins, with each type activating a different cellular response. The pathway from first messengers to target proteins is common to all G protein–coupled receptors.

As long as a G protein–coupled receptor is bound to a first messenger, the receptor keeps the G protein active. The activated G protein, in turn, keeps the effector active in generating second messengers. If the first messenger is released from the receptor, or if the receptor is taken into the cell by endocytosis, GTP is hydrolyzed to GDP, which inactivates the G protein. As a result, the effector becomes inactive, turning "off" the response pathway.

The importance of G proteins to cellular metabolism is underscored by the fact that they are targets of toxins released by some infecting bacteria. The cholera toxin produced by *Vibrio cholerae,* the pertussis toxin that causes whooping cough produced by

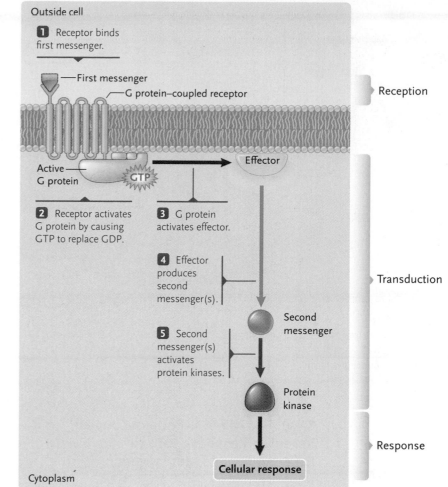

Figure 8.9

Response pathways activated by G protein–coupled receptors, in which protein kinase activity is separate from the receptor. The signal molecule is called the first messenger; the effector is an enzyme that generates one or more internal signal molecules called second messengers. The second messengers directly or indirectly activate the protein kinases of the pathway, leading to the cellular response.

Bordetella pertussis, and a toxin produced by a disease-causing form of *Escherichia coli* are all enzymes that modify the G proteins, making them continuously active and keeping their response pathways turned "on" at high levels. For example, the cholera toxin prevents a G protein from hydrolyzing GTP, keeping the G protein switched on and the pathway in a permanently active state. Among other effects, the pathway opens ion channels in intestinal cells, causing severe diarrhea through a massive release of salt and water from the body into the intestinal tract. Unless the resulting dehydration is relieved, death can result quickly. The *E. coli* toxin, which has similar but milder effects, is the cause of many cases of traveller's diarrhea.

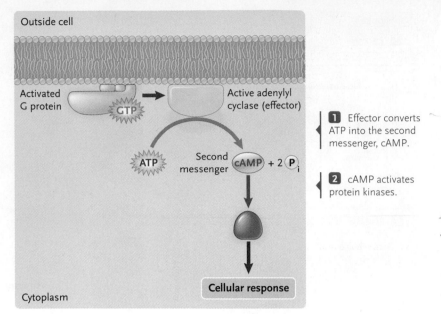

Figure 8.10

The operation of cAMP–response pathways. The second messenger of the pathway, cAMP, activates one or more cAMP-dependent protein kinases, which add phosphate groups to target proteins to initiate the cellular response.

1 Effector converts ATP into the second messenger, cAMP.

2 cAMP activates protein kinases.

8.4b Two Major G Protein–Coupled Receptor–Response Pathways Involve Different Second Messengers

Activated G proteins bring about a cellular response through two major receptor–response pathways in which different effectors generate different second messengers. One pathway involves the second messenger **cyclic AMP (cAMP)**, a relatively small, water-soluble molecule derived from ATP **(Figure 8.10)**. The effector that produces cAMP is the enzyme *adenylyl cyclase,* which converts ATP to cAMP **(Figure 8.11)**. cAMP diffuses through the cytoplasm and activates protein kinases that add phosphate groups to target proteins. The other pathway involves two second messengers: **inositol triphosphate (IP$_3$)** and **diacylglycerol (DAG)**. The effector of this pathway, an enzyme called *phospholipase C,* produces both of these second

messengers by breaking down a membrane phospholipid **(Figure 8.12)**. IP$_3$ is a small, water-soluble molecule that diffuses rapidly through the cytoplasm. DAG is hydrophobic; it remains and functions in the plasma membrane.

The primary effect of IP$_3$ in animal cells is to activate transport proteins in the endoplasmic reticulum (ER), which release Ca^{2+} stored in the ER into the cytoplasm. The released Ca^{2+}, either alone or in combination with DAG, activates a protein kinase cascade that brings about the cellular effect.

Both major G protein–coupled receptor–response pathways are balanced by reactions that constantly eliminate their second messengers. cAMP is quickly degraded by *phosphodiesterase,* an enzyme that is continuously active in the cytoplasm (see Figure 8.11). The rapid elimination of the second messengers provides another highly effective off switch for the pathways, ensuring that protein kinases are inactivated quickly if the receptor becomes inactive. Still another off switch is provided by protein phosphatases that remove the phosphate groups added to proteins by the protein kinases.

As in the receptor tyrosine kinase pathways, the activities of the pathways controlled by cAMP and IP$_3$/DAG second messengers are also stopped by endocytosis of receptors and their bound extracellular signals. As with all cell signalling pathways, cells vary in their response to cAMP or IP$_3$/DAG pathways depending on the type of G protein–coupled receptors on the cell surface and the kinds of protein kinases present in the cytoplasm.

The cAMP pathway is limited to animals and some fungi. The IP$_3$/DAG pathway is universally distributed among eukaryotic organisms, including both vertebrate and invertebrate animals, fungi, and plants. The cAMP pathway occurs in animals and fungi, but its presence in plants is uncertain.

Specific Examples of Cyclic AMP Pathways. Many hormones act as first messengers for cAMP pathways in animals. The receptors that bind these hormones control such varied cellular responses as the uptake and oxidation of glucose, glycogen breakdown or synthesis,

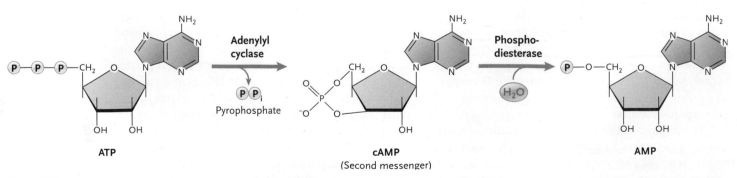

Figure 8.11

cAMP. The second messenger, cAMP, is made from ATP by adenylyl cyclase and is broken down to AMP by phosphodiesterase.

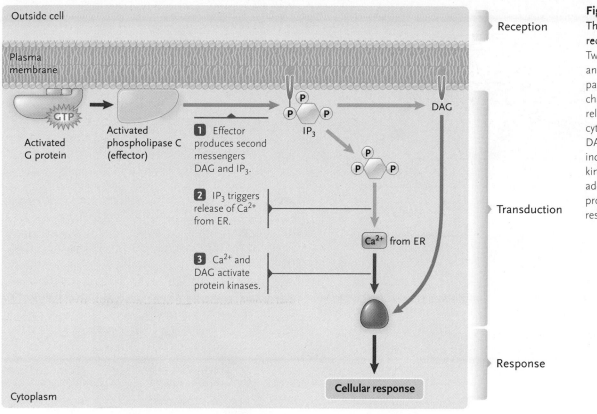

Figure 8.12

The operation of IP$_3$/DAG receptor–response pathways. Two second messengers, IP$_3$ and DAG, are produced by the pathway. IP$_3$ opens Ca^{2+} channels in ER membranes, releasing the ion into the cytoplasm. The Ca^{2+}, with DAG in some cases, directly or indirectly activates the protein kinases of the pathway, which add phosphate groups to target proteins to initiate the cellular response.

ion transport, the transport of amino acids into cells, and cell division.

A cAMP pathway is involved in the regulation of the level of glucose, the fundamental fuel of cells. When the level of blood glucose falls too low in mammals, cells in the pancreas release the peptide hormone glucagon. Binding of the hormone by a G protein–coupled glucagon receptor on the surface of liver cells triggers the cAMP pathway (see Figure 8.10). The cAMP produced activates a protein kinase cascade that amplifies the effects of the pathway at each step. Two enzymes are end targets of the protein kinase cascades. One enzyme is *glycogen phosphorylase,* which catalyzes the breakdown of glycogen into glucose units that pass from the liver cells into the bloodstream and increase the glucose level in the blood; it is activated by the cascades. The other enzyme is *glycogen synthase,* which adds glucose units to glycogen; it is inactivated by the cascades, ensuring that glucose is not converted back into glycogen in the liver cells.

Specific Examples of IP$_3$/DAG Pathways. The IP$_3$/DAG-response pathways are also activated by a large number of peptide hormones (including growth factors) and neurotransmitters, leading to responses as varied as sugar and ion transport, glucose oxidation, cell growth and division, and movements such as smooth muscle contraction.

Among the vertebrate hormones that activate the pathways are vasopressin, angiotensin, and norepinephrine. Vasopressin, also known as antidiuretic hormone, helps the body conserve water by reducing the output of urine. **Angiotensin** helps maintain blood volume and pressure. Norepinephrine, together with epinephrine, brings about the fight-or-flight response in threatening or stressful situations.

Many growth factors operate through IP$_3$/DAG pathways. Defects in the receptors or other parts of the pathways that lead to higher-than-normal levels of DAG in response to growth factors are often associated with the progression of some forms of cancer. This is because DAG, in turn, causes an overactivity of the protein kinases responsible for stimulating cell growth and division. Also, plant substances in a group called *phorbol esters* resemble DAG so closely that they can promote cancer in animals by activating the same protein kinases.

In plants, IP$_3$/DAG pathways control responses to conditions such as water loss and changes in light intensity or salinity. Plant hormones—relatively small, nonprotein molecules such as *auxin* (a derivative of the amino acid tryptophan) and the *cytokinins* (derivatives of the nucleotide base adenine)—act as first messengers activating some of the IP$_3$/DAG pathways of these organisms.

Example of a Signalling Pathway That Combines a Receptor Tyrosine Kinase with a G Protein. Some pathways important in gene regulation link certain receptor tyrosine kinases to a specific type of G protein called Ras. When

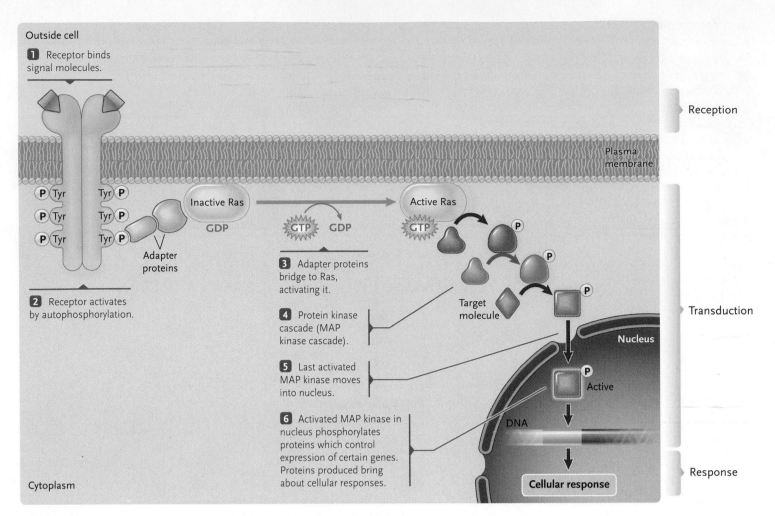

Outside cell

1 Receptor binds signal molecules.

Reception

Plasma membrane

P Tyr   Tyr **P**
P Tyr   Tyr **P**
P Tyr   Tyr **P**

Adapter proteins

Inactive Ras

GDP

GTP   GDP

Active Ras

GTP

3 Adapter proteins bridge to Ras, activating it.

2 Receptor activates by autophosphorylation.

4 Protein kinase cascade (MAP kinase cascade).

5 Last activated MAP kinase moves into nucleus.

6 Activated MAP kinase in nucleus phosphorylates proteins which control expression of certain genes. Proteins produced bring about cellular responses.

Cytoplasm

Target molecule

P

P

P

Nucleus

P

Active

DNA

Transduction

Response

Cellular response

Figure 8.13

The pathway from receptor tyrosine kinases to gene regulation, including the G protein, Ras, and MAP kinase.

the receptor tyrosine kinase receives a signal (**Figure 8.13,** step 1), it activates by autophosphorylation (step 2). Adapter proteins then bind to the phosphorylated receptor and bridge to Ras, stimulating the activation of Ras (step 3). Like other G proteins, Ras is activated by binding GTP. The activated Ras sets in motion a phosphorylation cascade that involves a series of three enzymes known as *mitogen-activated protein kinases* (MAP kinases; step 4). The last MAP kinase in the cascade, when activated, enters the nucleus (step 5) and phosphorylates other proteins, which then change the expression of certain genes, particularly activating those involved in cell division (step 6). (A *mitogen* is a substance that controls cell division, hence the name of the kinases.) Changes in gene expression can have far-reaching effects on the cell, such as determining whether a cell divides or how frequently it divides. The Ras proteins are of major interest to investigators because of their role in linking receptor tyrosine kinases to gene regulation, as well as their major roles in the development of many types of cancer when their function is altered.

In this section, we have surveyed major response pathways linked to surface receptors that bind peptide hormones, growth factors, and neurotransmitters.

We now turn to the other major type of signal receptor: the internal receptors binding signal molecules.

STUDY BREAK

1. What is the role of the first messenger in a G protein–coupled receptor-controlled pathway?
2. What is the role of the effector?
3. For a cAMP second-messenger pathway, how is the pathway turned off if no more signal molecules are present in the extracellular fluids?

8.5 Pathways Triggered by Internal Receptors: Steroid Hormone Nuclear Receptors

Cells of many types have internal receptors that respond to signals arriving from the cell exterior. Unlike the signal molecules that bind to surface receptors, these signals, primarily, but not exclusively, steroid hormones, penetrate through the plasma membrane and bind to receptors in the cytoplasm. The receptor-hormone complex enters the nucleus and interacts directly with the genome. Although the receptors are often referred to as steroid nuclear receptors, other hormones can act via nuclear receptors. Thyroxine, a nonsteroidal hormone that has many developmental effects, including the control of development from tadpole to frog, acts via nuclear receptors. The internal receptors, called **steroid hormone receptors**, are typically control proteins that turn on specific genes when they are activated by binding a signal molecule.

The same steroid hormones that activate internal receptors may also have different effects when they activate membrane receptors. The membrane receptors may be on different cells or on the same cells.

8.5a Steroid Hormones Have Widely Different Effects That Depend on Relatively Small Chemical Differences

Steroid hormones are relatively small, nonpolar molecules derived from cholesterol, with a chemical structure based on four carbon rings. Steroid hormones combine with hydrophilic carrier proteins that mask their hydrophobic groups and hold them in solution in the blood and extracellular fluids. When a steroid

hormone–carrier protein complex collides with the surface of a cell, the hormone is released and penetrates directly through the nonpolar part of the plasma membrane. On the cytoplasmic side, the hormone binds to its internal receptor.

The various steroid hormones differ only in the side groups attached to their carbon rings. Although the differences are small, they are responsible for highly distinctive effects. For example, the male and female sex hormones of mammals, testosterone and estrogen, respectively, which are responsible for many of the structural and behavioural differences between male and female mammals, differ only in minor substitutions in side groups at two positions. The differences cause the hormones to be recognized by different receptors, which activate specific regulatory DNA regions of target genes, leading to development of individuals as males or females.

8.5b The Response of a Cell to Steroid Hormones Depends on Its Internal Receptors and the Genes They Activate

Steroid nuclear hormone receptors are proteins with two major domains **(Figure 8.14)**. One domain recognizes and binds a specific steroid hormone. The other domain

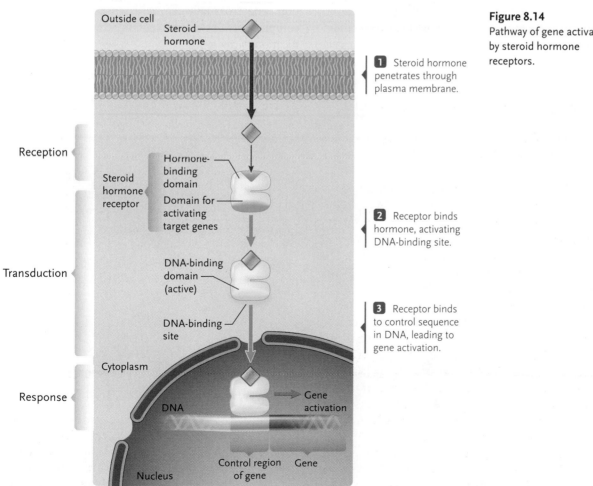

Figure 8.14
Pathway of gene activation by steroid hormone receptors.

Outside cell

Steroid hormone

1 Steroid hormone penetrates through plasma membrane.

Reception

Steroid hormone receptor

Hormone-binding domain

Domain for activating target genes

2 Receptor binds hormone, activating DNA-binding site.

Transduction

DNA-binding domain (active)

DNA-binding site

3 Receptor binds to control sequence in DNA, leading to gene activation.

Cytoplasm

Response

Gene activation

DNA

Nucleus

Control region of gene

Gene

interacts with the regions of target genes that control their expression. When a steroid hormone combines with the hormone-binding domain, the gene activation domain changes shape, thus enabling the complex to bind to the DNA control regions of the target genes that the hormone affects. For most steroid hormone receptors, binding of the activated receptor to a gene control region activates that gene, although some may suppress the expression of the target gene.

Steroid hormones, like peptide hormones, are released by cells in one part of an organism and are carried by the organism's circulation to other cells. Whether a cell responds to a steroid hormone depends on whether it has a receptor for the hormone. For responses to steroids mediated by internal receptors, the type of response depends on the genes that are recognized and turned on by an activated receptor. Depending on the receptor type and the particular genes it recognizes, even the same steroid hormone can have highly varied effects on different cells.

Taken together, the various types of receptor tyrosine kinases, G protein–coupled receptors, and steroid hormone nuclear receptors prime cells to respond to a stream of specific signals that continuously fine-tune their function. How are the signals integrated within the cell and organism to produce harmony rather than chaos? The next section shows how the various signal pathways are integrated into a coordinated response. Not all receptors can be classified as surface receptors or internal receptors. The plant hormone ethylene acts via membrane receptors that are inside the cell (see *Molecule Behind Biology*).

STUDY BREAK

1. What distinguishes a steroid nuclear receptor from a receptor tyrosine kinase receptor or a G protein–coupled receptor?
2. By what means does a specific steroid hormone result in a specific cellular response?

8.6 Integration of Cell Communication Pathways

Cells are under the continual influence of many simultaneous signal molecules. The cell signalling pathways may communicate with one another to integrate their responses to cellular signals. The interpathway interaction is called **cross-talk**; a conceptual example that involves two second-messenger pathways is shown in **Figure 8.15.** A protein kinase in one pathway might phosphorylate a site on a target protein in another signal transduction pathway, activating or inhibiting that protein, depending on the site of the phosphorylation. The cross-talk can be extensive, resulting in a complex network of interactions between cell communication pathways.

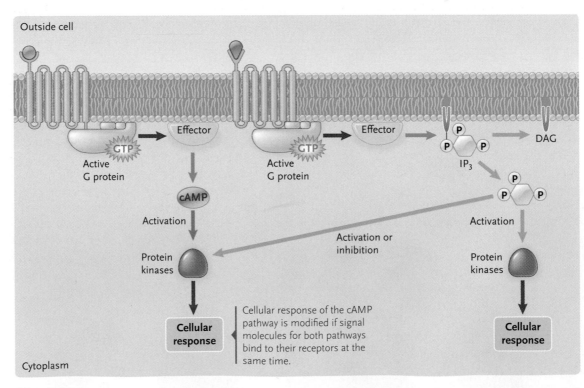

Figure 8.15
Cross-talk, the interaction between cell communication pathways to integrate the responses to signal molecules.

Ethylene

Ethylene is a structurally simple molecule that has dramatic effects on the physiology of plants throughout their life history. As discussed in Chapter 31, ethylene influences such fundamental physiological processes as seed germination, response to wounding, flowering, fruit ripening, and senescence. Several characteristics of ethylene and its action are interesting in the context of this chapter.

First, this molecule is strikingly simple in structure compared to the peptide or steroid hormones of animals and the auxin or cytokinin hormones of plants. Second, it is one of very few hormones that is a gas at physiological temperature (nitric oxide is another). It is soluble in both water and lipids, and as such, it can readily diffuse to, *and into*, target cells. Third, the receptors for ethylene are a family of membrane-bound proteins found not on the cell surface but within the cell on the ER. Fourth, whereas the membrane receptors discussed in this chapter have binding sites that protrude away from the membrane, the binding site for ethylene is within the transmembrane portion of the receptor protein. That is, ethylene diffuses inside the ER membrane to find its receptor. Fifth, in the absence of ethylene, the cascade of proteins involved in ethylene response is actively repressed and inactive. However,

Figure 1
Ethylene: a gaseous plant hormone.

when ethylene binds a receptor, kinase activity and conformational changes activate the pathway, ultimately resulting in production of transcription factors that, in turn, regulate the expression of hundreds of genes.

Cross-talk often leads to modifications of the cellular responses controlled by the pathways. Such modifications fine-tune the effects of combinations of signal molecules binding to the receptors of a cell. For example, cross-talk between second-messenger pathways is involved in particular types of olfactory (smell) signal transduction in rats and probably in many animals. The two pathways involved are activated upon stimulation with distinct odours. One pathway involves cAMP as the second messenger, and the other involves IP$_3$. However, the two olfactory second-messenger pathways do not work independently; rather, they operate in an antagonistic way. That is, experimentally blocking key enzymes of one signal transduction cascade inhibits that pathway while simultaneously augmenting the activity of the other pathway. The cross-talk may be a way to refine the animal's olfactory sensory perception by helping discriminate different odour molecules more effectively.

Cross-talk networks may also involve inputs from other cellular response systems, such as those triggered by cell adhesion molecules as a result of specific contact between cells. Cell adhesion molecules are receptor-like glycoproteins in plasma membranes; they link cells together or bind them to molecules of the extracellular matrix. Many of these surface molecules also trigger cellular responses. For example, when the surface molecule *integrin* binds to another cell or to a molecule of the extracellular matrix, such as collagen, it triggers a cellular response, often including cross-talk steps that link the reactions to the cAMP and IP$_3$/DAG pathways. The responses triggered by the cell adhesion molecules include changes in the rate of cell division and gene activity and alterations in cell motility, development, and differentiation.

Direct channels of communication may also be involved in a cross-talk network. For example, gap junctions between the cytoplasms of adjacent cells admit ions and small molecules, including the Ca^{2+}, cAMP, and IP$_3$ second messengers released by the receptor–response pathways. Thus, one cell that receives a signal through its surface receptors can transmit the signal to other cells in the same tissue via the connecting gap junctions, thereby coordinating the functions of those cells. For instance, cardiac muscle cells are connected by gap junctions, and the Ca^{2+} flow regulates coordinated muscle fibre contractions.

The entire system integrating cellular response mechanisms, tied together by many avenues of cross-talk between individual pathways, creates a sensitively balanced control mechanism that regulates and coordinates the activities of individual cells into the working unit of the organism.

STUDY BREAK

What cell communication pathways might be integrated in a cross-talk network?

Intercellular signal molecules control many cellular activities; therefore, it is not surprising that many laboratories are extensively researching the mechanisms involved. Experimental goals include determining the molecular details of the receptor structures and how they interact with and change when a signal molecule binds, identifying and characterizing all of the components of the transduction steps, detailing how the final activated component of the transduction steps triggers the cellular responses, and understanding the regulation of signal transduction pathways.

What are the prospects for treating human diseases caused by signal transduction pathway malfunctions?

Receptor tyrosine kinase–mediated signalling is critical for cell growth, division, differentiation, and development. Some human diseases and developmental abnormalities result from mutations in the genes for receptor tyrosine kinases and from overexpression of those genes.

Examples are dwarfism, heritable cancer susceptibility, vein malformations, and piebaldism. Researchers are determining the exact nature of the receptor gene mutations in order to explore how the mutations cause the malfunctions of the signal transduction pathways. They have found that some mutations affect the ability of the receptor to form a dimer when the signal molecule binds, and others affect the kinase activity of the cytoplasmic side of the receptor. In fact, there are a surprisingly large number of different mutations that affect receptor tyrosine kinases, meaning that there are many ways that their functions can be affected. In terms of treating human diseases resulting from receptor tyrosine kinase mutations, research is at a relatively early stage. Prospects for therapeutic approaches to treat these diseases include developing anti–tyrosine kinase drugs. Clearly, an increased understanding of receptor tyrosine kinases' signalling and function is crucial for progress to be made in the diagnosis and treatment of human diseases resulting from mutations that cause abnormal regulation of receptor tyrosine kinase function.

Review

Go to CENGAGENOW™ at http://hed.nelson.com/ to access quizzing, animations, exercises, articles, and personalized homework help.

8.1 Cell Communication: An Overview

- Cells communicate with one another through direct channels of communication, specific contact between cells, and intercellular chemical messengers.

- In communication that involves an intercellular chemical messenger, a controlling cell releases a signal molecule that causes a response of target cells. To respond, the target cell must have a receptor for the specific signal molecule. The target cell processes the signal in three steps: reception, transduction, and response. The series of events from reception to response is called signal transduction.

8.2 Characteristics of Cell Communication Systems with Surface Receptors

- Cell communication systems based on surface receptors have three components: (1) extracellular signal molecules, (2) surface receptors that receive the signals, and (3) internal response pathways triggered when receptors bind a signal.

- The systems based on surface receptors respond to hormones and neurotransmitters.

- Hormones include peptides and steroids. A special class of peptide hormones is the growth factors, which affect cell growth, division, and differentiation. Neurotransmitters include small peptides, individual amino acids or their derivatives, and other chemical substances.

- Surface receptors are integral membrane proteins that extend entirely through the plasma membrane. Binding a signal molecule induces a molecular change in the receptor that activates its cytoplasmic end.

- Cellular response pathways operate by activating protein kinases. Phosphate groups added by the protein kinases stimulate or inhibit the activities of the target proteins,

thereby accomplishing the cellular response. The response is reversed by protein phosphatases that remove phosphate groups from target proteins. In addition, receptors are removed by endocytosis when signal transduction has run its course.

- Each step of a response pathway catalyzed by an enzyme is amplified because each enzyme can activate hundreds or thousands of proteins that enter the next step in the pathway. Amplification allows a full cellular response when a few signal molecules bind to their receptors.

8.3 Surface Receptors with Built-in Protein Kinase Activity: Receptor Tyrosine Kinases

- When receptor tyrosine kinases bind a signal molecule, it moves together with another protein kinase to form a dimer, activating the kinase. The active dimer adds phosphate groups to tyrosines in the receptor itself and to target proteins. The phosphate groups added to the cytoplasmic end of the receptor are recognition sites for proteins that are activated by binding to the receptor.

8.4 G Protein–Coupled Receptors

- In the pathways activated by G protein-coupled receptors, binding of the extracellular signal molecule (the first messenger) activates a site on the cytoplasmic end of the receptor.

- An activated receptor turns on a G protein, which acts as a molecular switch. The G protein is active when it is bound to GTP and inactive when it is bound to GDP.

- When a G protein is active, it switches on the effector of the pathway, an enzyme that generates small internal signal molecules called second messengers. The second messengers activate the protein kinases of the pathway.

- In one of the two major pathways triggered by G protein–coupled receptors, the effector, adenylyl cyclase, generates cAMP as second messenger. cAMP activates specific protein kinases.

- In the other major pathway, the activated effector, phospholipase C, generates two second messengers, IP_3 and DAG. IP_3 activates transport proteins in the ER, which release stored Ca^{2+} into the cytoplasm. The released Ca^{2+}, alone or in combination with DAG, activates specific protein kinases that add phosphate groups to their target proteins.

- Both the cAMP and IP_3/DAG pathways are balanced by reactions that constantly eliminate their second messengers. Both pathways are also stopped by protein phosphatases that continually remove phosphate groups from target proteins and by endocytosis of receptors and their bound extracellular signals.

- Some pathways important in gene regulation link certain receptor tyrosine kinases to a specific G protein called Ras. When the receptor binds a signal molecule, it phosphorylates itself, and adapter proteins then bind, bridging to Ras, activating it. Activated Ras turns on the MAP kinase cascade. The last MAP kinase in the cascade, when activated, phosphorylates target proteins in the nucleus, activating them to turn on specific genes. Many of those genes control cell division.

8.5 Pathways Triggered by Internal Receptors: Steroid Hormone Nuclear Receptors

- In addition to their effects on membrane receptors, steroid hormones also penetrate through the plasma membrane to bind to receptors within the cell. The internal receptors are regulatory proteins that turn on specific genes when they are activated by binding a signal molecule, thereby producing the cellular response.

- Steroid hormone nuclear receptors have a domain that recognizes and binds a specific steroid hormone and a domain that interacts with the controlling regions of target genes.

- Steroids may act on membrane and nuclear receptors in the same cells or on different cells. The type of response involving nuclear receptors depends on the genes that are turned on by an activated receptor.

8.6 Integration of Cell Communication Pathways

- In cross-talk, cell signalling pathways such as the cAMP and IP_3 pathways communicate with one another to integrate responses to cellular signals. Cross-talk may result in a complex network of interactions between cell communication pathways.

- Cross-talk often results in modifications of the cellular responses controlled by the pathways, fine-tuning the effects of combinations of signal molecules binding to the receptors of a cell.

- In animals, inputs from other cellular response systems, including cell adhesion molecules, as well as molecules arriving through gap junctions, also can become involved in the cross-talk network.

Questions

Self-Test Questions

1. In signal transduction, which of the following is *not* a target protein? hormone hair aprotein
   a. proteins that regulate gene activity.
   b. hormones that activate the receptor.
   c. enzymes of pathways.
   d. transport proteins.
   e. enzymes of cell reactions.

2. A cell that responds to a signal molecule is distinguished from a cell that does not respond by the fact that it has
   a. a cell adhesion molecule.
   b. cAMP.
   c. a first-messenger molecule.
   d. a receptor.
   e. a protein kinase.

3. In a stepwise pathway activated by a small number of signal molecules binding to their receptors, which of the following enables enzymes to activate thousands of molecules?
   a. autophosphorylation.
   b. second-messenger enhancement.
   c. amplification.
   d. ion channel regulation.
   e. G protein turn-on.

4. Which of the following is *incorrect* about pathways activated by G protein–coupled receptors?
   a. The extracellular signal is the first messenger.
   b. When activated, plasma membrane–bound G protein can switch on an effector.
   c. Second messengers enter the nucleus.
   d. ATP converts to cAMP to activate protein kinases.
   e. Protein kinases phosphorylate molecules to change cellular activity.

5. Which of the following would *not* inhibit signal transduction?
   a. Phosphate groups are removed from proteins.
   b. Endocytosis acts on receptors and their bound signals.
   c. Receptors and signals separate.
   d. Receptors and bound signals enter lysosomes.
   e. Autophosphorylation targets the cytoplasmic portion of the receptor.

Questions for Discussion

1. Describe the possible ways in which a G-protein–coupled receptor pathway could become defective and not trigger any cellular responses.

2. What factors might have contributed to the evolution of two internal mechanisms: one using switching molecules that bind ATP and the other binding GTP?

3. What experiments would you do to determine whether a receptor is located on the cell surface or inside the cell?

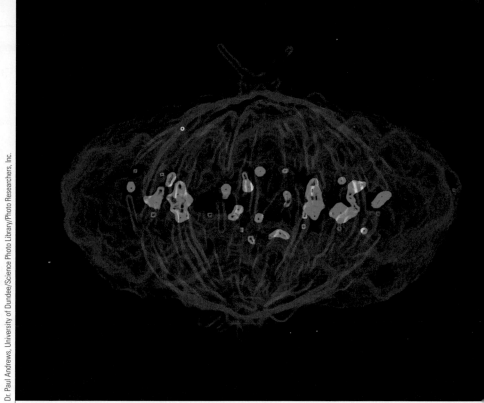

A cell in mitosis (fluorescence micrograph). The spindle (red) is separating copies of the cell's chromosomes (green) prior to cell division.

Dr. Paul Andrews, University of Dundee/Science Photo Library/Photo Researchers, Inc.

9 Cell Cycles

WHY IT MATTERS

As the rainy season recedes in Northern India, rice paddies and other flooded areas begin to dry. These shallow seasonal pools have provided an environment of slow-moving warm water for zebrafish (*Danio rerio*) to spawn **(Figure 9.1, p. 180)**. Over the past few months, many millions of cell divisions have fuelled the growth and development of single fertilized eggs into the complex multicellular tissues and organs of these small, boldly striped fish. Most cells in the adults have now stopped dividing and are dedicated to particular functions.

Moving into the fast-running streams that feed the Ganges River, the young zebrafish encounter larger predators, such as knifefish (*Notopterus notopterus*). Imagine for a moment that a zebrafish is attacked by a knifefish; the prey narrowly escapes but not without leaving one of its fins behind in the mouth of the predator. In an amazing feat of cell cycle regulation, the entire zebrafish fin will be regenerated—skin, nerves, muscles, bones, and all—within a week!

As a model system for vertebrate development, the zebrafish has provided a popular tool for researchers to identify the stages of regeneration at the molecular level. (See *The Chemical and Physical Foundations*

Figure 9.1
Zebrafish
(*Danio rerio*).

of Biology pages for more information about zebrafish as model organisms.) In the first step, existing skin cells migrate to close the wound and prevent bleeding. Then cells just under the new skin transform into "regeneration cells" that form a temporary tissue called a blastema. Blastema cells exhibit two important characteristics: (1) they reenter the cell cycle and divide up to 50 times faster than usual, and (2) they expand their previously restricted range of function. The blastema provides large numbers of daughter cells capable of maturing into new bone, nerve, muscle, and blood vessel cells in response to signal proteins produced by the skin. Once the regenerated fin has reached its normal size and shape, cell cycling returns to its normally quiescent state.

Although regenerating lost fins is dramatic, zebrafish can also regenerate lost heart muscle. Studies are under way to explore the possibility that human hearts could be stimulated to repair themselves following heart attack damage rather than just form scar tissue.

Since multicellular organisms are made (and sometimes remade) almost entirely of cells and their products, understanding organismal development and structure is really a problem of understanding the regulation of cell division and differentiation. Which conditions stimulate cells to divide? Which make them stop? How do cells "learn" their original function, and how do they "relearn" a new one? This chapter is dedicated to helping you better understand the factors that influence and guide cell division. The differentiation of cells for specialized functions in various organisms is discussed in Chapters 14, 20, and 31.

9.1 The Cycle of Cell Growth and Division: An Overview

If we were to show you a living cell and ask, "What does the future hold for this cell?" you would likely reply, "It will grow and divide, grow and divide." You might be correct. If the cell is a prokaryote such as *Escherichia coli* or a single-celled eukaryote such as baker's yeast, then, yes, it would be a safe bet to predict reproduction as frequently as environmental conditions allow.

However, if this cell is from inside the cheek of a moose or from a yellow rose petal, the future may hold neither growth nor cell division. In fact, some cells may even be programmed to die immediately!

The increasing size, developmental complexity, and diversity of functioning of multicellular eukaryotic organisms require strict control of cell division that ultimately results in a mature body composed of different subpopulations of cells. Whereas most mature cells divide infrequently, if at all, relatively small populations in the meristem tissues of plants, as well as the stem cells of animals, are actively dividing by the process of mitosis. The new progeny cells are needed for growth (new leaves), asexual reproduction, and replacement of cells lost to wear (shedding skin and gut lining) and tear (wound repair, virus infection) **(Figure 9.2)**. Before dividing, most cells enter a period of growth in which they synthesize proteins, lipids, and carbohydrates and (during one particular stage) replicate their nuclear DNA. After this growth period, the nuclei divide, and, usually, cytokinesis (the division of the cytoplasm; cyto = cell, derived from "hollow vessel"; kinesis = movement) follows, partitioning nuclei to each of two daughter cells. Each daughter nucleus contains a copy of the original DNA. This sequence of events—a period of growth followed by nuclear division and cytokinesis—is known as the **cell cycle**.

a.

b.

Figure 9.2
Actively dividing cells provide for new growth of skin **(a)** and leaves **(b)**.

9.1a The Products of Mitosis Are Genetic Duplicates of the Dividing Cell

As long as eukaryotes require their daughter cells to be exact genetic copies of the **parental** cell, mitosis serves very well to divide the replicated DNA equally and precisely. This is the result of three elegantly interrelated systems. One component is an elaborate master program of molecular checks and balances that ensures an orderly and timely progression through the cell cycle. Within the overall regulation of the cell cycle, the process of DNA synthesis replicates each DNA chromosome into two copies with almost perfect fidelity (see Section 13.3). The final system is a structural and mechanical web of interwoven "cables" and "motors" of the mitotic cytoskeleton that separates the DNA copies precisely into the daughter cells (see Figure 9.13).

However, at a certain stage of the life cycle of sexually reproducing organisms, some cells are needed that are decidedly *different* from the parent cells. A different type of cell division process is required. **Meiosis** produces the necessary daughter nuclei—different in that they have only half the number of chromosomes as the parental nuclei that began the process. Also, many of the genetic traits carried by these daughter nuclei are in different combinations from those of the parent cell. The cells that are the products of meiosis may function as gametes in animals (fusing with other gametes to make a zygote) and as spores in plants and many fungi (dividing by mitosis).

This chapter concentrates on the mechanical and regulatory aspects of cell division in eukaryotes and prokaryotes; meiosis and its role in eukaryotic sexual reproduction are addressed in the next chapter. We begin our discussion with **chromosomes**, the nuclear units of genetic information that are divided and distributed by mitotic cell division.

9.1b Chromosomes Are the Genetic Units Divided by Mitosis

In all eukaryotes, the hereditary information of the nucleus is distributed among several linear DNA molecules. These DNA molecules are combined with proteins that stabilize the DNA, assist in packaging DNA during cell division, and influence the expression of individual genes. Each chromosome (*chroma* = colour, when stained with dyes used in light microscopy; *soma* = body; **Figure 9.3**) in a cell is composed of one of these linear DNA molecules along with its associated proteins.

Most eukaryotes have two copies of each type of chromosome in their nuclei, and their chromosome complement is said to be **diploid**, or 2*n*. For example, humans have 23 different pairs of chromosomes for a diploid number of 46 chromosomes (2*n* = 46). Other eukaryotes, mostly microorganisms, may have only one copy of each type of chromosome in their

Figure 9.3
Eukaryotic chromosomes (blue).

Conly Rieder

nucleus, so their chromosome complement is said to be **haploid**, or *n*. Baker's yeast (*Saccharomyces cerevisiae*) is an example of an organism that can grow as a diploid (2*n* = 32) and as a haploid (*n* = 16). Still others, such as many plant species, have three, four, or even more complete sets of chromosomes in each cell. The number of chromosome sets is called the **ploidy** of a cell or species. See Chapter 18 for a look at the role of ploidy in the formation of new species.

Replication of the DNA of each individual chromosome creates two identical molecules called **sister chromatids.** Newly formed sister chromatids are held together until mitosis separates them, placing one in each of the two daughter nuclei. As a result of this precise division, each daughter nucleus receives exactly the same number and types of chromosomes, and contains the same genetic information, as the parent cell entering the division. The equal distribution of daughter chromosomes to each of the two cells that result from cell division is called **chromosome segregation.**

The precision of chromosome replication and segregation in the mitotic cell cycle creates a group of cells called a clone. Except for rare chance mutations, all cells of a clone are genetically identical. Since all the diverse cell types of a complex multicellular organism arose by mitosis from a single zygote, they should all contain the same genetic information. Forensic scientists rely on this feature of organisms when, for instance, they match the genetic profile of a small amount of tissue (e.g., cells in dog saliva recovered from a bite victim) with that of a blood sample from the suspected animal.

STUDY BREAK

1. What are the three interrelated systems that contribute to the eukaryotic cell cycle?
2. What is a chromosome composed of?

Growing Cell Clones in Culture

How can investigators safely test whether a particular substance is toxic to human cells or whether it can cure or cause cancer? One widely used approach is to work with **cell cultures**—living cells grown in laboratory vessels. Many types of prokaryotic and eukaryotic cells can be grown in this way.

When cell cultures are started from single cells, they form **clones:** barring mutations, all the individuals descending from the original cell are genetically identical. Clones are ideal for experiments in genetics, biochemistry, molecular biology, and medicine because the cells lack genetic differences that could affect the experimental results.

Microorganisms such as yeasts and many bacteria are easy to grow in laboratory cultures. For example, the human intestinal bacterium *E. coli* can be grown in solutions (growth media) that contain only an organic carbon source such as glucose, a nitrogen source, and inorganic salts. Under optimal conditions, the cycle of cell growth and division of *E. coli* cells takes 20 minutes. As a result, large numbers of cells are produced in a short time. The cells may be grown in liquid suspensions or on the surface of a solid growth medium such as an agar gel (agar is a **polysaccharide** extracted from an alga). Many thousands of bacterial strains are used in a wide variety of experimental studies.

Many types of plant cells can also be cultured as clones in specific growth media. With the addition of plant growth hormones, complete plants can often be grown from single cultured cells. Growing plants from cultured cells is particularly valuable in genetic engineering, in which genes introduced into cultured cells can be tracked in fully developed plants. Plants that have been engineered successfully can then be grown simply by planting their seeds.

Animal cells vary in what is needed to culture them. For many types, the culture medium must contain **essential amino acids**—that is, the amino acids that the cells cannot make for themselves. In addition, mammalian cells require specific growth factors provided by adding blood serum, the fluid part of the blood left after red and white blood cells are removed.

Even with added serum, many types of normal mammalian cells cannot be grown in long-term cultures. Eventually, the cells stop dividing and die. By contrast, tumour cells often form cultures that grow and divide indefinitely.

The first successful culturing of cancer cells was performed in 1951 in the laboratory of George and Margaret Gey (Johns Hopkins University, Baltimore, MD). Gey and Gey's cultures of normal cells died after a few weeks, but the researchers achieved success with a culture of tumour cells from a cancer patient. The cells in culture continued to grow and divide; in fact, descendants of those cells are still being cultured and used for research today. The cells were given the code name *HeLa*, from the first two letters of the patient's first and last names—Henrietta Lacks. Unfortunately, the tumour cells in Henrietta's body also continued to grow, and she died within two months of her cancer diagnosis.

Other types of human cells have since been grown successfully in culture, derived either from tumour cells or normal cells that have been "immortalized" by inducing genetic changes that transformed them into tumour-like cells.

9.2 The Mitotic Cell Cycle

If cells show a repeating phase of growth and division, they can be thought of as moving through a mitotic cell "cycle." Although the cell cycle is usually a smooth continuum of change in nature, it is helpful to describe discrete "phases" for discussion purposes. If we choose to let the formation of a new daughter cell mark the beginning of the mitotic cell cycle, then the first and longest phase is interphase. During interphase, the cell grows and replicates its DNA in preparation for mitosis (also called the *M phase*) and cytokinesis **(Figure 9.4).** Internal regulatory controls trigger each phase, ensuring that the processes of one phase are completed successfully before the next phase can begin. Various internal mechanisms also regulate the overall number of cycles that a cell is allowed. These internal controls may be subject to various "external" influences caused by other cells or viruses as well as signal molecules, including hormones, growth factors, and death factors.

9.2a Interphase Extends from the End of One Mitosis to the Beginning of the Next Mitosis

Interphase begins as a daughter cell from a previous division cycle enters an initial period of cytoplasmic growth. During this initial growth stage, called the G_1 **phase** of the cell cycle, the cell makes various RNAs, proteins, and other types of cellular molecules but not nuclear DNA (the G in G_1 stands for *gap*, referring to the absence of DNA synthesis). Then, if the cell is going to divide, DNA replication begins, initiating the **S phase** of the cell cycle (S stands for *synthesis*, meaning DNA synthesis).

During the S phase, the cell duplicates the **chromosomal proteins** as well as the DNA and continues the synthesis of other cellular molecules. As the

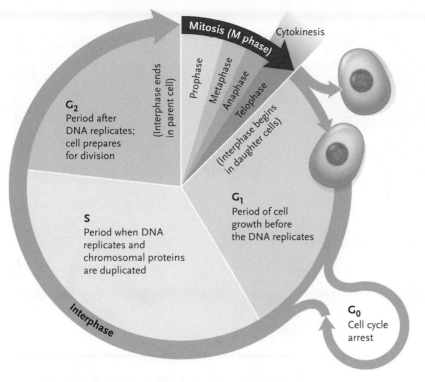

G₂
Period after DNA replicates; cell prepares for division

(Interphase ends in parent cell)

Mitosis (M phase)   Cytokinesis

Prophase
Metaphase
Anaphase
Telophase

(Interphase begins in daughter cells)

G₁
Period of cell growth before the DNA replicates

S
Period when DNA replicates and chromosomal proteins are duplicated

Interphase

G₀
Cell cycle arrest

Figure 9.4

The cell cycle. The length of G_1 varies, but for a given cell type, the timing of S phase, G_2 phase, and mitosis is usually relatively uniform. Cytokinesis (red segment) usually begins while mitosis is in progress and reaches completion as mitosis ends. Cells in a state of division arrest are considered to enter a side loop (or shunt) from G_1 phase called G_0 phase.

S phase is completed, the cell enters the **G_2 phase** of the cell cycle (G_2 refers to the second gap during which there is no DNA synthesis). During G_2, the cell continues to synthesize RNAs and proteins, including those required for mitosis, and the cell continues to grow. At the end of G_2, which marks the end of interphase, mitosis begins. During all the steps of interphase, the chromosomes are relatively loose, but organized, in the nucleus **(Figure 9.5)**.

Figure 9.5

Chromosomes from the muntjac deer are individually "painted" with fluorescent stain. Note that there are two cells in this picture. The metaphase cell shows six long, condensed chromosomes with homologues stained the same colour. The interphase nucleus shows the homologous DNA organized in close proximity rather than randomly distributed.

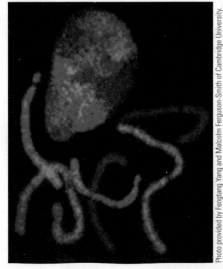

Photo provided by Fengtang Yang and Malcolm Ferguson-Smith of Cambridge University.

Usually, G_1 is the only phase of the cell cycle that varies in length for a given species. Thus, whether cells divide rapidly or slowly primarily depends on the length of G_1. Once DNA replication begins, most mammalian cells take about 10 to 12 hours to proceed through the S phase, about 4 to 6 hours to go through G_2, and about 1 to 4 hours to complete mitosis. G_1 is also the stage in which many cell types stop dividing. This state of division arrest is often designated the **G_0 phase** (see Figure 9.4). For example, in humans, cells of the nervous system normally enter G_0 once they are fully mature.

The events of interphase are an important focus of research, particularly the regulatory controls for the transition from the G_1 phase to the S phase and, with it, the commitment to cell division. Understanding the molecular events that regulate the G_1/S phase transition is important because one of the hallmarks of cancer is the loss of normal control of that transition.

9.2b After Interphase, Mitosis Proceeds in Five Stages

If you watch a cell going through mitosis **(Figures 9.6, p. 184, and 9.7, p. 185)**, you will notice several dramatic changes that signal the progression through different "stages": prophase (*pro* = before), prometaphase (*meta* = between), metaphase, anaphase (*ana* = back), and telophase (*telo* = end).

Prophase During **prophase**, the greatly extended chromosomes that were replicated during interphase begin to *condense* into compact, rod-like structures (see **chromatin** packaging in Section 13.5). Each diploid human cell, although only about 40 to 50 µm in diameter, contains *2 metres* of DNA distributed among 23 pairs of chromosomes. Condensation during prophase packs these long DNA molecules into units small enough to be divided successfully during mitosis. As they condense, the chromosomes appear as thin threads under the light microscope. The word *mitosis* (*mitos* = thread) is derived from this thread-like appearance.

While condensation is in progress, the **nucleolus** becomes smaller and eventually disappears in most species. The disappearance reflects a shutdown of all types of RNA synthesis, including the ribosomal RNA made in the nucleolus.

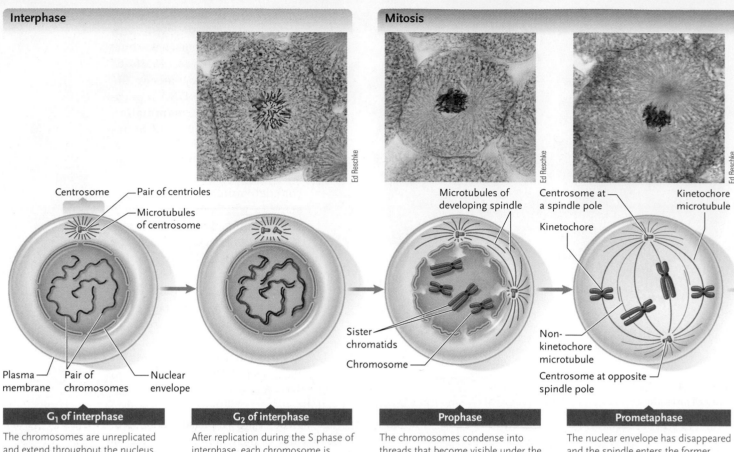

Ed Reschke
Ed Reschke
Ed Reschke

Centrosome — Pair of centrioles

— Microtubules
of centrosome

Microtubules of
developing spindle

Centrosome at
a spindle pole

Kinetochore
microtubule

Kinetochore

Sister
chromatids

Chromosome

Non-
kinetochore
microtubule

Centrosome at opposite
spindle pole

Plasma
membrane

Pair of
chromosomes

Nuclear
envelope

G₁ of interphase	**G₂ of interphase**	**Prophase**	**Prometaphase**
The chromosomes are unreplicated and extend throughout the nucleus. For simplicity we show only two pairs of chromosomes. One of each pair was inherited from one parent, and the other was inherited from the other parent.	After replication during the S phase of interphase, each chromosome is double at all points and now consists of two sister chromatids. The centrioles within the centrosome have also doubled into pairs.	The chromosomes condense into threads that become visible under the light microscope. Each chromosome is double as a result of replication. The centrosome has divided into two parts, which are generating the spindle as they separate.	The nuclear envelope has disappeared and the spindle enters the former nuclear area. Microtubules from opposite spindle poles attach to the two kinetochores of each chromosome.

Figure 9.6
The stages of mitosis. Light micrographs show mitosis in an animal cell (whitefish embryo). Diagrams show mitosis in an animal cell with two pairs of chromosomes.

In the cytoplasm, the mitotic **spindle** (**Figure 9.8, p. 186**; see also Figure 9.12) begins to form between the two centrosomes as they start migrating toward the opposite ends of the cell to form the **spindle poles**. The spindle develops as bundles of microtubules that radiate from the spindle poles.

Prometaphase At the end of prophase, the nuclear envelope breaks down, heralding the beginning of **prometaphase**. Bundles of spindle microtubules grow from centrosomes at the opposing spindle poles toward the centre of the cell. Some of the developing spindle enters the former nuclear area and attaches to the chromosomes.

Although seldom visible as a double structure at this point, it is important for you to remember that each chromosome is made up of two identical sister chromatids held together only at their **centromeres**. By this time, a complex of several proteins, a **kinetochore**, has formed on each chromatid at the centromere. Kinetochore microtubules bind to the kinetochores. These connections determine the outcome of mitosis because they attach the sister chromatids of each chromosome to microtubules leading to the opposite

spindle poles (see Figure 9.8). Microtubules that do not attach to kinetochores overlap those from the opposite spindle pole.

Metaphase During **metaphase**, the spindle reaches its final form and the spindle microtubules move the chromosomes into alignment at the spindle midpoint, also called the metaphase plate. The chromosomes complete their condensation in this stage and assume their characteristic shape as determined by the location of the centromere and the length and thickness of the chromatid arms.

Only when the chromosomes are all assembled at the spindle midpoint, with the two sister chromatids of each one attached to microtubules leading to opposite spindle poles, can metaphase give way to actual separation of chromatids.

Although chromosomes are generally thought of as "X" shapes, it is important to realize that few chromosomes actually ever look like this. Only chromosomes with their centromere near the middle could appear as an "X." Even so, during most of the cell cycle, such chromosomes would be too loosely packaged to take on any shape at all.

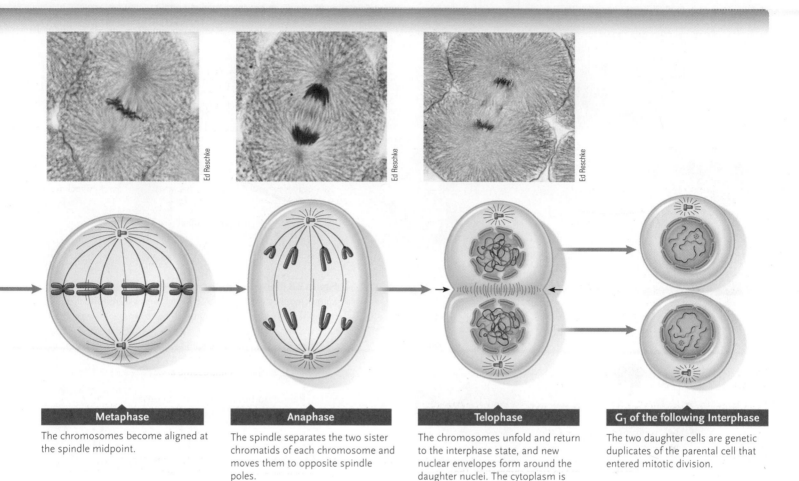

Metaphase	Anaphase	Telophase	G₁ of the following Interphase
The chromosomes become aligned at the spindle midpoint.	The spindle separates the two sister chromatids of each chromosome and moves them to opposite spindle poles.	The chromosomes unfold and return to the interphase state, and new nuclear envelopes form around the daughter nuclei. The cytoplasm is beginning to divide by furrowing at the points marked by arrows.	The two daughter cells are genetic duplicates of the parental cell that entered mitotic division.

The complete collection of metaphase chromosomes, arranged according to size and shape, forms the **karyotype** of a given species. In many cases, the karyotype is so distinctive that a species can be identified from this characteristic alone. **Figure 9.9 (p. 186)** shows a human karyotype.

Anaphase During **anaphase**, sister chromatids separate and move to opposite spindle poles. The first signs of chromosome movement can be seen at the centromeres as the kinetochores are the first sections to move toward opposite poles. The movement continues until the separated chromatids, now called daughter chromosomes, have reached the two poles. At this point, chromosome segregation has been completed.

Telophase During **telophase**, the spindle disassembles and the chromosomes at each spindle pole decondense and return to the extended state typical of interphase. As decondensation proceeds, the nucleolus reappears, RNA transcription resumes, and a new nuclear envelope forms around the chromosomes at each pole, producing the two daughter nuclei. At this point, nuclear division is complete, and the cell has two nuclei.

9.2c Cytokinesis Completes Cell Division by Dividing the Cytoplasm between Daughter Cells

Cytokinesis, the division of the cytoplasm, usually follows the nuclear division stage of mitosis and produces two daughter cells, each containing one of the daughter nuclei. In most cells, cytokinesis begins during telophase or even late anaphase. By the time cytokinesis is completed, the daughter nuclei have progressed to the interphase stage and entered the G₁ phase of the next cell cycle.

Cytokinesis proceeds by different pathways in the different kingdoms of eukaryotic organisms. In animals, protists, and many fungi, a groove, the **furrow**, girdles the cell and gradually deepens until it cuts the cytoplasm into two parts. In plants, a new cell wall, called the **cell plate**, forms between the daughter nuclei and grows laterally until it divides the cytoplasm. In both cases, the plane of cytoplasmic division is determined by the layer of microtubules that persist at the former spindle midpoint.

Furrowing In furrowing, the layer of microtubules that remains at the former spindle midpoint expands

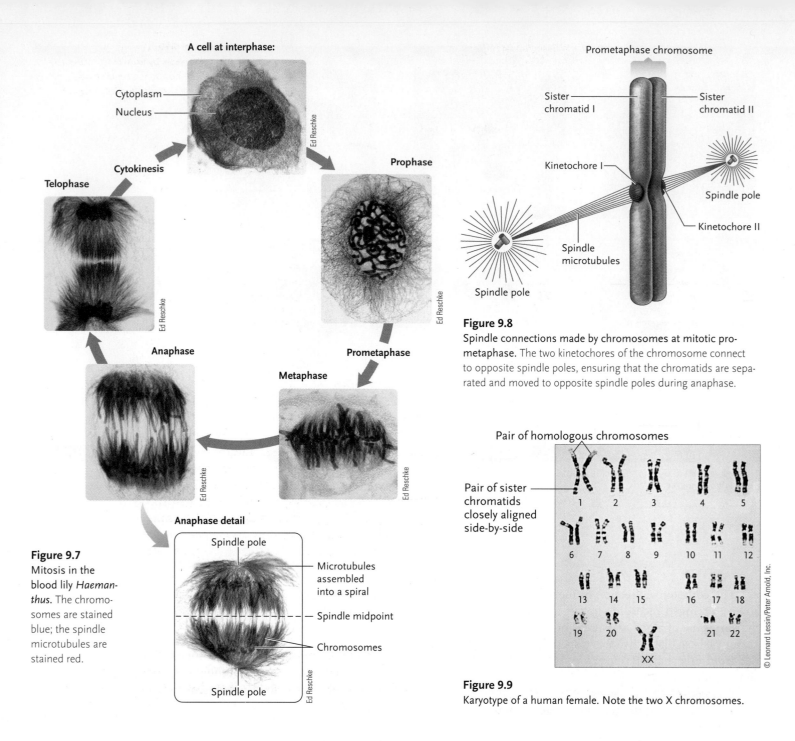

A cell at interphase:

Cytoplasm

Nucleus

Ed Reschke

Cytokinesis

Telophase

Ed Reschke

Prophase

Ed Reschke

Anaphase

Prometaphase

Metaphase

Ed Reschke

Ed Reschke

Figure 9.7
Mitosis in the blood lily *Haemanthus*. The chromosomes are stained blue; the spindle microtubules are stained red.

Anaphase detail

Spindle pole

Microtubules assembled into a spiral

Spindle midpoint

Chromosomes

Spindle pole

Ed Reschke

Prometaphase chromosome

Sister chromatid I

Sister chromatid II

Kinetochore I

Spindle pole

Spindle microtubules

Kinetochore II

Spindle pole

Figure 9.8
Spindle connections made by chromosomes at mitotic prometaphase. The two kinetochores of the chromosome connect to opposite spindle poles, ensuring that the chromatids are separated and moved to opposite spindle poles during anaphase.

Pair of homologous chromosomes

Pair of sister chromatids closely aligned side-by-side

© Leonard Lessin/Peter Arnold, Inc.

Figure 9.9
Karyotype of a human female. Note the two X chromosomes.

laterally until it stretches entirely across the dividing cell **(Figure 9.10)**. As the layer develops, a band of microfilaments forms just inside the plasma membrane, forming a belt that follows the inside boundary of the cell in the plane of the microtubule layer (microfilaments are discussed in Section 2.4). Powered by motor proteins, the microfilaments slide together, tightening the band and constricting the cell. The constriction forms a groove—the furrow—in the plasma membrane. The furrow gradually deepens, much like the tightening of a drawstring, until the daughter cells are completely separated. The cytoplasmic division isolates the daughter nuclei in the two cells and, at the same time, distributes the organelles and other structures (which have also doubled) approximately equally.

Cell Plate Formation In cell plate formation, the layer of microtubules that persists at the former spindle midpoint serves as an organizing site for vesicles produced by the endoplasmic reticulum (ER) and Golgi complex **(Figure 9.11)**. As the vesicles collect, the layer expands until it spreads entirely across the dividing cell. During this expansion, the vesicles fuse together and their contents assemble into a new cell wall—the cell plate—stretching completely across the former spindle midpoint. The junction separates the cytoplasm and its organelles into two parts and isolates the daughter nuclei in separate cells. The plasma membranes that line the two surfaces of the cell plate are derived from the vesicle membranes.

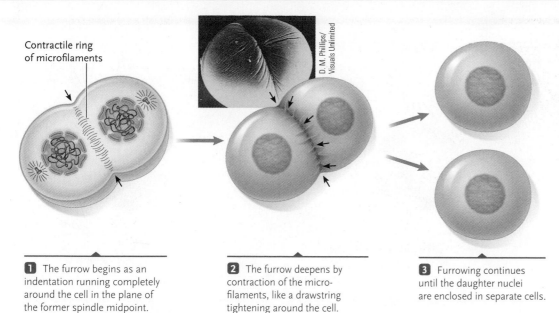

Contractile ring
of microfilaments

D. M. Phillips /
Visuals Unlimited

Figure 9.10
Cytokinesis by furrowing. The micrograph shows a furrow developing in the first division of a fertilized egg cell.

1 The furrow begins as an indentation running completely around the cell in the plane of the former spindle midpoint.

2 The furrow deepens by contraction of the microfilaments, like a drawstring tightening around the cell.

3 Furrowing continues until the daughter nuclei are enclosed in separate cells.

STUDY BREAK

1. During which stage(s) of the cell cycle is a chromosome composed of two chromatids?
2. What are the conditions under which a chromosome could appear as an "X" shape under the microscope?
3. How does cytokinesis differ in plant and animal cells?

9.3 Formation and Action of the Mitotic Spindle

The mitotic spindle is central to both mitosis and cytokinesis. The spindle is made up of microtubules and their proteins, and its activities depend on their changing patterns of organization during the cell cycle.

Microtubules form a major part of the interphase cytoskeleton of eukaryotic cells. (Section 2.4 outlines the patterns of microtubule organization in the cytoskeleton.) As mitosis approaches, the microtubules disassemble from their interphase arrangement and reorganize into the spindle, which grows until it fills almost the entire cell. This reorganization follows one of two pathways in different organisms, depending on the presence or absence of a *centrosome* during interphase. However, once organized, the basic function of the spindle is the same, regardless of whether a centrosome is present.

9.3a Animals and Plants Form Spindles in Different Ways

Animal cells and many protists have a **centrosome**, a site near the nucleus from which microtubules radiate outward in all directions (**Figure 9.12, p. 188** step 1).

Figure 9.11
Cytokinesis by cell plate formation in plant cells.

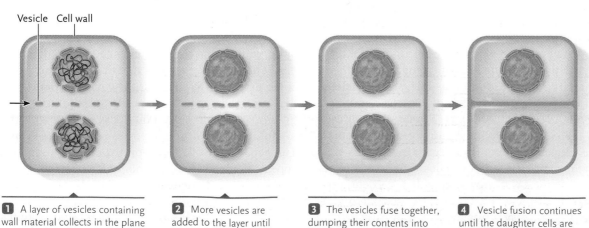

Vesicle   Cell wall

R. Calentine / Visuals Unlimited

1 A layer of vesicles containing wall material collects in the plane of the former spindle midpoint (arrow).

2 More vesicles are added to the layer until it extends across the cell.

3 The vesicles fuse together, dumping their contents into a gradually expanding wall between the daughter cells.

4 Vesicle fusion continues until the daughter cells are separated by a continuous new wall, the cell plate.

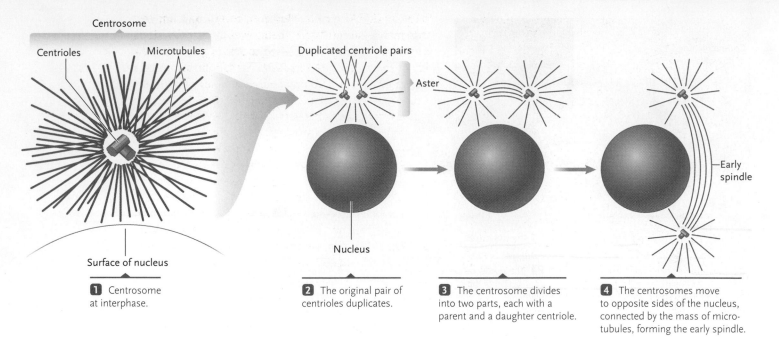

Figure 9.12

The centrosome and its role in spindle formation.

Labels in figure:
Centrosome
Centrioles Microtubules
Surface of nucleus
Duplicated centriole pairs
Aster
Nucleus
Early spindle

1 Centrosome at interphase.

2 The original pair of centrioles duplicates.

3 The centrosome divides into two parts, each with a parent and a daughter centriole.

4 The centrosomes move to opposite sides of the nucleus, connected by the mass of microtubules, forming the early spindle.

The centrosome is the main **microtubule organizing centre (MTOC)** of the cell, anchoring the microtubule cytoskeleton during interphase and positioning many of the cytoplasmic organelles. The centrosome contains a pair of **centrioles**, usually arranged at right angles to each other. Although centrioles originally appeared to be important in the construction of the mitotic spindle, it has now been shown that they can be removed with no ill effect. The primary function of centrioles is actually to generate the microtubules needed for flagella or cilia, the whiplike extensions that provide cell motility.

When DNA replicates during the S phase of the cell cycle, the centrioles within the centrosome also duplicate, producing two pairs of centrioles (see Figure 9.12, step 2). As prophase begins in the M phase, the centrosome separates into two parts (step 3). The duplicated centrosomes, with the centrioles inside them, continue to separate until they reach opposite ends of the nucleus (step 4). As centrosomes move apart, the microtubules between them lengthen and increase in number.

By late prophase, when the centrosomes are fully separated, the microtubules that extend between them form a large mass around one side of the nucleus called the early spindle. When the nuclear envelope subsequently breaks down at the end of prophase, the spindle moves into the region formerly occupied by the nucleus and continues growing until it fills the cytoplasm. The microtubules that extend from the centrosomes also grow in length and extent, producing radiating arrays that appear starlike under the light microscope. Initially named by early microscopists, **asters** are the centrosomes at the spindle tips, which form the poles of the spindle. By dividing

the duplicated centrioles, the spindle ensures that, when the cytoplasm divides during cytokinesis, the daughter cells each receive a pair of centrioles.

No centrosome or centrioles are present in angiosperms (flowering plants) or in most gymnosperms, such as conifers. Instead, the spindle forms from microtubules that assemble in all directions from multiple MTOCs surrounding the entire nucleus (see prophase in Figure 9.7). When the nuclear envelope breaks down at the end of prophase, the spindle moves into the former nuclear region, as in animals.

9.3b Mitotic Spindles May Move Chromosomes by a Combination of Two Mechanisms

When fully formed at metaphase, the spindle may contain from hundreds to many thousands of microtubules, depending on the species **(Figure 9.13)**. In almost all eukaryotes, these microtubules are divided into two groups. Some, called kinetochore microtubules, connect the chromosomes to the spindle poles **(Figure 9.14a)**. Others, called nonkinetochore microtubules, extend between the spindle poles without connecting to chromosomes; at the spindle midpoint, these microtubules from one pole overlap with the microtubules from the opposite pole **(Figure 9.14b)**. The separation of the chromosomes at anaphase appears to result from a combination of separate but coordinated movements produced by the two types of microtubules.

The exact mechanism by which chromosomes move is still uncertain; at one time, it was believed that microtubules pulled the chromosomes toward the

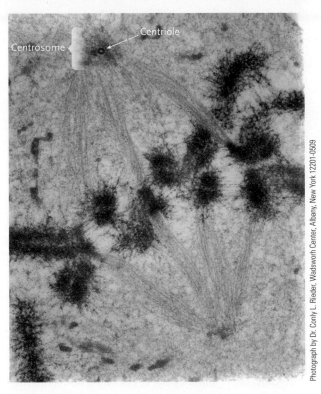

Centrosome
Centriole

Photograph by Dr. Conly L. Rieder, Wadsworth Center, Albany, New York 12201-0509

Figure 9.13
A fully developed spindle in a mammalian cell. Only microtubules connected to chromosomes have been caught in the plane of this section. One of the centrioles is visible in cross section in the centrosome at the top of the micrograph (arrow). Original magnification ×14 000.

poles of dividing cells. However, recent data suggest that chromosomes "walk" themselves to the poles along stationary microtubules, using motor proteins in their kinetochores **(Figure 9.15, p. 190)**. The tubulin subunits of the kinetochore microtubules disassemble as the kinetochores pass along them; thus, the microtubules become shorter as the movement progresses (see Figure 9.14a). The movement is similar to pulling yourself, hand over hand, up a rope as it falls apart behind you.

Evidence supporting kinetochore-based movement comes from experiments in which researchers tagged kinetochore microtubules with a microscopic beam of ultraviolet light, producing bleached sites that could be seen in the light microscope **(Figure 9.16, p. 190)**. As the chromosomes moved to the spindle poles, the bleached sites stayed in the same place. This result showed that the kinetochore microtubules do not move much with respect to the poles during the anaphase movement.

In nonkinetochore microtubule–based movement, the entire spindle is lengthened, pushing the poles farther apart (see Figure 9.14b). The pushing movement is presumably produced by microtubules sliding over one another in the zone of overlap, powered by proteins acting as microtubule motors. In many species, the nonkinetochore microtubules also push the poles apart by growing in length as they slide.

Figure 9.14
The two microtubule-based movements of the anaphase spindle.

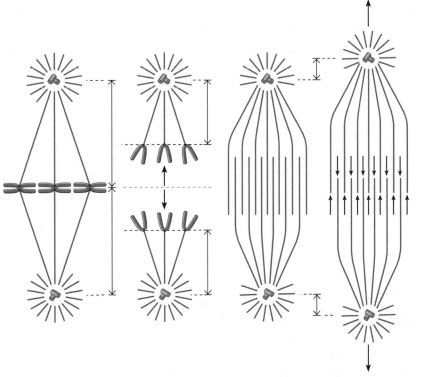

→ separation

a. The kinetochore microtubules connected to the kinetochores of the chromosomes become shorter, lessening the distance from the chromosomes to the poles.

b. Sliding of the nonkinetochore microtubules in the zone of overlap at the spindle midpoint pushes poles farther apart and increases the total length of the spindle.

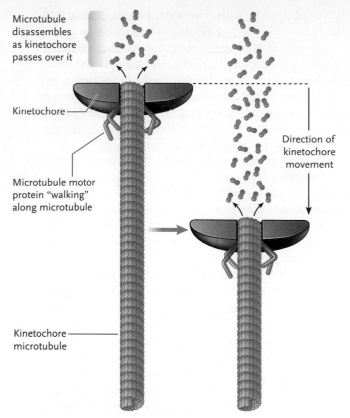

Microtubule disassembles as kinetochore passes over it

Kinetochore

Microtubule motor protein "walking" along microtubule

Direction of kinetochore movement

Kinetochore microtubule

Figure 9.15
Microtubule motor proteins "walking" the kinetochore of a chromosome along a microtubule.

STUDY BREAK

1. What is the role of the centrosome?
2. What is the role of the kinetochore?

9.4 Cell Cycle Regulation

We have noted that a number of internal and external regulatory mechanisms control the mitotic cell cycle. As part of the internal controls, the cell cycle has built-in **checkpoints** to prevent critical phases from beginning until the previous phases are completed. Hormones, growth factors, and other external controls coordinate the cell cycle with the needs of an organism by stimulating or inhibiting division. Some key research contributing to our understanding of cell cycle regulation, particularly defining the genes involved and their protein products, was done using yeast. The *Experimental Research Organisms* section describes yeast and its role in research in more detail.

9.4a Cyclins and Cyclin-Dependent Kinases Are the Internal Controls that Directly Regulate Cell Division

Cyclin-dependent kinases (CDK) are major players in the regulation of cell division, directly affecting progression through the cell cycle. CDKs are protein kinases, enzymes that add phosphate groups to target proteins. CDK enzymes are called "cyclin dependent" because they are "switched on" only when combined with another protein called a **cyclin**. Since the concentration of the cyclins rises and falls during the cell cycle, so does the enzyme activity of the CDKs (even though the concentration of CDK proteins remains constant). The name *cyclin* reflects these cyclic fluctuations in its concentration. R. Timothy Hunt, of the Imperial Cancer Research Fund in London, UK, received a Nobel Prize in 2001 for discovering cyclins.

Several different cyclin:CDK combinations regulate cell cycle transitions at different "checkpoints." For example, the cyclin:CDK combination that controls the cell cycle at the G_1-to-S checkpoint is shown in **Figure 9.17**. At the G_1-to-S checkpoint, cyclin E has reached a concentration high enough to form a complex with CDK2 and activate it. The CDK2 then phosphorylates a number of cell-cycle control target proteins, which trigger the cell to make the transition into the S phase. After the transition is made, the cyclin E is degraded, less is available for binding to CDK2, and therefore kinase activity decreases. CDK2 becomes activated again when cyclin E levels rise at the next G_1-to-S checkpoint, after mitosis. Similar events, with a different cyclin:CDK combination, occur to release the G_2-to-M checkpoint referred to below.

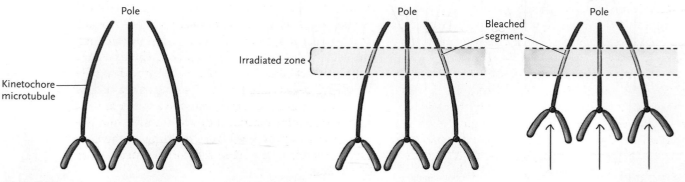

Pole

Kinetochore microtubule

Irradiated zone

Pole

Pole

Bleached segment

Figure 9.16
Experiment demonstrating that kinetochore microtubules remain stationary as chromosomes move during anaphase.

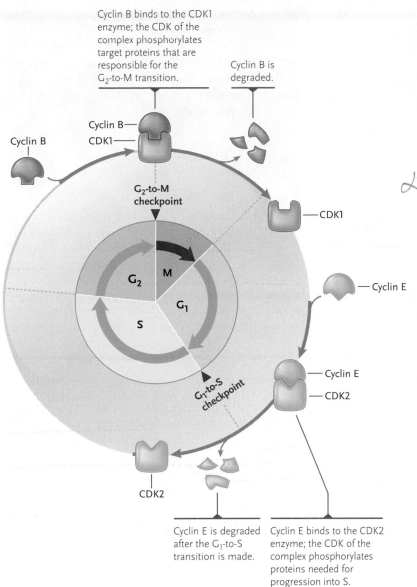

Cyclin B binds to the CDK1 enzyme; the CDK of the complex phosphorylates target proteins that are responsible for the G_2-to-M transition.

Cyclin B is degraded.

Cyclin B

Cyclin B
CDK1

G_2-to-M checkpoint

CDK1

G_2

M

G_1

S

Cyclin E

Cyclin E

CDK2

G_1-to-S checkpoint

CDK2

Cyclin E is degraded after the G_1-to-S transition is made.

Cyclin E binds to the CDK2 enzyme; the CDK of the complex phosphorylates proteins needed for progression into S.

Figure 9.17
Cyclin:CDK control of the G_1-to-S and G_2-to-M transitions of the cell cycle.

9.4b   Internal Checkpoints Stop the Cell Cycle if Stages Are Incomplete

The cyclin:CDK combinations directly control the cell cycle, but other factors within the cell act as indirect controls by altering the activity of the cyclin:CDK complexes. At each key checkpoint, regulatory events block the cyclin:CDK complex from triggering the associated cell cycle transition until the actions of a previous phase are successfully completed. For example, the cyclin B:CDK1 complex stimulates the cell to enter the M phase out of the G_2 phase. However, until the cell is ready to enter mitosis, phosphorylation of a site on CDK1 keeps it inactive even though it is bound to cyclin B. When the cell is ready, a phosphatase removes the inhibitory phosphate, the CDK1 becomes active, and the cell is moved into mitosis.

Control at checkpoints is exerted in many types of circumstances. For instance, if some of the DNA

remains unreplicated during the S phase, the cell slows its progress during the G_2 phase to allow more time for replication to be completed. Similarly, if radiation or chemicals damage DNA, inhibitory events prevent the onset of S phase to give the cell an opportunity to repair the damage.

9.4c   External Controls Coordinate the Mitotic Cell Cycle of Individual Cells with the Overall Activities of the Organism

The internal controls that regulate the cell cycle are modified by signal molecules that originate from outside the dividing cells. In animals, these signal molecules include the peptide hormones and similar proteins called growth or death factors.

Many of these external factors bind to receptors at the cell surface, which respond by triggering reactions inside the cell. These reactions often include steps that add inhibiting or stimulating phosphate groups to the cyclin:CDK complexes, particularly to the CDKs. The reactions triggered by the activated receptor may also directly affect the same proteins regulated by the cyclin:CDK complexes. The overall effect is to speed, slow, or stop the progress of cell division, depending on the particular hormone or factor and the internal pathway that is stimulated. Some growth factors are even able to break the arrest of cells shunted into the G_0 stage and return them to active division. (Hormones, growth factors, and other signal molecules are part of the cell communication system, as discussed in Chapter 8.)

Cell-surface receptors in animal cells also recognize contact with other cells or with molecules of the extracellular matrix. The contact triggers internal reaction pathways that inhibit division by arresting the cell cycle, usually in the G_1 phase. The response, called **contact inhibition**, stabilizes cell growth in fully developed organs and tissues. As long as the cells of most tissues are in contact with one another or with the extracellular matrix, they are shunted into the G_0 phase and prevented from dividing. If the contacts are broken, the freed cells often enter rounds of division.

Contact inhibition is easily observed in cultured mammalian cells grown on a glass or plastic surface.

In such cultures, division proceeds until all the cells are in contact with their neighbours in a continuous, unbroken, single layer. At this point, division stops. If a researcher then scrapes some of the cells from the surface, cells at the edges of the "wound" are released from inhibition and divide until they form a continuous layer and all the cells are again in contact with their neighbours.

9.4d Cells Cannot Divide Indefinitely

In 1961, Leonard Hayflick and Paul Moorhead reported that normal human skin cells eventually stopped dividing when grown in artificial culture. This loss of proliferative ability over time is called **cellular senescence**, and scientists have been searching for the "Hayflick factors" that are responsible for it. We consider two candidates: DNA damage and telomere shortening.

The progressive accumulation of random damage to a cell's DNA sequence, or its chromosome structure, or even the genes coding for the enzyme machinery needed to repair such damage, is perhaps the most intuitive Hayflick factor. One would expect "older" cells to have diminished function if they have suffered mutations in genes controlling critical activities.

Telomeres are repetitive DNA sequences that are added to the ends of chromosomes by the enzyme telomerase. Since DNA replication machinery is unable to replicate the entire ends of linear chromosomes, telomere sequence is lost at each round of replication (see Figure 13.15). Once telomeres diminish to a certain minimum length, cells stop dividing (senesce) and may die.

You might wonder why we do not just take a pill to stimulate our telomerase, rejuvenate our cells, and extend our life span. It turns out that cellular senescence is an important anti-tumour mechanism. Some researchers have stimulated the telomerase of cultured cells: they become "immortal" and divide out of control. Mice that have been engineered to lack telomerase, and therefore suffer faster senescence, are significantly *resistant* to cancer. It seems that by the time cells are short on telomeres, many of them are also a long way toward cancerous growth, as described below.

9.4e Cell Cycle Controls Are Lost in Cancer

Cancer occurs when cells lose the normal controls that determine when and how often they will divide. Cancer cells divide continuously and uncontrollably, producing a rapidly growing mass called a tumour **(Figure 9.18)**. Cancer cells also typically lose their adhesions to other cells and often become actively mobile. As a result, in a process called metastasis, they tend to break loose from an original tumour, spread

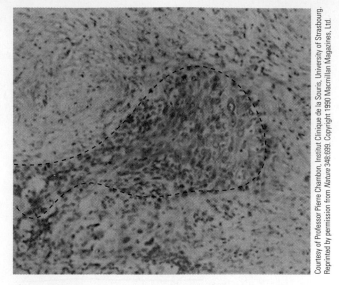

Figure 9.18
A mass of tumour cells (dashed line) embedded in normal tissue. As is typical, the tumour cells appear to be more densely packed because they have less cytoplasmic volume than normal cells. Original magnification ×270.

Courtesy of Professor Pierre Chambon, Institut Clinique de la Souris, University of Strasbourg. Reprinted by permission from *Nature* 348:699. Copyright 1990 Macmillan Magazines, Ltd.

throughout the body, and grow into new tumours in other body regions. Metastasis is promoted by changes that defeat contact inhibition and alter the cell-surface molecules that link cells together or to the extracellular matrix.

Growing tumours damage surrounding normal tissues by compressing them and interfering with blood supply and nerve function. Tumours may also break through barriers such as the outer skin, internal cell layers, or the gut wall. The breakthroughs cause bleeding, open the body to infection by microorganisms, and destroy the separation of body compartments necessary for normal function. Both compression and breakthroughs can cause pain that, in advanced cases, may become extreme. As tumours increase in mass, the actively growing and dividing cancer cells may deprive normal cells of their required nutrients, leading to generally impaired body functions, muscular weakness, fatigue, and weight loss.

Cancer cells have typically accumulated mutations in a variety of different genes that promote uncontrolled cell division or metastasis. Before they undergo mutation, many of these genes code for components of the cyclin:CDK system that regulates cell division; others encode proteins that regulate gene expression, form cell surface receptors, or make up elements of the signalling pathways controlled by the receptors. When mutated, the genes, called **oncogenes**, encode altered versions of these products.

For example, a mutation in a gene that codes for a surface receptor might result in a protein that is constantly active even without binding the intended extracellular signal molecule. As a result, the internal

Roscovitine

Screening of a wide variety of artificially modified adenine molecules has led to the discovery of a group of compounds related to plant cytokinin hormones that selectively inhibit cyclin-dependent kinases by competing for (and blocking) their ATP binding site. The example shown below, roscovitine, has antitumour and antiviral activity resulting from stimulation of apoptosis in affected cells. Note the adenine in each molecule (rectangle).

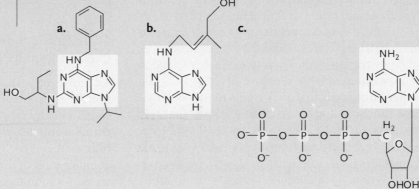

(a) Roscovitine. (b) The plant cytokinin hormone zeatin. (c) ATP.

---

reaction pathways triggered by the receptor, which induce cell division, are continually stimulated. Another mutation, this time in a cyclin gene, could result in increased cyclin:CDK binding that triggers DNA replication and the rest of the cell cycle. Cancer, oncogenes, and the alterations that convert normal genes to oncogenes are discussed in further detail in Chapter 15.

9.4f Some Cells Are Programmed to Die

Normal development of multicellular organisms is a highly regulated balance between cell proliferation and cell death. "Programmed cell death," called **apoptosis**, appears to be a very ancient mechanism common to all multicellular eukaryotes studied so far. Initiation of cell death can result from either internal or external signals. The nematode *Caenorhabditis elegans* is one useful model organism to study this signalling because all adult animals have exactly the same number of cells **(Figure 9.19a)**.

In addition, the fate of each of these cells, from the zygote to the adult, can be tracked with a light microscope. Detailed studies of the 1090 cells that are generated to form an adult reveal that 131 of them not only stop dividing—they stop living.

The apoptosis machinery in *C. elegans* is available in all its cells, waiting in an inactive state for the right trigger. The main "executioner" enzyme is one of a family of normally inactive proteases, called **caspases**, and is coded by the "cell death abnormal" gene, *ced-3* **(Figure 9.19b)**. If a cell is destined to die by apoptosis, the cascade begins when

internal developmental cues stimulate expression of a gene called "egg laying deficient," *egl-1*. EGL-1 protein then binds to CED-9 protein, resulting in the release of bound CED-4 protein and the formation

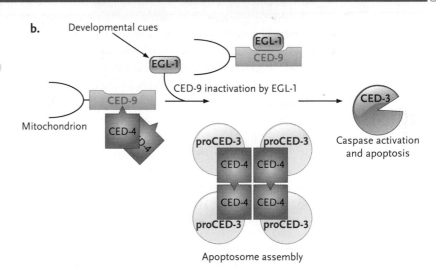

Courtesy of Dr. Sydney Brenner

Figure 9.19

(a) The adult nematode "worm" *Caenorhabditis elegans* is about 1 mm long and is composed of 959 living cells. **(b)** The main cascade of programmed cell death in *C. elegans*. Cells destined to die express EGL-1 protein that, by binding to mitochondrial-bound CED-9, releases CED-4 protein. A complex of CED-4 then activates the main "executioner" caspase protease enzyme, CED-3.

of an active apoptosome. CED-3 caspase is thus activated, and cell death ensues. The causes of death are nuclear DNA degradation and disrupted mitochondrial function. The corpses of dead cells are engulfed and eaten by neighbouring cells. The 2002 Nobel Prize in Physiology or Medicine was awarded jointly to Sydney Brenner, Robert Horvitz, and John Sulston for their discoveries concerning "genetic regulation of organ development and programmed cell death" in *C. elegans*. The Experimental Research Organisms (see The Chemical and Physical Foundations of Biology pages) section describes *C. elegans* and its role in research in more detail.

Removing cells that are surplus for development is one function of apoptosis, but why are other cells programmed to die? We hope you will agree that it would be beneficial for an organism to provoke apoptosis in cells suffering severe DNA damage, viral infection, or mutations leading to uncontrolled division. Sometimes perfectly normal and healthy cells die by apoptosis. For instance, the cells that make up xylem elements in the vascular tissue of woody plants actually function as "skeletons." They must die to fulfill their function as hollow, water-conducting pipes.

The overview of the mitotic cell cycle and its regulation presented in this chapter only hints at the complexity of cell growth and division. The likelihood of any given cell dividing is determined by weighing a variety of internal signals in the context of external cues from the environment. If a cell is destined to divide, then the problem of accurately replicating and partitioning its DNA requires a highly regulated, intricately inter-related series of mechanisms. Although male Australian Jack Jumper ants (*Myrmecia pilosula*) have only one chromosome to deal with, think of the problems faced by the fern *Ophioglossum pycnostichum*, which has 1260 chromosomes in each cell!

STUDY BREAK

1. Explain how the *activity* of cyclin-dependent kinases can rise and fall with each "turn" of the cell cycle, whereas the *concentration* of these enzymes remains constant.
2. What observation do "Hayflick factors" explain?
3. What is metastasis?

9.5 Cell Division in Prokaryotes

Prokaryotes undergo a cycle of cytoplasmic growth, DNA replication, and cell division, producing two daughter cells from an original parent cell. The entire mechanism of prokaryotic cell division is called **binary fission**—that is, splitting or dividing into two parts. Although binary fission is regulated, the small size of prokaryotic cells makes it particularly difficult to discover just how the chromosomes move. Although actin-like proteins have been found in bacteria, their role in chromosome segregation remains unclear.

9.5a Replication Occupies Most of the Cell Cycle in Rapidly Dividing Prokaryotic Cells

All prokaryotes use DNA as their hereditary information. The vast majority of prokaryotic species have a single, circular DNA molecule known as the **bacterial chromosome** (**Figure 9.20**, step 1). When prokaryotic cells divide at the maximum rate, DNA replication occupies most of the period between cytoplasmic divisions. As soon as replication is complete, the cytoplasm divides to complete the cell cycle. For example, in populations of *E. coli* cells, which can double every 20 minutes, DNA replication occupies 19 minutes of the division cycle.

9.5b Replicated Chromosomes Are Distributed Actively to the Halves of the Prokaryotic Cell

In the 1960s, François Jacob of The Pasteur Institute, Paris, France, proposed a model for the segregation of bacterial chromosomes to the daughter cells in which the two chromosomes attach to the plasma membrane near the middle of the cell and separate as a new plasma membrane is added between the two sites during cell elongation. The essence of this model is that chromosome separation is passive. However, current research indicates that bacterial chromosomes rapidly separate in an active way that is linked to DNA replication events and is independent of cell elongation. The new model is shown in Figure 9.20.

Replication of the bacterial chromosome commences at a specific region called the **origin of replication** (ori). The ori is in the middle of the cell where the enzymes for DNA replication are located. Once the ori has been duplicated, the two origins migrate toward the two ends (poles) of the cell as replication continues for the rest of the chromosome. This active movement distributes the two replicated chromosomes to the two ends of the cell. How this movement occurs is unknown.

Next, cytoplasmic division in prokaryotes occurs through an inward growth of the plasma membrane, along which new cell wall material is assembled to cut the cell into two parts (see Figure 9.20, step 5). The new wall divides the two replicated DNA molecules

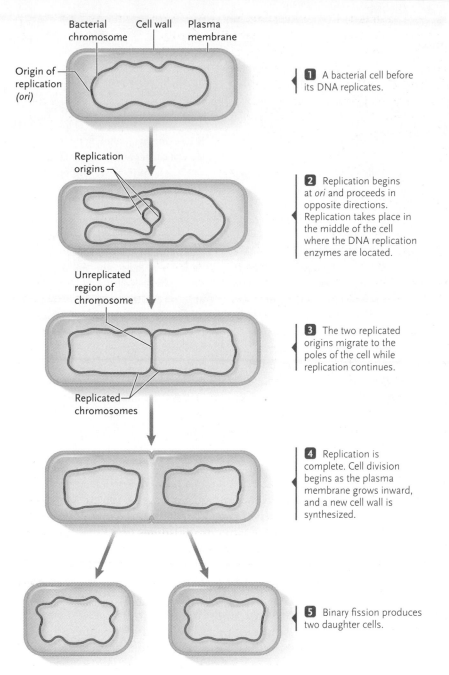

Origin of replication (*ori*)

Bacterial chromosome   Cell wall   Plasma membrane

1 A bacterial cell before its DNA replicates.

Replication origins

2 Replication begins at *ori* and proceeds in opposite directions. Replication takes place in the middle of the cell where the DNA replication enzymes are located.

Unreplicated region of chromosome

3 The two replicated origins migrate to the poles of the cell while replication continues.

Replicated chromosomes

4 Replication is complete. Cell division begins as the plasma membrane grows inward, and a new cell wall is synthesized.

5 Binary fission produces two daughter cells.

Figure 9.20
Model for the segregation of replicated bacterial chromosomes to daughter cells.

and the cytoplasmic structures and molecules equally between the daughter cells.

9.5c Mitosis Evolved from Binary Fission

The prokaryotic mechanism works effectively because most prokaryotic cells have only a single chromosome. Thus, if a daughter cell receives at least one copy of the chromosome, its genetic information is complete. By contrast, the genetic information of eukaryotes is divided among several chromosomes, with each chromosome containing a much greater length of DNA than a bacterial chromosome does. If

a daughter cell fails to receive a copy of even one chromosome, the effects are usually lethal. The evolution of mitosis solved the mechanical problems associated with distributing long DNA molecules without breakage. Mitosis provided the level of precision required to ensure that each daughter cell receives a complete complement of chromosomes.

Scientists believe that the ancestral division process was binary fission and that mitosis evolved from that process. Variations in the mitotic apparatus in modern-day organisms illuminate possible intermediates in this evolutionary pathway. For example, in many primitive eukaryotes, such as dinoflagellates (a type of single-celled alga), the nuclear envelope remains intact during mitosis, and the chromosomes bind to the inner membrane of the nuclear membrane. When the nucleus divides, the chromosomes are segregated.

A more advanced form of the mitotic apparatus is seen in yeasts and diatoms (another type of single-celled alga). In these organisms, the mitotic spindle forms and chromosomes segregate to daughter nuclei without the disassembly and reassembly of the nuclear envelope. Currently, scientists think that the type of mitosis seen in yeasts and **diatoms** and the type of mitosis in animals and higher plants evolved separately from a common ancestral type. Mitotic cell division, the subject of this chapter, produces two cells that have the same genetic information as the parental cell entering division. In the next chapter, you will learn about meiosis, a specialized form of cell division that produces cells with half the number of chromosomes as the parent cells that enter into division.

STUDY BREAK

What are the three main steps in prokaryotic binary fission?

John Dick, University of Toronto

One of the best places to find actively cycling cells in a vertebrate body is in bone marrow. It is here that hematopoietic stem cells divide to produce progeny cells capable of proliferating and differentiating into the various specialized cells needed to maintain the liquid tissue called blood.

One of the best places to try to understand this developmental process, as well as the mechanisms underlying human blood disorders and cancer (leukemia), is the laboratory of Dr. John Dick at the University of Toronto. Dr. Dick is a professor of medical genetics and microbiology, a fellow of the Royal Society of Canada, and Canada Research Chair in Stem Cell Biology. Originally from rural Manitoba, he now heads a team of coworkers and international collaborators from his office in the

MaRS Discovery District in downtown Toronto.

One of Dr. Dick's most powerful tools, one that gained him international recognition, is his system for modelling the production of blood by establishing human hematopoietic cells in mice. That is, he creates mice that make human blood instead of their usual mouse blood. Mice that make human blood also show human blood disorders, and Dr. Dick's team has been able to study the initiation and progression of human leukemia entirely in mice. This mouse model system provides an opportunity to better understand the genetic changes involved in leukemia and the effectiveness of emerging therapies.

Dr. Dick's sustained success arises from his ability to locate stem cells and

understand their biology. His original discovery of the role of aberrant stem cells at the root of leukemia is now seen as the opening line of a story that is fundamentally altering the prevailing view of cancer and its treatment. If Dr. Dick is correct in his hypothesis that many cancers are initiated and fed by the progeny of relatively slow cycling, genetically aberrant, stem cells (as is suggested by a growing body of research), then traditional therapies designed to indiscriminately kill rapidly cycling cancer cells are understandably "hit and miss." Dr. Dick has been able to identify and sort colon cancer cells into two fractions: those that can reproduce new tumours and those that cannot. This ability to specifically target cancer stem cells will be at the centre of the future development of anticancer therapies.

UNANSWERED QUESTIONS

This chapter has indicated that complex, interacting molecular networks within cells fine-tune the division of each cell in both unicellular and multicellular organisms. Identifying the genes and proteins involved in these networks is crucial both for a complete understanding of cell growth and division and for developing models for diseases caused by cell cycle defects. For example, zebrafish can regenerate damaged heart tissue, but humans cannot. Why might this be?

Review

Go to CENGAGENOW™ at http://hed.nelson.com/ to access quizzing, animations, exercises, articles, and personalized homework help.

9.1 The Cycle of Cell Growth and Division: An Overview

- In mitotic cell division, DNA replication is followed by the equal separation—that is, segregation—of the replicated DNA molecules and their delivery to daughter cells. The process ensures that the two cell products of a division have the same genetic information as the parent cell entering division.
- Mitosis is the basis for growth and maintenance of body mass in multicelled eukaryotes and for the reproduction of many single-celled eukaryotes.

- The chromosomes of eukaryotic cells are individual, linear DNA molecules with associated proteins.
- DNA replication and the duplication of chromosomal proteins convert each chromosome into a structure composed of two exact copies known as sister chromatids.

9.2 The Mitotic Cell Cycle

- Mitosis and interphase constitute the mitotic cell cycle. Mitosis occurs in five stages. In prophase (stage 1), the chromosomes condense into short rods and the spindle forms in the cytoplasm (see Figures 9.4 and 9.6).

- In prometaphase (stage 2), the nuclear envelope breaks down, the spindle enters the former nuclear area, and the sister chromatids of each chromosome make connections to opposite spindle poles. Each chromatid has a kinetochore that attaches to spindle microtubules (see Figures 9.4 and 9.8).
- In metaphase (stage 3), the spindle is fully formed and the chromosomes, moved by the spindle microtubules, become aligned at the metaphase plate (see Figure 9.4).
- In anaphase (stage 4), the spindle separates the sister chromatids and moves them to opposite spindle poles. At this point, chromosome segregation is complete (see Figures 9.4 and 9.6).
- In telophase (stage 5), the chromosomes decondense and return to the extended state typical of interphase. A new nuclear envelope forms around the chromosomes (see Figures 9.4 and 9.6).
- Cytokinesis, the division of the cytoplasm, completes cell division by producing two daughter cells, each containing a daughter nucleus produced by mitosis (see Figures 9.4 and 9.6).
- Cytokinesis in animal cells proceeds by furrowing, in which a band of microfilaments just under the plasma membrane contracts, gradually separating the cytoplasm into two parts (see Figure 9.10).
- In plant cytokinesis, cell wall material is deposited along the plane of the former spindle midpoint; the deposition continues until a continuous new wall, the cell plate, separates the daughter cells (see Figure 9.11).

9.3 Formation and Action of the Mitotic Spindle

- In animal cells, the centrosome divides and the two parts move apart. As they do so, the microtubules of the spindle form between them. In plant cells with no centrosome, the spindle microtubules assemble around the nucleus (see Figure 9.12).
- In the spindle, kinetochore microtubules run from the poles to the kinetochores of the chromosomes, and nonkinetochore microtubules run from the poles to a zone of overlap at the spindle midpoint without connecting to the chromosomes (see Figure 9.14).
- During anaphase, the kinetochores move along the kinetochore microtubules, pulling the chromosomes to the poles. The nonkinetochore microtubules slide over each other, pushing the poles farther apart (see Figures 9.14 and 9.15).

9.4 Cell Cycle Regulation

- The cell cycle is controlled directly by complexes of cyclins and a cyclin-dependent protein kinase (CDK). A CDK is activated when combined with a cyclin and then adds phosphate groups to target proteins, activating them. The activated proteins trigger the cell to progress to the next cell cycle stage. Each major stage of the cell cycle begins with activation of one or more cyclin:CDK complexes and ends with deactivation of the complexes by breakdown of the cyclins (see Figure 9.17).
- Important internal controls create checkpoints to ensure that the reactions of one stage are complete before the cycle proceeds to the next stage.
- External controls are based primarily on surface receptors that recognize and bind signals such as peptide hormones and growth factors, surface groups on other cells, or molecules of the extracellular matrix. The binding triggers internal reactions that speed, slow, or stop cell division.
- Most cells in multicellular eukaryotes progressively lose the ability to divide over time by a process called cellular senescence. Factors that contribute to senescence include accumulating DNA damage and shortening telomeres.
- In cancer, control of cell division is lost and cells divide continuously and uncontrollably, forming a rapidly growing mass of cells that interferes with body functions. Cancer cells also break loose from their original tumour (metastasize) to form additional tumours in other parts of the body.
- Certain cells may undergo programmed cell death called apoptosis. Such a fate would be appropriate for cells that are, for instance, surplus for development, damaged, infected, or functional only after death.

9.5 Cell Division in Prokaryotes

- Replication of the bacterial chromosome begins at a site called the "origin" through reactions catalyzed by enzymes located in the middle of the cell. Once the origin of replication is duplicated, the two origins migrate to the two ends of the cells. Division of the cytoplasm then occurs through a partition of cell wall material that grows inward until the cell is separated into two parts (see Figure 9.20).

Questions

Self-Test Questions

1. During the cell cycle, the DNA mass of a cell
   a. decreases during G_1 phase.
   b. decreases during metaphase.
   c. increases during the S phase.
   d. increases during G_2.
   e. decreases during interphase.

2. Imagine that you are in a job interview for a pharmaceutical company and are asked to suggest a good target for an anticancer drug. You should suggest a drug whose action results in

   a. decreased apoptosis.
   b. decreased binding of cyclin to CDK.
   c. increased CDK activity.
   d. increased telomerase.
   e. decreased caspase.

3. Honeybee eggs that are not fertilized develop into fertile, haploid males called "drones." Fertilized eggs can develop into diploid females, one of which might become a "queen." (Fertilized eggs might also become males, but they are taken out and killed by the drones.)

If the queen has 32 chromosomes in her body cells, how many chromatids would be present in a G_2 drone cell?
- a. 8.
- b. 16.
- c. 24.
- d. 32.
- e. 64.

4. The major microtubule organizing centre of the animal cell is
- a. chromosomes, composed of chromatids.
- b. the centrosome, composed of centrioles.
- c. the chromatin, composed of chromatids.
- d. chromosomes, composed of centromere.
- e. centrioles, composed of centrosome.

5. For a given cell, the number of _____ is *higher* at the end of S phase than at the beginning.
- a. nuclei.
- b. chromatids.
- c. chromosomes.
- d. CDK2 molecules.
- e. Both b and c are correct.

6. Which of the following statements about mitosis is *incorrect*?
- a. Microtubules can bind to kinetochores and interact with other microtubules from opposite poles.
- b. In anaphase, the spindle separates sister chromatids and pulls them apart.
- c. Chromosomes congregate near the centre of the cell during metaphase.
- d. Cytokinesis describes the movement of chromosomes.
- e. Both the animal cell furrow and the plant cell plate form at their former spindle midpoints.

7. Mitomycin C is an anticancer drug that stops cell division by inserting itself between the strands of DNA and binding them together. You would predict this drug to have its major effect at
- a. late G_1 phase, early S phases.
- b. late G_2 phase.
- c. prophase.
- d. metaphase.
- e. anaphase.

8. Which of the following statements about cell cycle regulation is *incorrect*?
- a. Cyclin is synthesized during the S phase.
- b. Caspase is activated by cyclin binding.
- c. CDKs combine with cyclin to phosphorylate target proteins.
- d. Telomere shortening stops cell cycling.
- e. Stem cells divide more often than other somatic cells.

9. Which of the following is *not* characteristic of cancer cells?
- a. metastasis.
- b. contact inhibition.
- c. avoidance of "Hayflick" factors.
- d. oncogene overactivation of cyclin.
- e. extra growth factor receptors.

10. In bacteria,
- a. several chromosomes undergo mitosis.
- b. binary fission produces four daughter cells.
- c. replication begins at the ori and the DNA strand separates.
- d. replication occurs in the same direction off each opposite strand.
- e. the daughter cells receive different genetic information from the parent cell.

Questions for Discussion

1. You have a means of measuring the amount of DNA in a single cell. You first measure the amount of DNA during G_1. At what point(s) during the remainder of the cell cycle would you expect the amount of DNA per cell to change?

2. A cell has 38 chromosomes. After mitosis and cell division, 1 daughter cell has 39 chromosomes and the other has 37. What might have caused these abnormal chromosome numbers? What effects do you suppose this might have on cell function? Why?

3. Taxol (Bristol-Myers Squibb, New York), a substance derived from the Pacific yew (*Taxus brevifolia*), is effective in the treatment of breast and ovarian cancers. It works by stabilizing microtubules, thereby preventing them from disassembling. Why would this activity slow or stop the growth of cancer cells?

4. Many chemicals in the food we eat potentially have effects on cancer cells. Chocolate, for example, contains a number of flavonoid compounds, which act as natural antioxidants. Design an experiment to determine whether any of the flavonoids in chocolate inhibit the cell cycle of breast cancer cells growing in culture.

5. The genes and proteins involved in cell cycle regulation are very different in prokaryotes and eukaryotes. However, both types of organisms use similar molecular regulatory reactions to coordinate DNA synthesis with cell division. What does this observation mean from an evolutionary perspective?

Mating octopus.

© VOLVOX Inc. Tsuneo Nakamura Marine Photo Office

10 Genetic Recombination

WHY IT MATTERS

A couple clearly shows mutual interest. First, he caresses her with one arm, then another—then another, another, and another. She reciprocates. This interaction goes on for hours—a hug here, a squeeze there. At the climactic moment, the male reaches deftly under his mantle and removes a packet of sperm, which he inserts under the mantle of the female. For every one of his sperm that successfully performs its function, a fertilized egg can develop into a new octopus.

For the octopus, sex is an occasional event, preceded by a courtship ritual that involves intermingled tentacles. For another marine animal, the slipper limpet, sex is a lifelong group activity. Slipper limpets are relatives of snails. Like many other animals, a slipper limpet passes through a free-living immature stage before it becomes a sexually mature adult. When the time comes for an immature limpet to transform into an adult, it settles onto a rock or other firm surface. If the limpet settles by itself, it develops into a female. If instead it settles on top of a female, it develops into a male. If another slipper limpet settles down on that male, it, too, becomes a male. Adult slipper limpets almost always live in such piles, with the one on the bottom always being a female. All the male limpets continually contribute sperm that fertilize eggs shed by the female. If the one female dies, the surviving male at the bottom of the pile changes into a female and reproduction continues.

The life history of these octopuses and slipper limpets illustrates a tension in biology between sameness and difference. On the one hand, the growth and repair of their multicellular tissues depend on faithful replication of deoxyribonucleic acid (DNA) during mitotic cell division, as described in the previous chapter. At the level of the organism, it is important that all the individual cells in the body of a slipper limpet, for example, are genetically identical. However, on the other hand, at the level of the population, it is important that the individual limpets are genetically *different*. Evolutionary changes in populations arise from natural selection of particular individuals over others in each generation. Populations must have heritable genetic diversity if they are to evolve.

The ultimate source of genetic diversity is mutation of the DNA sequence, often resulting from errors during DNA replication. Since mutations are relatively rare, diversity is amplified through various mechanisms that shuffle existing mutations into different combinations. This process, of literally cutting and pasting DNA backbones into new combinations, is called genetic recombination and is very widespread in nature. Genetic **recombination** allows "jumping genes" to move, inserts some viruses into the chromosome of their hosts, underlies the spread of antibiotic resistance among bacteria, and is at the heart of meiosis in eukaryotes. Genetic recombination puts the "sexual" in sexual reproduction; without genetic recombination, reproduction is "asexual," and offspring are simply identical clones of their parent. We begin this chapter with a look at the basic mechanism of DNA recombination.

10.1 Mechanism of Genetic Recombination

Biologists who study **genetic recombination** have developed several models to explain precisely how the process proceeds in various situations. In its most general sense, genetic recombination requires the following: two DNA molecules that differ from one another in at least two places, a mechanism for bringing the DNA molecules into close proximity, and a collection of enzymes to "cut," "exchange," and "paste" the DNA back together. **Figure 10.1** conveys a very simple model for recombination that, although lacking the details of more sophisticated models, highlights the basic steps involved.

The elegant double helix of DNA represented in Figure 10.1 is one of the most widely recognized biological molecules, and we expect that you can discern the "backbone" of the helix winding around the interior "steps" of paired bases. The sugar–phosphate backbone is held together by strong covalent bonds, whereas the bases pair with their partners through relatively weak hydrogen bonds. (If these ideas are new to you, see Chapter 13 for a more comprehensive look at DNA structure.) Figure 10.1a shows two similar double helixes lying close together as the first step in recombination. Most of the recombination discussed in this chapter occurs between regions of DNA that are very similar, but not identical, in the sequence of bases. Such regions, which may be as short as a few base pairs or as long as an entire chromosome, are called **homologous**. Homology allows different DNA molecules to line up and recombine precisely. Once homologous regions of DNA are paired, enzymes break a covalent bond in each of the four sugar–phosphate backbones. The free ends of each backbone are then exchanged and reattached to those of the other DNA molecule, as shown in Figure 10.1b and c.

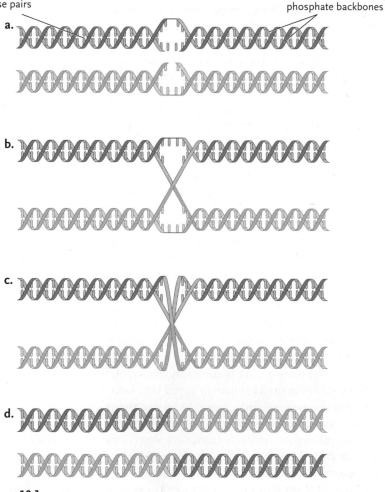

Hydrogen-bonded base pairs

Covalently bonded sugar phosphate backbones

a.

b.

c.

d.

Figure 10.1

A simplified model of genetic recombination. **(a)** Two molecules of DNA with similar sequence are brought into close proximity. **(b)** Enzymes nick the DNA backbones, exchange the ends, and reattach them. **(c and d)** In this case, the final result is two recombined DNA molecules.

The final result is two recombined molecules in which the originally red DNA is now covalently bound to blue DNA, and vice versa. In this chapter, we consider all the steps shown in Figure 10.1 to comprise a single recombination event. This idea is worth restating: cutting and pasting *four* DNA backbones results in *one* recombination event.

As we move through diverse examples of recombination in this chapter, from plasmids to meiotic crossing-over, to transposons, the characteristics of the participating DNA molecules will be different, the enzymes will change, and the results of recombination will have quite different consequences for the organism in question. However, you can always return to Figure 10.1 to remind yourself of the basic underlying mechanism.

STUDY BREAK

What would happen if two circular DNA molecules were involved in a single recombination event?

10.2 Genetic Recombination in Bacteria

Genetic recombination was historically first associated with meiosis in sexually reproducing eukaryotes. Genetic and microscopic research in the early decades of the twentieth century characterized recombination and culminated in the construction of the first genetic maps of chromosomes. However, by the middle of that century, improved techniques for studying the genetics of bacteria and their viruses enabled researchers to look for evidence of genetic recombination even though prokaryotes do not reproduce sexually by meiosis. They found plenty, and we begin our discussion of recombination with a look at prokaryotes. The data showed that, for particular bacteria, there are mechanisms to bring DNA from different cells together and that this DNA recombines to create offspring that are different from either parent cell. Bacteria clearly have a type of sex in their lives. It may be surprising for you to learn that, in some types of bacterial recombination, one of the participating cells is dead. Watch for this.

Escherichia coli, the most extensively studied prokaryote, is named in honour of its discoverer, a Viennese pediatrician named Dr. Theodor Escherich, who isolated it from dirty diapers during an outbreak of diarrhea in 1885. Ready availability and ease of growth in the laboratory have made *E. coli* a workhorse of bacterial genetics that has helped lay the foundations for our understanding of the role of DNA as the genetic material, as well as the molecular structure, expression, and recombination of genes. (See more information about *E. coli* as a model research organism in *The Chemical and Physical Foundations of Biology* pages.)

10.2a Genetic Recombination Occurs in *E. coli*

In 1946, two scientists at Yale University, Joshua Lederberg and Edward L. Tatum, set out to determine if genetic recombination occurs in bacteria, using *E. coli* as their experimental organism. In essence, they were testing whether bacteria had a kind of sexuality in their reproduction process. In order to understand Lederberg and Tatum's work, you first need to know how bacteria are grown in the laboratory.

E. coli and many other bacteria can be grown in a **minimal medium** containing water, an organic carbon source such as glucose, and a selection of inorganic salts, including one, such as ammonium chloride, that provides nitrogen. The growth medium can be in liquid form or in the form of a gel made by adding agar to the liquid medium. (Agar is a polysaccharide material, indigestible by most bacteria, that is extracted from algae.) Since it is not practical to study a single bacterium for most experiments, researchers developed techniques for starting bacterial cultures from a single cell, generating cultures with a large number of genetically identical cells. Cultures of this type are called **clones.** To start bacterial clones, the scientist spreads a drop of a bacterial culture over a sterile agar gel in a culture dish. The culture is diluted enough to ensure that cells will be widely separated on the agar surface. Each cell divides many times to produce a clump of identical cells called a "colony." Cells can be removed from a colony and introduced into liquid media or spread on agar and grown in essentially any quantity.

Now, in order for Lederberg and Tatum to detect genetic recombination, they needed some sort of detectable differences that could be shown to occur in changing combinations. The difference that proved most useful was related to nutrition. Cells require various amino acids for synthesis of proteins. Strains that are able to synthesize the necessary amino acids are called **prototrophs.** Mutant strains that are unable to synthesize amino acids are called **auxotrophs;** they can grow only if the required amino acid is provided for them in the growth medium. A strain that cannot manufacture its own arginine is represented by the genetic shorthand arg^-. In this shorthand, arg refers to the gene that governs a cell's ability to synthesize arginine from simple inorganic molecules. A given strain of bacteria might carry this gene in its normal form, arg^+, or its mutant form, arg^-. These alternative forms of the gene are called alleles and might differ by as little as one base pair in their respective DNA sequence. Prokaryotes typically have one circular chromosome that carries one particular allele for each of their genes.

Using mutagens such as X-rays or ultraviolet light, Lederberg and Tatum isolated two different strains of *E. coli* carrying distinctive combinations of alleles for various metabolic genes. See **Figure 10.2 (p. 202)** to understand how these auxotrophic strains could

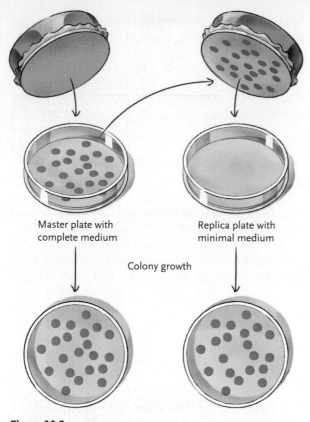

Figure 10.2

Replica plating transfers cells from complete media to minimal media where auxotrophs fail to grow.

Master plate with complete medium

Replica plate with minimal medium

Colony growth

be isolated by **replica** plating. One particular strain could grow only if the vitamin biotin and the amino acid methionine were added to the culture medium. A second mutant strain did not need biotin or methionine but could grow only if the amino acids leucine and threonine were added along with the vitamin

thiamine. These two multiple-mutant strains of *E. coli* were represented in genetic notation as

$$\text{bio}^- \text{met}^- \text{leu}^+ \text{thr}^+ \text{thi}^+$$

Strain 1

$$\text{bio}^+ \text{met}^+ \text{leu}^- \text{thr}^- \text{thi}^-$$

Strain 2

Lederberg and Tatum mixed about 100 million cells of the two mutant strains together and placed them on a minimal medium **(Figure 10.3).** Several hundred colonies grew even though, individually, none of the original cells carried all of the normal alleles needed for growth. You might be thinking, "They are mutants. Maybe some of the originally mutated alleles went back to normal." This possibility was easily discounted by plating large numbers of cells from each original strain onto minimal medium separately. If mutation was responsible for the initial results with mixed cultures, then colonies should also appear when strains were plated separately. There were none. Some form of recombination between the DNA molecules of the two parental types must have produced the necessary combination with normal alleles for each of the five genes:

$$\text{bio}^+ \text{met}^+ \text{leu}^+ \text{thr}^+ \text{thi}^+$$

10.2b Bacterial Conjugation Brings DNA of Two Cells into Close Proximity

How was DNA from two different bacterial cells able to recombine? We will see in Section 10.3 that genetic recombination in eukaryotes occurs in diploid cells by an exchange of segments between pairs of chromosomes. However, bacteria are haploid organisms; each cell typically has its own single, circular

Figure 10.3

Experimental evidence for genetic recombination in bacteria.

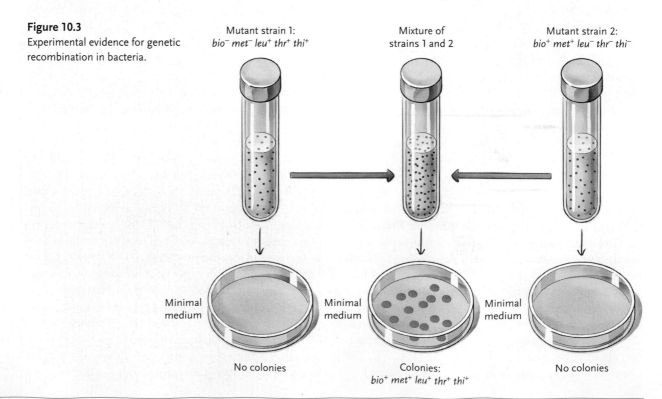

Mutant strain 1:
bio⁻ met⁻ leu⁺ thr⁺ thi⁺

Mixture of strains 1 and 2

Mutant strain 2:
bio⁺ met⁺ leu⁻ thr⁻ thi⁻

Minimal medium

Minimal medium

Minimal medium

No colonies

Colonies:
bio⁺ met⁺ leu⁺ thr⁺ thi⁺

No colonies

chromosome. So where do the "pairs" of chromosomes come from in bacteria? Although bacterial cells were first thought to bring their DNA together by fusing, it was later established that transfer of genetic information is unidirectional, from one cell to the other. Instead of fusing, bacterial cells *conjugate*. That is, cells contact each other by a long tubular structure called a *sex pilus* and then form a cytoplasmic bridge **(Figure 10.4a, b)**. During **conjugation**, a copy of part of the DNA of one cell moves through the cytoplasmic bridge into the other cell. Once DNA from one cell enters the other, genetic recombination can occur. Through this unidirectional transfer of a part of the chromosome, bacterial conjugation thus facilitates a kind of sexual reproduction in prokaryotes.

The F Factor and Conjugation. Conjugation is initiated by a bacterial cell that contains a small circle of DNA in addition to the main circular chromosomal DNA **(Figures 10.5 and 10.6, p. 204)**. Such small circles are called plasmids, and this particular one is known as the "fertility" plasmid or "the F factor." Like all plasmids, the F factor carries several genes as well as a replication origin that permits a copy to be passed on to each daughter cell during the usual process of bacterial cell division. This is an example of "vertical" inheritance from one generation to the next that you are familiar with. However, during conjugation, the

a. Attachment by sex pilus

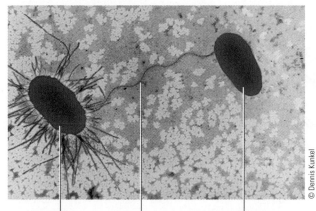

Donor cell with F factor

Sex pilus

Recipient cell lacking F factor

b. Cytoplasmic bridge formed

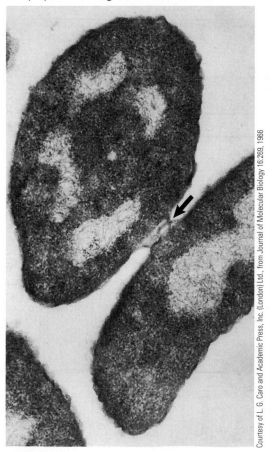

Courtesy of L. G. Caro and Academic Press, Inc. (London) Ltd., from Journal of Molecular Biology 16:269, 1986

Figure 10.4
Conjugating *E. coli* cells. **(a)** Initial attachment of two cells by the sex pilus. **(b)** A cytoplasmic bridge (arrow) has formed between the cells, through which DNA moves from one cell to the other.

a. Bacterial DNA released from cell

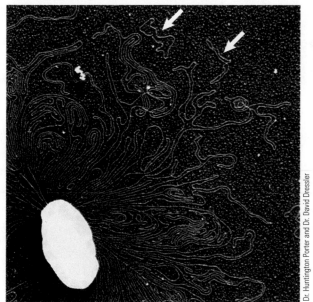

Dr. Huntington Porter and Dr. David Dressler

b. Plasmid

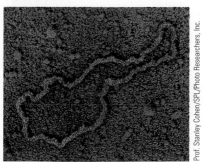

Prof. Stanley Cohen/SPL/Photo Researchers, Inc.

Figure 10.5
Electron micrographs of DNA released from a disrupted bacterial cell. **(a)** Plasmids (arrows) near the mass of chromosomal DNA. **(b)** A single plasmid at higher magnification (colourized).

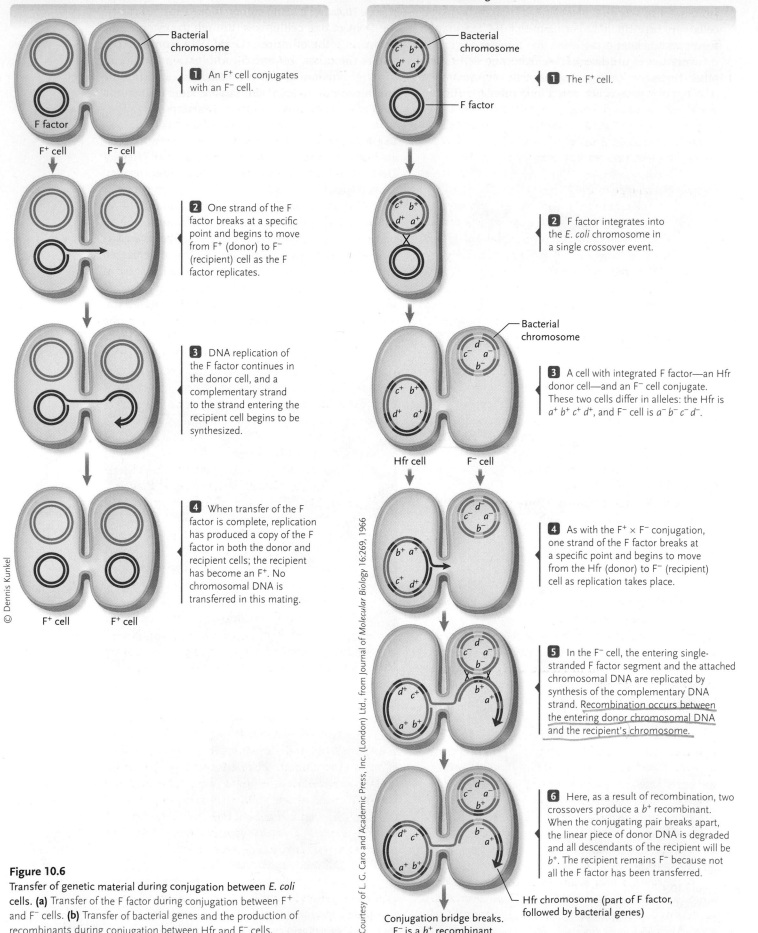

a. Transfer of the F factor

Bacterial chromosome

F factor

F⁺ cell   F⁻ cell

1 An F⁺ cell conjugates with an F⁻ cell.

2 One strand of the F factor breaks at a specific point and begins to move from F⁺ (donor) to F⁻ (recipient) cell as the F factor replicates.

3 DNA replication of the F factor continues in the donor cell, and a complementary strand to the strand entering the recipient cell begins to be synthesized.

4 When transfer of the F factor is complete, replication has produced a copy of the F factor in both the donor and recipient cells; the recipient has become an F⁺. No chromosomal DNA is transferred in this mating.

F⁺ cell   F⁺ cell

© Dennis Kunkel

b. Transfer of bacterial genes

Bacterial chromosome

c^+ b^+
d^+ a^+

F factor

1 The F⁺ cell.

2 F factor integrates into the *E. coli* chromosome in a single crossover event.

Bacterial chromosome

3 A cell with integrated F factor—an Hfr donor cell—and an F⁻ cell conjugate. These two cells differ in alleles: the Hfr is a^+ b^+ c^+ d^+, and F⁻ cell is a^- b^- c^- d^-.

Hfr cell   F⁻ cell

4 As with the F⁺ × F⁻ conjugation, one strand of the F factor breaks at a specific point and begins to move from the Hfr (donor) to F⁻ (recipient) cell as replication takes place.

5 In the F⁻ cell, the entering single-stranded F factor segment and the attached chromosomal DNA are replicated by synthesis of the complementary DNA strand. Recombination occurs between the entering donor chromosomal DNA and the recipient's chromosome.

6 Here, as a result of recombination, two crossovers produce a b^+ recombinant. When the conjugating pair breaks apart, the linear piece of donor DNA is degraded and all descendants of the recipient will be b^+. The recipient remains F⁻ because not all the F factor has been transferred.

Hfr chromosome (part of F factor, followed by bacterial genes)

Conjugation bridge breaks. F⁻ is a b^+ recombinant.

Courtesy of L. G. Caro and Academic Press, Inc. (London) Ltd., from *Journal of Molecular Biology* 16:269, 1966

Figure 10.6
Transfer of genetic material during conjugation between *E. coli* cells. **(a)** Transfer of the F factor during conjugation between F⁺ and F⁻ cells. **(b)** Transfer of bacterial genes and the production of recombinants during conjugation between Hfr and F⁻ cells.

F factor also has the ability to be copied and passed directly from one cell, called the donor, to another, called the recipient. This is an example of "horizontal" inheritance.

Donor cells are called **F$^+$ cells** because they contain the F factor. They are able to mate with recipient cells but not with other donor cells. Recipient calls lack the F factor and, hence, are called **F$^-$ cells.** The F factor carries about 20 or so genes. Several of them encode proteins of the **sex pilus,** also called the **F pilus** (plural pili) (see Figures 10.4 and 10.6a, step 1).

During conjugation, the F plasmid replicates using a special type of DNA replication called "rolling circle". To understand this mechanism, first picture a site, called the origin of transfer, on the F plasmid. Then imagine a break in just one strand of the double helix at this site. Now, with your imaginary fingers, gently pull the free end of the single strand of DNA away from the F factor, through the cytoplasmic bridge, and into the recipient cell. As the single strand is pulled, the remaining strand—still a circle—"rolls" like the spool on a tape dispenser. DNA synthesis fills in the complementary bases to ensure that the F factor is double-stranded in both the donor and the recipient cells. When the entire F factor strand has transferred and replicated, it circularizes again (see Figure 10.6a, step 4). It is important to understand that although the recipient cell becomes F$^+$, no chromosomal DNA is transferred between cells in this process. *That is, no genetic recombination occurs between the DNA of two different cells in such a mating.*

So why are we including F factor conjugation in this chapter if it does not recombine DNA of different cells? The answer lies in the Hfr cells described in the next section.

Hfr Cells and Genetic Recombination. In some F$^+$ cells, the F factor comes into close proximity with the main chromosome and, lining up in a short region of homology, suffers a recombination event. When two circular DNA molecules recombine, (by the mechanism shown in Figure 10.1) they simply fuse together into one larger circle. In this way, the F factor actually becomes a part of the main bacterial chromosome (see Figure 10.6b, step 2). These special donor cells are known as **Hfr cells** (Hfr = high-frequency recombination). It is important not to be confused at this point; although a recombination event integrated the F factor into the host chromosome, this is recombination within one cell, not between the chromosomes of different cells. Hfr cells are called "high-frequency recombination" because they can "export" copies of chromosomal genes to another cell, as described below.

When the F factor is integrated into the bacterial chromosome, its genes are still active. Therefore, these Hfr cells make sex pilli and can conjugate with an F$^-$ cell. Figure 10.6b, step 3, shows an Hfr $\times$ F$^-$ mating where the two cell types differ in alleles for the genes a, b, c, and d. Note that a segment of the F factor moves through the conjugation bridge into the recipient, bringing the single-stranded chromosomal DNA behind it (see Figure 10.6b, steps 4 and 5). This is, again, rolling circle replication in which both donor and recipient cells restore the DNA to double-strandedness. In this situation, the circle that rolls is the entire Hfr donor chromosome. Although DNA transfer often continues long enough for several genes to be transferred, the conjugation bridge between the mating cells soon breaks. It is rare for the entire donor chromosome to be transferred.

At this point, it is important for you to recall that when the F factor transfers by itself, as described in the previous section, the recipient cells often become F$^+$. However, in Hfr cells, the origin of transfer is near the middle of the integrated F factor. As a result, only half of the F factor DNA is transferred at the front of the chromosomal DNA. (Think of the engine of a train.) The other half of the F factor (the dining car at the end of the train) can follow only after the rest of the entire chromosome (see Figure 10.6b, steps 4 to 6). As a result, it is very unusual for a recipient cell to obtain the entire F factor and become Hfr as well. Most likely, the recipient cell will become a **partial diploid;** it will have two copies of only those genes that came through the conjugation bridge on the donor chromosomal DNA segment.

For our example, the recipient cell in Figure 10.6b, step 5, has become, for the moment, $a^+ b^+/a^- b^-$. Although the DNA carrying + alleles for genes a and b differs slightly from that carrying − alleles, these regions are homologous and can pair for recombination. In fact, Figure 10.6 shows two recombination events, one on either side of the b gene, resulting in the exchange of the donor allele with that of the recipient (see Figure 10.6b, step 5). As a result, the recipient cell has become an $a^- b^+$ **recombinant.** Since enzymes in the recipient cell degrade the linear Hfr chromosome soon after recombination occurs, any incoming alleles that are not recombined onto the chromosome are lost. Following recombination, the bacterial DNA replicates and the cell divides normally, producing a clone of cells with the new combination of alleles.

In other pairs in the mating population, recombination events at different locations would lead to different recombinant recipients; perhaps the *a* gene could recombine with the homologous recipient gene, or both *a* and *b* genes could recombine to give $a^+ b^+$ recipients. The various genetic recombinants observed in the Lederberg and Tatum experiment described earlier were produced in this general way.

Mapping Genes by Conjugation. The use of conjugation for genetic mapping was discovered by two scientists, François Jacob (the same scientist who proposed the operon model for the regulation of gene expression in bacteria; see Section 14.1) and Elie L. Wollman, at the Pasteur Institute in Paris. They began their experiments by mating Hfr and F cells that differed in a number of alleles. At regular intervals after conjugation commenced, they removed some of the cells and agitated them in a blender to break apart mating pairs. They then cultured the separated cells and analyzed them for recombinants. They found that the longer they allowed cells to conjugate before separation, the greater the number of donor genes that entered the recipient and produced recombinants. By noting the order and time at which genes were transferred, Jacob and Wollman were able to map and assign the relative positions of several genes in the *E. coli* chromosome.

10.2c Transformation and Transduction Provide Additional Sources of DNA for Recombination

The discovery of conjugation and genetic recombination in *E. coli* showed that genetic recombination is not restricted to eukaryotes. Further discoveries demonstrated that DNA can transfer from one bacterial cell to another by two additional mechanisms, transformation and transduction. Like conjugation, these mechanisms transfer DNA in one direction and create partial diploids in which recombination can occur between alleles in the homologous DNA regions. Unlike conjugation, in which both donor and recipient cells are living, transformation and transduction enable recipient cells to recombine with DNA obtained from dead donors.

Transformation. In **transformation**, bacteria simply take up pieces of DNA that are released into the environment as other cells disintegrate. Fred Griffith, a medical officer in the British Ministry of Health, London, discovered this phenomenon in 1928 while trying to understand how bacteria cause pneumonia in mice. Cells of the virulent strains of *Streptococcus pneumoniae* were surrounded by a polysaccharide **capsule**, whereas the nonvirulent strains were not. Griffith found that a mixture of heat-killed virulent cells plus living nonvirulent cells still caused pneumonia. One interpretation of this observation was that the living nonvirulent cells had been transformed to virulence by something released from the dead cells. In 1944, Oswald Avery and his colleagues at New York University found that the substance derived from the killed virulent cells, the substance capable of transforming nonvirulent bacteria to the virulent form, was DNA (discussed in Section 13.1).

Subsequently, geneticists established that in the transformation of *Streptococcus*, the linear DNA fragments taken up from disrupted virulent cells recombine with the chromosomal DNA of the nonvirulent

cells in much the same way as genetic recombination takes place in conjugation. In this case, the recombination introduces the normal allele for capsule formation into the DNA of the nonvirulent cells; expression of that normal allele generates a capsule around the cell and its descendants, making them virulent.

Only some species of bacteria can take up DNA from the surrounding medium by natural mechanisms, and *E. coli* is not one of them. Fortunately for molecular biologists, *E. coli* cells can be induced to take up DNA in the laboratory by a variety of artificial transformation techniques involving exposure to calcium ions and/or pulses of electric current. Artificial transformation is often used to insert recombinant DNA plasmids into *E. coli* cells as part of cloning or genetic engineering techniques. (DNA cloning and genetic engineering are discussed further in Chapter 16.)

Transduction. In **transduction**, DNA is transferred from donor to recipient cells inside the head of an infecting bacterial virus. The infection cycles of viruses that infect bacteria, called **bacteriophage** (or just phage), are described in Chapter 22. For the purposes of this chapter, the basic details of phage infection are shown in **Figures 10.7 and 10.8, p. 208**. In general, transduction begins when new phages assemble in an infected bacterial cell; they sometimes incorporate fragments of the host cell DNA along with, or instead of, the viral DNA. After the host cell is killed, the new phages that are released may then attach to another cell and inject the bacterial DNA (and the viral DNA if it is present) into that recipient cell. The introduction of this DNA, as in conjugation and transformation, makes the recipient cell a partial diploid and allows recombination to take place. Recipients are not killed because they have received bacterial DNA rather than infective viral DNA. Lederberg and his graduate student, Norton Zinder, then at the University of Wisconsin at Madison, discovered transduction in 1952 in experiments with the bacterium *Salmonella typhimurium* and phage P22. Lederberg received a Nobel Prize in 1958 for his discovery of conjugation and transduction in bacteria.

There are two different types of transduction, generalized and specialized, arising from the different infection cycles of the phage involved. **Generalized transduction**, in which all donor genes are equally likely to be transferred, is associated with some **virulent bacteriophages**, which kill their host cells during each cycle of infection (the **lytic cycle**). Notice in Figure 10.7 that, during infection by the virulent phage, the host bacterial chromosome is degraded to provide raw material for synthesis of new phage chromosomes. However, sometimes a fragment of host chromosome avoids degradation and is packed into the head of a new phage *by mistake*. This particular phage now contains a small random sample of bacterial genes *instead of* phage genes. When the host cell

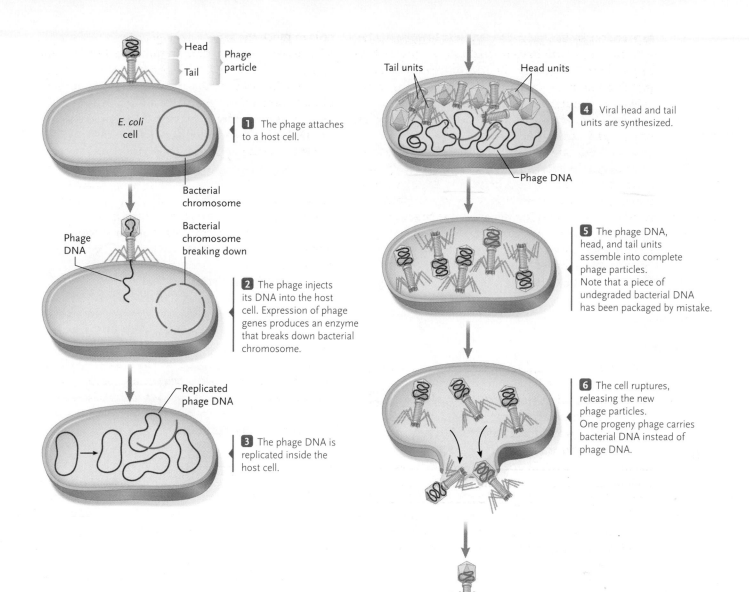

Figure 10.7

Generalized transduction: movement of bacterial DNA from one cell to another inside the head of a lytic bacteriophage.

1 The phage attaches to a host cell.

2 The phage injects its DNA into the host cell. Expression of phage genes produces an enzyme that breaks down bacterial chromosome.

3 The phage DNA is replicated inside the host cell.

4 Viral head and tail units are synthesized.

5 The phage DNA, head, and tail units assemble into complete phage particles. Note that a piece of undegraded bacterial DNA has been packaged by mistake.

6 The cell ruptures, releasing the new phage particles. One progeny phage carries bacterial DNA instead of phage DNA.

7 Bacterial DNA is injected into the next host where it can recombine with similar regions on the host chromosome.

is burst to release the new phage, this "transducing phage" can mechanically infect a recipient cell. However, it will deliver a linear piece of DNA from the donor cell rather than an infectious phage chromosome. The newly infected (and incredibly lucky) recipient cell will survive; incoming DNA may then pair, and recombine, with homologous regions on the recipient chromosome.

One of the most extensively studied bacteriophages is phage lambda (), which infects *E. coli*. Again, a mistake in the infection cycle can result in the transfer of bacterial genes from a donor to a recipient cell. However, in this case, a different type

of mistake, in a different infection cycle, gives rise to a different type of transduction: **specialized transduction** (shown in Figure 10.8). Lambda is a **temperate bacteriophage.** That is, when it first infects a new host, it determines whether the host is likely to be a good one. Is it starving? Is it suffering from DNA damage? If the host cell passes this molecular health checkup, then the lambda chromosome lines up with a small region of homology on the bacterial chromosome and a phage-coded enzyme catalyzes a single recombination event. The phage is thus integrated into the host chromosomal DNA and, in this state, is called a **prophage.** (Overall, this mechanism is very

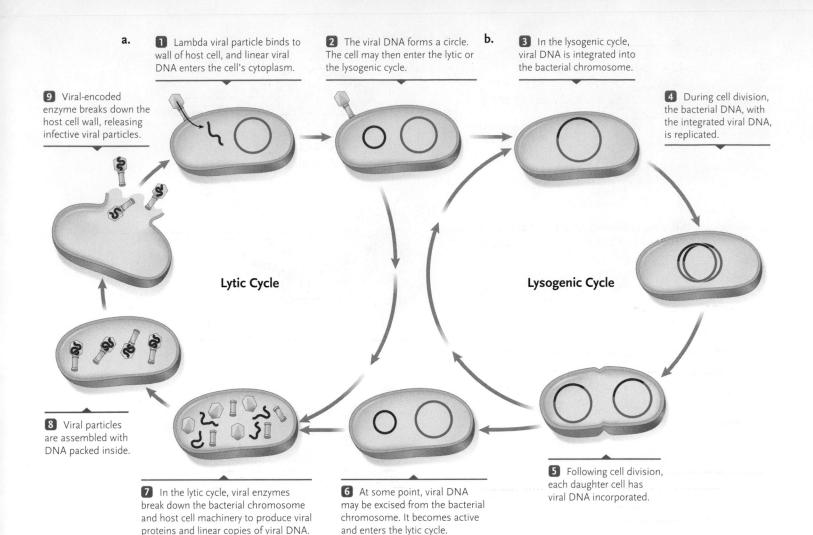

a.

1 Lambda viral particle binds to wall of host cell, and linear viral DNA enters the cell's cytoplasm.

2 The viral DNA forms a circle. The cell may then enter the lytic or the lysogenic cycle.

b.

3 In the lysogenic cycle, viral DNA is integrated into the bacterial chromosome.

9 Viral-encoded enzyme breaks down the host cell wall, releasing infective viral particles.

4 During cell division, the bacterial DNA, with the integrated viral DNA, is replicated.

Lytic Cycle

Lysogenic Cycle

8 Viral particles are assembled with DNA packed inside.

7 In the lytic cycle, viral enzymes break down the bacterial chromosome and host cell machinery to produce viral proteins and linear copies of viral DNA.

6 At some point, viral DNA may be excised from the bacterial chromosome. It becomes active and enters the lytic cycle.

5 Following cell division, each daughter cell has viral DNA incorporated.

Figure 10.8
The infective cycle of lambda, an example of a temperate phage, which can go through the lytic cycle **(a)** or the lysogenic cycle **(b)**.

similar to the integration of the F factor discussed previously.) The prophage is then replicated and passed to daughter cells along with the rest of the bacterial chromosome as long as conditions remain favourable (the **lysogenic cycle** in Figure 10.8).

If, however, the host cell becomes inhospitable (perhaps as a result of ultraviolet-induced DNA damage), the prophage activates several genes, releases itself from the chromosome by a recombination event, and proceeds to manufacture new phage, which are released as the cell bursts as a result of lytic growth.

In specialized transduction, the "mistake" occurs when the prophage is excised from the chromosome. Sometimes this recombination event is imprecise; bacterial DNA is removed from the host chromosome, and some prophage DNA is left behind. As a result, this bacterial DNA is packaged into new phage and carried to recipient cells. Since the transducing phage is defective, having left some of its genes behind in the host, it does not kill its new host. We hope that you can see that in the case of specialized transduction only bacterial genes that are close to the integration site of the phage will ever be incorporated into the phage chromosome by the recombination mistake. Typically, only genes coding for

galactose and biotin metabolism are transferred at high frequency by phage lambda.

Conjugation, transformation, and transduction are all ways in which DNA from two different bacterial cells is brought into close proximity. Homologous regions may then pair and recombine to give rise to a recipient cell that carries a different collection of alleles than it had previously. Overall, these processes create more diversity in the DNA sequence among members of a population than would arise by mutation and binary fission alone. More diversity leads to a higher likelihood that at least some individuals will be well suited to survive changes in the environment.

These basic principles also apply to single and multicellular eukaryotes. The next section of this chapter introduces genetic recombination in eukaryotes as it occurs within the overall process of meiosis. Notice how DNA from two different individuals is brought close together in the same cell following fertilization. Also watch for extensive homology that now extends the full length of large linear chromosomes. Finally, notice the genetic recombination at the centre of this process, which generates novel chromosomes with new combinations of alleles.

10.3 Genetic Recombination in Eukaryotes: Meiosis

The octopuses and slipper limpets described at the opening of this chapter are engaged in forms of **sexual reproduction**, the production of offspring through the union of male and female **gametes**—for example, eggs and sperm cells in animals. Sexual reproduction depends on **meiosis**, a specialized process of cell division that recombines DNA sequences and produces cells with half the number of chromosomes present in the **somatic cells** (body cells) of a species. The derivation of the word *meiosis* (*meioun* = to diminish) reflects this reduction. At **fertilization**, the nuclei of an egg and sperm cell fuse, producing a cell called the **zygote**, in which the chromosome number typical of the species is restored. Without the halving of chromosome number by the meiotic divisions, fertilization would double the number of chromosomes in each subsequent generation.

Both meiosis and fertilization also mix genetic information into new combinations; thus, none of the offspring of a mating pair are likely to be genetically identical to either their parents or their siblings. This genetic variability is the raw material for the process of evolution as described in Chapter 19.

The biological foundations of sexual reproduction are the mixing of genetic information into new combinations and the halving of the chromosome number, both of which occur through meiosis, as well as the restoration of the original chromosome number by fertilization. Intermingled tentacles in octopuses, communal sex among limpets, clouds of pollen in the wind, and the courting and mating rituals of humans are nothing more or less than variations of the means for achieving fertilization, thus bringing DNA together for recombination.

10.3a Meiosis Occurs in Different Places in Different Organismal Life Cycles

Although the life cycle of nearly all eukaryotes alternates between a stage with one basic set of chromosomes (haploid) and a stage with two basic sets of chromosomes (diploid), **Figure 10.9** shows that evolution has produced wide variety in the relative timing of mitosis, meiosis, and fertilization among different species. The life cycles of plants, algae, and fungi may be unfamiliar to you and can be better understood by noticing the function of the cells that are the immediate

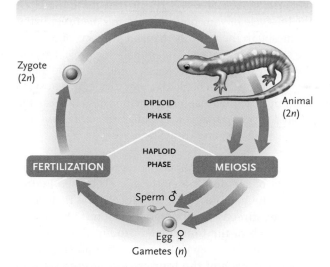

a. Animal life cycles

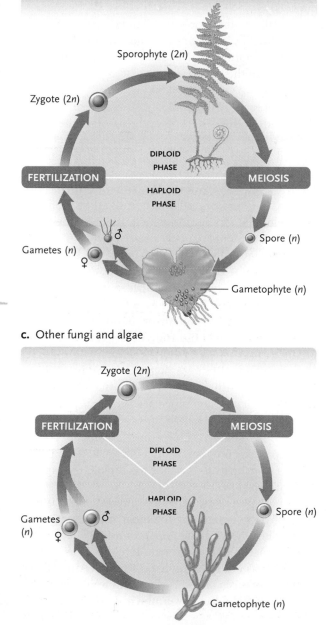

b. All plants and some fungi and algae (fern shown; relative length of the two phases varies widely in plants)

c. Other fungi and algae

Figure 10.9
Variations in the time and place of meiosis in eukaryotes. The diploid phase of the life cycles is shaded in blue; the haploid phase is shaded in yellow. *n* refers to the haploid number of chromosomes; 2*n* refers to the diploid number. **(a)** Meiosis in animal life cycles. Only zygotes divide by mitosis. **(b)** Meiosis in most plants and some fungi and algae. Spores and zygotes divide by mitosis. **(c)** Meiosis in other fungi and algae. Only spores divide by mitosis.

products of meiosis. Notice that the assumption that "meiosis makes gametes" is true only for animals. In the life cycle of your house plants and the fungi living in the soil in the park, the haploid products of meiosis are spores, not gametes. In animals, the diploid zygote divides by mitosis. However, in some fungi and algae, this is reversed; the haploid spores divide by mitosis to form multicellular haploid gametophytes, whereas the diploid zygote remains unicellular. In plants, both the zygote and the spores divide by mitosis.

Animals. Animals follow the pattern in which the diploid phase dominates the life cycle (see Figure 10.9a), the haploid phase is reduced, and meiosis is followed directly by gamete formation. In male animals, each of the four nuclei produced by meiosis is enclosed in a separate cell by cytoplasmic divisions, and each of the four cells differentiates into a functional sperm cell. In female animals, only one of the four nuclei becomes functional as an egg cell nucleus.

Fertilization restores the diploid phase of the life cycle. Thus, animals are haploids only as sperm or eggs, and no mitotic divisions occur during the haploid phase of the life cycle.

Most Plants and Fungi. Most plants and some algae and fungi follow the life cycle pattern shown in Figure 10.9b. These organisms alternate between haploid and diploid generations in which, depending on the organism, either generation may dominate the life cycle, and mitotic divisions occur in both phases. In these organisms, fertilization produces the diploid generation, in which the individuals are called **sporophytes** (*spora* = seed; *phyta* = plant). After the sporophytes grow to maturity by mitotic divisions, some of their cells undergo meiosis, producing haploid, genetically different, reproductive cells called **spores**. The spores are not gametes; they germinate and grow directly by mitotic divisions into a generation of haploid individuals called **gametophytes** (*gameta* = gamete). At maturity, the nuclei of some cells in gametophytes develop into egg or sperm nuclei. All the egg or sperm nuclei produced by a particular gametophyte are genetically identical because they arise through mitosis; meiosis does not occur in gametophytes. Fusion of a haploid egg and sperm nucleus produces a diploid zygote nucleus that divides by mitosis to produce the diploid sporophyte generation again.

In all plants (except bryophytes), the diploid sporophyte generation is the most visible part of the plant. The gametophyte generation is reduced to an almost microscopic stage that develops in the reproductive parts of the sporophytes—in flowering plants, in the structures of the flower. The female gametophyte remains in the flower; the male gametophyte is released from flowers as microscopic pollen grains. When pollen contacts a flower of the same species, it releases a haploid nucleus that fertilizes a haploid egg cell of a female gametophyte in the flower. The resulting cell reproduces by mitosis to form a sporophyte.

Sphagnum moss (commonly known as "peat moss") is a good example of a plant in which the gametophyte is the most visible and familiar stage of the life cycle. In this case, the sporophyte is reduced and develops from a zygote within the body of the gametophyte. Vast peatlands of *Sphagnum* gametophytes are industrially harvested in many parts of the world for fuel and horticultural use.

Some Fungi. The life cycle of some fungi and algae follows the third life cycle pattern (see Figure 10.9c). In these organisms, the diploid phase is limited to a single cell, the zygote, produced by fertilization. Immediately after fertilization, the diploid zygote undergoes meiosis to produce the haploid phase. Mitotic divisions occur only in the haploid phase.

During fertilization, two haploid gametes, usually designated simply as positive (+) or negative (−) because they are similar in structure, fuse to form a diploid nucleus. This nucleus immediately enters meiosis, producing four haploid cells. These cells develop directly or after one or more mitotic divisions into haploid spores. These spores germinate to produce haploid individuals, the gametophytes, which grow or increase in number by mitotic divisions. Eventually, positive and negative gametes are formed in these individuals by differentiation of some of the cells produced by the mitotic divisions. Because the gametes are produced by mitosis, all the gametes of an individual are genetically identical.

10.3b Meiosis Changes Both Chromosome Number and DNA Sequence

In order to understand the mechanism of meiosis, it is helpful to keep the "big picture" in mind. Chapter 8 made the point that the essence of mitotic cell division is "sameness." That is, chromosomes are replicated and partitioned to ensure that cells produced by the process have the same number of chromosomes, with the same DNA sequence, as the cell that began the process. In this way, somatic cells are produced for most of the requirements of multicellular bodies. However, the essence of meiosis is "difference"—actually two kinds of difference: halved chromosome number and recombined chromosomal DNA sequence. The products of meiosis are not intended to contribute to the body of the organisms that make them. In multicellular animals and plants, you would find that meiosis occurs only in specialized tissues that produce gametes or spores, respectively.

Both types of difference mentioned above arise from the very different behaviour of chromosomes in meiosis relative to mitosis. If you understand the significance of the chromosome pairs in diploid organisms as described below, then the differences in chromosome behaviour in meiosis and mitosis will make sense more easily.

As discussed in Section 8.1, the two representatives of each chromosome in a diploid cell constitute a *homologous pair*—they have the same genes, arranged in the same order in the DNA of the chromosomes. One chromosome of each homologous pair, the **paternal chromosome**, is derived from the male parent of the organism, and the other chromosome, the **maternal chromosome**, is derived from its female parent. Although two homologous chromosomes carry the same genes arranged in the same order, different *versions* of these genes, **alleles**, may be present on either chromosome. Recall from the bacterial conjugation material at the beginning of this chapter that different alleles of a given gene have similar, but distinct, DNA sequences. They therefore likely encode variations of the given ribonucleic acid (RNA) or protein gene product, which may then have a different structure, different biochemistry, or both.

For example, all the different breeds of dogs normally have 78 chromosomes in their cells, made up of 39 homologous pairs. However, each individual has a unique combination of the alleles carried by the two chromosomes of each homologous pair. The distinct set of alleles, arising from the mixing mechanisms of meiosis and fertilization in the parents, gives each individual offspring his or her unique combination of inherited traits, including attributes such as size, coat colour, susceptibility to certain diseases and disorders, and aspects of behaviour and intelligence.

One of the more dramatic accomplishments of meiosis in an organism like a dog is the separation of the members of each homologous pair into different cells, thereby reducing the diploid or 2*n* number of chromosomes to the haploid or *n* number. Each cell produced by meiosis carries only one member of each homologous pair. An egg or sperm cell contains 39 chromosomes, one of each pair. When the egg and sperm combine in sexual reproduction to produce the zygote—the first cell of the new puppy—the diploid number of 78 chromosomes (39 pairs) is regenerated. The processes of DNA replication and mitotic cell division ensure that this diploid number is maintained in the body cells as the zygote divides and develops (see Chapter 8).

The second significant consequence of meiotic cell division is, of course, genetic recombination of the actual DNA sequence on chromosomes. Referring back to Figure 10.1, recall that recombination involves the precise breaking of covalently bonded DNA backbones, exchanging the "ends" with those of the other homologue and reforming the bonds. As a result, each chromosome passed on to offspring is composed of a novel mixture of both maternal and paternal DNA sequence.

The following sections describe how the ability of homologues to find their respective partners, and pair intimately along their length, allows both the partitioning of homologues into separate cells and the process of recombination to occur during the first part of the two-step process of meiosis.

10.3c Meiosis Produces Four Genetically Different Daughter Cells

Cells that are destined to divide by meiosis (called **meiocytes**) move through their last turn of the cell cycle as usual, replicating DNA and making more chromosomal proteins during S phase. (See Chapter 13 for details of DNA replication.) The resulting G_2 cells carry replicated chromosomes, each composed of two identical sister chromatids (**Figure 10.10, p. 212**). Following this premeiotic interphase, cells enter the first of the two meiotic divisions: **meiosis I** and **meiosis II**. During meiosis I, chromosomes behave dramatically differently than they do during mitosis. That is, early in meiosis I, homologous chromosomes find their partners and pair lengthwise, gene for gene, in a process called synapsis. During this intimate pairing, recombination occurs, and chromosomal segments are exchanged. As the meiocyte continues through to the end of the first division, the members of each homologous pair are separated into one or the other of the two daughter cells. These daughter cells still contain replicated chromosomes with two chromatids each; however, the number of such chromosomes is only half that of the original meiocyte. During the second meiotic division, meiosis II, the sister chromatids are separated into different cells. A total of four cells, each with the haploid number of chromosomes and a novel collection of alleles, is the final result of the two meiotic divisions.

For convenience, biologists separate each meiotic division into the same key stages as mitosis: *prophase, prometaphase, metaphase, anaphase,* and *telophase*. The stages are identified as belonging to the two divisions, meiosis I and meiosis II, by a *I* or a *II*, as in *prophase I* and *prophase II*. A brief interphase called **interkinesis** separates the two meiotic divisions, *but no DNA replication occurs during interkinesis.*

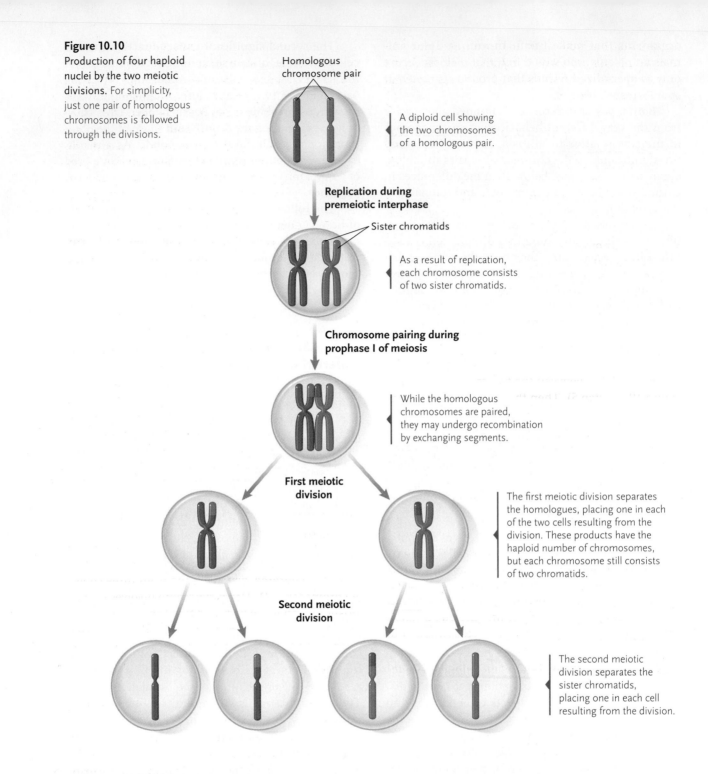

Figure 10.10
Production of four haploid nuclei by the two meiotic divisions. For simplicity, just one pair of homologous chromosomes is followed through the divisions.

Homologous chromosome pair

A diploid cell showing the two chromosomes of a homologous pair.

Replication during premeiotic interphase

Sister chromatids

As a result of replication, each chromosome consists of two sister chromatids.

Chromosome pairing during prophase I of meiosis

While the homologous chromosomes are paired, they may undergo recombination by exchanging segments.

First meiotic division

The first meiotic division separates the homologues, placing one in each of the two cells resulting from the division. These products have the haploid number of chromosomes, but each chromosome still consists of two chromatids.

Second meiotic division

The second meiotic division separates the sister chromatids, placing one in each cell resulting from the division.

Prophase I. At the beginning of prophase I, the replicated chromosomes, each consisting of two sister chromatids, begin to fold and condense into threadlike structures in the nucleus (**Figure 10.11, p. 214,** step 1). The two chromosomes of each homologous pair then come together and line up side by side in a zipperlike way; this process is called **pairing** or **synapsis** (step 2). The fully paired homologues are called **tetrads**, referring to the fact that each homologous pair consists of four chromatids. Note that chromosomes do not behave like this in mitosis.

While they are paired, the chromatids of homologous chromosomes physically exchange segments (step 3). This physical exchange, genetic recombination, is the step that mixes the alleles of the homologous chromosomes into new combinations and contributes to the generation of variability in sexual reproduction. (This is the process that underlies recombination frequency mapping described in Chapter 12.) As prophase I finishes, a spindle forms in the cytoplasm by the same basic mechanisms described in Chapter 8.

Prometaphase I. In prometaphase I, the nuclear envelope breaks down and the spindle enters the former nuclear area (see Figure 10.11, step 4). The two chromosomes of each pair attach to kinetochore microtubules leading to opposite spindle poles. That is, both sister chromatids of one homologue attach to microtubules leading to one spindle pole, whereas both sister chromatids of the other homologue attach to microtubules leading to the opposite pole. Notice, again, how this is different from the spindle attachments during mitosis.

Metaphase and Anaphase I. At metaphase I, movements of the spindle microtubules have aligned the recombined tetrads on the equatorial plane—the *metaphase plate*—between the two spindle poles (see Figure 10.11, step 5). Then the two chromosomes of each homologous pair separate and move to opposite spindle poles during anaphase I (step 6). The movement segregates homologous pairs, delivering a haploid set of chromosomes to each pole of the spindle. However, all the chromosomes at the poles are still double structures composed of two sister chromatids.

Telophase I and Interkinesis. Telophase I is a brief, transitory stage in which there is little or no change in the chromosomes (see Figure 10.11, step 7). New nuclear envelopes form in some species but not in others. Telophase I is followed by an interkinesis in which the single spindle of the first meiotic division disassembles and the microtubules reassemble into two new spindles for the second division. There is no DNA replication between the first and the second division.

Prophase II, Prometaphase II, and Metaphase II. Although the chromosome behaviour during meiosis II is superficially similar to that in a mitotic division, it is important to remember that these two processes are quite distinct. Meiosis II is not "just like mitosis." Meiosis II occurs only in reproductive tissue, there is no immediately preceding S phase, and the resulting daughter cells are not genetically identical.

During prophase of meiosis II, the chromosomes condense and the spindle begins to form (see Figure 10.11, step 8). During prometaphase II, the nuclear envelope breaks down, the spindle enters the former nuclear area, and spindle microtubules leading to opposite spindle poles attach to the two kinetochores of each chromosome (step 9). At meta-phase II, movements of the chromosomes within the spindle bring them to rest on the metaphase plate (step 10).

Anaphase and Telophase II. Anaphase II begins as the sister chromatids of each chromosome separate from each other and move to opposite spindle poles (see Figure 10.11, step 11). At the completion of anaphase II, the separated chromatids—now called chromosomes—have been segregated to the two poles. During telophase II, the chromatids decondense to the extended interphase state, the spindles disassemble, and new nuclear envelopes form around the masses of chromatin (step 12). The result is four haploid cells, each with a nucleus containing half the number of chromosomes present in a somatic cell of the same species. These chromosomes all carry various new combinations of maternal and paternal alleles.

Nondisjunction. Rarely, chromosome segregation fails at either meiosis I or II. For example, during meiosis I, both chromosomes of a homologous pair may connect to the same spindle pole in anaphase I. In the resulting nondisjunction, as it is called, the spindle fails to separate the homologous chromosomes of the tetrad. As a result, one pole receives both chromosomes of the homologous pair, whereas the other pole has no copies of that chromosome. Meiosis II will proceed to separate the chromatids of the extra chromosome as usual, with the result that gametes will have two copies of this chromosome (instead of one). Zygotes that receive an extra chromosome because of nondisjunction therefore have three copies of a given chromosome instead of two. In humans, most zygotes of this kind do not result in live births. One exception is Down syndrome, which results from three copies of chromosome 21. Down syndrome involves characteristic alterations in body and facial structure, mental retardation, and significantly reduced fertility (see Chapter 12 for a more detailed discussion of Down syndrome).

Sex Chromosomes. In many eukaryotes, including most animals, one or more pairs of chromosomes, called the sex chromosomes, are different in male and female individuals of the same species. For example, in fruit flies, the cells of females contain a pair of sex chromosomes called the *XX* pair. Male flies contain a pair of sex chromosomes that consist of one X chromosome and a smaller chromosome called the Y chromosome. The two X chromosomes in females are fully homologous, whereas the male X and Y chromosomes are homologous only through a short region. The X and Y chromosomes behave as homologues during meiosis in males. As a result of meiosis, a gamete formed in females may receive either member of the X pair. A gamete formed in males receives either an X or a Y chromosome. (See Chapter 12 for a discussion of the inheritance of genes on sex chromosomes.)

First meiotic division

Prophase I

Plasma membrane · Duplicated centrioles · Nuclear envelope

Tetrad

Homologous chromosomes · Two sister chromatids

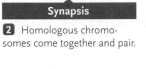

Condensation of chromosomes

1 At the beginning of prophase I the chromosomes begin to condense into threadlike structures. Each consists of two sister chromatids, as a result of DNA replication during premeiotic interphase. The chromosomes of two homologous pairs, one long and one short, are shown.

Synapsis

2 Homologous chromosomes come together and pair.

Recombination

3 While they are paired, the chromatids of homologous chromosomes undergo recombination by exchanging segments. The enlarged circle shows a site undergoing recombination (arrow).

Prometaphase I

4 In prometaphase I, the nuclear envelope breaks down, and the spindle moves into the former nuclear area. Kinetochore microtubules connect to the chromosomes—kinetochore microtubules from one pole attach to both sister kinetochores of one duplicated chromosome, and kinetochore microtubules from the other pole attach to both sister ki-net-o-chores of the other duplicated chromosome.

Figure 10.11

The meiotic divisions. The sequence is shown as it would occur in a two X chromosomes are shown; therefore, female animal also shown are equivalent stages in a plant, the lily (*Lilium* regale). (Two homologous pairs of chromosomes are shown.) Micrographs with thanks to the John Innes Foundation Trustees.

Second meiotic division

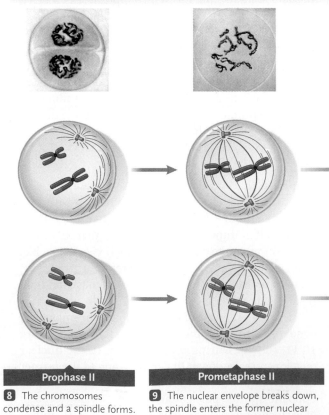

Prophase II

8 The chromosomes condense and a spindle forms.

Prometaphase II

9 The nuclear envelope breaks down, the spindle enters the former nuclear area, and kinetochore microtubules from the opposite spindle poles attach to the kinetochores of each chromosome.

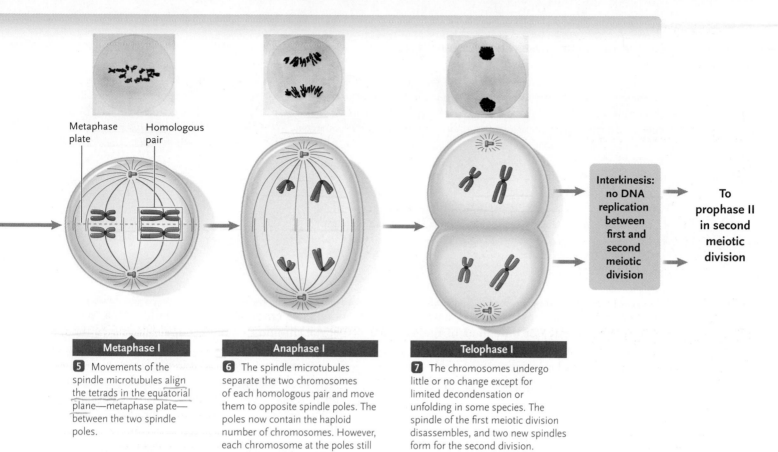

Metaphase plate

Homologous pair

Metaphase I

5 Movements of the spindle microtubules align the tetrads in the equatorial plane—metaphase plate—between the two spindle poles.

Anaphase I

6 The spindle microtubules separate the two chromosomes of each homologous pair and move them to opposite spindle poles. The poles now contain the haploid number of chromosomes. However, each chromosome at the poles still contains two chromatids.

Telophase I

7 The chromosomes undergo little or no change except for limited decondensation or unfolding in some species. The spindle of the first meiotic division disassembles, and two new spindles form for the second division.

Interkinesis: no DNA replication between first and second meiotic division

To prophase II in second meiotic division

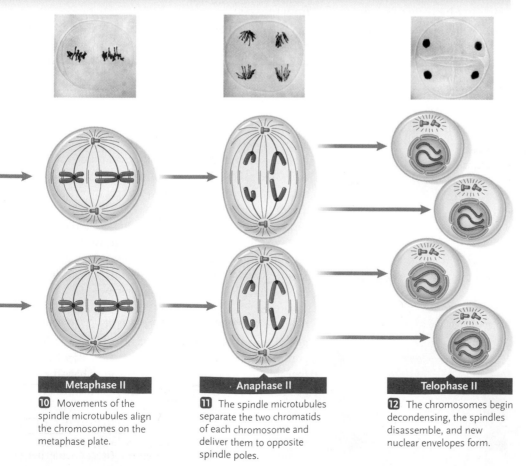

Metaphase II

10 Movements of the spindle microtubules align the chromosomes on the metaphase plate.

Anaphase II

11 The spindle microtubules separate the two chromatids of each chromosome and deliver them to opposite spindle poles.

Telophase II

12 The chromosomes begin decondensing, the spindles disassemble, and new nuclear envelopes form.

Bisphenol A and the Grandmother Effect

Although this chapter documented the role of meiosis in generating genetically diverse offspring, one type of diversity that must be avoided is differences in chromosome number. Cells (or organisms) that have more, or less, than the normal number of chromosomes are called "aneuploid"; agents that promote this problem are known as "aneugens." The formation of gametes by meiosis is under hormonal control in mammals, and it is not surprising to learn that synthetic chemicals influencing the action of reproductive hormones can be aneugenic. Bisphenol A, a chemical monomer used in the manufacture of polycarbonate plastics and resins, binds to estrogen receptors in mice. Exposure to relatively high concentrations has been shown to elevate the incidence of aneuploid gametes and offspring. Since meiosis is active in females before they are born, exposure of pregnant mouse mothers resulted in aneuploid gametes produced by their daughters, which, in turn, gave rise to aneuploid grandchildren.

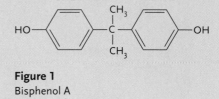

Figure 1
Bisphenol A

The sequence of steps in the two meiotic divisions accomplishes the major outcomes of meiosis: the generation of genetic variability and the reduction in chromosome number. (Figure 10.13, reviews the two meiotic divisions and compares them with the single division of mitosis.)

10.3d Several Mechanisms Contribute Genetic Diversity

The generation of genetic variability by meiosis is a prime evolutionary advantage of sexual reproduction **(Figure 10.12)**. Such variability increases the chance that at least some offspring will have combinations of alleles that will be successful in surviving and reproducing in changing environments. In fact, some scientists argue that meiosis exists not to create just any variability but to generate "repaired" chromosomes to be passed on to the next generation (see *People Behind Biology*). As you work through the ideas in this section, try to envision how you could pass a "perfect" copy of chromosome 6 to your children even though both copies of chromosome 6 you inherited from your parents are damaged (in different places).

The variability produced by sexual reproduction is apparent all around us, particularly in the human population. Except for identical twins (or identical triplets, identical quadruplets, and so forth), no two humans look alike, act alike, or have identical biochemical and physiological characteristics, even if they are members of the same immediate family. Other species that reproduce sexually show equivalent variability arising from meiosis.

During meiosis and fertilization, genetic variability arises from four sources: (1) genetic recombination, (2) the differing combinations of maternal and paternal chromosomes segregated to the poles during anaphase I, (3) the differing combinations of recombinant chromatids segregated to the poles during anaphase II, and (4) the particular sets of male and female gametes that unite in fertilization. The four mechanisms, working together, produce so much total variability that no two products of meiosis produced by the same or different individuals and no two zygotes produced by union of the gametes are likely to have the same genetic makeup. Each of these sources of variability is discussed in further detail in the following sections. **Figure 10.13 (p. 218),** contrasts the genetically identical daughter cells arising from mitosis with the diverse daughter cells produced by meiosis.

Genetic Recombination. Recombination, the key genetic event of prophase I, starts when homologous chromosomes pair **(Figure 10.14 (p. 220),** step 1). Recall that although homologous chromosomes have the same genes in the same order, they likely carry different versions of those genes (alleles). This means that the underlying DNA sequence is similar enough to form the basis of meiotic pairing yet different enough to generate novel combinations after recombination. (Recall Lederberg's

Figure 10.12
Genetic variability as shown in the appearance of domestic cats.

Marc Henrie/Dorling Kindersley/Getty Images

Dave King/Dorling Kindersley/Getty Images

Elena Butinova/Shutterstock

Dave King/Dorling Kindersley/Getty Images

Lexx/Shutterstock

Dave King/Dorling Kindersley/Getty Images

Aurora Nedelcu, University of New Brunswick

Whereas the octopuses and limpets mentioned at the opening of this chapter have no choice but to undergo meiosis and follow the remaining steps of their sexual life cycle, prokaryotes and many lower eukaryotes become sexual only in response to suboptimal environmental conditions, such as elevated temperature or nutrient deficiency. This observation led Dr. Aurora Nedelcu and her colleagues in The Green Lab at the University of New Brunswick to gather evidence to test the hypothesis that sex originally evolved as one of several responses available to cells dealing with stress.

A variety of external stresses all eventually cause internal oxidative stress resulting from increased concentration of damaging reactive oxygen species (ROS). Using her multicellular algal model system (*Volvox carteri*), Dr. Nedelcu has shown that stress-induced increase in ROS does indeed stimulate the expression of sex-related genes **(Figure 1)**. She believes that the cells experiencing oxidative stress "turn on" their sex genes in order to benefit from the possibility that meiotic recombination will repair DNA damage caused by ROS.

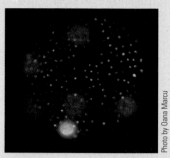

Figure 1
Volvox carteri under heat stress. ROS indicated by green fluorescence.

multiple auxotrophic *E. coli* mutants here; the idea is the same.) As the homologous chromosomes pair, they are held together tightly by a protein framework called the **synaptonemal complex (Figure 10.15, p. 220).** Supported by this framework, regions of homologous chromatids exchange segments, producing new combinations of alleles (see Figure 10.14, step 2). Recall that the exchange process is very precise and involves the breakage and rejoining of DNA molecules by enzymes (Figure 10.1). When the exchange is complete toward the end of prophase I, the synaptonemal complex disassembles and disappears. If you now follow meiosis I and II through to the end in your mind, notice that each of the four resulting nuclei receives one of these four chromatids (see Figure 10.14, step 3); two receive unchanged chromatids, and two receive chromatids that have new combinations of alleles due to recombination.

The physical effect of recombination can be seen later in prophase I, when increased condensation of the chromosomes thickens the chromosomes enough to make them visible under the light microscope (see Figure 10.11, steps 3 and 4). Regions in which non-sister chromatids cross one another, called **crossovers** or **chiasmata** (singular, *chiasma* = crosspiece), clearly show that two of the four chromatids have exchanged segments. Because of the shape produced, the recombination process is also called **crossing-over.**

Note that illustrations of recombination usually show chromosomes "paired" side by side, with only the closest chromatids participating in recombination (see Figure 10.14); however, chromosomes actually pair "one on top of the other" such that any two of the four chromatids can participate in a given recombination event. Recombination takes place largely at random, at almost any position along the chromosome arms.

Several events likely occur at various locations along all chromatids.

Notice in Figure 10.14 that a recombination event does not just "switch" the alleles of a given gene in a localized area. All of the DNA sequence stretching from the site of recombination to the ends of the participating chromatids is exchanged.

Random Segregation. Random segregation of chromosomes of maternal and paternal origin accounts for the second major source of genetic variability in meiosis. Recall that the maternal and paternal members of each homologous pair are different in that they typically carry different alleles of many of the genes on that chromosome. During prometaphase I, spindle microtubules make connections to kinetochores. For each homologous pair, one chromosome makes spindle connections leading to one pole and the other chromosome connects to the opposite pole. In making these connections, all the maternal chromosomes may connect to one pole and all the paternal chromosomes may connect to the opposite pole. Or, as is most likely, a random combination of maternal and paternal chromosomes may be segregated to a given spindle pole **(Figure 10.16, p. 221).**

The number of possible combinations depends on the number of chromosome pairs in a species. For example, the 39 chromosome pairs in dogs allow 2^{39} different combinations of maternal and paternal chromosomes to be delivered to the poles, producing potentially 500 billion genetically different gametes from this source of variability alone. Note that this random partitioning of maternal and paternal chromosomes is responsible for the independent assortment of the alleles of two genes in Mendel's experiments with garden peas described in Chapter 11.

Alternative Combinations at Meiosis II. If you look carefully at the cells drawn in metaphase II in Figure 10.13, you will see that the chromosomes are still replicated and, as a result of recombination in prophase I, each chromosome carries one recombinant chromatid and one nonrecombinant chromatid. Notice that, in this case, the chromosomes have aligned at metaphase II with both recombinant chromatids attached to the same spindle pole. However, since the attachment of spindles to kinetochores is random at this stage, we hope that you can see that it is just as likely that these chromosomes *could* have lined up, with the smaller chromosome sending its recombinant chromatid to one pole and the larger chromosome sending its recombinant chromatid to the opposite pole. The resulting daughter cells will be genetically different, depending on how the chromosomes align in metaphase II.

Random Fertilization. The haploid products of meiosis are genetically diverse. The rather random combination of these cells (or their descendants) during fertilization is a matter of chance that amplifies the variability of sexual reproduction. For example, if we consider only the variability available from random separation of homologous chromosomes at meiosis I along with that from random fertilization, the possibility that two children of the same human parents could receive the same combination of maternal and paternal chromosomes is 1 chance out of $(2^{23})^2$ or 1 in 70 368 744 000 000 (~70 trillion), a number that far exceeds the number of humans who have ever lived. The further variability introduced by recombination and shuffling at meiosis II makes it practically impossible for humans and most other sexually reproducing organisms to produce genetically identical gametes or offspring. The only exception is identical twins (or identical triplets, identical quadruplets, and so forth), which arise not from the combination of identical gametes during fertilization but from mitotic division of a single fertilized egg into separate cells that give rise to genetically identical individuals.

We have just seen that meiosis has three outcomes that are vital to sexual reproduction. This process reduces the chromosomes to the haploid number so that they can be brought together with those of another individual without doubling the usual chromosome number during fertilization. Through genetic recombination and random separation of maternal and paternal chromosomes, meiosis produces genetic variability in gametes; further variability is provided by the random combination of gametes in fertilization. These ideas form the "mechanics" that underlie the patterns of inheritance of traits in sexually reproducing organisms discovered by Mendel and described in Chapter 11.

STUDY BREAK

1. Which phase (diploid or haploid) dominates the life cycles of animals, plants, and fungi?
2. What are the two functions of meiosis?
3. What are the four sources of genetic variability in sexually reproducing organisms?
4. What is nondisjunction, and how does it occur?

Figure 10.13
Comparison of key steps in meiosis and mitosis. Both diagrams use an animal cell as an example. Maternal chromosomes are shown in red; paternal chromosomes are shown in blue.

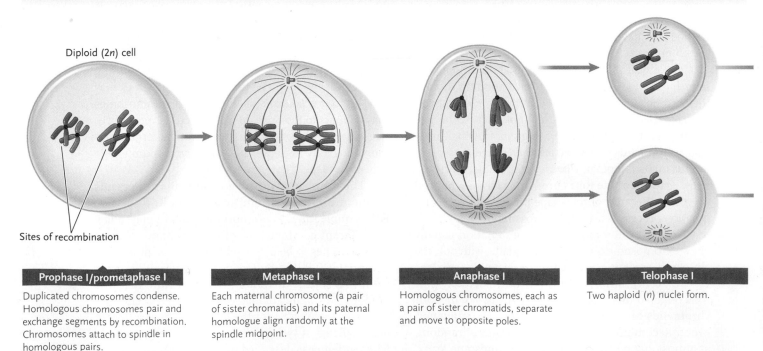

Meiosis I

Diploid (2*n*) cell

Sites of recombination

Prophase I/prometaphase I	**Metaphase I**	**Anaphase I**	**Telophase I**
Duplicated chromosomes condense. Homologous chromosomes pair and exchange segments by recombination. Chromosomes attach to spindle in homologous pairs.	Each maternal chromosome (a pair of sister chromatids) and its paternal homologue align randomly at the spindle midpoint.	Homologous chromosomes, each as a pair of sister chromatids, separate and move to opposite poles.	Two haploid (*n*) nuclei form.

10.4 Mobile Elements

Our examples have so far involved two participating DNA molecules that have always been at least partially homologous and that have always originated from two different individuals. However, one of the most interesting examples of genetic recombination in nature shows neither of these characteristics. All organisms appear to contain particular segments of DNA, called **mobile elements**, that can move from one place to another; they cut and paste DNA backbones using a type of recombination that does not require homology.

Sometimes called "jumping genes," these elements normally move from place to place *within the genome of a given cell*. The following section describes these fascinating elements in more detail.

10.4a Insertion Sequence Elements and Transposons Are the Two Major Types of Prokaryotic Mobile Elements

Mobile elements are also known by the more specific term **transposable elements (TEs)**, and their mechanism of movement, involving nonhomologous recombination, is called **transposition.** Transposition

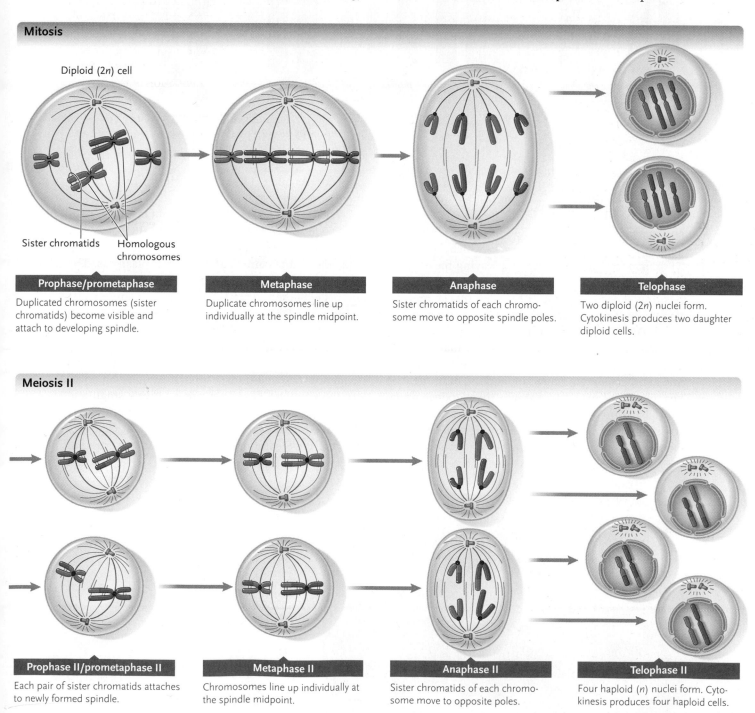

Mitosis

Diploid (2*n*) cell

Sister chromatids   Homologous chromosomes

| **Prophase/prometaphase** | **Metaphase** | **Anaphase** | **Telophase** |

Duplicated chromosomes (sister chromatids) become visible and attach to developing spindle.

Duplicate chromosomes line up individually at the spindle midpoint.

Sister chromatids of each chromosome move to opposite spindle poles.

Two diploid (2*n*) nuclei form. Cytokinesis produces two daughter diploid cells.

Meiosis II

| **Prophase II/prometaphase II** | **Metaphase II** | **Anaphase II** | **Telophase II** |

Each pair of sister chromatids attaches to newly formed spindle.

Chromosomes line up individually at the spindle midpoint.

Sister chromatids of each chromosome move to opposite poles.

Four haploid (*n*) nuclei form. Cytokinesis produces four haploid cells.

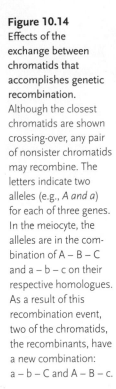

Figure 10.14
Effects of the exchange between chromatids that accomplishes genetic recombination. Although the closest chromatids are shown crossing-over, any pair of nonsister chromatids may recombine. The letters indicate two alleles (e.g., *A and a*) for each of three genes. In the meiocyte, the alleles are in the combination of A – B – C and a – b – c on their respective homologues. As a result of this recombination event, two of the chromatids, the recombinants, have a new combination: a – b – C and A – B – c.

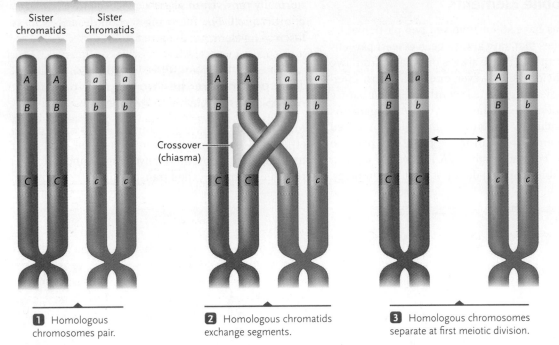

1 Homologous chromosomes pair.

2 Homologous chromatids exchange segments.

3 Homologous chromosomes separate at first meiotic division.

usually occurs at a low frequency in either of two ways, depending on the type of element: (1) a cut-and-paste process, in which the TE leaves its original location and transposes to a new location **(Figure 10.17a, p. 222)**, and (2) a copy-and-paste process, in which a copy of a TE transposes to a new location, leaving the original TE behind **(Figure 10.17b, p. 222)**. For most TEs, transposition starts with contact between the TE and the target site. This also means that TEs do not exist free of the DNA in which they are integrated; hence, that popular name of "jumping genes" is actually inaccurate. TEs are never "in the air" between one location and another. TEs are important because of the genetic changes they cause. For example, they produce mutations by transposing into genes and knocking out their functions, and they increase or decrease gene expression by transposing into regulatory sequences

of genes. As such, TEs are biological mutagens that increase genetic variability.

Bacterial TEs were discovered in the 1960s. They have been shown to move from site to site within the bacterial chromosome, between the bacterial chromosome and plasmids, and between plasmids. The frequency of transposition is low but constant for a given TE. Some bacterial TEs insert randomly, at any point in the DNA, whereas others recognize certain sequences as "hot spots" for insertion and insert preferentially at these locations.

The two major types of bacterial TEs are **insertion sequences** (IS) and **transposons**. Insertion sequences are the simplest TEs. They are relatively small and contain only genes for their transposition, notably the gene for **transposase**, an enzyme that catalyzes some of the recombination reactions for inserting or

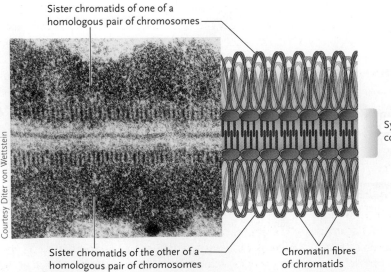

Sister chromatids of one of a homologous pair of chromosomes

Sister chromatids of the other of a homologous pair of chromosomes

Chromatin fibres of chromatids

Synaptonemal complex

Courtesy Diter von Wettstein

Figure 10.15
The synaptonemal complex as seen in a meiotic cell of the fungus *Neotiella*. The relationship of the complex to the chromatin fibres of the paired chromosomes is shown.

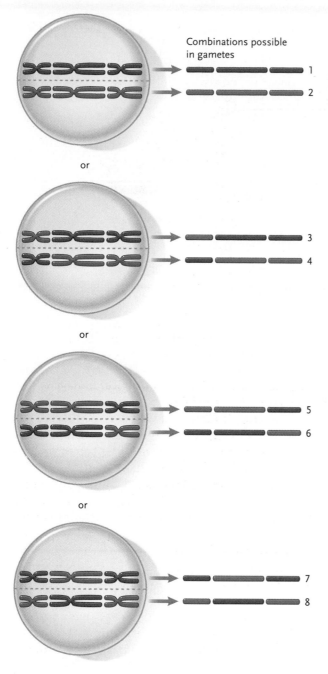

Combinations possible
in gametes

1

2

or

3

4

or

5

6

or

7

8

Figure 10.16
Possible outcomes of the random spindle connections of three pairs of chromosomes at metaphase I of meiosis. Maternal chromosomes are red; paternal chromosomes are blue. There are four possible patterns of connections, giving eight possible combinations of maternal and paternal chromosomes in gametes (labelled 1–8).

removing the TE from the DNA **(Figure 10.18, p. 222)**. At each of the two ends of an IS is a short **inverted repeat** sequence—the same DNA sequence running in opposite directions (shown by directional arrows in the figure). The inverted repeat sequences enable the transposase enzyme to identify the ends of the TE when it catalyzes transposition. The inverted repeat sequence is an IS element on both the F factor and the bacterial chromosome that provides the homology needed for the creation of the Hfr strains described in Section 10.2.

The second type of bacterial TE, called a transposon, has an inverted repeat sequence at each end enclosing a central region with one or more genes. In a number of bacterial transposons, the inverted repeat sequences are insertion sequences, which provide the transposase for movement of the element (see Figure 10.18). Additional genes in the central region typically code for antibiotic resistance; they originated from the main bacterial DNA circle or from plasmids. These non-IS genes included in transposons are carried along as the TEs move from place to place.

Many antibiotics, such as penicillin, erythromycin, tetracycline, ampicillin, and streptomycin, that were once successful in curing bacterial infections have lost much of their effectiveness because of resistance genes carried in transposons. Movements of the transposons, particularly to plasmids that can be transferred by conjugation within and between bacterial species, greatly increase the spread of genes, providing antibiotic resistance to infecting cells. Resistance genes have made many bacterial diseases difficult or impossible to treat with standard antibiotics.

10.4b Transposable Elements Were First Discovered in Eukaryotes

TEs were first discovered in a eukaryote, maize (corn), in the 1940s by Barbara McClintock, a geneticist working at the Cold Spring Harbor Laboratory in New York. McClintock noted that some mutations affecting kernel and leaf colour appeared and disappeared rapidly under certain conditions. Mapping the alleles by linkage studies produced a surprising result: the map positions changed frequently, indicating that the alleles could move from place to place in the corn chromosomes. Some of the movements were so frequent that changes in their effects could be noticed at different times in a single developing kernel **(Figure 10.19, p. 223)**.

When McClintock first reported her results, her findings were regarded as an isolated curiosity, possibly applying only to corn. This was because the then-prevailing opinion among geneticists was that genes are fixed in the chromosomes and do not move to other locations. Her conclusions were widely accepted only after TEs were detected and characterized in bacteria in the 1960s. By the 1970s, further examples of TEs were discovered in other eukaryotes, including yeast and mammals. McClintock was awarded a Nobel Prize in 1983 for her pioneering work, after these discoveries confirmed her early findings that TEs are probably universally distributed among both prokaryotes and eukaryotes.

10.4c Eukaryotic Transposable Elements Are Classified as Transposons or Retrotransposons

Eukaryotic TEs fall into two major classes, transposons and retrotransposons, distinguished by the way the TE sequence moves from place to place in

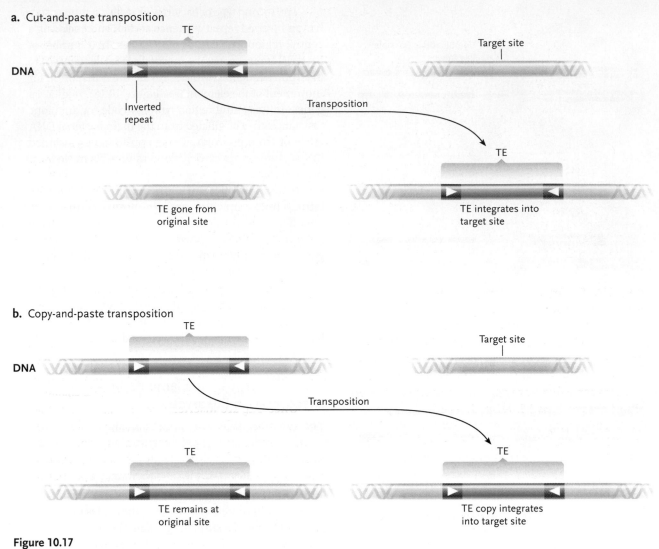

a. Cut-and-paste transposition

TE

DNA

Target site

Inverted repeat

Transposition

TE

TE gone from original site

TE integrates into target site

b. Copy-and-paste transposition

TE

DNA

Target site

Transposition

TE

TE

TE remains at original site

TE copy integrates into target site

Figure 10.17

Two transposition processes for transposable elements. (a) Cut-and-paste transposition, in which the TE leaves one location in the DNA and moves to a new location. **(b)** Copy-and-paste transposition, in which a copy of the TE moves to a new location, leaving the original TE behind.

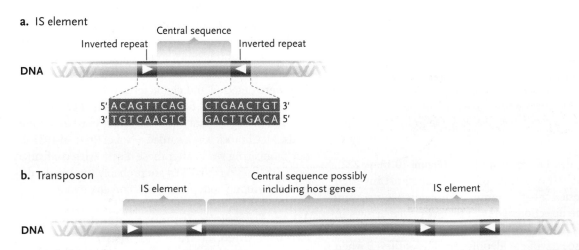

a. IS element

Central sequence

Inverted repeat

Inverted repeat

DNA

5′ ACAGTTCAG   CTGAACTGT 3′
3′ TGTCAAGTC   GACTTGACA 5′

b. Transposon

IS element

Central sequence possibly including host genes

IS element

DNA

Figure 10.18

Types of bacterial transposable elements. **(a)** Insertion sequence. **(b)** Transposon.

Nik Kleinberg

Figure 10.19
Barbara McClintock and corn kernels showing different colour patterns due to the movement of transposable elements. As TEs move into or out of genes, controlling pigment production in developing kernels, the ability of cells and their descendants to produce the dark pigment is destroyed or restored. The result is random patterns of pigmented and colourless (yellow) segments in individual kernels.

the DNA. Eukaryotic transposons are similar to bacterial transposons in their general structure and in the ways they transpose. However, members of the other class of eukaryotic TEs, the **retrotransposons**, transpose by a copy-and-paste mechanism that is unlike any of the other TEs we have discussed. Retrotransposons have this name because transposition occurs via an intermediate RNA copy of the TE **(Figure 10.20)**. First, the retrotransposon, which is a DNA element integrated into the chromosomal DNA, is transcribed into a complementary RNA copy. Next, an enzyme called **reverse transcriptase**, which is

encoded by one of the genes of the retrotransposon, uses the RNA as a template to make a DNA copy of the retrotransposon.

The DNA copy is then inserted into the DNA at a new location, leaving the original in place. This insertion step involves breaking and rejoining DNA backbones, as we have seen several times in this chapter.

Once TEs are inserted into chromosomes, they become more or less permanent residents, duplicated and passed on during cell division along with the rest of the DNA. TEs inserted into the DNA of reproductive cells may be inherited, thereby becoming a permanent

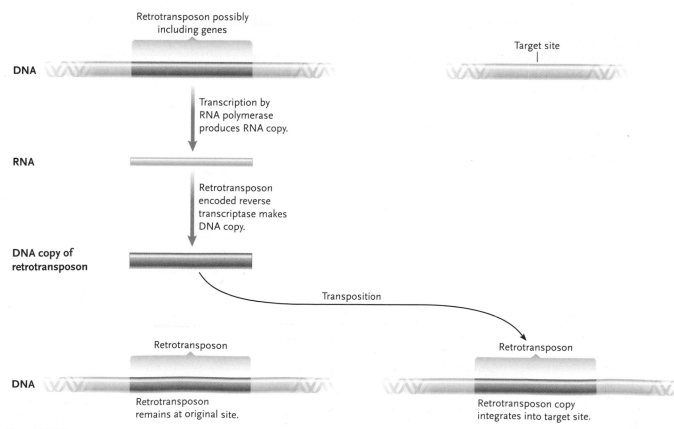

Figure 10.20
Transposition of a eukaryotic retrotransposon to a new location by means of an intermediate RNA copy.

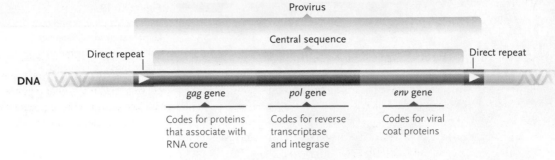

Figure 10.21

A mammalian retrovirus in the provirus form in which it is inserted into chromosomal DNA. The direct repeats at either end contain sequences capable of acting as enhancer, promoter, and termination signals for transcription. The central sequence contains genes coding for proteins, concentrated in the *gag*, *pol*, and *env* regions. The provirus of human immunodeficiency virus (HIV), the virus that causes acquired immune deficiency syndrome (AIDS), takes this form.

part of the genetic material of a species. Long-standing TEs are subject to mutation along with other sequences in the DNA. Such mutations may accumulate in a TE, gradually altering it into a nonmobile, residual sequence in the DNA. The DNA of many eukaryotes, including humans, contains a surprising amount of nonfunctional TE sequence likely created in this way.

10.4d Retrotransposons Are Similar to Retroviruses

The RNA to DNA reverse transcription associated with retrotransposon movement is strikingly similar to that employed by a class of eukaryotic viruses called **retroviruses**. When a retrovirus infects a host cell, a reverse transcriptase carried in the virus particle is released and copies the single-stranded RNA genome into a double-stranded DNA copy. The viral DNA is then inserted into the host DNA (by genetic recombination), where it is replicated and passed to progeny cells during cell division. Similar to the prophage of bacteria, the inserted viral DNA is known as a **provirus** (Figure 10.21).

Retroviruses are found in a wide range of organisms, with most so far identified in vertebrates. You, as well as most other humans and mammals, probably contain from 1 to as many as 100 or more retroviruses in your genome as proviruses. In total, retrotransposons and retroviruses of all types occupy some 40% of the human genome!

Although many of the retroviruses do not produce infectious virus particles, they sometimes cause DNA rearrangements such as deletions and translocations. Such changes may alter the relative position of DNA sequences on the chromosome and, in turn, disturb the normal regulation of gene expression. Given your knowledge of transduction by bacterial viruses described earlier in this chapter, you will not be surprised to hear that retroviruses sometimes pick up host eukaryotic genes and move them to recipients. Such genes may become abnormally active through the effects of regulatory sequences located in the TE itself or the DNA nearby. Certain forms of cancer

have been linked to this type of abnormal activation of genes that are important in regulating cell division (see Section 14.4). In one of the most dramatic examples, a cellular gene is transported to an infected cell by the avian sarcoma retrovirus. The cellular gene is overexpressed in the new environment, resulting in uncontrolled growth of infected cells, leading to tumours in infected birds.

STUDY BREAK

Among eukaryotic mobile elements, how do transposons, retrotransposons, and retroviruses differ?

This has been a long chapter. We hope that, taken together, all of these ideas will help you understand the balance that biology must strike between the stability and the plasticity of the genetic material. On the one hand, DNA must be faithfully replicated and passed to the next generation. Lack of quality control at this step would allow widespread random mutations to undermine the selection and preservation of good combinations of alleles. On the other hand, any system that made only perfectly "photocopied" DNA available for the next generation would be doomed as well; a wide variety of diverse "solutions" are needed for a population to survive in constantly changing environments that are impossible to anticipate.

Genetic recombination is central to many processes that contribute changes to the sequence of DNA in all forms of life. (And we did not even discuss interesting examples of developmental genetic recombination in infecting parasites or the cells of the developing immune system, or foreign DNA taken up by rotifers.) The genetic elements discussed in this chapter, particularly plasmids and retroviruses, often act as natural genetic engineers by moving genes between species. Chapter 16 describes how human genetic engineers manipulate and clone DNA and how they analyze genomes at the DNA level.

The overall mechanism and outcomes of meiosis have been known for a long time, since the turn of the twentieth century. However, despite the fundamental importance of meiosis in sexual reproduction, the biochemical, genetic, and molecular mechanisms of meiosis are poorly understood. For example, how do homologous chromosomes recognize their appropriate pairing partners? How do they become aligned in a configuration that allows the formation of crossovers?

How is the number of crossover events regulated to ensure that each chromosome pair will have a crossover? Developing a deeper understanding of the molecular mechanisms that regulate meiosis is highly important in human biology because missegregation of chromosomes during meiosis I is a major cause of birth defects and the leading cause of miscarriages.

Review

Go to CENGAGENOW™ at http://hed.nelson.com/ to access quizzing, animations, exercises, articles, and personalized homework help.

10.1 Mechanism of Genetic Recombination

- Genetic recombination requires two DNA molecules that differ from one another in at least two places, a mechanism for bringing the DNA molecules into close proximity and a collection of enzymes to "cut," "exchange," and "paste" the DNA back together.

- Homology allows DNA on different molecules to line up and recombine precisely.

- Enzymatic cutting and pasting of both DNA backbones from each of the two DNA molecules is required for each recombination event.

- Two circular molecules "fuse" together as a result of a single recombination event.

10.2 Genetic Recombination in Bacteria

- Study of bacterial recombination requires detectable genetic differences between strains.

- Lederberg and Tatum created strains that were different in their ability to manufacture certain amino acids and vitamins.

- In bacteria, the DNA of the bacterial chromosome may recombine with DNA brought into close proximity from another cell.

- Three primary mechanisms bring DNA into bacterial cells from the outside: conjugation, transformation, and transduction.

- In conjugation, which is the basis of a kind of sexual reproduction in bacteria, two bacterial cells form a cytoplasmic bridge and part or all of the DNA of one cell moves into the other through the bridge. The donated DNA can then recombine with homologous sequences of the recipient cell's DNA.

- *E. coli* bacteria that are able to act as DNA donors in conjugation have an F plasmid, making them F^+; recipients have no F plasmid and are F^-. In Hfr strains of *E. coli*, the F plasmid is within the main chromosome. As a result, genes of the main chromosome are often transferred into F^- cells along with a portion of the F plasmid DNA. Researchers have mapped genes on the *E. coli* chromosome by noting the order in which they are transferred from Hfr to F^- cells during conjugation.

- In transformation, intact cells of some species absorb pieces of DNA released from cells that have disintegrated. The entering DNA fragments can recombine with the recipient cell's DNA.

- In transduction, DNA is transferred from one cell to another "by mistake" inside the head of an infecting virus.

- Since generalized transduction transfers random fragments of the host chromosome, all host genes are transferred at equal frequency. Specialized transduction only transfers genes lying close to the point of insertion of the prophage.

10.3 Genetic Recombination in Eukaryotes: Meiosis

- The time and place of meiosis follow one of three major pathways in the life cycles of eukaryotes, which reflect the portions of the life cycle spent in the haploid and diploid phases and whether mitotic divisions intervene between meiosis and the formation of gametes.

- In animals, the diploid phase is dominant, and the haploid phase is reduced. Meiosis is followed by gamete formation. Plants and most fungi alternate between haploid and diploid generations, either of which may dominate the life cycle, and both of which will divide by mitosis. The diploid sporophytes are produced by fertilization, and the haploid gametophytes are produced by mitotic divisions of the spores formed by meiosis. In some fungi, the diploid phase is limited to a single cell produced by fertilization, which then immediately undergoes meiosis.

- In animals, the products of meiosis are haploid gametes. The diploid phase of the life cycle is then restored when one gamete fuses with another. In plants, meiosis occurs in some of the cells of the diploid sporophytes and produces a generation of haploid spores. These spores then divide by mitosis to produce multicellular gametophytes.

- The functions of meiosis are to reduce the chromosome number (from diploid to haploid) and to generate genetic diversity in sexually reproducing organisms.

- Meiosis occurs only in eukaryotes that reproduce sexually and only in organisms that are at least diploid—that is, organisms that have at least two representatives of each chromosome.

- DNA replicates and the chromosomal proteins are duplicated during the premeiotic interphase, producing two copies, the sister chromatids, of each chromosome.

- During prophase I of the first meiotic division (meiosis I), the replicated chromosomes condense and come together and pair as the spindle forms in the cytoplasm.

- While they are paired, the chromatids of homologous chromosomes undergo recombination by breaking the covalent bonds of the DNA backbones, exchanging the ends and restoring the bonds.

- During prometaphase I, the nuclear envelope breaks down, the spindle enters the former nuclear area, and kinetochore microtubules leading to opposite spindle poles attach to one kinetochore of each pair of sister chromatids of homologous chromosomes.

- At metaphase I, spindle microtubule movements have aligned the tetrads on the metaphase plate, the equatorial plane between the two spindle poles. The connections of kinetochore microtubules to opposite poles ensure that the homologous pairs separate and move to opposite spindle poles during anaphase I, reducing the chromosome number to the haploid value. Each chromosome at the poles still contains two chromatids.

- Telophase I and interkinesis are brief and transitory stages; no DNA replication occurs during interkinesis. During these stages, the single spindle of the first meiotic division disassembles and the microtubules reassemble into two new spindles for the second division.

- During prophase II, the chromosomes condense and a spindle forms. During prometaphase II, the nuclear envelope breaks down, the spindle enters the former nuclear area, and spindle microtubules leading to opposite spindle poles attach to the two kinetochores of each chromosome. At metaphase II, the chromosomes become aligned on the metaphase plate. The connections of kinetochore microtubules to opposite spindle poles ensure that during anaphase II, the chromatids of each chromosome are separated and segregate to those opposite spindle poles.

- During telophase II, the chromosomes decondense to their extended interphase state, the spindles disassemble, and new nuclear envelopes form. The result is four haploid cells, each containing half the number of chromosomes present in a G_1 nucleus of the same species.

- Meiosis II differs from mitosis in that meiosis II occurs only in reproductive tissue, is not preceded by an S phase, and results in genetically different daughter cells.

- Nondisjunction occurs when both members of a pair of homologous chromosomes connect to spindles from the same pole. Following anaphase, one pole then receives both copies of the pair, and the other pole receives none. The overall result (following normal meiosis II) is gametes that have two copies of a chromosome. After fertilization, the resulting zygote will therefore have three copies of the chromosome instead of two.

- In many eukaryotes, including most animals, one or more pairs of chromosomes, called the sex chromosomes, are different in male and female individuals of the same species.

- Recombination is the first source of the genetic variability produced by meiosis. During recombination, chromatids generate new combinations of alleles by physically exchanging segments. The exchange process involves precise breakage and joining of DNA mol-

ecules. It is catalyzed by enzymes and occurs while the homologous chromosomes are held together tightly by the synaptonemal complex. The crossovers visible between the chromosomes at late prophase I reflect the exchange of chromatid segments that occurred during the molecular steps of genetic recombination.

- The random segregation of homologous chromosomes is the second source of genetic variability produced by meiosis. The homologous pairs separate at anaphase I of meiosis, segregating random combinations of maternal and paternal chromosomes to the spindle poles.

- Random segregation of the chromatids of replicated chromosomes at meiosis II is a third mechanism for generating diversity.

- Random joining of male and female gametes in fertilization is the fourth source of genetic variability.

10.4 Mobile Elements

- Both prokaryotes and eukaryotes contain TEs (transposable elements)—DNA sequences that can move from place to place in the DNA. The TEs may move from one location in the DNA to another or generate duplicated copies that insert in new locations while leaving the "parent" copy in its original location.

- Genes of the host cell DNA may become incorporated into a TE and may be carried with it to a new location. There the genes may become abnormally active when placed near sequences that control the activity of genes within the TE or near the control elements of active host genes.

- Eukaryotic TEs occur as transposons, which release from one location in the DNA and insert at a different site, or as retrotransposons, which move by making an RNA copy, which is then replicated into a DNA copy that is inserted at a new location. The "parent" copy remains at the original location. Like retrotransposons, retroviruses integrate into chromosomal DNA by making a DNA copy of their RNA genome. Retroviruses may have evolved from retrotransposons.

- TE-instigated abnormal activation of genes regulating cell division has been linked to the development of some forms of cancer in humans and other complex animals.

Questions

Self-Test Questions

1. If recombination occurred between bacteria as shown in the figure, the result would be

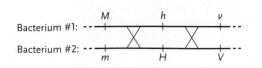

Bacterium #1:
Bacterium #2:

a. MHv and mhV.
b. MHV and mhv.
c. Mhv and mHv.
d. MHV and mhV.
e. mhv and MhV.

2. Which of the following is *not* correct for bacterial conjugation?
   a. Both Hfr and F⁺ bacteria have the ability to code for a sex pilus.
   b. After an F⁻ cell has conjugated with an F⁺, its plasmid holds the F⁺ factor.
   c. The recipient cell usually becomes Hfr following conjugation.
   d. In an Hfr × F⁻ mating, DNA of the main chromosome moves to a recipient cell.
   e. Genes on the F factor encode proteins of the sex pilus.

3. Which of the following is *not* correct for bacterial transformation?
   a. Artificial transformation is used in cloning procedures.
   b. Avery was able to transform live noninfective bacteria with DNA from dead infective bacteria.
   c. The cell wall and plasma membrane must be penetrated for transformation to proceed.

    d.   A virus is required for the process.
    e.   Electroporation is a form of artificial transformation used to introduce DNA into cells.

4. Transduction
    a.   may allow recombination of newly introduced DNA with host cell DNA.
    b.   is the movement of DNA from one bacterial cell to another by means of a plasmid.
    c.   can cause the DNA of the donor to change but not the DNA of the recipient.
    d.   is the movement of viral DNA but not bacterial DNA into a recipient bacterium.
    e.   requires physical contact between two bacterium.

5. A virus in its lysogenic cycle is
    a.   lysing the host cell.
    b.   transducing a bacterial cell.
    c.   assembling viral particles for cell rupture.
    d.   damaging the host cell.
    e.   embedded in host DNA and is called a prophage.

6. The diploid number of this individual is 6.

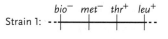

This figure represents
    a.   mitotic metaphase.
    b.   meiotic metaphase I. → tetraploid –
    c.   meiotic metaphase II.
    d.   a gamete.
    e.   six nonhomologous chromosomes.

7. Chiasmata
    a.   form during metaphase II of meiosis.
    b.   occur between two nonhomologous chromosomes.
    c.   represent chromosomes independently assorting.
    d.   are sites of DNA exchange between homologous chromatids.
    e.   ensure that the resulting cells are identical to the parent cell.

8. If $2n$ is four, the number of possible combinations in the resulting gametes is
    a.   1.
    b.   2.
    c.   4.
    d.   8.
    e.   16.

9. The number of human chromosomes in a cell in prophase I of meiosis is ___ and in telophase II is ___.
    a.   92; 46
    b.   46; 23
    c.   23; 23
    d.   23; 16
    e.   4; 2

10. The DNA content in a diploid cell in G_2 is X. If that cell goes into meiosis at its metaphase II, the DNA content would be
    a.   0.1X.
    b.   0.5X.
    c.   X.
    d.   2X.
    e.   4X.

11. In the human gamete,
    a.   there must be one chromosome of each type, except for the sex chromosomes, where both an X chromosome and a Y chromosome are present.
    b.   a chromosome must be represented from each parent.
    c.   there must be an unequal mixture of chromosomes from both parents.
    d.   there must be representation of chromosomes from only one parent.
    e.   there is the possibility of 2^{46} different combinations of maternal and paternal chromosomes.

12. Which of the following is *not* correct about transposable elements?
    a.   They can be recognized by their ends of inverted transposable elements.
    b.   They have an internal portion that can be transcribed.
    c.   They encode a transposase enzyme.
    d.   They have no harmful effects on cell function.
    e.   They move by a cut-and-paste or copy-and-paste mechanism.

13. Which is *not* correct about retroviruses?
    a.   They are RNA viruses.
    b.   They are believed to be the source of retrotransposons.
    c.   They encode an enzyme for their insertion into host cell DNA.
    d.   They encode single-stranded viral DNA from viral RNA.
    e.   They encode a reverse transcriptase enzyme for RNA to DNA synthesis.

Questions for Discussion

1. You set up an experiment like the one carried out by Lederberg and Tatum, mixing millions of *E. coli* of two strains with the following genetic constitutions.

Among the bacteria obtained after mixing, you find some

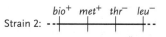

Strain 1: bio^- met^- thr^+ leu^+

Strain 2: bio^+ met^+ thr^- leu^-

cells that do not require threonine, leucine, or biotin to grow but still need methionine. How might you explain this result?

2. You have a technique that allows you to measure the amount of DNA in a cell nucleus. You establish the amount of DNA in a sperm cell of an organism as your baseline. Which multiple of this amount would you expect to find in a nucleus of this organism at G_2 of premeiotic interphase? At telophase I of meiosis? During interkinesis? At telophase II of meiosis?

3. Mutations are changes in DNA sequences that can create new alleles. In which cells of an individual, somatic or meiotic cells, would mutations be of greatest significance to that individual? What about to the species to which the individual belongs?

4. Experimental systems have been developed in which transposable elements can be induced to move under the control of a researcher. Following the induced transposition of a yeast TE element, two mutants were identified with altered activities of enzyme X. One of the mutants lacked enzyme activity completely, whereas the other had five times as much enzyme activity as normal cells did. Both mutants were found to have the TE inserted into the gene for enzyme X. Propose hypotheses for how the two different mutant phenotypes were produced.

Mice, showing genetic variation in coat colour.

Carolyn A. McKeone/Science Photo Library/Photo Researchers, Inc.

11 Mendel, Genes, and Inheritance

WHY IT MATTERS

Parties and champagne were among the last things on Ernest Irons's mind on New Year's Eve, 1904. Irons, a medical intern, was examining a blood specimen from a new patient and was sketching what he saw through his microscope—peculiarly elongated red blood cells **(Figure 11.1, p. 230)**. He and his supervisor, James Herrick, had never seen anything like them. The shape of the cells was reminiscent of a sickle, a cutting tool with a crescent-shaped blade.

The patient had complained of weakness, dizziness, shortness of breath, and pain. His father and two sisters had died from mysterious ailments that had damaged their lungs or kidneys. Did those deceased family members also have sickle-shaped red cells in their blood? Was there a connection between the abnormal cells and the ailments? How did the cells become sickled?

The medical problems that baffled Irons and Herrick killed their patient when he was only 32 years old. The patient's symptoms were characteristic of a genetic disorder now called *sickle cell disease*. This disease develops when a person has received two copies of a gene (one from each parent) that codes for an altered subunit of hemoglobin, the oxygen-transporting protein in red blood cells. When oxygen supplies

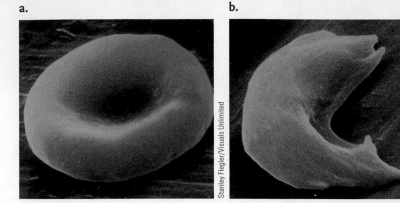

a.

b.

Stanley Flegler/Visuals Unlimited

Stanley Flegler/Visuals Unlimited

Figure 11.1
Red blood cell shape in sickle cell disease. **(a)** A normal red blood cell. **(b)** A sickled red blood cell.

are low, the altered hemoglobin forms long, fibrous, crystal-like structures that push red blood cells into the sickle shape. The altered protein differs from the normal protein by just a single amino acid.

The sickled red blood cells are too elongated and inflexible to pass through the capillaries, the smallest vessels in the circulatory system. As a result, the cells block the capillaries. The surrounding tissues become starved for oxygen and saturated with metabolic wastes, causing the symptoms experienced by Irons' and Herrick's patient. The problem worsens as oxygen concentration falls in tissues and more red blood cells are pushed into the sickled form. (You will learn more about sickle cell disease in this chapter and in Chapter 12.)

Researchers have studied sickle cell disease in great detail at both the molecular and the clinical levels. You may find it curious, however, that our understanding of sickle cell disease—and all other heritable traits—actually began with studies of pea plants in a monastery garden.

Fifty years before Ernest Irons sketched sickled red blood cells, a scholarly monk named Gregor Mendel **(Figure 11.2)** used garden peas to study patterns of

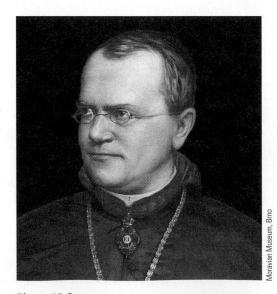

Moravian Museum, Brno

Figure 11.2
Gregor Mendel (1822–1884), the founder of genetics.

inheritance. To test his hypotheses about inheritance, Mendel bred generation after generation of pea plants and carefully observed the patterns by which parents transmit traits to their offspring. Through his experiments and observations, Mendel discovered the fundamental rules that govern inheritance. His discoveries and conclusions founded the science of genetics and still have the power to explain many of the puzzling and sometimes devastating aspects of inheritance that continue to occupy our attention.

11.1 The Beginnings of Genetics: Mendel's Garden Peas

Until about 1900, scientists and the general public believed in the **blending theory of inheritance**, which suggested that hereditary traits blend evenly in offspring through mixing of the parents' blood, much like the effect of mixing coffee and cream. Even today, many people assume that parental characteristics such as skin colour, body size, and facial features blend evenly in their offspring, with the traits of the children appearing about halfway between those of their parents. Yet if blending takes place, why don't extremes, such as very tall and very short individuals, gradually disappear over generations as repeated blending takes place? Also, why do children with blue eyes keep turning up among the offspring of brown-eyed parents?

Gregor Mendel's experiments with garden peas, performed in the 1860s, provided the first answers to these questions and many more. Mendel was an Augustinian monk who lived in a monastery in Brünn, now part of the Czech Republic. But he had an unusual education for a monk in the mid-nineteenth century. He had studied mathematics, chemistry, zoology, and botany at the University of Vienna under some of the foremost scientists of his day. He had also been reared on a farm and was well aware of agricultural principles and their application. He kept abreast of breeding experiments published in scientific journals. Mendel also won several awards for developing improved varieties of fruits and vegetables.

In his work with peas, Mendel studied a variety of heritable characteristics called **characters**, such as flower colour or seed shape. A variation in a character, such as purple or white flower colour, is called a **trait**. Mendel established that characters are passed to offspring in the form of discrete hereditary factors, which now are known as genes. Mendel observed that, rather than blending evenly, many parental traits appear unchanged in offspring, whereas others disappear in one generation to reappear unchanged in the next. Although Mendel did not know it, the inheritance patterns he observed are the result of the segregation of chromosomes, on which the genes are located, to gametes in meiosis (see Chapter 10). Mendel's methods illustrate, perhaps as well as any experiments in the history of science, how rigorous scientific work is conducted: through observation, making hypotheses, and testing the hypotheses with experiments.

11.1a Mendel Chose True-Breeding Garden Peas for His Experiments

Mendel chose the garden pea (*Pisum sativum*) for his research because the plant could be grown easily in the monastery garden, without elaborate equipment. As in other flowering plants, gametes are produced in structures of the flowers (see **Figure 11.3**). The male gametes are sperm nuclei contained in the pollen, which is produced in the *anthers* of the flower. The female gametes are egg cells, produced in the *carpel* of the flowers. Normally, pea plants **self-fertilize** (also known as **self-pollinate**, or more simply, *self*): sperm nuclei in pollen produced by anthers fertilize egg cells housed in the carpel of the same flower. However, for his experiments, Mendel prevented self-fertilization simply by cutting off the anthers. Pollen to fertilize these flowers must then come from a different plant. This technique is called **cross-pollination**, or more simply, a *cross*. This technique allowed Mendel to test the effects of mating pea plants of different parental types.

To begin his experiments, Mendel chose pea plants that were known to be **true-breeding** (also called *pure-breeding*); that is, when self-fertilized, or more simply, *selfed*, they passed traits without change from one generation to the next.

11.1b Mendel First Worked with Single-Character Crosses

Flower colour was among the seven characters Mendel selected for study; one true-breeding variety of peas had purple flowers, and the other true-breeding variety had white flowers (see Figure 11.3). Would these traits blend evenly if plants with purple flowers were cross-pollinated with plants with white flowers?

To answer this question, Mendel took pollen from the anthers of plants with purple flowers and placed it in the flowers of white-flowered plants. He placed the pollen on the *stigma*, the part of the carpel that receives pollen in flowers (see Figure 11.3). He also performed the reciprocal experiment by placing pollen from white-flowered plants on the stigmas of purple-flowered plants. Seeds were the result of the crosses; each seed contains a zygote, or embryo, that will develop into a new pea plant. The plants that develop from the seeds produced by the cross—the first generation of offspring from the cross—are the F_1 **generation** (F stands for *filial; filius* = son). The plants used in the initial cross are called the parental or **P generation**. The plants that grew from the F_1 seeds all formed purple flowers, as if the trait for white flowers had disappeared. The flowers showed no evidence of blending.

Mendel then allowed the purple-flowered F_1 plants to self, producing seeds that represented the F_2 **generation**.

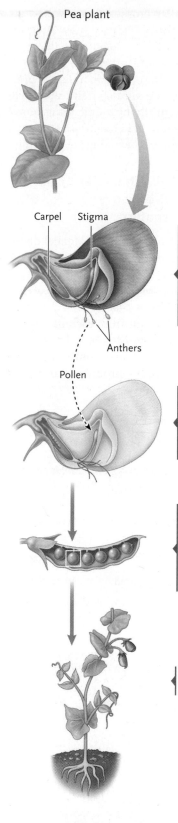

Pea plant

Carpel Stigma

Anthers

Pollen

a. This flower has been sectioned to show the location of its anthers and of the carpel with its attached stigma. Pollen grains form in the anthers. Egg cells develop, fertilization takes place, and seeds mature inside the carpel.

b. Pollen from one plant is brushed onto the stigma of a second plant. The anthers have been cut from the second plant so that it cannot self-fertilize.

c. The cross-fertilized plant produces seeds, which may be scored for seed traits, such as smooth or wrinkled shape, or may be grown into plants for scoring of adult traits, such as flower color.

d. The adult pea plant (F_1 generation)

Figure 11.3
The garden pea (*Pisum sativum*), the focus of Mendel's experiments.

When he planted the F_2 seeds produced by this cross, the white-flowered trait reappeared: both purple-flowered and white-flowered plants were produced. Mendel counted 705 plants with purple flowers and 224 with white flowers, in a ratio that he noted was close to 3:1, or about 75% purple-flowered plants and 25% white-flowered plants.

Mendel made similar crosses that involved six other characters with pairs of traits (**Figure 11.4**); for example, the character of seed colour has the traits yellow and green. In all cases, he observed a uniform F_1 generation, in which only one of the two traits was present. In the F_2 generation, the missing trait reappeared, and both traits were present among the offspring. Moreover, the trait present in the F_1 generation was present in a definite, predictable proportion among the offspring.

11.1c Mendel's Single-Character Crosses Led Him to Propose the Principle of Segregation

Using his knowledge of mathematics, Mendel developed a set of hypotheses to explain the results of his crosses. His first hypothesis was that *the adult plants carry a pair of factors that govern the inheritance of each character.* He correctly deduced that for each character, an organism inherits one factor from each parent.

In modern terminology, Mendel's factors are called *genes,* which are located on chromosomes; the different versions of a gene, producing different traits of a character, are **alleles** of the gene. Although Mendel did not use the modern terms *genes* and *alleles,* we use them in this chapter in our description of Mendel's work. Thus, there are two alleles of the gene that govern flower colour in garden peas: one allele for purple flower colour and the other allele for white flower colour. Organisms with two copies of each gene are now known as diploids; the two alleles of a gene in a diploid individual may be identical or different.

How can the disappearance of one of the traits, such as white flowers, in the F_1 generation and its reappearance in the F_2 generation be explained? Mendel deduced that the trait that had seemed to "disappear" in the F_1 generation actually was present but was masked in some way by the "stronger" allele. Mendel called the masking effect **dominance.** Accordingly, Mendel's second hypothesis stated that *if an individual's pair of genes consists of different alleles, one allele is dominant over the other.* This hypothesis assumes that one allele is **dominant** and the other allele is **recessive.** When a dominant allele for a trait is paired with a recessive allele for the same trait, the dominant allele is expressed.

Figure 11.4
Mendel's crosses with seven different characters in peas, including his results and the calculated ratios of offspring.

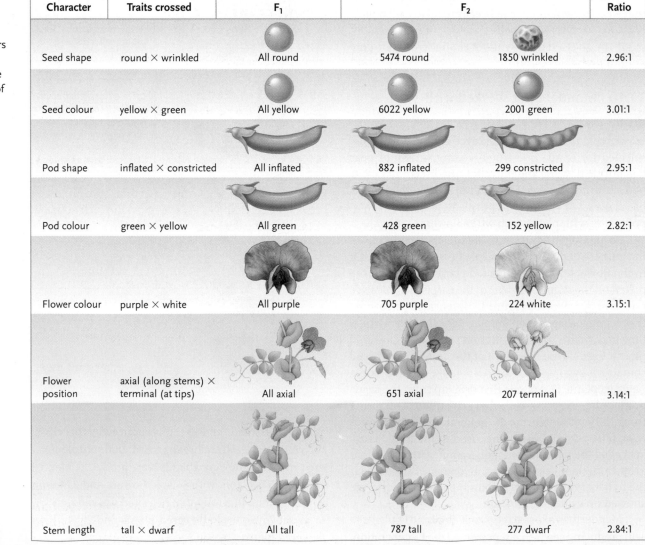

Character	Traits crossed	F_1	F_2		Ratio
Seed shape	round × wrinkled	All round	5474 round	1850 wrinkled	2.96:1
Seed colour	yellow × green	All yellow	6022 yellow	2001 green	3.01:1
Pod shape	inflated × constricted	All inflated	882 inflated	299 constricted	2.95:1
Pod colour	green × yellow	All green	428 green	152 yellow	2.82:1
Flower colour	purple × white	All purple	705 purple	224 white	3.15:1
Flower position	axial (along stems) × terminal (at tips)	All axial	651 axial	207 terminal	3.14:1
Stem length	tall × dwarf	All tall	787 tall	277 dwarf	2.84:1

By contrast, a recessive allele is expressed only when two copies of the allele are present. For example, for flower colour in Mendel's experiments, the allele for purple flowers was dominant and the allele for white flowers was recessive.

As a third hypothesis, Mendel proposed the following: *The pairs of alleles that control a character segregate (separate) as gametes are formed; half the gametes carry one allele, and the other half carry the other allele.* This hypothesis is now known as Mendel's **Principle of Segregation.** During fertilization, fusion of the haploid maternal and paternal gametes produces a diploid nucleus called the *zygote nucleus.* The zygote nucleus receives one allele for the character from the male gamete and one allele for the same character from the female gamete, reuniting the pairs.

Mendel's three hypotheses explained the results of the crosses **(Figure 11.5).** Both alleles of the gene that governs flower colour in the original, true-breeding parent plant with purple flowers are the same. The symbol *P* is used here to designate this allele, with the capital letter indicating that it is dominant, which gives this true-breeding parent the *PP* combination of alleles. Such an individual is called a **homozygote** (*homo* = same) and is said to be **homozygous** for the *P* allele. In other words, the individual has two copies of the same allele of the flower colour gene. Therefore, when the individual produces gametes and the paired alleles separate, all the gametes of this individual will receive a *P* allele (see the left side heading in **Figure 11.5a**).

In the original true-breeding parent with white flowers, both alleles of the gene are also the same. The symbol *p* is used here to designate this allele, with the lowercase letter indicating that it is recessive, which gives this true-breeding plant the homozygous *pp* combination of alleles. These alleles also separate during gamete formation, producing gametes with one *p* allele (see the top heading in Figure 11.5a). (Mendel originated the practice of using uppercase and lowercase letters to designate dominant and recessive alleles.)

All the F$_1$ plants produced by crossing purple-flowered and white-flowered plants—the cross *PP* × *pp*—receive the same combination of alleles, *Pp* (see the cell in Figure 11.5a). An individual of this type, with two different alleles of a gene, is called a **heterozygote** (*hetero* = different) and is said to be **heterozygous** for the trait. Because *P* is dominant over *p*, all the *Pp* plants have purple flowers, even though they also carry the allele for white flowers. An F$_1$ heterozygote produced from a cross that involves a single character is called a **monohybrid** (*mono* = one; *hybrid* = an offspring of parents with different traits).

According to Mendel's hypotheses, all the *Pp* plants in the F$_1$ generation produce two kinds of gametes. Because the heterozygous *Pp* pair separates during gamete formation, half of the gametes receive the *P* allele and half receive the *p* allele. **Figure 11.5b** shows how these gametes can combine during selfing of F$_1$

plants. Generally, a cross between two individuals that are each heterozygous for the same pair of alleles—*Pp* × *Pp* here—is called a **monohybrid cross.** The gametes are entered in both the rows and columns in Figure 11.5b; the cells show the possible combinations. Combining two gametes that both carry the *P* allele produces a *PP* F$_2$ plant; combining *P* from one parent and *p* from the other produces a *Pp* plant; and combining *p* from both F$_1$ parents produces a *pp* F$_2$ plant. The homozygous *PP* and heterozygous *Pp* plants in the F$_2$ generation have purple flowers, the dominant trait; the homozygous *pp* offspring have white flowers, the recessive trait.

Mendel's hypotheses explain how individuals may differ genetically but still look the same. The *PP* and *Pp* plants, although genetically different, both have purple flowers. In modern terminology, **genotype** refers to the *genetic constitution of an organism,* and **phenotype** (Greek *phainein* = to show) refers to its *outward appearance.* In this case, the two different genotypes *PP* and *Pp* produce the same purple-flower phenotype.

Thus, the results of Mendel's crosses support his three hypotheses:

1. The genes that govern genetic characters occur in pairs in individuals.
2. If different alleles are present in an individual's pair of genes, one allele is dominant over the other.
3. The two alleles of a gene segregate and enter gametes singly.

11.1d Mendel Could Predict Both Classes and Proportions of Offspring from His Hypotheses

Mendel could predict both classes and proportions of offspring from his hypotheses. To understand how Mendel's hypotheses allowed him to predict the proportions of offspring resulting from a genetic cross, let's

a.

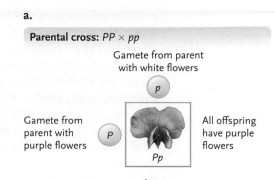

Parental cross: *PP* × *pp*

Gamete from parent with white flowers: *p*

Gamete from parent with purple flowers: *P*

Pp

All offspring have purple flowers

Mendel's parental cross between true-breeding pea plants with purple flowers and white flowers, producing an F$_1$ generation consisting of all purple-flowered plants.

b.

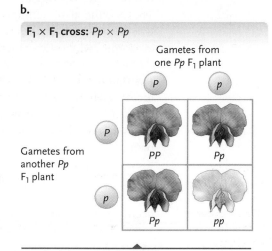

F$_1$ × F$_1$ cross: *Pp* × *Pp*

Gametes from one *Pp* F$_1$ plant: *P*, *p*

Gametes from another *Pp* F$_1$ plant: *P*, *p*

PP *Pp*

Pp *pp*

Mendel's cross between F$_1$ plants with purple flowers, producing an F$_2$ generation consisting of $^3/_4$ purple-flowered and $^1/_4$ white-flowered plants.

Figure 11.5
The principle of segregation in Mendel's crosses studying the inheritance of flower colour in garden peas.

review the mathematical rules that govern **probability**—that is, the possibility that an outcome will occur if it is a matter of chance, as in the random fertilization of an egg by a sperm cell that contains one allele or another.

In the mathematics of probability, the likelihood of an outcome is predicted on a scale of 0 to 1. An outcome that is certain to occur has a probability of 1, and an outcome that cannot possibly happen has a probability of 0. The standard game die, a cube with one of the numbers 1 through 6 on each face, is a familiar model to demonstrate working with probability. In general, we determine the probability of any given outcome (rolling a 4) by dividing that outcome by the total number of possible outcomes. For obtaining 4 in rolling a die, the probability is 1 divided by 6, or 1/6. The likelihood of rolling an even number (2, 4, 6) would be 3/6 = 1/2. The probabilities of all the possible outcomes, when added together, must equal 1.

The Product Rule in Probability. If you were to roll two dice together, what is the chance of rolling double fours? Because the outcome of one die has no effect on the other one, the two rolls are independent. When two or more events are independent, the probability that they will both occur is calculated using the **product rule**—their individual probabilities are multiplied. That is, the probability that events A and B *both* will occur equals the probability of event A *multiplied* by the probability of event B. For example, the probability of getting a 4 on the first die is 1/6; the probability of a 4 on the second die is also 1/6 **(Figure 11.6)**. Because the events are independent, the probability of getting a 4 on both dice is 1/6 × 1/6 = 1/36. Applying this

a. Likelihood of rolling a double four.

1/6 x 1/6 = 1/36
Likelihood of rolling a double 4

b. Likelihood of rolling a seven in any combination.

Figure 11.6
Rules of probability. **(a)** For each die, the probability of a 4 is 1/6. Because the outcome of one die is independent of that of the other, the combined probability of rolling a 4 on both dice at the same time is calculated by multiplying the individual probabilities (product rule). **(b)** Since there are six different outcomes, each of which adds up to 7, the total likelihood of rolling a 7 is calculated by adding the individual probabilities (sum rule).

principle to human families, the sex of one child has no effect on the sex of the next child; therefore, the probability of having four girls in a row is the product of their individual probabilities (very close to 1/2 for each birth): 1/2 × 1/2 × 1/2 × 1/2 = 1/16.

The Sum Rule in Probability. Another relationship, the **sum rule**, applies when several different events all give the same outcome; that is, the probability that *either* event A *or* event B *or* event C will occur equals the probability of event A *plus* the probability of event B *plus* the probability of event C. Returning to the two dice example, what is the probability of rolling a 7? Several different events all give the same total. One could make a total of 7 from a 1 on the first die and a 6 on the second, or a 5 on the first and a 2 on the second, or a 4 on the first and a 3 on the second. Each of these three combinations would be expected to occur at a frequency of 1/6 × 1/6 = 1/36. Hopefully, you can see three more possible combinations that are just the reciprocal of the first three, that is, 6 on the first die and a 1 on the second, and so on, for a total of six different ways to roll "7." That is, there are six ways of obtaining the same outcome. Therefore, for the probability of rolling a 7, we sum the individual probabilities to get the final probability: 1/36 + 1/36 + 1/36 + 1/36 + 1/36 + 1/36 = 6/36 = 1/6. On average, you could expect to roll a combination of numbers totalling 7 once in every six attempts.

Probability in Mendel's Crosses. Since the randomness inherent in meiosis is comparable to the randomness inherent in rolling dice, the same rules of probability just discussed apply to genes carried on chromosomes in Mendel's crosses. For example, in the crosses that involve the purple-flowered and white-flowered traits, half of the gametes of the F_1 generation contain the P allele of the gene and half contain the p allele (see Figure 11.5b). To produce a PP zygote, two P gametes must combine. The probability of selecting a P gamete from one F_1 parent is 1/2, and the probability of selecting a P gamete from the other F_1 parent is also 1/2. Therefore, the probability of producing a PP zygote from this monohybrid cross is 1/2 × 1/2 = 1/4. That is, by the product rule, one-fourth of the offspring of the F_1 cross $Pp \times Pp$ are expected to be PP, which have purple flowers **(Figure 11.7a)**. By the same line of reasoning, one-fourth of the F_2 offspring are expected to be pp, which have white flowers **(Figure 11.7b)**.

What about the production of Pp offspring? The cross $Pp \times Pp$ can produce Pp in two different ways. A P gamete from the first parent can combine with a p gamete from the second parent (Pp), or a p gamete from the first parent can combine with a P gamete from the second parent (pP) **(Figure 11.7c)**. Because there are two different ways to get the same outcome, we apply the sum rule to obtain the combined probability. Each of the ways to get Pp has an individual probability of 1/4; when we add these individual probabilities, we have 1/4 + 1/4 = 1/2.

Therefore, half of the offspring are expected to be *Pp*, which have purple flowers. We could get the same result from the requirement that all of the individual probabilities must add up to 1. If the probability of *PP* is 1/4 and the probability of *pp* is 1/4, then the probability of the remaining possibility, *Pp*, must be 1/2, because the total of the individual probabilities must add up to 1: 1/4 + 1/4 + 1/2 = 1.

What if we want to know the probability of obtaining purple flowers in the cross *Pp* × *Pp*? In this case, the rule of addition applies, because there are two ways to get purple flowers: genotypes *PP* and *Pp*. Adding the individual probabilities of these combinations, 1/4 *PP* + 1/2 *Pp*, gives a total of 3/4, indicating that three-fourths of the F₂ offspring are expected to have purple flowers. Because the total probabilities must add up to 1, the remaining one-fourth of the offspring are expected to have white flowers (1/4 *pp*). These proportions give the ratio 3:1, which is close to the ratio Mendel obtained in his cross.

What we have just stepped through in describing Figure 11.7 is the **Punnett square** method for determining the genotypes of offspring and their expected proportions. To use the Punnett square, write the probability of obtaining gametes with each type of allele from one parent at the top of the diagram and write the chance of obtaining each type of allele from the other parent on the left side. Then fill in the cells by combining the alleles from the top and from the left and multiply their individual probabilities.

11.1e Mendel Used a Testcross to Check the Validity of His Hypotheses

Mendel realized that he could assess the validity of his hypotheses by determining whether they could be used successfully to *predict* the outcome of a cross of a different type than he had tried so far. Accordingly, he crossed an F₁ plant with purple flowers, assumed to have the heterozygous genotype *Pp*, with a true-breeding white-flowered plant, with the homozygous genotype *pp*. In this cross, *Pp* × *pp*, all the gametes of the *pp* plant contain a single *p* allele. Therefore, the probability that a gamete from this parent contains *p* is 1. The gamete and its probability of 1 are entered as the row heading of the Punnett square in **Figure 11.8.** The *Pp* parent produces two types of gametes, half that contain the *P* allele and half that contain the *p* allele. These values, 1/2 *P* and 1/2 *p*, are entered as the column headings. Filling in the possible combinations in the cells gives the two expected classes, *Pp* and *pp*, both with a probability of 1/2. Thus, half the offspring of this cross are expected to have purple flowers and half are expected to have white flowers; the ratio is 1:1. Mendel's actual results in this cross were 85 purple-flowered plants and 81 white-flowered plants, which closely approach the expected 1:1 ratio. Mendel also made the same type of cross with all the other traits

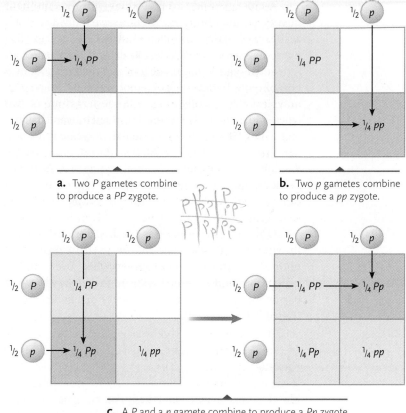

a. Two *P* gametes combine to produce a *PP* zygote.

b. Two *p* gametes combine to produce a *pp* zygote.

c. A *P* and a *p* gamete combine to produce a *Pp* zygote in two squares, for a total of 1/4 *Pp* + 1/4 *Pp* = 1/2 *Pp*.

Figure 11.7
Punnett square method for predicting offspring and their ratios in genetic crosses. The example is the F₁ × F₁ cross of purple-flowered plants from Figure 11.5. Each cell shows the genotype and proportion of one type of zygote.

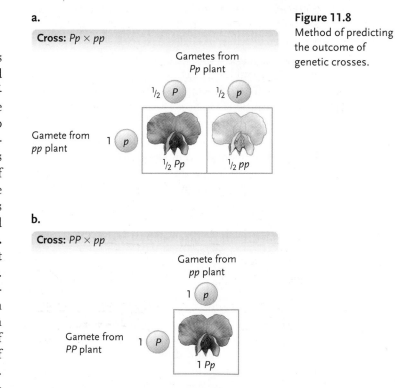

a.

Cross: *Pp* × *pp*

Gametes from *Pp* plant

Gamete from *pp* plant

1/2 *Pp*   1/2 *pp*

b.

Cross: *PP* × *pp*

Gamete from *pp* plant

Gamete from *PP* plant

1 *Pp*

Figure 11.8
Method of predicting the outcome of genetic crosses.

used in his study, including those traits affecting seed shape, seed colour, and plant height, and found the same 1:1 ratio.

A cross between an individual with the dominant phenotype and a homozygous recessive individual, such as the one described, is called a **testcross**. Geneticists use a testcross as a standard test to determine whether an individual with a dominant trait is a heterozygote or a homozygote, because these cannot be distinguished phenotypically. If the offspring of the testcross are of two types, with half displaying the dominant trait and half the recessive trait, then the individual in question must be a heterozygote (see Figure 11.8). If all the offspring display the dominant trait, the individual in question must be a homozygote. For example, the cross $PP \times pp$ gives all Pp progeny, which show the dominant purple phenotype (see Figure 11.8).

Obviously, the testcross method cannot be used for humans. However, it can be used in reverse by noting the traits present in families over several generations and working backward to deduce whether a parent must have been a homozygote or a heterozygote (see also Chapter 12).

11.1f Mendel Tested the Independence of Different Genes in Crosses

Mendel next asked what happens in crosses when more than one character is involved. Would the alleles of different characters be inherited independently, or would they interact to alter their expected proportions in offspring?

To answer these questions, Mendel crossed parental stocks that had differences in two of the hereditary characters he was studying: seed shape and seed colour. His single-character crosses had shown that each was controlled by a pair of alleles. For seed shape, the RR or Rr genotypes produce round seeds and the rr genotype produces wrinkled seeds. For seed colour, yellow is dominant. The homozygous YY and heterozygous Yy genotypes produce yellow seeds; the homozygous yy genotype produces green seeds.

Mendel crossed plants that bred true for the production of round and yellow seeds ($RR\ YY$) with plants that bred true for the production of wrinkled and green seeds ($rr\ yy$) **(Figure 11.9)**. The cross, $RR\ YY \times rr\ yy$, yielded an F_1 generation that consisted of all round yellow seeds, with the genotype $Rr\ Yy$. A zygote produced from a cross that involves two characters is called a **dihybrid** (di = two).

Mendel then planted the F_1 seeds, grew the plants to maturity, and selfed them; that is, he crossed the F_1 plants to themselves. A cross between two individuals that are heterozygous for two pairs of alleles—here $Rr\ Yy \times Rr\ Yy$—is called a **dihybrid cross** (see Figure 11.9). The seeds produced by these plants, representing the F_2 generation, included 315 round yellow seeds, 101 wrinkled yellow seeds, 103 round green seeds, and 32 wrinkled green seeds. Mendel noted that these numbers were close to a 9:3:3:1 ratio (3:1 for round: wrinkled, and 3:1 for yellow:green).

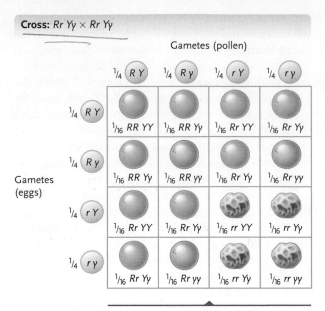

Cross: $Rr\ Yy \times Rr\ Yy$

Phenotypic ratio: 9 round yellow:3 round green: 3 wrinkled yellow:1 wrinkled green

Figure 11.9
The Principle of Independent Assortment in Mendel's crosses involving two hereditary characters in garden peas, seed shape, and seed colour.

This 9:3:3:1 ratio was consistent with Mendel's previous findings if he added one further hypothesis: *The alleles of the genes that govern the two characters segregate independently during formation of gametes.* That is, the allele for seed shape that the gamete receives (R or r) has no influence on which allele for seed colour it receives (Y or y) and vice versa. The two events are completely independent. Mendel termed this assumption **independent assortment;** it is now known as Mendel's **Principle of Independent Assortment.**

To understand the effect of independent assortment in the cross, assume that the $RR\ YY$ parent produces only $R\ Y$ gametes and the $rr\ yy$ parent produces only $r\ y$ gametes. In the F_1 generation, all possible combinations of these gametes produce only one genotype, $Rr\ Yy$, in the offspring. As observed, all the F_1 will be round yellow seeds.

If the alleles that control seed shape and seed colour assort independently in gamete formation, each F_1 plant grown from the seeds would produce four types of gametes. The R allele for seed shape can be delivered independently to a gamete with either the Y or y allele for seed colour, and, similarly, the r allele can be delivered to a gamete with either the Y or y allele. Thus, the independent assortment of genes from the $Rr\ Yy$ parents is expected to produce four types of gametes with equal probability: $1/4\ R\ Y$, $1/4\ R\ y$, $1/4\ r\ Y$, and $1/4\ r\ y$. These gametes and their probabilities are entered as the row and column headings of the Punnett square in Figure 11.9.

Filling in the cells of the diagram (see Figure 11.9) gives 16 combinations of alleles, all with an equal probability of 1 in every 16 offspring. Of these, the genotypes *RR YY*, *RR Yy*, *Rr YY*, and *Rr Yy* all have the same phenotype: round yellow seeds. These combinations occur in 9 of the 16 cells in the diagram, giving a total probability of 9/16. The genotypes *rr YY* and *rr Yy*, which produce the wrinkled yellow seeds, are found in three cells, giving a probability of 3/16 for this phenotype. Similarly, the genotypes *RR yy* and *Rr yy*, which yield round green seeds, occur in three cells, giving a probability of 3/16. Finally, the genotype *rr yy*, which produces wrinkled green seeds, is found in only one cell and therefore has a probability of 1/16.

These probabilities of round yellow seeds, wrinkled yellow seeds, round green seeds, and wrinkled green seeds, in a 9:3:3:1 ratio, closely approximate the actual results of 315:101:108:32 obtained by Mendel. Thus, Mendel's first three hypotheses, with the added hypothesis of independent assortment, explain the observed results of his dihybrid cross. Mendel's testcrosses completely confirmed his hypotheses; for example, the testcross *Rr Yy* × *rr yy* produced 55 round yellow seeds, 51 round green seeds, 49 wrinkled yellow seeds, and 53 wrinkled green seeds. This distribution corresponds well with the expected 1:1:1:1 ratio in the offspring. (Try to set up a Punnett square for this cross and predict the expected classes of offspring and their frequencies.)

Mendel's first three hypotheses provided a coherent explanation of the pattern of inheritance for alternate traits of the same character, such as purple and white for flower colour. His fourth hypothesis, independent assortment, addressed the inheritance of traits for different characters, such as seed shape, seed colour, and flower colour, and showed that, instead of being inherited together, the traits of different characters were distributed independently to offspring.

11.1g Mendel's Research Founded the Field of Genetics

Mendel's techniques and conclusions were so advanced for his time that their significance was not immediately appreciated. Mendel's success was based partly on a good choice of experimental organism. He was also lucky. The characters he chose all segregate independently; that is, none of them are physically near each other on the chromosomes, a condition that would have given ratios other than 9:3:3:1, showing that they do not assort independently. Mendel's findings anticipated in detail the patterns by which genes and chromosomes determine inheritance. Yet, when Mendel first reported his findings, during the nineteenth century, the structure and function of chromosomes and the patterns by which they are separated and distributed to gametes were unknown; meiosis remained to be discovered. In addition, his use of mathematical analysis was a new and radical departure from the usual biological techniques of his day.

Mendel reported his results to a small group of fellow intellectuals in Brünn and presented his results in 1866 in a natural history journal published in the city. His article received little notice outside of Brünn, and those who read it were unable to appreciate the significance of his findings. His work was overlooked until the early 1900s, when three investigators—Hugo de Vries in Holland, Carl Correns in Germany, and Erich von Tschermak in Austria—independently performed a series of breeding experiments similar to Mendel's and reached the same conclusions. These investigators, in searching through previously published scientific articles, discovered to their surprise Mendel's article about his experiments conducted 34 years earlier. Each gave credit to Mendel's discoveries, and the quality and far-reaching implications of his work were at last realized. Mendel died in 1884, 16 years before the rediscovery of his experiments and conclusions; thus, he never received the recognition that he so richly deserved during his lifetime.

Mendel was unable to relate the behaviour of his "factors" (genes) to cell structures because the critical information he required was not obtained until later, through the discovery of meiosis during the 1890s. The next section describes how a genetics student familiar with meiosis was able to make the connection between Mendel's factors and chromosomes.

11.1h Sutton's Chromosome Theory of Inheritance Related Mendel's Genes to Chromosomes

By the time Mendel's results were rediscovered in the early 1900s, critical information from studies of meiosis was available. It was not long before a genetics student, Walter Sutton, recognized the similarities between the inheritance of the genes discovered by Mendel and the behaviour of chromosomes in meiosis and fertilization **(Figure 11.10, p. 238)**.

In a historic article published in 1903, Sutton, then a graduate student at Columbia University in New York, drew all the necessary parallels between genes and chromosomes:

- Chromosomes occur in pairs in sexually reproducing, diploid organisms, as do the alleles of each gene.
- The chromosomes of each pair are separated and delivered singly to gametes, as are the alleles of a gene.
- The separation of any pair of chromosomes in meiosis and gamete formation is independent of the separation of other pairs (see Figure 11.10), as in the independent assortment of the alleles of different genes in Mendel's dihybrid crosses.

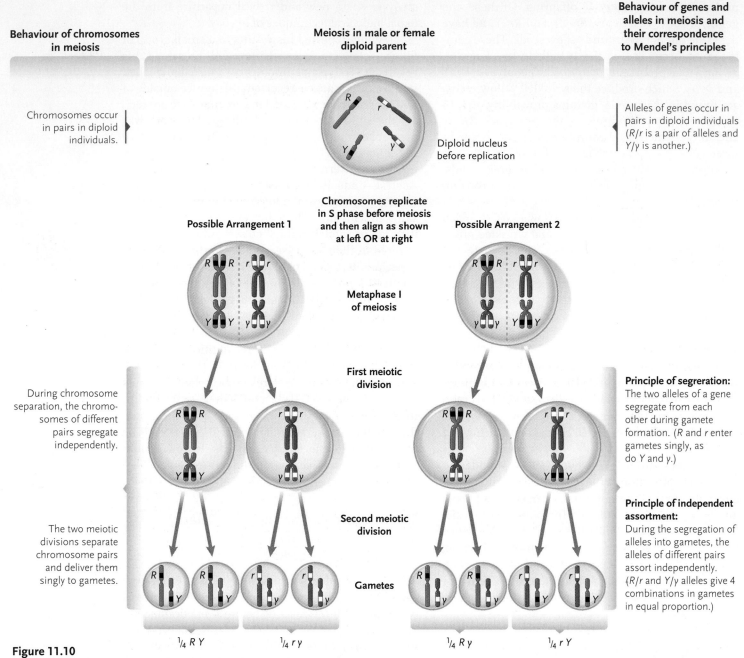

Figure 11.10
The parallels between the behaviour of chromosomes and genes and alleles in meiosis. The gametes show four different combinations of alleles produced by independent segregation of chromosome pairs.

• Finally, one member of each chromosome pair is derived in fertilization from the male parent, and the other member is derived from the female parent, in an exact parallel with the two alleles of a gene.

From this total coincidence in behaviour, Sutton correctly concluded that genes and their alleles are carried on the chromosomes, a conclusion known today as the **chromosome theory of inheritance.**

The exact parallel between the principles set forth by Mendel, and the behaviour of chromosomes and genes during meiosis, is shown in Figure 11.10 for an *Rr Yy* diploid. For a cross of *Rr Yy* × *Rr Yy*, when the gametes fuse randomly, the progeny will show a phenotypic ratio of 9:3:3:1. This mechanism explains the

same ratio of gametes and progeny as the *Rr Yy* × *Ry Yy* cross in Figure 11.9.

The particular site on a chromosome at which a gene is located is called the **locus** (plural, *loci*) of the gene. The locus is a particular DNA sequence that encodes a protein or ribonucleic acid (RNA) product responsible for the phenotype controlled by the gene. A locus for a gene with two alleles, *A* and *a*, on a homologous pair of chromosomes is shown in **Figure 11.11.** At the molecular level, different alleles consist of small differences in the DNA sequence of a gene, which may result in functional differences in the protein or RNA product encoded by the gene. These differences are detected as distinct phenotypes in the offspring of a cross.

All the genetics research conducted since the early 1900s has confirmed Mendel's basic hypotheses about

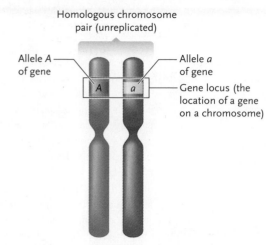

Homologous chromosome pair (unreplicated)

Allele *A* of gene

Allele *a* of gene

Gene locus (the location of a gene on a chromosome)

Figure 11.11

A locus, the site occupied by a gene on a pair of homologous chromosomes. Two alleles, *A* and *a*, of the gene are present at this locus in the homologous pair. These alleles have differences in the DNA sequence of the gene.

inheritance. This research has shown that Mendel's conclusions apply to all types of organisms, from yeast and fruit flies to humans, and has led to the rapidly growing field of human genetics. In humans, a number of easily seen traits show inheritance patterns that follow Mendelian principles **(Figure 11.12)**; for example, albinism, the lack of normal skin colour, is recessive to normal skin colour, and fingers with webs between them are recessive to normally separated fingers. Similarly, achondroplasia, the most frequent form of short-limb dwarfism, is a recessive trait that involves abnormal bone growth. Many human disorders that cannot be seen easily also show simple inheritance patterns. For instance, cystic fibrosis, in which a defect in the membrane transport of chloride ions leads to pulmonary and digestive dysfunctions and eventually death, is a recessive trait.

The post-Mendel research has demonstrated additional patterns of inheritance (see the next section) that were not anticipated by Mendel and, in some circumstances, require modifications or additions to his hypotheses.

STUDY BREAK

1. What characteristics of the garden pea made this organism a good model system for Mendel?
2. How does independent assortment explain Mendel's dihybrid cross data?
3. How is an allele related to a locus?

11.2 Later Modifications and Additions to Mendel's Hypotheses

The rediscovery of Mendel's research in the early 1900s produced an immediate burst of interest in genetics. The research that followed greatly expanded our understanding of genes and their inheritance. The discovery that the alleles of many genes are neither fully dominant nor fully recessive was among these new findings. Some alleles show incomplete dominance, in which recessive alleles do have some effect on the phenotype of heterozygotes. Other alleles are codominant; that is, they have different and approximately equal effects in heterozygotes.

Further research also demonstrated that more than two alleles of a gene may be present among all the members of a population. This condition, called multiple alleles, is still consistent with Mendel's conclusions because each sexually reproducing, diploid individual in a population has only two alleles of each gene—a pair—which are inherited and passed on according to Mendel's principles.

Geneticists also found that the activity of one gene can influence the activity of a different gene, a phenomenon called epistasis. Furthermore, some characters are explained by polygenic inheritance, in which several different genes each contribute to the phenotype. In addition, alterations in a single gene sometimes affect more than one phenotype in an organism; this phenomenon is called pleiotropy. The following sections discuss each of these so-called extensions of Mendel's fundamental principles.

11.2a In Incomplete Dominance, Dominant Alleles Do Not Completely Mask Recessive Alleles

Incomplete dominance occurs when the effects of recessive alleles can be detected to some extent in heterozygotes. Flower colour in snapdragons shows incomplete dominance

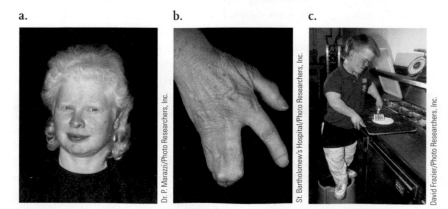

a.   b.   c.

Dr. P. Marazzi/Photo Researchers, Inc.

St. Bartholomew's Hospital/Photo Researchers, Inc.

David Frazier/Photo Researchers, Inc.

Figure 11.12

Human traits showing inheritance patterns that follow Mendelian principles. **(a)** Lack of normal skin colour (albinism). **(b)** Webbed fingers. **(c)** Achondroplasia, or short-limbed dwarfism.

Why Mendel's Dwarf Pea Plants Were So Short

Two independent research teams worked out the molecular basis for one of the seven characters Mendel studied—dwarfing, which is governed by stem length in garden peas. The investigators, including Diane Lester and her colleagues at the University of Tasmania in Australia and David Martin and his coworkers at Oregon State University, were interested in learning the molecular differences in the alleles of the gene that produced tall or dwarf plants. The dominant *T* allele (*T* = tall) of the gene produces plants of normal height; the recessive *t* allele produces dwarf plants with short stems. How can a single gene control the overall height of a plant?

Lester's team discovered that the gene codes for an enzyme that carries out a preliminary step in the synthesis of the plant hormone gibberellin, which, among other effects, causes the stems of plants to elongate. Martin's group cloned the gene and determined its complete DNA sequence. (Cloning techniques and DNA sequencing are described in Sections 16.1 and 16.3.) The sequence showed that the *T* and *t* alleles of the gene encode two versions of the enzyme that catalyzes gibberellin synthesis, which differ by only a single amino acid. Lester's group found that the faulty enzyme encoded by the *t* allele carries out its step (addition of a hydroxyl group to a precursor) much more slowly than the enzyme encoded by the normal *T* allele. As a result, plants with the *t* allele have only about 5% as much gibberellin in their stems as *T* plants. The reduced gibberellin levels limit stem elongation, producing the dwarf plants.

Thus, the methods of molecular biology allowed contemporary researchers to study a gene first discovered in the mid-nineteenth century. The findings leave little doubt that a change in a single amino acid leads to the dwarf phenotype Mendel observed in his monastery garden.

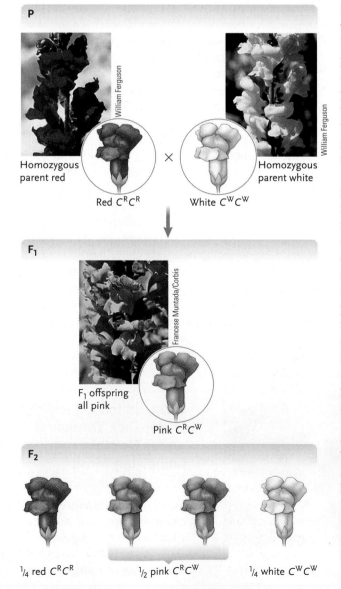

Figure 11.13
Incomplete dominance in the inheritance of flower colour in snapdragons.

(**Figure 11.13**). If true-breeding, red-flowered and white-flowered snapdragon plants are crossed, all the F_1 offspring have pink flowers (see Figure 11.13). The pink colour might make it appear that the pure red and white colours have blended out and disappeared—mixing red and white makes pink—until two F_1 plants are crossed. The cross demonstrates that the red and white traits both reappear in the F_2 generation, which has red, pink, and white flowers in numbers approximating a 1:2:1 ratio.

This outcome can be explained by incomplete dominance between a C^R allele for red colour and a C^W allele for white colour. When one allele is not completely dominant to the other, we use a superscript to signify the character. In this case, C signifies the character for flower colour and the superscripts indicate the alleles (R for red and W for white). Therefore, the initial cross is $C^R C^R$ (red) $\times$ $C^W C^W$ (white), which produces $C^R C^W$ F_1 (pink) plants. The C^R allele encodes an enzyme that produces a red pigment, but two alleles ($C^R C^R$) are necessary to produce enough of the active form of the enzyme to produce fully red flowers. The enzyme is completely inactive in $C^W C^W$ plants, which produce colourless flowers that appear white because of the scattering of light by cell walls and other structures. With their single C^R allele, the $C^R C^W$ heterozygotes of the F_1 generation can produce only enough pigment to give the flowers a pink colour. When the pink $C^R C^W$ F_1 plants are crossed, the fully red and white colours reappear, together with the pink colour, in the F_2 generation, in a ratio of 1/4 $C^R C^R$ (red), 1/2 $C^R C^W$ (pink), and 1/4 $C^W C^W$ (white). This ratio is exactly the same as the ratio of genotypes produced from a cross of two heterozygotes in Mendel's experiments (for example, see Figure 11.7, pp. 233).

Some human disorders show incomplete dominance. For example, sickle cell disease (see the introduction to

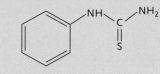
this chapter) is characterized by an alteration in the hemoglobin molecule that changes the shape of red blood cells when oxygen levels are low. An individual with sickle cell disease is homozygous for a recessive allele that encodes a defective form of one of the polypeptides of the hemoglobin molecule. Individuals heterozygous for that recessive allele and the normal allele have a condition known as *sickle cell trait,* which is a milder form of the disease because the individuals still produce normal polypeptides from the normal allele.

Familial hypercholesterolemia is another example of incomplete dominance. The gene involved encodes the low-density lipoprotein (LDL) receptor, a cell membrane protein responsible for removing excess cholesterol from the blood (see Section 5.5). Individuals with familial hypercholesterolemia are homozygous for a defective LDL receptor gene, produce no LDL receptors, and have a severe form of the disease. These individuals have six times the normal level of cholesterol in the blood and therefore are very prone to atherosclerosis (hardening of the arteries). Many individuals with familial hypercholesterolemia have heart attacks as children. Heterozygous individuals have half the normal number of receptors, which results in a milder form of the disease. Their symptoms are twice the normal blood cholesterol level, an unusually high risk of atherosclerosis, and a high risk of heart attacks before age 35.

Many alleles that appear to be completely dominant are actually incomplete in their effects when analyzed at the biochemical or molecular level. For example, for pigments that produce fur or flower colours, biochemical studies often show that even though heterozygotes may produce enough pigment to make them look the same externally as homozygous dominants, a difference in the amount of pigment is measurable at the biochemical level. Thus, whether dominance between alleles is complete or incomplete often depends on the level at which the effects of the alleles are examined.

A similar situation occurs in humans who carry the recessive allele that causes Tay–Sachs disease. Children who are homozygous for the recessive allele do not have a functional version of an enzyme that breaks down gangliosides, a type of membrane lipid. As a result, gangliosides accumulate in the brain, leading to mental impairment and eventually to death. Heterozygotes are without symptoms of the disease, even though they have one copy of the recessive allele. However, at the biochemical level, reduced breakdown of gangliosides can be detected in heterozygotes, evidently due to a reduced quantity of the active enzyme.

11.2b In Codominance, the Effects of Different Alleles Are Equally Detectable in Heterozygotes

Codominance occurs when alleles have approximately equal effects in individuals, making the alleles equally detectable in heterozygotes. The inheritance of the human blood types, M, MN, and N, is an example of codominance. These are different blood types from the familiar blood types of the ABO blood group. The L^M and L^N alleles of the MN blood group gene that control this character encode different forms of a glycoprotein molecule located on the surface of red blood cells. If the genotype is $L^M L^M$, only the M form of the glycoprotein is present and the blood type is M; if it is $L^N L^N$, only the N form is present and the blood type is N. In heterozygotes with the $L^M L^N$ genotype, both glycoprotein types are present and can be detected, producing the blood type MN. Because each genotype has a different phenotype, the inheritance pattern for the MN blood group alleles is generally the same as for incompletely dominant alleles. That is, you would not be able to distinguish between codominance and incomplete dominance just by comparing the ratio of offspring from crosses.

The MN blood types do not affect blood transfusions and have relatively little medical importance. However, they have been invaluable in tracing human evolution and prehistoric migrations, and they are frequently used in initial tests to determine the paternity of a child. Among their primary advantages in research and paternity determination is that the genotype of all individuals, including heterozygotes, can be detected directly—and inexpensively—from their phenotype, with no requirement for further genetic tests or analysis.

11.2c In Multiple Alleles, More Than Two Alleles of a Gene Are Present in a Population

One of Mendel's major and most fundamental assumptions was that alleles occur in pairs in individuals; in the pairs, the alleles may be the same or different. After the rediscovery of Mendel's principles, it soon became apparent that although alleles do indeed occur in pairs in individuals, **multiple alleles** (more than two different alleles of a gene) may be present if all the individuals of a population are taken into account. For example, for a gene B, there could be the normal allele, B, and several alleles with alterations in the gene named, for example, b_1, b_2, b_3, and so on. Some individuals in a population may have the B and b_1 alleles of a gene; others, the b_2 and b_3 alleles; still others, the b_3 and b_5 alleles; and so on, for all possible combinations. Thus, although any one individual can have only two alleles of the gene, there are more than two alleles in the population as a whole. Genes may certainly occur in many more than the four alleles of the example; for instance, one of the genes that plays a part in the acceptance or rejection of organ transplants in humans has more than 200 different alleles.

The multiple alleles of a gene each contain differences at one or more points in their DNA sequences **(Figure 11.14)**, which cause detectable alterations in the structure and function of gene products encoded by the alleles. Multiple alleles present no real difficulty in genetic analysis because each diploid individual still has only two of the alleles, allowing gametes to be predicted and traced through crosses by the usual methods.

Human ABO Blood Group. The human *ABO* blood group provides another interesting example of multiple

Table 11.1	Blood Types of the Human ABO Blood Group		
Blood Type	Antigens	Antibodies	Blood Types Accepted in a Transfusion
A	A	Anti-B	A or O
B	B	Anti-A	B or O
AB	A and B	None	A, B, AB, or O
O	None	Anti-A, anti-B	O

alleles, in a system that also exhibits both dominance and codominance. The ABO blood group was discovered in 1901 by Karl Landsteiner, an Austrian biochemist who was investigating the sometimes fatal outcome of attempts to transfer whole blood from one person to another. Landsteiner found that only certain combinations of four blood types, designated A, B, AB, and O, can be mixed safely in transfusions **(Table 11.1).**

Landsteiner determined that, in the wrong combinations, red blood cells from one blood type are agglutinated or clumped by an agent in the serum of another type (the serum is the fluid in which the blood cells are suspended). The clumping was later found to depend on the action of an **antibody** in the blood serum. (Antibodies, protein molecules that interact with specific substances called antigens, are discussed in Chapter 44.)

The antigens responsible for the blood types of the ABO blood group are the carbohydrate parts of glycoproteins located on the surfaces of red blood cells (unrelated to the glycoprotein carbohydrates responsible for the blood types of the MN blood group). People with type A blood have *antigen A* on their red blood cells, and people with type B blood have *antigen B* on their red blood cells. At the same time, people with type A blood have antibodies against antigen B, and people with type B blood have antibodies against antigen A. People with type O blood have neither antigen A nor antigen B on their red blood cells, but they have antibodies against both of these antigens. People with type AB blood have neither anti-A nor anti-B antibodies, but they have both the A and B antigens, and their red blood cells are clumped by antibodies in the blood of all the other groups.

The four blood types—A, B, AB, and O—are produced by different combinations of multiple (three) alleles of a single gene I **(Figure 11.15).** The three alleles, designated I^A, I^B, and i, produce the following blood types:

$I^A I^A$ = type A blood		$I^B I^B$ = type B blood	
$I^A i$ = type A blood		$I^B i$ = type B blood	
$I^A I^B$ = type AB blood		ii = type O blood	

In addition, I^A and I^B are codominant alleles that are each dominant to the i allele.

B allele   ...ATGCAGATACCGATTACAGACCATAGG...

b_1 allele   ...ATGCAGAGACCGATTACAGACCATAGG...

b_2 allele   ...ATGCAGATGCCGATTACAGACCATAGG...

b_3 allele   ...ATGCAGATACCGATTACAGGCCATAGG...

Figure 11.14

Multiple alleles. Multiple alleles consist of small differences in the DNA sequence of a gene at one or more points, which result in detectable differences in the structure of the protein encoded by the gene. The B allele is the normal allele, which encodes a protein with normal function. The three b alleles each have alterations of the normal protein-coding DNA sequence that may adversely affect the function of that protein.

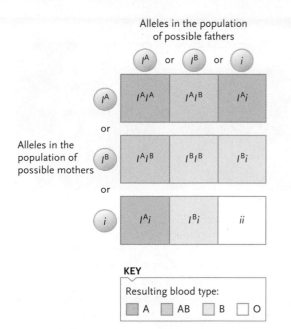

Figure 11.15
Inheritance of the blood types of the human ABO blood group. Note that although there are three possible alleles in the population, each individual parent carries only two.

11.2d In Epistasis, Genes Interact, with the Activity of One Gene Influencing the Activity of Another Gene

The genetic characters discussed so far in this chapter, such as flower colour, seed shape, and the blood types of the ABO group, are all produced by the alleles of single genes, with each gene functioning on its own. This is not the case for every gene. In **epistasis** (*epi* = on or over; *stasis* = standing or stopping), genes interact, with one or more alleles of a gene at one locus inhibiting or masking the effects of one or more alleles of a gene at a different locus. The result of epistasis is that some expected phenotypes do not appear among offspring.

Labrador retrievers (Labs) may have black, chocolate brown, or yellow fur **(Figure 11.16)**. The different colours result from variations in the amount and distribution in hairs of a brownish black pigment called melanin. One gene, coding for an enzyme involved in melanin production, determines how much melanin is produced. The dominant *B* allele of this gene produces black fur colour in *BB* or *Bb* Labs; less pigment is produced in *bb* dogs, which are chocolate brown. However, another gene at a different locus determines whether the black or chocolate colour appears at all, by controlling the deposition of pigment in hairs. A dominant allele *E* of this second gene permits pigment deposition, so that the black colour in *BB* or *Bb* individuals, or the chocolate colour in *bb* individuals, actually appears in the fur. Pigment deposition is almost completely blocked in homozygous recessive *ee* individuals, so the fur lacks melanin and has a yellow colour whether the genotype for the *B* gene is *BB*, *Bb*, or *bb*. Thus, the *E* gene is epistatic to the *B* gene (that is, *E* and *B* interact).

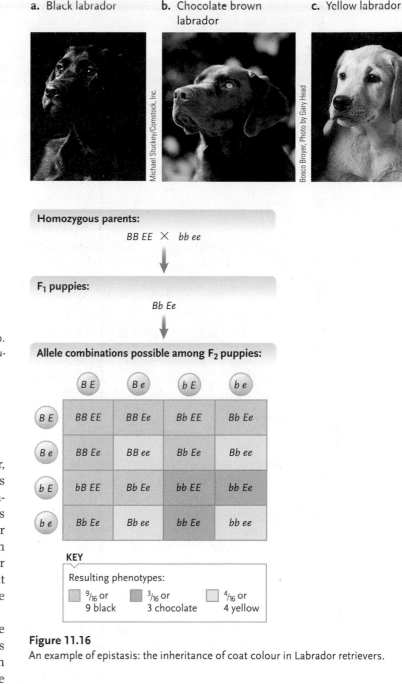

Figure 11.16
An example of epistasis: the inheritance of coat colour in Labrador retrievers.

Epistasis by the *E* gene eliminates some of the expected classes from crosses among Labs. Rather than two separate classes, as would be expected from a dihybrid cross without epistasis, the *BB ee, Bb ee, bB ee,* and *bb ee* genotypes produce a single yellow phenotype, giving the distribution: 9/16 black, 3/16 chocolate, and 4/16 yellow. That is, the ratio is 9:3:4 instead of the expected 9:3:3:1 ratio. Many other dihybrid crosses that involve epistatic interactions produce distributions that differ from the expected 9:3:3:1 ratio.

In human biology, researchers believe that gene interactions and epistasis are common. The current thinking is that epistasis is an important factor in determining an individual's susceptibility to common human diseases. That is, the different degrees of susceptibility are the result of different gene interactions

a. Students at Brigham Young University, arranged according to height

b. Actual distribution of individuals in the photo according to height

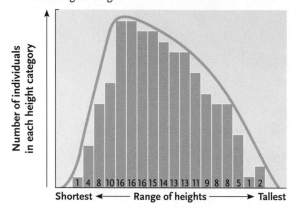

Number of individuals in each height category

1 4 8 10 16 16 16 15 14 13 13 11 9 8 8 5 1 2

Shortest ← Range of heights → Tallest

c. Idealized bell-shaped curve for a population that displays continuous variation in a trait

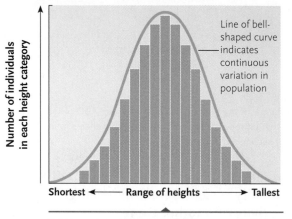

Number of individuals in each height category

Line of bell-shaped curve indicates continuous variation in population

Shortest ← Range of heights → Tallest

If the sample in the photo included more individuals, the distribution would more closely approach this ideal.

Figure 11.17
Continuous variation in height due to polygenic inheritance.

in the individuals. A specific example is insulin resistance, a disorder in which muscle, fat, and liver cells do not use insulin correctly, with the result that glucose and insulin levels become high in the blood. This disorder is believed to be determined by several genes often interacting with one another.

11.2e In Polygenic Inheritance, a Character Is Controlled by the Common Effects of Several Genes

Some characters follow a pattern of inheritance in which there is a more or less even gradation of types, forming a continuous distribution, rather than "on" or "off" (discontinuous) effects such as the production of purple or white flowers in pea plants. For example, in the human population, people range from short to tall, in a continuous distribution of gradations in height between limits of about 1 and 2 metres. Typically, a continuous distribution of this type is the result of **polygenic inheritance**, in which several to many different genes contribute to the same character. Other characters that undertake a similar continuous distribution include skin colour and body weight in humans, ear length in corn, seed colour in wheat, and colour spotting in mice. These characters are also known as *quantitative traits*.

Polygenic inheritance can be detected by defining classes of a variation, such as human body height of 180 cm in one class, 181 cm in the next class, 182 cm in the next class, and so on. The number of individuals in each class is then plotted as a graph. If the plot produces a bell-shaped curve, with fewer individuals at the extremes and the greatest numbers clustered around the midpoint, it is a good indication that the trait is quantitative **(Figure 11.17)**.

Polygenic inheritance is often modified by the environment. For example, height in humans is not the result of genetics alone. Poor nutrition during infancy and childhood is one environmental factor that can limit growth and prevent individuals from reaching the height expected from genetic inheritance; good nutrition can have the opposite effect. Thus, the average young adult in Japan today is several inches taller than the average adult in the 1930s, when nutrition was poorer. Similarly, individuals who live in cloudy, northern or southern climates usually have lighter skin colour than individuals with the same genotype who live in sunny climates.

At first glance, the effects of polygenic inheritance might appear to support the idea that the characteristics of parents are blended in their offspring. Commonly, people believe that the children in a family with one tall and one short parent will be of intermediate

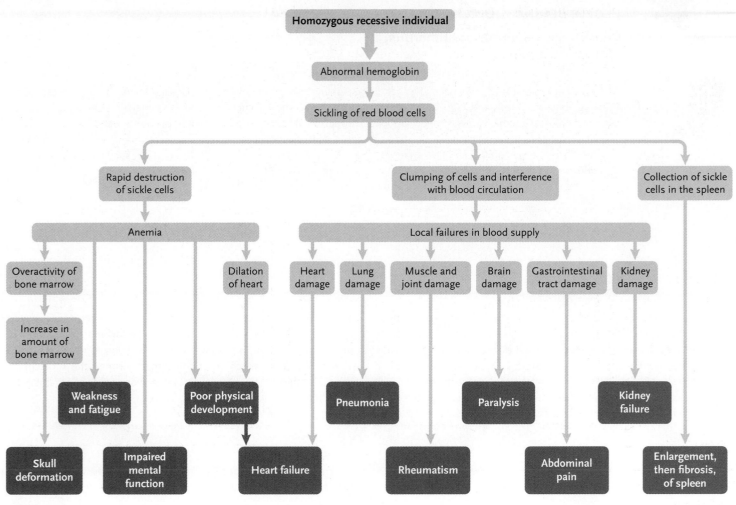

Figure 11.18

Pleiotropy, as demonstrated by the wide-ranging, multiple effects of the single mutant allele responsible for sickle cell disease.

height. Although the children of such parents are most likely to be of intermediate height, careful genetic analysis of many such families shows that their offspring actually range over a continuum from short to tall, forming a typical bell-shaped curve. Careful analysis of the inheritance of skin colour produces the same result: although the skin colour of children is most often intermediate between that of the parents, a typical bell-shaped distribution is obtained in which some children at the extremes are lighter or darker than either parent. Thus, genetic analysis does not support the idea of blending or even mixing of parental traits in polygenic characteristics such as body size or skin colour.

11.2f In Pleiotropy, Two or More Characters Are Affected by a Single Gene

In **pleiotropy**, single genes affect more than one character of an organism. For example, sickle cell disease (see earlier discussion) is caused by a recessive allele of a single gene that affects hemoglobin structure and function. However, the altered hemoglobin, the primary phenotypic change of the sickle cell mutation, leads to blood vessel blockage, which can damage many tissues and organs in the body and affect many body functions, producing such wide-ranging symptoms as fatigue, abdominal pain, heart failure, paralysis, and pneumonia **(Figure 11.18)**. Physicians recognize these wide-ranging pleiotropic effects as symptoms of sickle cell disease.

The next chapter describes additional patterns of inheritance that were not anticipated by Mendel, including the effects of recombination during meiosis. These additional patterns also extend, rather than contradict, Mendel's fundamental principles.

STUDY BREAK

1. Distinguish between alleles that are incompletely dominant and those that are codominant.
2. How might you know that a trait is polygenic?

Charles Scriver, Professor Emeritus, McGill University

A "paradigm" is a particular way of thinking about a subject, and as Charles Scriver began his career, the way of thinking about genetic disease was beginning to shift. The old paradigm of "nothing can be done" was giving way to an understanding that disease phenotypes have both a genetic *and* an environmental component. Through a combination of basic research, public education, newborn screening programs, and on-line archiving of hundreds of mutations, Dr. Scriver brought this paradigm shift to our understanding of the underlying biology, treatment, and prevention of diseases such as phenylketonuria, vitamin D–deficient rickets, Tay–Sachs disease, and thalassemia.

Unanswered Questions

The determination of genetic principles by Mendel and later geneticists involved crosses of plants and animals with visible traits, that is, phenotypes that could be seen by visual examination. Examples are smooth and wrinkled seeds of garden peas and red and white eyes of fruit flies. Until recently, it was impossible to determine the biochemical or molecular basis for traits. Even now, we do not know the molecular basis for most of the traits mentioned in this chapter, or for many others. For example, the molecular reason for the dwarf (short stem) phenotype of Mendel's peas was determined only as recently as the 1990s. Similar research is ongoing to determine the molecular basis for other visible genetic traits in a wide variety of organisms, including humans.

Review

Go to CENGAGENOW™ at http://hed.nelson.com/ to access quizzing, animations, exercises, articles, and personalized homework help.

11.1 The Beginnings of Genetics: Mendel's Garden Peas

- Mendel made a good choice of experimental organism in that garden peas offered simple cultivation, clearly defined, true-breeding, characters (such as flower colour or seed shape), and an opportunity to make controlled pollinations.

- By analyzing his results quantitatively, Mendel showed that traits are passed from parents to offspring as hereditary factors (now called genes and alleles) in predictable ratios and combinations, disproving the notion of blended inheritance (see Figures 11.3, 11.4, and 11.5).

- Mendel realized that his results with crosses that involve single characters (monohybrid crosses) could be explained if three hypotheses were true: (1) the genes that govern genetic characters occur in pairs in individuals; (2) if different alleles of a gene are present in a pair within an individual, one allele is dominant over the other; and (3) the two alleles of a gene segregate and enter gametes single (see Figures 10.5 and 10.7).

- Mendel confirmed his hypotheses by a testcross between an F1 heterozygote and a homozygous recessive parent. This type of testcross is still used to determine whether an individual is homozygous or heterozygous for a dominant allele (see Figure 11.8).

- To explain the results of his crosses with individuals showing differences in two characters—dihybrid crosses—Mendel added an additional hypothesis: the alleles of the genes that govern the two characters segregate independently during formation of gametes (see Figure 11.9). That is, the dihybrid cross $AaBa \times AaBa$ can be treated as two separate monohybrid crosses: $Aa \times Aa$ and $Bb \times$ Bb. The monohybrid crosses would give phenotypic ratios of 3/4 $A\_\_$: 1/4 aa and 3/4 $B\_\_$: 1/4 bb, respectively. The standard dihybrid ratios arise from combinations of these monohybrid ratios. That is, 9/16 $A\_\_$ $B\_\_$ results from 3/4 $A\_\_ \times$ 3/4 $B\_\_$, 3/16 aa $B\_\_$ results from 1/4 $aa \times$ 3/4 $B\_\_$, and so on.

- Walter Sutton was the first person to note the similarities between the inheritance of genes and the behaviour of chromosomes in meiosis and fertilization. These parallels made it obvious that genes and alleles are carried on the chromosomes, and are called the chromosome theory of inheritance (see Figure 11.10).

- A locus is the particular site where a given gene is found on the chromosomes of an organism (see Figure 11.11). An allele is just a particular version of the DNA sequence of a gene. Therefore, if an individual is heterozygous for the stem length gene of Mendel's peas, it would have a T allele on one homologue and a t allele on the other. These two alleles would each be located at exactly the same locus on their respective chromosomes.

11.2 Later Modifications and Additions to Mendel's Hypotheses

- Incomplete dominance arises when, in a heterozygote, the activity of one allele is insufficient to compensate for the inactivity of another. Codominance arises when, in a heterozygote, both alleles are equally active. In both cases, the phenotype of heterozygotes is different from that of either homozygote (see Figure 11.13).

- Many genes may have multiple alleles if all the individuals in a population are taken into account. However, any diploid individual in a population has only two alleles of these genes, which are inherited and passed on according to Mendel's principles (see Figures 11.14 and 11.15).

- In epistasis, genes interact, with one or more alleles of one locus inhibiting or masking the effects of one or more alleles at a different locus. The result is that some expected phenotypes do not appear among offspring (see Figure 11.16).

- A character that is subject to polygenic inheritance shows a more or less continuous variation from one extreme to another. Plotting the distribution of such characters among individuals typically produces a bell-shaped curve (see Figure 11.17).

- In pleiotropy, one gene affects more than one character of an organism (see Figure 11.18).

Questions

Self-Test Questions

1. The dominant C allele of a gene that controls colour in corn produces kernels with colour; plants homozygous for a recessive c allele of this gene have colourless or white kernels. What kinds of gametes, and in what proportions, would be produced by the plants in the following crosses? What seed colour, and in what proportions, would be expected in the offspring of the crosses?
   a. $CC \times Cc$ b. $Cc \times Cc$ c. $Cc \times cc$

2. In peas, the allele T produces tall plants and the allele t produces dwarf plants. The T allele is dominant to t. If a tall plant is crossed with a dwarf, the offspring are distributed about equally between tall and dwarf plants. What are the genotypes of the parents?

3. The ability of humans to taste the bitter chemical phenylthiocarbamide (PTC) is a genetic trait. People with at least one copy of the normal, dominant allele of the PTC gene can taste PTC; those who are homozygous for a mutant, recessive allele cannot taste it. Could two parents able to taste PTC have a nontaster child? Could nontaster parents have a child able to taste PTC? A pair of taster parents, both of whom had one parent able to taste PTC and one nontaster parent, are expecting their first child. What is the chance that the child will be able to taste PTC? Unable to taste PTC? Suppose the first child is a nontaster. What is the chance that their second child will also be unable to taste PTC?

4. One gene has the alleles A and a; another gene has the alleles B and b. For each of the following genotypes, what types of gametes will be produced, and in what proportions, if the two gene pairs assort independently?
   a. $AA\ BB$ c. $Aa\ bb$
   b. $Aa\ BB$ d. $Aa\ Bb$

5. What genotypes, and in what frequencies, will be present in the offspring from the following matings?
   a. $AA\ BB \times aa\ BB$ c. $Aa\ Bb \times aa\ bb$
   b. $Aa\ BB \times AA\ Bb$ d. $Aa\ Bb \times Aa\ Bb$

6. In addition to the two genes in problem 4, assume you now study a third independently assorting gene that has the alleles C and c. For each of the following genotypes, indicate what types of gametes will be produced:
   a. $AA\ BB\ CC$ c. $Aa\ BB\ Cc$
   b. $Aa\ BB\ cc$ d. $Aa\ Bb\ Cc$

7. A man is homozygous dominant for alleles at 10 different genes that assort independently. How many genotypically different types of sperm cells can he produce? A woman is homozygous recessive for the alleles of 8 of these 10 genes, but she is heterozygous for the other 2 genes. How many genotypically different types of eggs can she produce? What hypothesis can you suggest to describe the relationship between the number of different possible gametes and the number of heterozygous and homozygous genes that are present?

8. In guinea pigs, an allele for rough fur (R) is dominant over an allele for smooth fur (r); an allele for black coat (B) is dominant

over that for white (b). You have an animal with rough, black fur. What cross would you use to determine whether the animal is homozygous for these traits? What phenotype would you expect in the offspring if the animal is homozygous?

9. You cross a lima bean plant from a variety that breeds true for green pods with another lima bean from a variety that breeds true for yellow pods. You note that all the F_1 plants have green pods. These green-pod F_1 plants, when crossed, yield 675 plants with green pods and 217 with yellow pods. How many genes probably control pod colour in this experiment? Give the alleles letter designations. Which is dominant?

10. Some recessive alleles have such a detrimental effect that they are lethal when present in both chromosomes of a pair. Homozygous recessives cannot survive and die at some point during embryonic development. Suppose that the allele r is lethal in the homozygous rr condition. What genotypic ratios would you expect among the living offspring of the following crosses?
    a. $RR \times Rr$
    b. $Rr \times Rr$

11. In garden peas, the genotypes GG or Gg produce green pods and gg produces yellow pods; TT or Tt plants are tall and tt plants are dwarfed; RR or Rr produce round seeds and rr produces wrinkled seeds. If a plant of a true-breeding, tall variety with green pods and round seeds is crossed with a plant of a true-breeding, dwarf variety with yellow pods and wrinkled seeds, what phenotypes are expected, and in what ratios, in the F_1 generation? What phenotypes, and in what ratios, are expected if F_1 individuals are crossed?

12. In chickens, feathered legs are produced by a dominant allele F. Another allele f of the same gene produces featherless legs. The dominant allele P of a gene at a different locus produces pea combs; a recessive allele p of this gene causes single combs. A breeder makes the following crosses with birds 1, 2, 3, and 4; all parents have feathered legs and pea combs:

Cross	Offspring
1×2	all feathered, pea comb
1×3	3/4 feathered; 1/4 featherless, all pea comb
1×4	9/16 feathered, pea comb; 3/16 featherless, pea comb; 3/16 feathered, single comb; 1/16 featherless, single comb

    What are the genotypes of the four birds?

13. A mixup in a hospital ward caused a mother with O and MN blood types to think that a baby given to her really belonged to someone else. Tests in the hospital showed that the doubting mother was able to taste PTC (see problem 3). The baby given to her had O and MN blood types and had no reaction when the bitter PTC chemical was placed on its tongue. The mother had four other children with the following blood types and tasting abilities for PTC:
    a. Type A and MN blood, taster
    b. Type B and N blood, nontaster
    c. Type A and M blood, taster
    d. Type A and N blood, taster

Without knowing the father's blood types and tasting ability, can you determine whether the child is really hers? (Assume that all her children have the same father.)

14. In cats, the genotype *AA* produces tabby fur colour; *Aa* is also a tabby, and *aa* is black. Another gene at a different locus is epistatic to the gene for fur colour. When present in its dominant *W* form (*WW* or *Ww*), this gene blocks the formation of fur colour and all the offspring are white; *ww* individuals develop normal fur colour. What fur colours, and in what proportions, would you expect from the cross *Aa Ww* × *Aa Ww*?

15. Having malformed hands with shortened fingers is a dominant trait controlled by a single gene; people who are homozygous for the recessive allele have normal hands and fingers. Having woolly hair is a dominant trait controlled by a different gene; homozygous recessive individuals have normal, nonwoolly hair. Suppose a woman with normal hands and nonwoolly hair marries a man who has malformed hands and woolly hair. Their first child has normal hands and nonwoolly hair. What are the genotypes of the mother, the father, and the child? If this couple has a second child, what is the probability that it will have normal hands and woolly hair?

Questions for Discussion

1. The eyes of brown-eyed people are not alike but rather vary considerably in shade and pattern. What do you think causes these differences?

2. Explain how individuals of an organism that are phenotypically alike can produce different ratios of progeny phenotypes.

3. ABO blood type tests can be used to exclude paternity. Suppose a defendant who is the alleged father of a child takes a blood type test and the results do not exclude him as the father. Do the results indicate that he is the father? What arguments could a lawyer make based on the test results to exclude the defendant from being the father? (Assume the tests were performed correctly.)

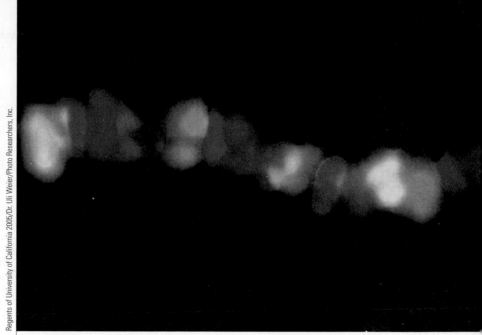

Fluorescent probes bound to specific sequences along human chromosome 10 (light micrograph). New ways of mapping chromosome structure yield insights into the inheritance of normal and abnormal traits.

Regents of University of California 2005/Dr. Uli Weier/Photo Researchers, Inc.

12 Genes, Chromosomes, and Human Genetics

WHY IT MATTERS

Imagine being 10 years old and trapped in a body that each day becomes more shrivelled, frail, and old. You are just tall enough to peer over the top of the kitchen counter, and you weigh less than 16 kilograms. Already you are bald, and you probably have only a few more years to live. But if you are like Mickey Hayes or Fransie Geringer **(Figure 12.1, p. 250),** you still have not lost your courage or your childlike curiosity about life. Like them, you still play, laugh, and celebrate birthdays.

Progeria, the premature aging that afflicts Mickey and Fransie, is caused by a genetic error that occurs once in every 8 million human births. The error is perpetuated each time cells of the embryo—then of the child—duplicate their chromosomes and divide. The outcome of that rare mistake is an acceleration of aging and a greatly reduced life expectancy.

Progeria affects both boys and girls. Usually, symptoms begin to appear before the age of 2. The rate of body growth declines to abnormally low levels. Skin becomes thinner, muscles become flaccid, and limb bones start to degenerate. Children with progeria never reach puberty, and most die in their early teens from a stroke or heart attack

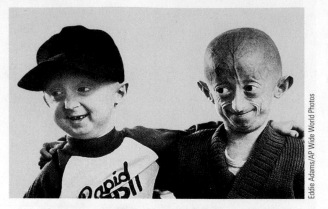

Figure 12.1
Two boys, both younger than 10, who have progeria, a genetic disorder characterized by accelerated aging and extremely reduced life expectancy.

brought on by hardening of the arteries, a condition typical of advanced age.

The plight of Mickey and Fransie provides a telling and tragic example of the dramatic effects that gene defects can have on living organisms. We are the products of our genes, and the characteristics of each individual, from humans to pine trees to protozoa, depend on the combination of genes, alleles, and chromosomes inherited from its parents, as well as on environmental effects. This chapter delves deeply into genes and the role of chromosomes in inheritance.

12.1 Genetic Linkage and Recombination

In his historic experiments, Gregor Mendel carried out crosses with seven different characters in garden peas, controlled by seven different genes. He found that his observations from crosses were consistent with the hypothesis that each of the genes assorted independently of all of the others in the formation of gametes. If Mendel had extended his study to additional characters, he would have found exceptions to this principle. This should not be surprising because an organism has far more genes than chromosomes. Conceptually, then, chromosomes contain many genes, with each gene at a particular locus. Genes located on different chromosomes assort independently in gamete formation because the two chromosomes behave independently of one another during meiosis. Genes located on the same chromosome may be inherited together in genetic crosses—that is, not assort independently—because the chromosome is inherited as a single physical entity in meiosis. Genes on the same chromosome are known as **linked genes**, and the phenomenon is called **linkage**.

12.1a The Principles of Linkage and Recombination Were Determined with *Drosophila*

In the early part of the twentieth century, Thomas H. Morgan and coworkers at Columbia University used the fruit fly, *Drosophila melanogaster*, as a model organism to investigate Mendel's principles in animals. (See more information about Drosophila as a model research organism in The Chemical and Physical Foundations of Biology pages.) Groups of genes that tended to assort together in crosses were believed to be carried on the same chromosome. It was Morgan's group, and an undergraduate student named Alfred Sturtevant working in the lab at the time, who developed the insight that resulted in the construction of the first genetic map showing the relative order of genes on a chromosome as well as a measure of the distance separating them. These brilliant and far-reaching hypotheses were typical of Morgan, who founded genetics research in the United States, developed *Drosophila* as a research organism, and made discoveries that were likely as significant to the development of genetics as those of Mendel.

Although it is tempting to assume that genetic maps could be made simply by looking down a microscope, finding the genes, and measuring the distance between them, the technology to do this was simply not available. Instead, Morgan's group used an indirect measure of "distance." They reasoned that genes sitting relatively far apart on a chromosome would be more likely to be separated from one another during meiotic crossing-over than genes lying closer together. Figure 10.14 illustrates this process of recombination occurring in the space separating two genes as they appear on chromosomes paired during meiosis. Obviously, if recombination is to be used as a measure of distance separating genes, it must be detectable. That is why the organism used in Figure 10.14 is heterozygous for all genes; the chromatids resulting from recombination are then different from the original, nonrecombinant, ones and can be identified. Following meiosis I and II, each of the four different chromatids will become a chromosome in a separate gamete (review the basic mechanisms of meiosis in Figure 10.10). Which chromosome, recombinant or not, is carried by a given gamete is actually revealed only in offspring resulting from fertilization with a homozygous recessive gamete. That is why, in the following cross, which was originally done by Morgan in 1911, you will notice that one parent is heterozygous and the other is homozygous recessive.

To understand the following crosses, you need to learn to work with the genetic symbolism developed by Morgan instead of the *A/a* system used in Chapter 11. Although *Drosophila* notation might appear counterintuitive at first, understanding a few basic principles will help you see the logic behind it. First, note that geneticists working with fruit flies have all agreed on a "normal," or "wild-type," genotype; any change from wild type is, by definition, a mutant. Mutant alleles are named based on the phenotype of the organism that expresses them. The names for dominant mutant alleles are written in uppercase, whereas those for recessive mutant alleles are written in lowercase.

For example, a dominant mutant allele transforming an **antenna** into a leg is called Antennapedia (Antp), whereas a recessive mutant allele altering eye colour is called vermilion (v). The notation for a wild-type allele is always made by simply adding a superscripted plus (+) sign to the mutant allele notation. You know you understand this system if you agree that Antp+ is a *recessive* allele giving a normal phenotype when homozygous.

Morgan began a specific breeding program using true-breeding fruit flies with normal red eyes and normal wing length, genotype $pr^+pr^+ vg^+vg^+$, along with a true-breeding fly with the recessive traits of purple eyes and vestigial (that is, short and crumpled) wings, genotype $prpr\ vgvg$ (**Figure 12.2, p. 252**, step 1).

The F_1 (first-generation) offspring were all dihybrid $pr^+pr\ vg^+vg$, and because of the dominance of the wild-type alleles, they had red eyes and normal wings (see Figure 12.2, step 2). Morgan then selected these wild-type F_1 females as the dihybrid parent and mated them to homozygous recessive males (with purple eyes and vestigial wings) as the testcross parent. If the purple and vestigial genes were carried on different chromosomes, Mendel's principle of independent assortment (see Section 11.1) would predict four classes of phenotypes in the offspring, in the approximate 1:1:1:1 ratio of red eyes, normal wings: purple, vestigial: red, vestigial: purple, normal. Given over 2800 offspring from several females, about 700 should have been in each class. However, Morgan observed two types of progeny in which the counts were much higher than 700 (red, normal and purple, vestigial) and two types with counts that were much less (red, vestigial, and purple, normal (see Figure 12.2, step 4).

Morgan's hypothesis to explain this non-Mendelian distribution is illustrated in **Figure 12.3 (p. 253)**. He suggested that the two genes are linked genetically—physically associated on the same chromosome. That is, *pr* and *vg* are linked genes. He further hypothesized that the behaviour of these linked genes is explained by *chromosome recombination* during meiosis. Furthermore, he proposed that the frequency of this recombination is a function of the distance between linked genes.

The $pr^+pr\ vg^+vg$ F_1 dihybrid parents produce four types of gametes (see Figure 12.3, step 1). The two parental gametes, $pr^+\ vg^+$ and $pr\ vg$, are generated by simple segregation of the chromosomes during meiosis without any crossing-over (recombination) between the genes. The two recombinant gametes, $pr^+\ vg$ and $pr\ vg^+$, result from crossing-over between the homologous chromatids when they are paired in prophase I of meiosis (see Figures 10.10 and 10.14). The offspring of the cross are produced by fusion of each of these four gametes with a *pr vg* gamete produced by the *prpr vgvg* male parent. The phenotypes of the offspring directly reflect the genotypes of the gametes produced by the dihybrid parent. Students of genetics sometimes assume that the wild-type and purple vestigial offspring

are called "parental" because they *look like* the parents. However, the term "parental" actually refers to genotype, not phenotype; parental offspring are the ones that inherit chromosomes unchanged from their dihybrid parent. Parental offspring do not always resemble the parents of the cross. Although Morgan could not look down a microscope and measure the distance between genes directly, he could look down a microscope and identify recombinant offspring from dihybrid testcrosses. Thus, the relative frequency of recombinant progeny became his "measure" of the distance separating genes. The example in Figure 12.3 reveals that purple eyes and vestigial wings are on the same chromosome separated by a **recombination frequency** of 10.7%.

12.1b Recombination Frequency Can Be Used to Map Chromosomes

The recombination frequency of 10.7% for the *pr* and *vg* genes of *Drosophila* means that 10.7% of the gametes originating from the $pr^+pr\ vg^+vg$ parent contained recombined chromosomes. That recombination frequency is characteristic for those two genes. In other crosses that involve linked genes, Morgan found that the recombination frequency was characteristic of the two genes involved, varying from less than 1 to 50% (see the next section).

From these observations, Alfred Sturtevant realized that the variation in recombination frequencies could be used as a means of mapping genes on chromosomes. Sturtevant himself later recalled his lightbulb moment:

> I suddenly realized that the variations in the strength of linkage already attributed by Morgan to difference in the spatial separation of the gene offered the possibility of determining sequence in the linear dimensions of a chromosome. I went home and spent most of the night (to the neglect of my other homework) producing the first chromosome map.

Therefore, recombination frequencies can be used to make a **linkage map** of a chromosome showing the relative locations of genes. For example, assume that the three genes *a*, *b*, and *c* are carried together on the same chromosome. Crosses reveal a 9.6% recombination frequency for *a* and *b*, an 8% recombination frequency for *a* and *c*, and a 2% recombination frequency for *b* and *c*. These frequencies allow the genes to be arranged in only one sequence on the chromosomes as follows:

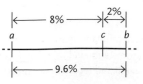

Figure 12.2
Evidence for gene linkage.

QUESTION: Do the purple-eye vestigial-wing genes of *Drosophila* assort independently?

EXPERIMENT: Morgan crossed true-breeding wild-type flies with red eyes and normal wings with purple-eyed, vestigial-winged flies. The F₁ dihybrids were all wild-type in phenotype. Next he crossed the F₁ dihybrid flies with purple-eyed, vestigial-winged flies (this is a testcross) and analyzed the phenotypes of the progeny.

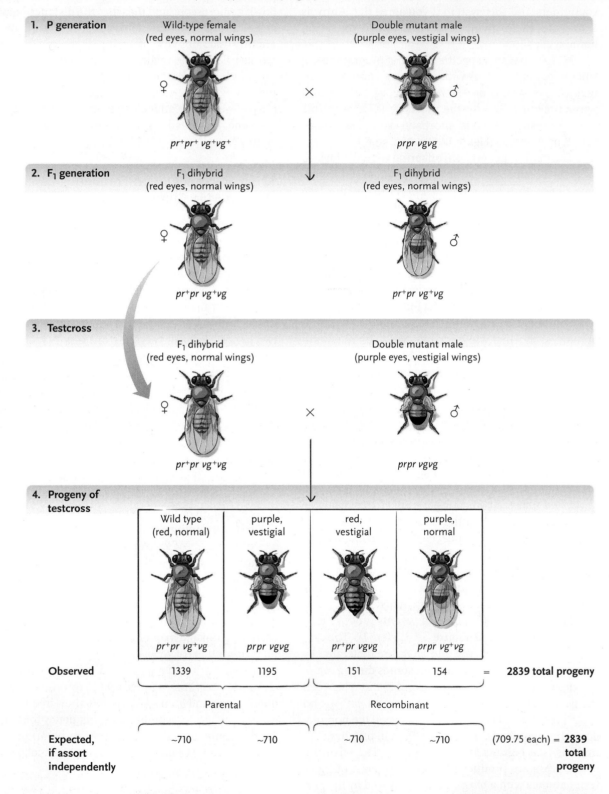

1. **P generation**
   Wild-type female (red eyes, normal wings) ♀ $pr^+pr^+\ vg^+vg^+$
   ×
   Double mutant male (purple eyes, vestigial wings) ♂ $prpr\ vgvg$

2. **F₁ generation**
   F₁ dihybrid (red eyes, normal wings) ♀ $pr^+pr\ vg^+vg$
   F₁ dihybrid (red eyes, normal wings) ♂ $pr^+pr\ vg^+vg$

3. **Testcross**
   F₁ dihybrid (red eyes, normal wings) ♀ $pr^+pr\ vg^+vg$
   ×
   Double mutant male (purple eyes, vestigial wings) ♂ $prpr\ vgvg$

4. **Progeny of testcross**

	Wild type (red, normal)	purple, vestigial	red, vestigial	purple, normal	
	$pr^+pr\ vg^+vg$	$prpr\ vgvg$	$pr^+pr\ vgvg$	$prpr\ vg^+vg$	
Observed	1339	1195	151	154	= **2839 total progeny**
	Parental		Recombinant		
Expected, if assort independently	~710	~710	~710	~710	(709.75 each) = **2839 total progeny**

RESULTS: 2534 of the testcross progeny flies were parental, wild-type and purple, vestigial, while 305 of the progeny were recombinant red, vestigial and purple, normal. If the genes assorted independently, the expectation is a 1:1:1:1 ratio for testcross progeny: approximately 1420 of both parental and recombinant progeny.

CONCLUSION: The purple-eye and vestigial-wing genes do not assort independently. The simplest alternative is that the two genes are linked on the same chromosome.

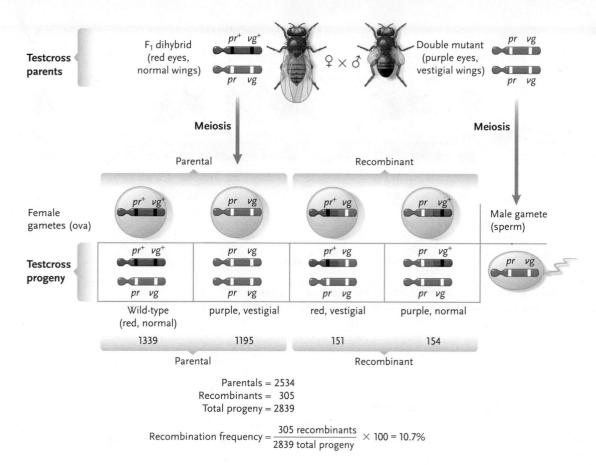

Testcross parents

F₁ dihybrid (red eyes, normal wings) pr^+ vg^+ / pr vg ♀ × ♂ Double mutant (purple eyes, vestigial wings) pr vg / pr vg

Meiosis Meiosis

Parental Recombinant

Female gametes (ova) pr^+ vg^+ pr vg pr^+ vg pr vg^+ Male gamete (sperm) pr vg

Testcross progeny

Wild-type (red, normal)	purple, vestigial	red, vestigial	purple, normal
1339	1195	151	154

Parental Recombinant

Parentals = 2534
Recombinants = 305
Total progeny = 2839

$$\text{Recombination frequency} = \frac{305 \text{ recombinants}}{2839 \text{ total progeny}} \times 100 = 10.7\%$$

You will note that the *a–b* recombination frequency does not exactly equal the sum of the *a–c* and *c–b* recombination frequencies. This is because genes farther apart on a chromosome are more likely to have more than one crossover occur between them. Whereas a single crossover between two genes gives recombinants, a double crossover (two single crossovers occurring in the same meiosis) between two genes gives parentals (and is therefore undetectable and would not be counted). You can see this simply by drawing single and double crossovers between two genes on a piece of paper. In our example, the undetectable double crossovers that occur between *a* and *b* have slightly decreased the recombination frequency between these two genes.

Using this method, Sturtevant created the first linkage map showing the arrangement of six genes on the *Drosophila* X chromosome. (A partial linkage map of a *Drosophila* chromosome is shown in **Figure 12.4, p. 254.**)

Since the time of Morgan, many *Drosophila* genes and those of other eukaryotic organisms widely used for genetic research, including *Neurospora* (a fungus), yeast, maize (corn), and the mouse, have been mapped using the same approach. Recombination frequencies, together with the results of other techniques, have been used to create linkage maps of the locations of genes in the DNA of prokaryotes such as the human intestinal bacterium *Escherichia coli*.

The unit of a linkage map, called a **map unit** (abbreviated mu), is equivalent to a recombination frequency of 1%. The map unit is also called the **centimorgan** in honor of Morgan's discoveries of linkage and recombination. Map units are not absolute physical distances in micrometres or nanometres; rather, they are *relative*, showing the positions of genes with respect to each other. One of the reasons that the units are relative and not absolute distances is that the frequency of crossing-over varies to some extent from one position to another on chromosomes.

In recent years, the linkage maps of a number of species have been supplemented by DNA sequencing of whole genomes, which shows the precise physical locations of genes on chromosomes.

12.1c Widely Separated Linked Genes Assort Independently

Genes can be so widely separated on a chromosome that recombination is likely to occur at some point between them in every cell undergoing meiosis. When this is the case, the genes assort independently even though they are on the same chromosome. The map distance separating them will be 50 mu.

To understand why this is, first recall Figure 10.14 showing that a recombination event in a given cell creates 2 recombinant and 2 nonrecombinant chromatids. Next, imagine 100 meiocytes going through meiosis as usual to yield 400 gametes. If a recombination event occurred in the space separating 2 given genes in 10 of those cells, then 20 recombinant chromatids would be produced during prophase I. Twenty gametes would eventually receive recombinant chromosomes, and

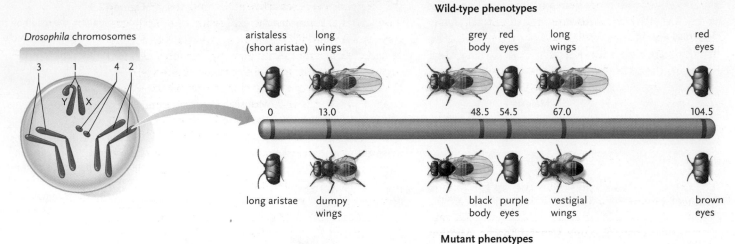

Wild-type phenotypes

Drosophila chromosomes

aristaless (short aristae) | long wings | grey body | red eyes | long wings | red eyes

0   13.0   48.5   54.5   67.0   104.5

long aristae | dumpy wings | black body | purple eyes | vestigial wings | brown eyes

Mutant phenotypes

Figure 12.4

Relative map locations of several genes on chromosome 2 of *Drosophila*, as determined by recombination frequencies. For each gene, the diagram shows the normal or "wild-type" phenotype on the top and the mutant phenotype on the bottom. Mutant alleles at two different locations alter wing structure, one producing the dumpy wing and the other the vestigial wing phenotypes; the normal allele at these locations results in normal long-wing structure. Mutant alleles at two different locations also alter eye colour.

20/400 = 5% of the total testcross progeny would be recombinant. We would conclude that these genes are 5 mu apart. Now assume that a recombination event occurs in the space separating two genes in *every one of the 100* cells going through meiosis. Two hundred recombinant offspring would result out of the total of 400; 50% would be recombinants; 50 mu would separate the genes.

Linkage between such widely separated genes can still be detected, however, by testing their linkage to one or more genes that lie between them. For example, the genes *a* and *c* in **Figure 12.5** are located so far apart that

they assort independently and show no linkage. However, crosses show that *a* and *b* are 23 mu apart (recombination frequency of 23%), and crosses that show *b* and *c* are 34 mu apart. Therefore, *a* and *c* must also be linked and carried on the same chromosome at 23 + 34 = 57 mu apart. Obviously, we could not see a recombination frequency of 57% in testcross progeny because the maximum frequency of recombinants is 50%.

We now know that some of the genes Mendel studied are actually on the same chromosome. For example, the genes for flower colour and seed colour are located on the same chromosome pair, but they are so far apart that the frequent recombination between them makes them assort independently.

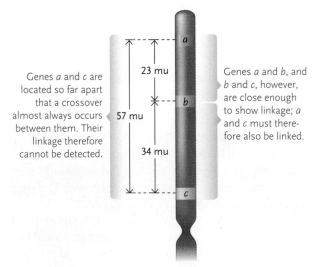

Genes *a* and *c* are located so far apart that a crossover almost always occurs between them. Their linkage therefore cannot be detected.

23 mu

57 mu

34 mu

a

b

c

Genes *a* and *b*, and *b* and *c*, however, are close enough to show linkage; *a* and *c* must therefore also be linked.

Figure 12.5

Genes far apart on the same chromosome. Genes *a* and *c* are far apart and will not show linkage, suggesting that they are on different chromosomes. However, linkage between such genes can be established by noting their linkage to another gene or genes located between them—gene *b* here.

STUDY BREAK

1. What type of cross can be used to discover whether two genes are linked or not?
2. How can two genes be on the same chromosome yet assort independently as if they were on separate chromosomes?

12.2 Sex-Linked Genes

In many organisms, one or more pairs of chromosomes are different in males and females. Genes located on these chromosomes, the *sex chromosomes*, are called **sex-linked genes**; they are inherited differently in males and females. (Note that the word *linked* in *sex-linked gene* means that the gene is on a sex chromosome, whereas the use of the term *linked* when considering two or more genes means that the genes are on the same chromosome, not necessarily a sex chromosome.) Chromosomes other than the sex chromosomes are called **autosomes**; genes on these chromosomes have the same patterns of inheritance in both sexes. In humans, chromosomes 1 to 22 are the autosomes.

12.2a Females Are XX and Males Are XY in Both Humans and Fruit Flies

In most species with sex chromosomes, females have two copies of a chromosome known as the **X chromosome**, forming a fully homologous XX pair, whereas males have only one X chromosome. Another chromosome, the Y chromosome, occurs in males but not in females. The Y chromosome has a short region of homology with the X chromosome that allows them to pair during meiosis. The XX human chromosome complement is shown in Figure 9.9.

Each normal gamete produced by an XX female carries an X chromosome. Half the gametes produced by an XY male carry an X chromosome and half carry a Y. When a sperm cell carrying an X chromosome fertilizes an X-bearing egg cell, the new individual develops into an XX female. Conversely, when a sperm cell carrying a Y chromosome fertilizes an X-bearing egg cell, the combination produces an XY male. The Punnet square (see **Figure 12.6**) shows that fertilization is expected to produce females and males with an equal frequency of 1/2. This expectation is closely matched in the human and *Drosophila* populations.

Other sex chromosome arrangements have been found, as in some insects with XX females and XO males (the O means there is no Y chromosome). In birds, butterflies, and some reptiles, the situation is reversed: males have a homologous pair of sex chromosomes (ZZ instead of XX), and females have the equivalent of an XY combination (ZW).

12.2b Human Sex Determination Depends on the *SRY* Gene

Although the human X and Y chromosomes are called "sex chromosomes," only a few genes they carry have any influence on sex determination or sexual function. For instance, most of the roughly 2400 known genes on the X chromosome code for phenotypes needed by both sexes, such as colour perception, blood clotting, and DNA replication. However, one gene carried on the Y chromosome, *SRY* (for sex-determining region of the Y), appears to be the "master switch" that directs development toward maleness at an early point in embryonic development.

For the first month or so of embryonic development in humans and other mammals, the rudimentary structures that give rise to reproductive organs and tissues are the same in XX or XY embryos. After 6 to 8 weeks,

the *SRY* gene becomes active in XY embryos, producing a protein that regulates the expression of other genes, thereby stimulating part of these structures to develop as testes. As a part of stimulation by hormones secreted in the developing testes and elsewhere, tissues degenerate that would otherwise develop into female structures such as the vagina and oviducts. The remaining structures develop into the penis and scrotum. In XX embryos, which do not have a copy of the *SRY* gene, development proceeds toward female reproductive structures. The rudimentary male structures degenerate in XX embryos because the hormones released by the developing testes in XY embryos are not present. Further details of the *SRY* gene and its role in human sex determination are presented in Chapter 48.

12.2c Sex-Linked Genes Were First Discovered in *Drosophila*

Since males and females have different sets of sex chromosomes, the genes carried on these chromosomes can be inherited in a distinctly non-Mendelian pattern called sex linkage. Sex linkage arises from two differences

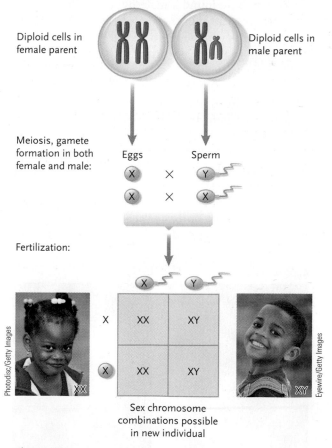

Figure 12.6

Sex chromosomes and the chromosomal basis of sex determination in humans. Females have two X chromosomes and produce gametes (eggs), all of which have the X sex chromosome. Males have one X and one Y chromosome and produce gametes, half with an X chromosome and half with a Y chromosome. Males transmit their Y chromosome to their sons, but not to their daughters. Males receive their X chromosome only from their mother.

Drosopterin

The brick red eyes of wild-type fruit flies owe their colour to a mixture of two types of pigment: bright red drosopterin and brown ommochrome. Drosopterin is the final product of a multistep biochemical pathway beginning with guanine. Mutations that alter the function of enzymes acting at different steps in this pathway result in novel eye colours such as purple, brown, or sepia.

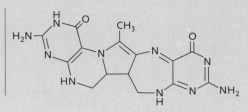

between males and females: (1) males have one X chromosome and therefore one allele for each gene on this chromosome; females have two copies of the X chromosome and therefore two alleles for all genes on the X chromosome; (2) males also have one copy of the Y chromosome and one allele for each gene on this chromosome; females have no Y chromosome and therefore no Y alleles at all. Y chromosomes are present in males but not females.

Morgan discovered sex-linked genes and their pattern of sex linkage in 1910. The story of discovery started when he found a male fly in his stocks with white eyes instead of the normal red eyes **(Figure 12.7)**. He crossed the white-eyed male with a true-breeding female with red eyes and observed that all the F_1 flies had red eyes **(Figure 12.8a)**. He concluded that the white-eye trait was recessive. Next, he allowed the F_1 flies to interbreed. Based on Mendel's principles, he expected that both male and female F_2 flies would show a 3:1 ratio of red-eyed flies to white-eyed flies. Morgan was surprised to find that all the F_2 females had red eyes, and half of the F_2 males had red eyes and half had white eyes **(Figure 12.8b)**.

Morgan hypothesized that the alleles segregating in the cross were of a gene located on the X chromosome—now termed a sex-linked gene. The white-eyed male

No children affected means => recessive

parent in the cross had the genotype X^wY: an X chromosome with a white (X^w) allele, and no other allele of that gene on the Y chromosome. The red-eyed female parent in the cross had the genotype $X^{w+}X^{w+}$: each X chromosome carries the dominant normal allele for red eyes, X^{w+}.

We can follow the alleles in this cross (see Figure 12.8a). The F_1 flies of a cross $X^{w+}X^{w+} \times X^wY$ are produced as follows. The X chromosome of the males comes from their mother; therefore, their genotype is $X^{w+}Y$, and their phenotype is red eyes. The females receive one X from each parent; therefore, their genotype is $X^{w+}X^w$, and their phenotype is red eyes due to the dominance of the X^{w+} allele.

In the F_2 generation, the females receive an X^{w+} allele from the male F_1 parent and either an X^{w+} or X^w allele from the female F_1 parent; these genotypes result in red eyes (see Figure 12.8a). The males receive their one X chromosome from the female F_1 parent, which has the genotype $X^{w+}X^w$. Therefore, F_2 males are half $X^{w+}Y$ (red eyes) and half X^wY (white eyes).

Morgan also made a *reciprocal cross* of the one just described; that is, the phenotypes were switched between the sexes. The reciprocal cross here was a white-eyed female (X^wX^w) with a red-eyed male ($X^{w+}Y$) (see Figure 12.8b). The F_1 males all had white eyes because they received the X^w-bearing chromosome from the female parent; thus, their genotype is X^wY. The F_1 females have red eyes; therefore, they are all heterozygous $X^{w+}X^w$. This result is clearly different from the cross in Figure 12.8a.

In the F_2 generation of this second cross, both male and female flies showed a 1:1 ratio of red eyes to white eyes (see Figure 12.8b). Again, this result differs markedly from that of the cross in Figure 12.8a.

In summary, Morgan's work showed that there is a distinctive pattern in the phenotypic ratios for reciprocal crosses in which the gene involved is on the X chromosome. A key indicator of this sex linkage is when all male offspring of a cross between a true-breeding mutant female and a wild-type male have the mutant phenotype. As we have seen, this occurs because a male receives his X chromosome from his female parent.

a.   b.

© Carolina Biological/Visuals Unlimited

© Terry Gleason/Carolina Biological/Visuals Unlimited

Figure 12.7

Eye colour phenotypes in *Drosophila*. **(a)** Normal, red wild-type eye colour. **(b)** Mutant white eye colour caused by a recessive allele of a sex-linked gene carried on the X chromosome.

Figure 12.8
Evidence for sex-linked genes.

QUESTION: How is the white eye gene of *Drosophila* inherited?

EXPERIMENT: Morgan crossed a white-eyed male *Drosophila* with a true-breeding female with red eyes and then crossed the F₁ flies to produce the F₂ generation. He also performed the reciprocal cross in which the phenotypes were switched in the parental flies—true-breeding white-eyed female × red-eyed male.

a. True-breeding red-eyed female × white-eyed male

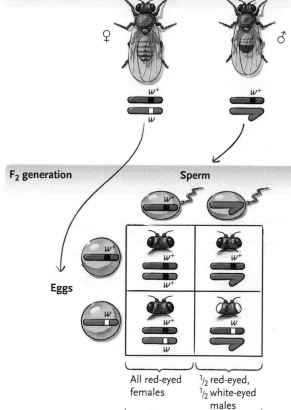

b. True-breeding white-eyed female × red-eyed male

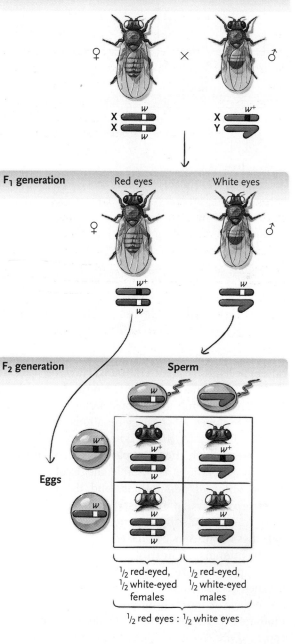

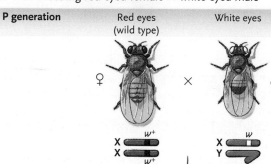

RESULTS: Differences were seen in both the F₁ and F₂ generations for the red ♀ × white ♂ and white ♀ × red ♂ crosses.

CONCLUSION: The segregation pattern for the white eye trait showed that the white eye gene is a sex-linked gene located on the X chromosome.

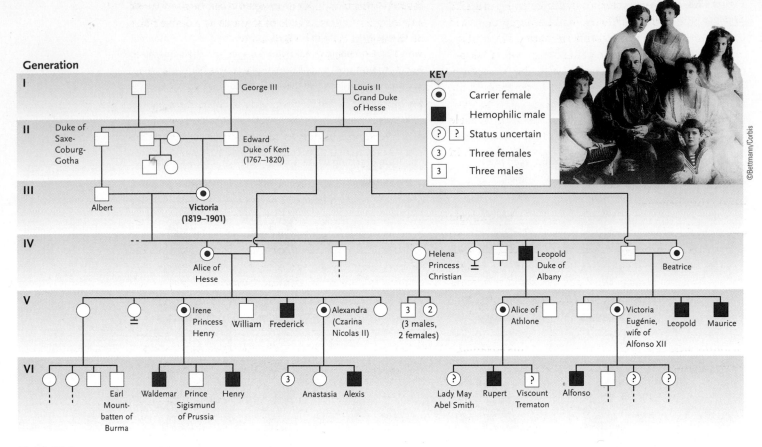

Generation

KEY
- ⊙ Carrier female
- ■ Hemophilic male
- (?) ? Status uncertain
- ③ Three females
- 3 (square) Three males

©Bettmann/Corbis

I: George III — Louis II Grand Duke of Hesse

II: Duke of Saxe-Coburg-Gotha — Edward Duke of Kent (1767–1820)

III: Albert — Victoria (1819–1901)

IV: Alice of Hesse — Helena Princess Christian — Leopold Duke of Albany — Beatrice

V: Irene Princess Henry — William — Frederick — Alexandra (Czarina Nicolas II) — 3 (3 males, 2 females) — Alice of Athlone — Victoria Eugénie, wife of Alfonso XII — Leopold — Maurice

VI: Earl Mount-batten of Burma — Waldemar — Prince Sigismund of Prussia — Henry — 3 — Anastasia — Alexis — Lady May Abel Smith — Rupert — Viscount Trematon — Alfonso

Figure 12.9

Inheritance of hemophilia in descendants of Queen Victoria of England. The photograph shows the Russian royal family in which the son, Crown Prince Alexis, had hemophilia. His mother was a carrier of the mutated gene.

12.2d Sex-Linked Genes in Humans Are Inherited as They Are in *Drosophila*

For obvious reasons, experimental genetic crosses cannot be conducted with humans. However, a similar analysis can be made by interviewing and testing living members of a family and reconstructing the genotypes and phenotypes of past generations from family records. The results are summarized in a chart called a **pedigree**, which shows all parents and offspring for as many generations as possible, the sex of individuals in the different generations, and the presence or absence of the trait of interest. Females are designated by a circle and males by a square; a solid circle or square indicates the presence of the trait.

In humans, as in fruit flies, sex-linked recessive traits appear more frequently among males than females because males need to receive only one copy of the allele on the X chromosome inherited from their mothers to develop the trait. Females must receive two copies of the recessive allele, one from each parent, to express the trait. Two examples of human sex-linked traits are red–green colour blindness, a recessive trait in which the affected individual is unable to distinguish between the colours red and green because of a defect in light-sensing cells in the retina, and hemophilia, a recessive trait in which affected individuals have a defect in blood clotting.

Hemophiliacs—people with hemophilia—are "bleeders"; that is, if they are injured, they bleed uncontrollably because a protein required for forming blood clots is not produced in functional form. Males are bleeders if they receive an X chromosome that carries the recessive allele. The disease also develops in females with the recessive allele on both of their X chromosomes—a rare combination. Although affected persons, with luck and good care, can reach maturity, their lives are tightly circumscribed by the necessity to avoid injury of any kind. Even internal bleeding from slight bruises can be fatal. The disease, which affects about 1 in 7000 males, can be treated by injection of the required clotting protein.

Hemophilia has had effects reaching far beyond individuals who inherit the disease. The most famous cases occurred in the royal families of Europe descended from Queen Victoria of England **(Figure 12.9)**. The disease was not recorded in Queen Victoria's ancestors, so the recessive allele for the trait probably appeared as a spontaneous mutation in the queen or one of her parents. Queen Victoria was heterozygous for the recessive hemophilia allele; that is, she was a **carrier**, meaning that she carried the mutant allele and could pass it on to her offspring, but she did not have symptoms of the disease. A carrier is indicated in a pedigree by a male or female symbol with a central dot.

Note in Queen Victoria's pedigree in Figure 12.9 that Leopold, Duke of Albany, had hemophilia, as did his grandson, Rupert, Viscount Trematon. The trait appears in males in alternate generations (i.e., it "skips" a generation) because it passes with the X chromosome from mother to son. Mothers do not express the trait because they are heterozygous carriers. The sons, in turn, pass the X chromosome with the affected allele to their daughters (and the Y chromsome to their sons), as did the Duke of Albany. The appearance of a trait in the males of alternate generations therefore indicates that the allele under study is recessive and carried on the X chromosome.

At one time, 18 of Queen Victoria's 69 descendants were affected males or female carriers. Because so many sons of European royalty were affected, the trait influenced the course of history. In Russia, Crown Prince Alexis was one of Victoria's hemophiliac descendants. His affliction drew together his parents, Czar Nicholas II and Czarina Alexandra (a granddaughter of Victoria and a carrier), and the hypnotic monk Rasputin, who manipulated the family to his advantage by convincing them that only he could control the boy's bleeding. The situation helped trigger the Russian Revolution of 1917, which ended the Russian monarchy and led to the establishment of a Communist government in the former Soviet Union, a significant event in twentieth-century history.

Hemophilia affected only sons in the royal lines but could have affected daughters if a hemophiliac son had married a carrier female. Because the disease is rare in the human population as a whole, the chance of such a mating is so low that only a few unions of this type have been recorded.

12.2e Inactivation of One X Chromosome Evens out Gene Effects

Although mammalian females have twice as many copies of genes carried on the X chromosome as males, it is unlikely that they require twice as much of the products of those genes. Theoretically, products from genes on the X chromosome could be equalized in males and females if (1) expression of genes on the single male X chromosome was doubled, or (2) expression of genes on both female X chromosomes was halved, or (3) one X chromosome was "turned off" in females. All of these dosage compensation mechanisms are known in nature, but mammals use the latter; females with two X chromosomes inactivate most of the genes on one X chromosome or the other in most body cells.

As a result of the equalizing mechanism, the activity of most genes carried on the X chromosome is essentially the same in the cells of males and females. The inactivation occurs by a condensation process that folds and packs the chromatin of one of the two X chromosomes into a tightly coiled state similar to the condensed state of chromosomes during cell division. The

inactive, condensed X chromosome can be seen at one side of the nucleus in cells of females as a dense mass of chromatin called the **Barr body.**

The inactivation occurs during embryonic development. Which of the two X chromosomes becomes inactive in a particular embryonic cell line is a random event. But once one of the X chromosomes is inactivated in a cell, that same X is inactivated in all descendants of the cell. Thus, within one female, one of the X chromosomes is active in particular cells and inactive in others and vice versa.

If the two X chromosomes carry different alleles of a gene, one allele will be active in cell lines in which one X chromosome is active, and the other allele will be active in cell lines in which the other X chromosome is active. For many sex-linked alleles, such as the recessive allele that causes hemophilia, random inactivation of either X chromosome has little overall whole-body effect in heterozygous females because the dominant allele is active in enough of the critical cells to produce a normal phenotype. However, for some genes, the inactivation of either X chromosome in heterozygotes produces recognizably different effects in distinct regions of the body.

For example, the orange and black patches of fur in calico cats result from inactivation of one of the two X chromosomes in regions of the skin of heterozygous females **(Figure 12.10)**. Males, which get only one of the two alleles, normally have either black or orange fur. Similarly, in humans, females who are heterozygous for an allele on the X chromosome that

Figure 12.10

A female cat with the calico colour pattern in which patches of orange and black fur are produced by random inactivation of one of the two X chromosomes. Two genes control the black and orange colours: the *O* gene on the X chromosome is for orange fur colour, and the *B* gene on an autosome is for black fur colour. A calico cat has the genotype *Oo BB* (or *Oo Bb*). An orange patch results when the X chromosome carrying the mutant *o* allele is inactivated. In this case, the *O* gene masks the expression of the *B* gene and orange fur is produced. (This example is of epistasis; see Section 11.2.) A black patch results when the X chromosome carrying the *O* allele is inactivated. In this case, the mutant *o* allele cannot mask *B* gene expression and black fur results. The white patches result from interactions with a different, autosomal gene that entirely blocks pigment deposition in the fur.

Ulrike Schanz/Animals, Animals - Earth Scenes

blocks development of sweat glands may have a patchy distribution of skin areas with and without the glands. Females with the patchy distribution are not seriously affected and may be unaware of the condition.

As we have seen, the discovery of genetic linkage, recombination, and sex-linked genes led to the elaboration and expansion of Mendel's principles of inheritance. Next, we examine what happens when patterns of inheritance are modified by changes in the chromosomes.

STUDY BREAK

1. What are the differences in sex chromosomes that underlie sex linkage inheritance patterns?
2. For a given gene, how could you determine if it was sex-linked or not?

12.3 Chromosomal Alterations That Affect Inheritance

Although chromosomes are relatively stable structures, they are sometimes altered by breaks in the DNA, which can be generated by agents such as radiation or certain chemicals or by enzymes encoded in some infecting viruses. The broken chromosome fragments may be lost, or they may reattach to the same or different chromosomes. The resulting changes in chromosome structure may have genetic consequences if alleles are eliminated, mixed in new combinations, duplicated, or placed in new locations by the alterations in cell lines that lead to the formation of gametes.

Genetic changes may also occur through changes in chromosome number, including addition or loss of one or more chromosomes or even entire sets of chromosomes. Both chromosomal alterations and changes in chromosome number can be a source of disease and disability, as well as a source of variability during evolution.

Figure 12.11
Chromosome
(a) deletion,
(b) duplication,
(c) translocation
(a reciprocal translocation is shown), and **(d)** inversion.

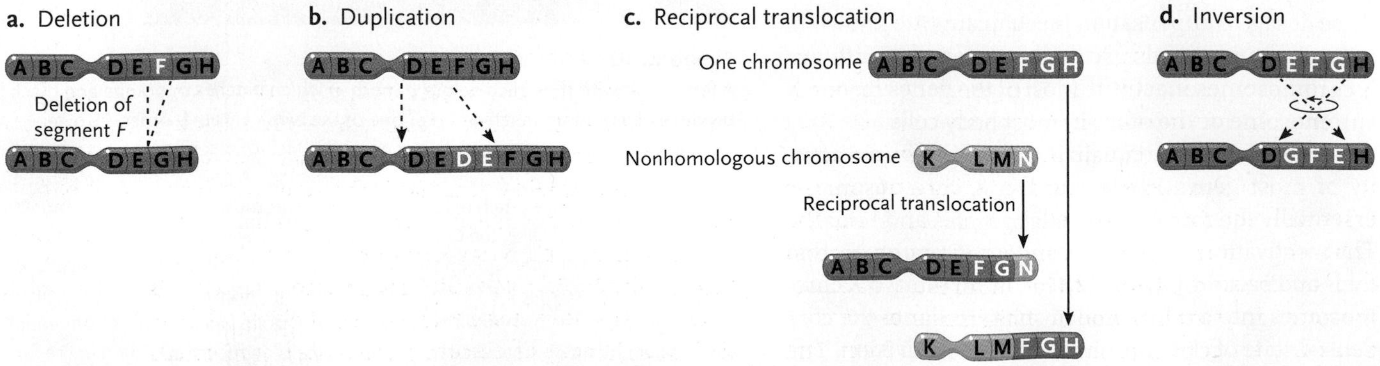

12.3a Deletions, Duplications, Translocations, and Inversions Are the Most Common Chromosomal Alterations

Chromosomal alterations after breakages occur in four major forms **(Figure 12.11)**:

1. A **deletion** occurs if a broken segment is lost from a chromosome.
2. A **duplication** occurs if a segment is broken from one chromosome and inserted into its homologue. In the receiving homologue, the alleles in the inserted fragment are added to the ones already there.
3. A **translocation** occurs if a broken segment is attached to a different, nonhomologous chromosome.
4. An **inversion** occurs if a broken segment reattaches to the same chromosome from which it was lost, but in reversed orientation, so that the order of genes is reversed.

To be inherited, chromosomal alterations must occur or be included in cells of the germ line leading to development of eggs or sperm.

Deletions and Duplications. A deletion (see Figure 12.11a) may cause severe problems if the missing segment contains genes that are essential for normal development or cellular functions. For example, one deletion from human chromosome 5 typically leads to severe mental retardation and a malformed larynx. The cries of an affected infant sound more like a meow than a human cry—hence the name of the disorder, *cri-du-chat* (meaning "cat's cry").

A duplication (see Figure 12.11b) may have effects that vary from harmful to beneficial, depending on the genes and alleles contained in the duplicated region. Although most duplications are likely to be detrimental, some have been important sources of evolutionary change. That is, because there are duplicate genes, one copy can mutate into new forms without seriously affecting the basic functions of the organism. For example, mammals have genes that encode several types of hemoglobin that are not present in vertebrates, such as sharks, which evolved earlier; the additional

a. Deletion

A B C D E F G H

Deletion of segment F

A B C D E G H

b. Duplication

A B C D E F G H

A B C D E D E F G H

c. Reciprocal translocation

One chromosome   A B C D E F G H

Nonhomologous chromosome   K L M N

Reciprocal translocation

A B C D E F G N

K L M F G H

d. Inversion

A B C D E F G H

A B C D G F E H

hemoglobin genes of mammals are believed to have appeared through duplications, followed by mutations in the duplicates that created new and beneficial forms of hemoglobin as further evolution took place. Duplications sometimes arise during recombination in meiosis, if crossing-over occurs unequally, so that a segment is deleted from one chromosome of a homologous pair and inserted in the other.

Translocations and Inversions. In a translocation, a segment breaks from one chromosome and attaches to another, nonhomologous chromosome. In many cases, a translocation is reciprocal, meaning that two nonhomologous chromosomes exchange segments (see Figure 12.11c). Reciprocal translocations resemble genetic recombination, except that the two chromosomes involved in the exchange do not contain the same genes.

For example, a particular cancer of the human immune system, Burkitt lymphoma, is caused by a translocation that moves a segment of human chromosome 8 to the end of chromosome 14. The break does not interrupt any genes required for normal cell function. The translocated segment contains genes that control cell division. These genes are precisely regulated at their normal location but are near the control regions of highly active genes in the new location, causing them to be overactive and leading to uncontrolled cell division and the development of a cancer.

In an inversion, a chromosome segment breaks and then reattaches to the same chromosome, but in reverse order (see Figure 12.11d). Inversions have essentially the same effects as translocations—genes may be broken internally by the inversion, with loss of function, or they may be transferred intact to a new location within the same chromosome, producing effects that range from beneficial to harmful.

Inversions and translocations have been important factors in the evolution of plants and some animals, including insects and primates. For example, five of the chromosome pairs of humans show evidence of translocations and inversions that are not present in one of our nearest primate relatives, gorillas, and therefore must have occurred after the gorilla and human evolutionary lineages split.

12.3b The Number of Entire Chromosomes May Also Change

At times, whole, single chromosomes are lost or gained from cells entering or undergoing meiosis, resulting in a change of chromosome number. Most often, these changes occur through **nondisjunction**, the failure of homologous pairs to separate during the first meiotic division, or through misdivision, the failure of chromatids to separate during the second meiotic division **(Figure 12.12)**. As a result, gametes are produced that lack one or more chromosomes or contain extra copies of the chromosomes. Note that

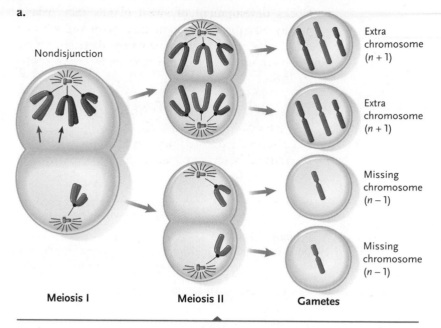

a.

Nondisjunction during the first meiotic division causes both chromosomes of one pair to be delivered to the same pole of the spindle. The nondisjunction produces two gametes with an extra chromosome and two with a missing chromosome.

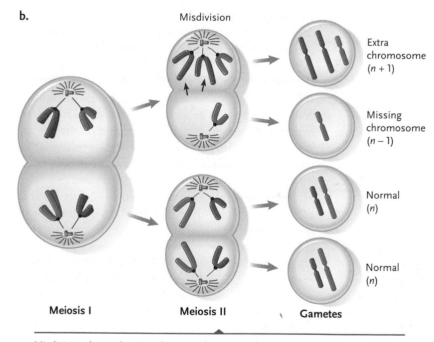

b.

Misdivision during the second meiotic division produces two normal gametes, one gamete with an extra chromosome and one gamete with a missing chromosome.

chromatids separate normally in meiosis II even if chromosomes do not disjoin properly in meiosis I. Fertilization by these gametes produces an individual with extra or missing chromosomes. Such individuals are called **aneuploids**, whereas individuals with a normal set of chromosomes are called **euploids.**

Changes in chromosome number can also occur through duplication of entire sets, meaning individuals may receive one or more extra copies of the entire haploid complement of chromosomes. Such individuals

Figure 12.12
(a) Nondisjunction during the first meiotic division and **(b)** misdivision during the second meiotic division.

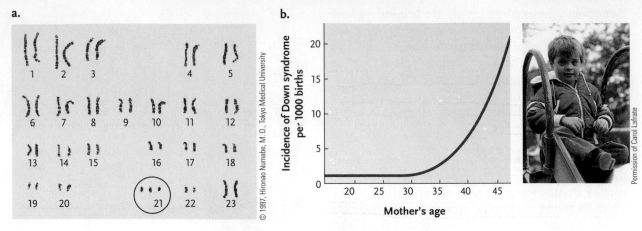

a.

1 2 3   4 5

6 7 8 9 10 11 12

13 14 15   16 17 18

19 20   21 22 23

b.

Incidence of Down syndrome per 1000 births

20

15

10

5

0

20 25 30 35 40 45

Mother's age

© 1997, Hironao Numabe, M. D., Tokyo Medical University

Permission of Carol Lafrate

Figure 12.13

Down syndrome. **(a)** The chromosomes of a human female with Down syndrome showing three copies of chromosome 21 (circled in red). **(b)** The increase in the incidence of Down syndrome with increasing age of the mother, from a study conducted in Victoria, Australia, between 1942 and 1957.

are called **polyploids**. *Triploids* have three copies of each chromosome instead of two; *tetraploids* have four copies of each chromosome. Multiples higher than tetraploids also occur.

Aneuploids. The effects of addition or loss of whole chromosomes vary depending on the chromosome and the species. In animals, aneuploidy of autosomes usually produces debilitating or lethal developmental abnormalities. These abnormalities also occur in humans; addition or loss of an autosomal chromosome causes embryos to develop so abnormally that they are aborted naturally. For reasons that are not understood, aneuploidy is as much as 10 times more frequent in humans than in other mammals. Of human embryos that have been miscarried and examined, about 70% are aneuploids.

In some cases, autosomal aneuploids survive. This is the case with humans who receive an extra copy of chromosome 21—one of the smallest chromosomes **(Figure 12.13a)**. Many of these individuals survive until young adulthood. The condition produced by the extra chromosome, called *Down syndrome* or *trisomy 21,* is characterized by short stature and moderate to severe mental retardation. About 40% of individuals with Down syndrome have heart defects, and skeletal development is slower than normal. Most do not mature sexually and remain sterile. However, with attentive care and appropriate educational opportunities, individuals with Down syndrome can participate with reasonable success in many activities.

Down syndrome arises from nondisjunction or misdivision of chromosome 21 during meiosis, primarily in women (about 5% of nondisjunctions that lead to Down syndrome occur in men). The nondisjunction occurs more frequently as women age, increasing the chance that a child may be born with the syndrome **(Figure 12.13b)**. Around the world, about 1 in every 800 children is born with Down syndrome, making it one of the most common serious human genetic defects.

Aneuploidy of sex chromosomes can also arise by nondisjunction or misdivision during meiosis (**Figure 12.14** and **Table 12.1**). Unlike autosomal aneuploidy, which usually has drastic effects on survival, altered numbers of X and Y chromosomes are often tolerated, producing individuals who progress through embryonic

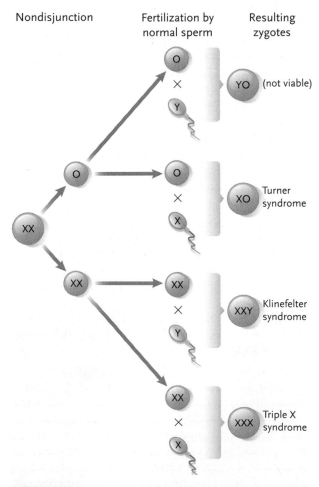

Nondisjunction   Fertilization by normal sperm   Resulting zygotes

O

×

Y

YO (not viable)

O

O

×

X

XO Turner syndrome

XX

XX

×

Y

XXY Klinefelter syndrome

XX

×

X

XXX Triple X syndrome

XX

Figure 12.14

Some abnormal combinations of sex chromosomes resulting from nondisjunction of X chromosomes in females.

development and grow to adulthood. In the case of multiple X chromosomes, the X-chromosome inactivation mechanism converts all but one of the X chromosomes to a Barr body, so the dosage of active X-chromosome genes is the same as in normal XX females and XY males. However, X chromosomes are not inactivated until about 15 to 16 days after fertilization. Expression of the extra X chromosome genes early in development results in some deleterious effects.

Because sexual development in humans is pushed toward male or female reproductive organs primarily by the presence or absence of the *SRY* gene on the Y chromosome, people with a Y chromosome are externally malelike, no matter how many X chromosomes are present. If no Y chromosome is present, X chromosomes in various numbers give rise to female-like individuals. (Table 12.1 lists the effects of some alterations in sex chromosome number.) Similar abnormal combinations of sex chromosomes also occur in other animals, including *Drosophila,* with varying effects on viability.

Polyploids. Polyploidy often originates from failure of the spindle to function normally during mitosis in cell lines leading to germ-line cells. In these divisions, the spindle fails to separate the duplicated chromosomes, which are incorporated into a single nucleus with twice the usual number of chromosomes. Eventually, meiosis takes place and produces gametes with two copies of each chromosome instead of one. Fusion of one such gamete with a normal haploid gamete produces a triploid, and fusion of two such gametes produces a tetraploid.

The effects of polyploidy vary widely between plants and animals. In plants, polyploids are often hardier and more successful in growth and reproduction than the diploid plants from which they were derived. As a result, polyploidy is common and has been an important source of variability in plant evolution. About half of all flowering plant species are polyploids, including important crop plants such as wheat and other cereals, cotton, strawberries, and bananas.

By contrast, among animals, polyploidy is uncommon because it usually has lethal effects during embryonic development. For example, in humans, all but about 1% of polyploids die before birth, and the few who are born die within a month. The lethality is probably due to disturbance of animal developmental pathways, which are typically much more complex than those of plants.

We now turn to a description of the effects of altered alleles on human health and development.

STUDY BREAK

What mechanisms are responsible for (a) duplication of a chromosome segment, (b) generation of a Down syndrome individual, (c) a chromosome translocation, and (d) polyploidy?

Table 12.1	Effects of Unusual Combinations of Sex Chromosomes in Humans	
Combination of Sex Chromosomes	Approximate Frequency	Effects
XO	1 in 5000 births	Turner syndrome: females with underdeveloped ovaries; sterile; intelligence and external genitalia are normal; typically, individuals are short in stature with underdeveloped breasts
XXY	1 in 2000 births	Klinefelter syndrome: male external genitalia with very small and underdeveloped testes; sterile; intelligence usually normal; sparse body hair and some development of the breasts; similar characteristics in XXXY and XXXXY individuals
XYY	1 in 1000 births	XYY syndrome: apparently normal males but often taller than average
XXX	1 in 1000 births	Triple-X syndrome: apparently normal female with normal or slightly retarded mental function

12.4 Human Genetics and Genetic Counselling

We have already noted a number of human genetic traits and conditions caused by mutant alleles or chromosomal alterations (see **Table 12.2** for a more detailed list). All of these traits are of interest as examples of patterns of inheritance that amplify and extend Mendel's basic principles. Those with harmful effects are also important because of their impact on human life and society.

Table 12.2	Examples of Human Genetic Traits
Trait	**Adverse Health Effects**
Autosomal Recessive Inheritance	
Albinism	Absence of pigmentation (melanin)
Attached ear lobes	None
Cystic fibrosis	Excess mucus in lungs and digestive cavities
Sickle cell disease	Severe tissue and organ damage
Galactosemia	Brain, liver, and eye damage
Phenylketonuria	Mental retardation
Tay–Sachs disease	Mental retardation, death
Autosomal Dominant Inheritance	
Free ear lobes	None
Achondroplasia	Defective cartilage formation that causes dwarfism
Early balding in males	None
Campodactyly	Rigid, bent small fingers
Curly hair	None
Huntington disease	Progressive, irreversible degeneration of nervous system
Syndactyly	Webbing between fingers
Polydactyly	Extra digits
Brachydactyly	Short digits
Progeria	Premature aging
X-Linked Inheritance	
Hemophilia A	Deficient blood clotting
Red–green colour blindness	Inability to distinguish red from green
Testicular feminizing syndrome	Absence of male organs, sterility
Changes in Chromosome Structure	
Cri-du-chat	Mental retardation, malformed larynx
Changes in Chromosome Number	
Down syndrome	Mental retardation, heart defects

12.4a In Autosomal Recessive Inheritance, Heterozygotes Are Carriers and Homozygous Recessives Are Affected by the Trait

Sickle cell anemia and cystic fibrosis are examples of human traits caused by recessive alleles on autosomes. Alleles of these particular traits code for defective proteins that function poorly, if at all. Many other human genetic traits follow a similar pattern of inheritance (see Table 12.2). These traits are passed on according to the pattern known as **autosomal recessive inheritance**, in which individuals who are homozygous for the dominant allele are free of symptoms and are not carriers; heterozygotes are usually symptom free but are carriers. People who are homozygous for the recessive allele show the trait.

For sickle cell anemia, between 10% and 15% of African Americans in the United States are carriers—that is, they have sickle cell trait (see Section 11.2). Although carriers make enough normal hemoglobin through the activity of the dominant allele to be essentially unaffected, the mutant, sickle cell form of the hemoglobin molecule is also present in their red blood cells. Carriers can be identified by a simple test for the mutant hemoglobin. In countries where malaria is common, including several countries in Africa, carriers are less susceptible to contraction of the disease, which helps explain the increased proportions of the recessive allele among races that originated in malarial areas.

Cystic fibrosis (CF), one of the most common genetic disorders among persons of Northern European descent, is another autosomal recessive trait **(Figure 12.15)**. About

Figure 12.15

A child affected by cystic fibrosis. Daily chest thumps, back thumps, and repositioning dislodge thick mucus that collects in airways to the lungs.

Achondroplastic Dwarfing by a Single Amino Acid Change

Researchers recently found that the gene responsible for achondroplastic dwarfing is on chromosome 4.

The gene codes for a receptor that binds the *fibroblast growth factor (FGF)*, a growth hormone that stimulates a wide range of mammalian cells to grow and divide. This fibroblast growth factor receptor (FGFR) gene is active in chondrocytes—cells that form cartilage and bone.

Arnold Munnich and his colleagues isolated the gene that encodes the FGFR and obtained its DNA sequence. They found two versions of the gene's sequence with a single difference—one version had an adenine–thymine (A-T) base pair and the other had a guanine–cytosine (G-C) base pair at the same position in the DNA sequence.

The change substitutes arginine for glycine at one position in the amino acid sequence of the encoded protein. These amino acids have very different chemical properties. The substitution occurs in a segment of the protein that extends across the membrane, connecting a hormone-binding site outside the cell with a site inside the cell that triggers the internal response.

The investigators then looked for the A-T–to–G-C substitution in the mutant form of the gene on chromosome 4 that causes achondroplastic dwarfing. The substitution was present in copies of the gene isolated from 6 families of achondroplastic dwarfs but absent in 120 people who lack the trait. This result supported the hypothesis that a mutant allele of the

FGFR on chromosome 4 is responsible for achondroplastic dwarfism.

How does the single amino acid substitution cause dwarfing? The cause is not known exactly. The change may inhibit the transmission of the signal triggered by a hormone binding to the receptor on the outer membrane. As a result, chondrocytes divide improperly and inhibit normal elongation of the limb bones. This helps explain why the achondroplasia mutation is dominant.

Identification of the gene responsible for achondroplastic dwarfing opens the future to finding a cure for the condition, possibly through gene therapy for infants or young children who carry the mutation.

---

1 in every 25 people from this line of descent is an unaffected carrier with one copy of the recessive allele, and about 1 in 2500 is homozygous for the recessive allele. The homozygous recessives have an altered membrane transport protein that results in excess Cl^- (chloride ions) in the extracellular fluids. Through pathways that are not completely understood, the alteration in chloride transport causes thick, sticky mucus to collect in airways of the lungs, in the ducts of glands such as the pancreas, and in the digestive tract. The accumulated mucus impairs body functions and, in the lungs, promotes pneumonia and other infections. With current management procedures, the life expectancy for a person with cystic fibrosis is about 40 years.

Another autosomal recessive disease, *phenylketonuria* (PKU), appears in about 1 of every 15 000 births. Affected individuals cannot produce an enzyme that converts the amino acid phenylalanine to another amino acid, tyrosine. As a result, phenylalanine builds up in the blood and is converted in the body into other products, including phenylpyruvate. Elevations in both phenylalanine and phenylpyruvate damage brain tissue and can lead to mental retardation. If diagnosed early enough, an affected infant can be placed on a phenylalanine-restricted diet, which can prevent the PKU symptoms. Screening newborns for PKU is routine in the developed world and is becoming more established in the developing world as well.

12.4b In Autosomal Dominant Inheritance, Only Homozygous Recessives Are Unaffected

Some human traits follow a pattern of **autosomal dominant inheritance** (see Table 12.2). In this case, the allele that causes the trait is dominant, and people who are either homozygous or heterozygous for the dominant allele are affected. Individuals homozygous for the recessive normal allele are unaffected.

Achondroplasia, a type of dwarfing that occurs in about 1 in 10 000 people, is caused by an autosomal dominant allele of a gene on chromosome 4. Of individuals with the dominant allele, only heterozygotes survive embryonic development; homozygous dominants are usually stillborn. When limb bones develop in heterozygous children, cartilage formation is defective, leading to disproportionately short arms and legs. The trunk and head, however, are of normal size. Affected adults are usually not much more than 122 centimetres tall. Achondroplastic dwarfs are of normal intelligence, are fertile, and can have children.

12.4c Males Are More Likely to Be Affected by X-Linked Recessive Traits

Red–green colour blindness and hemophilia have already been presented as examples of human traits that demonstrate **X-linked recessive inheritance**, that is, traits due to inheritance of recessive alleles carried on the X chromosome. Another X-linked recessive human disease trait is Duchenne muscular dystrophy. In affected individuals, muscle tissue begins to degenerate late in childhood; by the onset of puberty, most individuals with this disease are unable to walk. Muscular weakness progresses, with later involvement of the heart muscle; the average life expectancy for individuals with Duchenne muscular dystrophy is 25 years.

12.4d Human Genetic Disorders Can Be Predicted, and Many Can Be Treated

Each year, roughly 8 million children around the world are born with a severe disease or disability having a significant genetic component. The rate of such births in middle- and low-income countries is double that for high-income countries. Why might this be? One contributing factor has already been mentioned: in areas where malaria is endemic, the frequency of the sickle cell allele tends to be higher and the incidence of newborn sickle cell anemia is higher. Nutritional deficiencies, consanguinous (blood relative) marriage practices, and higher numbers of children born to older mothers may also elevate birth defect rates in certain societies. In addition to improvements in basic financial, health, and nutritional standards, programs offering genetic counselling, prenatal diagnosis, and genetic screening can help reduce the suffering associated with genetic disorders.

Genetic counselling allows prospective parents to assess the possibility that they might have an affected child. For example, parents may seek counselling if they, a close relative, or one of their existing children has a genetic disorder. Genetic counselling begins with identification of parental genotypes through family pedigrees or direct testing for an altered protein or DNA sequence. With this information in hand, counselors can often predict the chances of having a child with the trait in question. Couples can then make an informed decision about whether to have a child.

Genetic counselling is often combined with techniques of **prenatal diagnosis**, in which cells derived from a developing embryo or its surrounding tissues or fluids are tested for the presence of mutant alleles or chromosomal alterations. In **amniocentesis**, cells are obtained from the amniotic fluid—the watery fluid surrounding the embryo in the mother's uterus. In **chorionic villus sampling**, cells are obtained from portions of the placenta that develop from tissues of the embryo. More than 100 genetic disorders can now be detected by these tests. If prenatal diagnosis detects a serious genetic defect, the prospective parents can reach an informed decision about whether to continue the **pregnancy**, including religious and moral considerations, as well as genetic and medical advice.

Once a child is born, inherited disorders are identified by **genetic screening**, in which biochemical or molecular tests for disorders are routinely applied to children and adults or to newborn infants in hospitals. The tests can detect inherited disorders early enough to start any available preventive measures before symptoms develop. Worldwide newborn screening for PKU identifies affected children in time for them to avoid the debilitating symptoms of this disease. The first generation of people to ever survive childhood with PKU are now adults.

In addition to the characters and traits described so far in this chapter, some patterns of inheritance depend on genes located not in the cell nucleus, but in mitochondria or chloroplasts in the cytoplasm, as discussed in the following section.

STUDY BREAK

1. What inheritance pattern would suggest that a trait is dominant and carried on an autosome?
2. How are inherited disorders detected before symptoms arise?

12.5 Nontraditional Patterns of Inheritance

We consider two examples of nontraditional patterns of inheritance in this section. In **cytoplasmic inheritance**, the pattern of inheritance follows that of genes in the cytoplasmic organelles, mitochondria, or chloroplasts. In **genomic imprinting**, the expression of an allele of a particular nuclear gene is based on whether an individual organism inherits the allele from the male or female parent.

12.5a Cytoplasmic Inheritance Follows the Pattern of Inheritance of Mitochondria or Chloroplasts

Many people believe that offspring inherit half of their DNA from each parent. Although this idea is roughly true for nuclear DNA, recall that both chloroplasts and mitochondria also contain DNA. In many organisms, inheritance of these non-nuclear chromosomes occurs only through the "egg parent." Organelle DNA contains genes and alleles that, like nuclear genes, are also subject to being mutated. Mutant genes in some cases result in altered phenotypes, but the inheritance pattern of these mutant genes is fundamentally different from that of mutant genes carried on chromosomes in the nucleus. The two major differences are as follows: (1) ratios typical of Mendelian segregation are not found because genes are not segregating by meiosis, and (2) genes usually show uniparental inheritance from generation to generation. In *uniparental inheritance,* all progeny (both males and females) inherit the genotype of only one of the parents. For most multicellular eukaryotes, the mother's genotype is passed on, a phenomenon called *maternal inheritance.* Maternal inheritance occurs because the amount of cytoplasm in the female gamete usually far exceeds that in the male gamete. Hence, a zygote receives most of its cytoplasm, including mitochondria and (in plants) chloroplasts, from the female parent and little from the male parent.

In humans, several inherited diseases have been traced to mutations in mitochondrial genes **(Table 12.3).** Recall that the mitochondrion plays a critical role in synthesizing adenosine triphosphate (ATP), the energy source for many cellular reactions. The mutations producing the diseases in Table 12.3 are in mitochondrial genes that encode components of the ATP-generating system of the organelle. The resulting mitochondrial defects are especially destructive to the organ systems most dependent on mitochondrial reactions for energy: the central nervous system, skeletal and cardiac muscle, the liver, and the kidneys. These inherited diseases show maternal inheritance.

12.5b In Genomic Imprinting, the Allele Inherited from One of the Parents Is Expressed Whereas the Other Allele Is Silent

Genomic imprinting is a phenomenon in which the expression of an allele of a gene is determined by the parent that contributed it. In some cases, the paternally derived allele is expressed; in others, the maternally derived allele is expressed. The silent allele—that which is not expressed—is called the *imprinted allele.* The imprinted allele is not inactivated by mutation.

Table 12.3	Some Human Diseases Caused by Mutations in Mitochondrial Genes	
Disease	**Symptoms**
Kearns–Sayre syndrome	May include muscle weakness, mental deficiencies, abnormal heartbeat, short stature
Leber hereditary optic neuropathy	Vision loss from degeneration of the optic nerve, abnormal heartbeat
Mitochondrial myopathy and encephalomyopathy	May include seizures, strokelike episodes, hearing loss, progressive dementia, abnormal heartbeat, short stature
Myoclonic epilepsy	Vision and hearing loss, uncoordinated movement, jerking of limbs, progressive dementia, heart defects

Rather, it is silenced by chemical modification (methylation) of certain bases in its sequence.

As an example of how imprinting is involved in human disease, Prader–Willi syndrome (PWS) and Angelman syndrome (AS) in humans are each caused by genomic imprinting of a particular gene on a chromosome inherited from one parent, coincident with deletion of the same gene on the homologous chromosome inherited from the other parent. The syndromes differ with respect to the gene imprinted. Both PWS and AS occur in about 1 in 15 000 births and are characterized by serious developmental, mental, and behavioural problems. PWS individuals are compulsive overeaters (leading to obesity), have short stature, have small hands and feet, and show mild to moderate mental retardation. AS individuals are hyperactive, are unable to speak, have seizures, show severe mental retardation, and display a happy disposition with bursts of laughter.

How is genomic imprinting responsible for these two syndromes? PWS is caused when an individual has a normal maternally derived chromosome 15 and a paternally derived chromosome 15 with a deletion of a small region of several genes that includes the PWS gene. The PWS gene is imprinted, and therefore silenced, on maternally derived chromosomes. As a result, when there is no PWS gene on the paternally derived chromosome, there is no PWS gene activity and PWS results. Similarly, AS is caused when an individual has a normal paternally derived chromosome 15 and a maternally derived chromosome 15 with a deletion of the same region; that region also includes the AS gene, the normal function of which is also required for normal development. In this case, genomic imprinting silences the AS gene on the paternally derived chromosome, and because there is no AS gene on the maternally derived chromosome, there is no AS gene activity and AS syndrome develops.

The mechanism of imprinting involves the modification of the DNA in the region that controls the expression of a gene by the addition of methyl ($—CH_3$) groups to cytosine nucleotides. The methylation of the control region of a gene prevents it from being expressed. (Note that there are a few instances of methylation-activating genes.) The regulation of gene expression by methylation of DNA is discussed further in Chapter 15. Genomic imprinting occurs in the gametes where the allele destined to be inactive in the new embryo after fertilization—either the father's or the mother's, depending on the gene—is methylated. That methylated (silenced) state of the gene is passed on as the cells grow and divide to produce the somatic (body) cells of the organism.

A number of cancers are associated with the failure to imprint genes. For instance, the mammalian *Igf2* (insulin growth factor 2) gene encodes a growth factor, a molecule that stimulates cells to grow and divide. *Igf2* is an imprinted gene, with the paternally derived allele on and the maternally derived allele off.

In some cases, the imprinting mechanism for this gene does not work, resulting in both alleles of *Igf2* being active, a phenomenon known as **loss of imprinting.** The resulting double dose of the growth factor disrupts the cell division cycle, contributing to uncontrolled growth and cancer.

In this chapter, you have learned about genes and the role of chromosomes in inheritance. In the next chapter, you will learn about the molecular structure and function of the genetic material and about the molecular mechanism by which DNA is replicated.

UNANSWERED QUESTIONS

This chapter focused on recombination during meiosis, exchanging sections of homologous chromosomes. Recombination is also known to occur in somatic cells during development of specialized cells of the immune system and in most other cells as a mechanism for repair of chromosome breaks. What remains unclear is the role of recombination in aging and diseases such as cancer.

Influencing the expression of genes in offspring through imprinting by parents has only recently received substantial research attention. Overall, this mechanism provides a way for organisms to regulate gene expression over generations in response to the environment. We are just beginning to understand the implications of this interaction between "nature" and "nurture."

Review

Go to CENGAGENOW™ at http://hed.nelson.com/ to access quizzing, animations, exercises, articles, and personalized homework help.

12.1 Genetic Linkage and Recombination

- Genes, consisting of sequences of nucleotides in DNA, are arranged linearly in chromosomes.

- Genes carried on the same chromosome are linked together in their transmission from parent to offspring. Linked genes are inherited in patterns similar to those of single genes, except for changes in the linkage due to recombination (see Figure 12.2).

- As a result of recombination, the particular collection of alleles linked on any given chromosome is mixed up as a result of exchange with corresponding alleles on the other homologous chromosome. The exchanges occur while homologues pair during prophase I of meiosis.

- The amount of recombination between any two genes located on the same chromosome pair reflects the distance between them on the chromosome. The greater this distance, the greater the chance that chromatids will exchange segments at points between the genes and the greater the recombination frequency.

- The relationship between separation and recombination frequencies is used to produce chromosome maps in which genes are assigned relative locations with respect to each other (see Figure 12.4).

- Dihybrid testcrosses (*AaBb* × *aa bb*) can be used to detect linkage. If all progeny classes are equally frequent, then the genes are not linked.

- Genes carried on the same chromosome may not show genetic linkage (i.e., assort independently) if they are quite far apart.

12.2 Sex-Linked Genes

- Sex linkage is a pattern of inheritance produced by genes carried on sex chromosomes: chromosomes that differ in males and females. Sex-linked inheritance patterns arise because, in humans and fruit flies, females have two copies of the X chromosome and therefore two alleles for each gene. Males have only one copy of the X chromosome and therefore only one allele for each gene. Only males have an allele for genes carried on the Y chromosome.

- Sex linkage is suggested by a particular, non-Mendelian pattern of inheritance when the progeny of reciprocal crosses are different (see Figure 11.8).

- Since males have only one X chromosome, any recessive alleles that they inherit on that X chromosome will be expressed. Females must receive two copies of the recessive allele, one from each parent, to develop the trait (see Figures 12.6–12.8).

- In mammals, inactivation of one of the two X chromosomes in cells of the female makes the dosage of X-linked genes the same in males and females (see Figure 12.10).

- Parents can influence the expression of certain alleles in their offspring through DNA methylation called imprinting.

12.3 Chromosomal Alterations That Affect Inheritance

- Inheritance is influenced by processes that delete, duplicate, or invert segments within chromosomes or translocate segments between chromosomes (see Figure 12.11).

- Chromosomes also change in number by addition or removal of individual chromosomes or entire sets. Changes in single chromosomes usually occur through nondisjunction, in which homologous pairs fail to separate during meiosis I, or sister chromatids fail to separate during meiosis II. As a result, one set of gametes receives an extra copy of a chromosome and the other set is deprived of the chromosome.

- Polyploids have one or more extra copies of the entire chromosome set. Polyploids usually arise when the spindle fails to function during mitosis in cell lines leading to gamete formation, producing gametes that contain double the number of chromosomes typical for the species (see Figures 12.12–12.14).

12.4 Human Genetics and Genetic Counselling

- Three modes of inheritance are most significant in human heredity: autosomal recessive, autosomal dominant, and X-linked recessive inheritance.

- In autosomal recessive inheritance, males or females carry a recessive allele on an autosome. Heterozygotes are carriers that are usually unaffected, but homozygous individuals show symptoms of the trait. Affected children born to unaffected parents would suggest autosomal recessive inheritance.

- In autosomal dominant inheritance, a dominant gene is carried on an autosome. Individuals that are homozygous or heterozygous for the trait show symptoms of the trait; homozygous recessives are normal.

- In X-linked recessive inheritance, a recessive allele for the trait is carried on the X chromosome. Male individuals with the recessive allele on their X chromosome or female individuals with the recessive allele on both X chromosomes show symptoms of the trait. Heterozygous females are carriers but usually show no symptoms of the trait.

- Genetic counselling, based on identification of parental genotypes by constructing family pedigrees and prenatal diagnosis, allows prospective parents to reach an informed decision about whether to have a child or continue a pregnancy.

12.5 Nontraditional Patterns of Inheritance

- Cytoplasmic inheritance depends on genes carried on DNA in mitochondria or chloroplasts. Cytoplasmic inheritance follows the maternal line: it parallels the inheritance of the cytoplasm in fertilization, in which most or all of the cytoplasm of the zygote originates from the egg cell. That is, all of the offspring of affected mothers would be affected; none of the offspring of affected fathers would be affected.

- Genomic imprinting is a phenomenon in which the expression of an allele of a gene is determined by the parent that contributed it. In some cases, the allele inherited from the father is expressed; in others, the allele from the mother is expressed. Commonly, the silencing of the other allele is the result of methylation of the region adjacent to the gene that is responsible for controlling the expression of that gene.

Questions

Self-Test Questions

1. In humans, red–green colour blindness is an X-linked recessive trait. If a man with normal vision and a colour-blind woman have a son, what is the chance that the son will be colour-blind? What is the chance that a daughter will be colour-blind?

2. The following pedigree shows the pattern of inheritance of red–green colour blindness in a family. Females are shown as circles and males as squares; the squares or circles of individuals affected by the trait are filled in black.

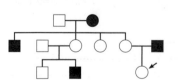

   What is the chance that a son of the third-generation female indicated by the arrow will be colour-blind if the father is a normal man? If the father is colour-blind?

3. Individuals affected by a condition known as polydactyly have extra fingers or toes. The following pedigree shows the pattern of inheritance of this trait in one family:

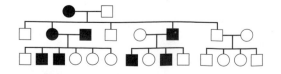

   From the pedigree, can you tell if polydactyly comes from a dominant or recessive allele? Is the trait sex-linked? As far as you can determine, what is the genotype of each person in the pedigree with respect to the trait?

4. A number of genes carried on the same chromosome are tested and show the following crossover frequencies. What is their sequence in the map of the chromosome?

Genes	Crossover Frequencies between Them
C and A	7%
B and D	3%
B and A	4%
C and D	6%
C and B	3%

5. In *Drosophila*, two genes, one for body colour and one for eye colour, are carried on the same chromosome. The wild-type grey body colour is dominant to black body colour, and wild-type red eyes are dominant to purple eyes. You make a cross between a fly with a grey body and red eyes and a fly with a black body and purple eyes. Among the offspring, about half have grey bodies and red eyes and half have black bodies and purple eyes. A small percentage have (a) black bodies and red eyes or (b) grey bodies and purple eyes. What alleles are carried together on the chromosomes in each of the flies used in the cross? What alleles are carried together on the chromosomes of the F$_1$ flies with black bodies and red eyes, and those with grey bodies and purple eyes?

6. Another gene in *Drosophila* determines wing length. The dominant wild-type allele of this gene produces long wings; a recessive allele produces vestigial (short) wings. A female that is true-breeding for red eyes and long wings is mated with a male that has purple eyes and vestigial wings. F_1 females are then crossed with purple-eyed, vestigial-winged males. From this second cross, a total of 600 offspring are obtained with the following combinations of traits:

$$\frac{30 + 42}{252 + 276 + 92 + 30} \times 100\%$$

$$= 12\%$$

    252 with red eyes and long wings
    276 with purple eyes and vestigial wings
    42 with red eyes and vestigial wings
    30 with purple eyes and long wings

Are the genes linked, unlinked, or sex-linked? If they are linked, how many map units separate them on the chromosome?

Drosophila with vestigial wings

Carolina Biological Supply Company

7. One human gene, which is suspected to be carried on the Y chromosome, controls the length of hair on men's ears. One allele produces nonhairy ears, and another produces hairy ears. If a man with hairy ears has sons, what percentage will also have hairy ears? What percentage of his daughters will have hairy ears?

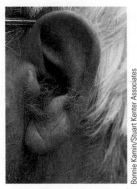

Male with hairy ears

Bonnie Kamin/Stuart Kenter Associates

8. You conduct a cross in *Drosophila* that produces only half as many male as female offspring. What might you suspect as a cause?

Questions for Discussion

1. Can a linkage map be made for a haploid organism that reproduces sexually?

2. Crossing-over does not occur between any pair of homologous chromosomes during meiosis in male *Drosophila*. From what you have learned about meiosis and crossing-over, propose one hypothesis for why this might be the case.

3. Even though X inactivation occurs in XXY (Klinefelter syndrome) humans, they do not have the same phenotype as normal XY males. Similarly, even though X inactivation occurs in XX individuals, they do not have the same phenotype as XO (Turner syndrome) humans. Why might this be the case?

4. All mammals have evolved from a common ancestor. However, the chromosome number varies among mammals. By what mechanism might this have occurred?

5. Assume that genes *a*, *b*, *c*, *d*, *e*, and *f* are linked. Explain how you would construct a linkage map that shows the order of these six genes and the map units between them.

A digital model of DNA (based on data generated by X-ray crystallography).

Kenneth Eward/Photo Researchers, Inc.

STUDY PLAN

13 DNA Structure, Replication, and Organization

WHY IT MATTERS

Imagine a scene 40 000 years ago in what is now called the Drachenlock Cave in Switzerland. Flickering torchlight reflects from a collection of large bear skulls as a Neanderthal shaman arranges one, then the next, to face toward the entrance to the cave. Now flash-forward to the present to find cave bear bones and teeth once again carefully arranged by human hands, this time on the bench of a modern, ultra-clean, research laboratory. The scientist is completely covered by a protective gown, gloves, and a face mask. The surface of the specimens is bleached and irradiated with high-intensity ultraviolet light. A small drill bores into the interior of a molar tooth, where researchers hope to recover ancient DNA (aDNA) from *Ursus spelaeus*, a long-extinct relative of modern bears.

As much as characterization of aDNA sequences promises to enhance our understanding of the genetic history and composition of modern populations, this field is overshadowed by two significant problems: DNA damage and contamination. The double helix of DNA is subject to breakages in one or both strands in addition to inappropriate cross-linking and chemical modification of individual bases. Living cells very successfully prevent or repair most of this

DNA damage, but postmortem degradation can be extensive after thousands of years. Sustained cold temperatures preserve a DNA relatively well, facilitating successful recovery of sequences from frozen mammoths and bison in permafrost, penguins in ice, and the human "Ice Man" frozen in a glacier. Ancient bacterial DNA sequences have been recovered from 500 000-year-old sections of ice cores.

The natural degradation of DNA over time usually means that aDNA sequences remaining in a given tissue sample are very rare and therefore prone to contamination by DNA from modern or ancient sources—hence the need for ultra-clean laboratories, decontamination procedures, and authentication protocols. Suspicions of contamination have clouded some of the most dramatic reports of aDNA recovery (from specimens 10 to 100 million years old).

As the future brings better techniques for the recovery and characterization of authentic aDNA sequences on Earth, we will undoubtedly turn these skills toward the search for evidence of past or present life on other planets. The Martian polar ice caps are very cold and very persistent, providing ideal conditions for preservation of DNA from any organisms that may have inhabited the Red Planet in the past.

Our current ability to find, characterize, and manipulate DNA arises ultimately from the work of a Swiss physician and physiological chemist, Johann Friedrich Miescher. In 1868, Miescher was engaged in a study of the composition of the cell nucleus. He collected pus cells from discarded bandages and extracted large quantities of an acidic substance with a high phosphorus content. He called the unusual substance "nuclein." Nuclein is now known by its modern name, **deoxyribonucleic acid**, or **DNA**, the molecule that is the genetic material of all living organisms and, as indicated by ancient DNA studies, all extinct organisms as well.

At the time of Miescher's discovery, scientists knew nothing about the molecular basis of heredity and very little about genetics. Although Mendel had already published the results of his genetic experiments with garden peas, the significance of his findings was not widely known or appreciated. It was not known which chemical substance in cells actually carries the instructions for reproducing parental traits in offspring. Not until 1952, more than 80 years after Miescher's discovery, did scientists fully recognize that the hereditary molecule was DNA.

After DNA was established as the hereditary molecule, the focus of research changed to the three-dimensional structure of DNA. Among the scientists striving to work out the structure were James D. Watson, a young American postdoctoral student at Cambridge University in England, and the Englishman Francis H.C. Crick, then a graduate student at the University of Cambridge. Using chemical and physical information about

Figure 13.1
James D. Watson and Francis H.C. Crick demonstrating their 1953 model for DNA structure, which revolutionized the biological sciences.

DNA, in particular Rosalind Franklin's analysis of the arrangement of atoms in DNA, the two investigators assembled molecular models from pieces of cardboard and bits of wire. Eventually, they constructed a model for DNA that fit all the known data **(Figure 13.1)**. Their discovery was of momentous importance in biology. The model enabled scientists to understand key processes in cells for the first time in terms of the structure and interaction of molecules. For example, the model immediately made it possible to understand how genetic information is stored in the structure of DNA and how DNA replicates. Unquestionably, the discovery launched a molecular revolution within biology, making it possible for the first time to relate the genetic traits of living organisms to a universal molecular code present in the DNA of every cell. In addition, Watson and Crick's discovery opened the way for numerous advances in fields such as medicine, forensics, pharmacology, and agriculture and eventually gave rise to the current rapid growth of the **biotechnology** industry.

13.1 Establishing DNA as the Hereditary Molecule

In the first half of the twentieth century, many scientists believed that proteins were the most likely candidates for the hereditary molecules because they appeared to offer greater opportunities for information coding than did nucleic acids. That is, proteins contain 20 types of amino acids, whereas nucleic acids have only 4 different nitrogenous bases available for coding. Other scientists believed that nucleic acids were the hereditary molecules. In this section, we describe the experiments showing that DNA, not protein, is the genetic material.

13.1a Experiments Began When Griffith Found a Substance That Could Genetically Transform Pneumonia Bacteria

In 1928, Frederick Griffith, a British medical officer, observed an interesting phenomenon in his experiments with the bacterium *Streptococcus pneumoniae,* which causes a severe form of pneumonia in mammals. Griffith was trying a make a vaccine to prevent pneumonia infections in the epidemics that occurred after World War I. He used two strains of the bacterium in his attempts. The smooth strain—*S*—has a polysaccharide capsule surrounding each cell and forms colonies that appear smooth and glossy when grown on a culture plate. When he injected the *S* strain into mice, it was virulent (highly infective, or pathogenic), causing pneumonia and killing the mice in a day or two (**Figure 13.2,** step 1). The rough strain—*R*—does not have a polysaccharide capsule and forms colonies with a nonshiny, rough appearance. When Griffith

injected the *R* strain into mice, it was avirulent (not infective, or nonpathogenic); the mice lived (step 2). Evidently, the capsule was responsible for the virulence of the *S* strain.

If Griffith killed the *S* bacteria by heating before injecting them into the mice, the mice remained healthy (step 3). However, quite unexpectedly, Griffith found that if he injected living *R* bacteria along with the heat-killed *S* bacteria, many of the mice died (step 4). Also, he was able to isolate living *S* bacteria with polysaccharide capsules from the infected mice. In some way, living *R* bacteria had acquired the ability to make the polysaccharide capsule from the dead *S* bacteria, and they had changed—transformed—into virulent *S* cells. The transformed bacteria were altered permanently; the smooth, infective trait was stably inherited by the descendants of the transformed bacteria. Griffith called the conversion of *R* bacteria to *S* bacteria *transformation* and called the agent responsible the *transforming principle.* What was the nature of the molecule responsible for the transformation? The most likely candidates were proteins or nucleic acids.

Figure 13.2
Griffith's experiment with infective and noninfective strains of *Streptococcus pneumoniae.*

QUESTION: What is the nature of the genetic material?

EXPERIMENT: Frederick Griffith studied the conversion of a nonvirulent (noninfective) *R* form of the bacterium *Streptococcus pneumoniae* to a virulent (infective) *S* form. The *S* form has a capsule surrounding the cell, giving colonies of it on a laboratory dish a smooth, shiny appearance. The *R* form has no capsule, so the colonies have a rough, nonshiny appearance. Griffith injected the bacteria into mice and determined how the mice were infected.

1. Mice injected with live, infective *S* cells (control to show effect of *S* cells)

RESULT: Mice die. Live, infective *S* cells in their blood; shows that *S* cells are virulent.

2. Mice injected with live, noninfective *R* cells (control to show effect of *R* cells)

RESULT: Mice live. No live *R* cells in their blood; shows that *R* cells are nonvirulent.

3. Mice injected with heat-killed *S* cells (control to show effect of dead *S* cells)

RESULT: Mice live. No live *S* cells in their blood; shows that live *S* cells are necessary to be virulent to mice.

4. Mice injected with heat-killed *S* cells plus live *R* cells

RESULT: Mice die. Live *S* cells in their blood; shows that living *R* cells can be converted to virulent *S* cells with some factor from dead *S* cells.

CONCLUSION: Griffith concluded that some molecules released when *S* cells were killed could change living *R* cells genetically to the virulent *S* form. He called the molecule the *transforming principle* and the process of genetic change *transformation.*

*Sulphur is a component of protein not DNA.

*Phosphorus is the component of DNA, not protein.

13.1b Avery and His Coworkers Identified DNA as the Molecule That Transforms Rough *Streptococcus* to the Infective Form

In the 1940s, Oswald Avery, a physician and medical researcher at the hospital at Rockefeller Institute for Medical Research, and his coworkers Colin MacLeod and Maclyn McCarty performed an experiment designed to identify the chemical nature of the transforming principle that can change *R Streptococcus* bacteria into the *S* infective form. Rather than working with mice, they attempted to reproduce the transformation using bacteria growing in culture tubes. They used heat to kill virulent *S* bacteria and then treated the macromolecules extracted from the cells with enzymes that break down each of the three main candidate molecules for the hereditary material—protein; DNA; or the other nucleic acid, ribonucleic acid (RNA). When they destroyed proteins or RNA, the researchers saw no effect; the extract of *S* bacteria still transformed *R* bacteria into virulent *S* bacteria—the cells had polysaccharide capsules and produced smooth colonies on culture plates. When they destroyed DNA, however, no transformation occurred—no smooth colonies were seen on culture plates.

In 1944, Avery and his colleagues published their discovery that the transforming principle was DNA. At the time, many scientists firmly believed that the genetic material was protein. So although their findings were clearly revolutionary, Avery and his colleagues presented their conclusions in the paper cautiously, offering several interpretations of their results. Some scientists accepted their results almost immediately. However, those who believed that the genetic material was protein argued that it was possible that not all protein was destroyed by their enzyme treatments and, as contaminants in their DNA transformation reaction, these remaining proteins were, in fact, responsible for the transformation. Further experiments were needed to convince all scientists that DNA is the hereditary molecule.

13.1c Hershey and Chase Found the Final Evidence Establishing DNA as the Hereditary Molecule

A final series of experiments conducted in 1952 by bacteriologist Alfred D. Hershey and his laboratory assistant Martha Chase at the Cold Spring Harbor Laboratory removed any remaining doubts that DNA is the hereditary molecule. Hershey and Chase studied the infection of the bacterium *Escherichia coli* by bacteriophage T2. *E. coli* is a bacterium normally found in the intestines of mammals. **Bacteriophages** (or simply **phages**; see Chapter 10) are viruses that infect bacteria. A **virus** is an infectious agent that contains either DNA or RNA surrounded by a protein coat. Viruses cannot reproduce except in a host cell. When a virus infects a cell, it can use the cell's resources to produce more virus particles.

The phage life cycle begins when a phage attaches to the surface of a bacterium. For phages such as T2, the infected cell quickly stops producing its own molecules and instead starts making progeny phages. After about 100 to 200 phages are assembled inside the bacterial cell, a viral enzyme breaks down the cell wall, killing the cell and releasing the new phages. The whole life cycle takes approximately 90 minutes.

The T2 phage that Hershey and Chase studied consists of only a core of DNA surrounded by proteins. Therefore, one of these molecules must be the genetic material that enters the bacterial cell and directs the infective cycle within. But which one? Hershey and Chase prepared two batches of phages, one with the protein tagged with a radioactive label and the other with the DNA tagged with a radioactive label. To obtain labelled phages, they added T2 to *E. coli* growing in the presence of either the radioactive isotope of sulphur (^{35}S) or the radioactive isotope of phosphorus (^{32}P) (**Figure 13.3**, step 1). The progeny phages produced in the ^{35}S medium had labelled proteins and unlabelled DNA because sulphur is a component of proteins but not of DNA. The phages produced in the ^{32}P medium had labelled DNA and unlabelled proteins because phosphorus is a component of DNA but not of proteins.

Hershey and Chase then infected separate cultures of *E. coli* with the two types of labelled phages (step 2). After a short period to allow the genetic material to enter the bacterial cell, they mixed the bacteria in a kitchen blender. They reasoned that only the genetic material was injected into the bacterial cell, leaving the rest of the phage outside. By mixing the cells in a blender, they could shear off the phage parts that did not enter the bacteria and collect them separately for analysis.

When they infected the bacteria with phages that contained labelled protein coats, they found no radioactivity in the bacterial cells but could easily measure it in the material removed by the blender (step 3, top). They also found no radioactivity in the progeny phages (step 4, top). However, if the infecting phages contained radioactive DNA, they found **radioactivity** inside the infected bacteria but none in the phage coats removed by the blender (step 3, bottom). In addition, radioactivity *was* seen in the progeny phages (step 4, bottom). The results were unequivocal: the genetic material of the phage was DNA, not protein.

When taken together, the experiments of Griffith, Avery and his coworkers, and Hershey and Chase established that DNA, not proteins, carries genetic information. Their research also established the term

Figure 13.3
The Hershey and Chase experiment demonstrating
that DNA is the hereditary molecule.

QUESTION: Is DNA or protein the genetic material?

EXPERIMENT: Hershey and Chase performed a definitive experiment to show whether DNA or protein is the genetic material. They used phage T2 for their experiment; it consists only of DNA and protein.

1. They infected *E. coli* growing in the presence of radioactive ^{32}P or ^{35}S with phage T2. The progeny phages were either labelled in their DNA with ^{32}P or in their protein with ^{35}S.

2. Fresh *E. coli* cells were infected with the radioactively labelled phages.

3. After infecting the bacteria, the cells were mixed in a blender to remove the phage coats from the cell surface. The components were analyzed for radioactivity.

4. Progeny phages analyzed for radioactivity.

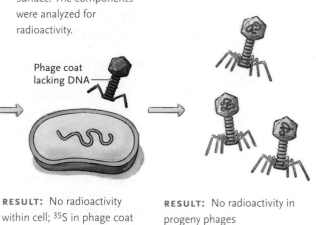

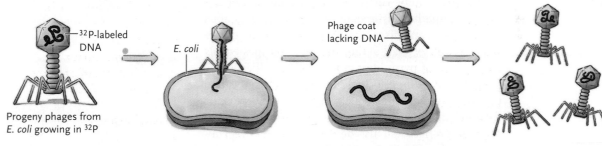

Progeny phages from *E. coli* growing in ^{35}S — ^{35}S-labeled protein

E. coli

Phage coat lacking DNA

RESULT: No radioactivity within cell; ^{35}S in phage coat

RESULT: No radioactivity in progeny phages

Progeny phages from *E. coli* growing in ^{32}P — ^{32}P-labeled DNA

E. coli

Phage coat lacking DNA

RESULT: ^{32}P within cell; not in phage coat

RESULT: ^{32}P in progeny phages

CONCLUSION: ^{32}P, the radioisotope used to label DNA, was found within phage-infected cells and in progeny phages, indicating that DNA is the genetic material. ^{35}S, the radioisotope used to label proteins, was found in phage coats after infection, but was not found in the infected cell or in progeny phages, showing that protein is not the genetic material.

transformation, which is still used in molecular biology. **Transformation** is the conversion of a cell's hereditary type by the uptake of DNA released by the breakdown of another cell, as in the Griffith and Avery experiments. Having identified DNA as the hereditary molecule, scientists turned next to determine its structure.

STUDY BREAK

How did Hershey and Chase exploit the life cycle of a phage to gain evidence for DNA as the hereditary material?

13.2 DNA Structure

The experiments that established DNA as the hereditary molecule were followed by a highly competitive scientific race to discover the structure of DNA. The race ended in 1953 when Watson and Crick elucidated the structure of DNA, ushering in a new era of molecular biology.

13.2a Watson and Crick Brought Together Information from Several Sources to Work Out DNA Structure

Before Watson and Crick began their research, other investigators had established that DNA contains four different nucleotides. Each nucleotide consists of the five-carbon sugar *deoxyribose* (carbon atoms on deoxyribose are numbered with primes from 1′ to 5′), a phosphate group, and one of the four nitrogenous bases—adenine (A), guanine (G), thymine (T), or cytosine (C) **(Figure 13.4).** Two of the bases, **adenine** and **guanine**, are *purines,* nitrogenous bases built from a pair of fused rings of carbon and nitrogen atoms. The other two bases, **thymine** and **cytosine**, are *pyrimidines,* built from a single carbon ring. An organic chemist, Erwin Chargaff, measured the amounts of nitrogenous bases in DNA and discovered that they occur in definite ratios. He observed that the amount of purines equals the amount of pyrimidines, but more specifically, the amount of adenine equals the amount of thymine, and the amount of guanine equals the amount of cytosine; these relationships are known as *Chargaff's rules.*

Researchers had also determined that DNA contains nucleotides joined to form a *polynucleotide chain.* In a polynucleotide chain, the deoxyribose sugars are linked by phosphate groups in an alternating sugar–phosphate–sugar–phosphate pattern, forming a **sugar–phosphate backbone** (highlighted in grey in Figure 13.4). Each phosphate group is a "bridge" between the 3′ carbon of one sugar and the 5′ carbon of the next sugar; the entire linkage, including the bridging phosphate group, is called a *phosphodiester bond.*

The polynucleotide chain of DNA has polarity, or directionality. That is, the two ends of the chain are not the same: at one end, a phosphate group is bound to the 5′ carbon of a deoxyribose sugar, whereas at the other end, a hydroxyl group is bonded to the 3′ carbon of a deoxyribose sugar (see Figure 13.4). Consequently, the two ends are called the **5′ end** and **3′ end**, respectively.

Those were the known facts when Watson and Crick began their collaboration in the early 1950s. However, the number of polynucleotide chains in a DNA molecule and the manner in which they fold or twist in DNA were unknown. Watson and Crick themselves did not conduct experiments to study the

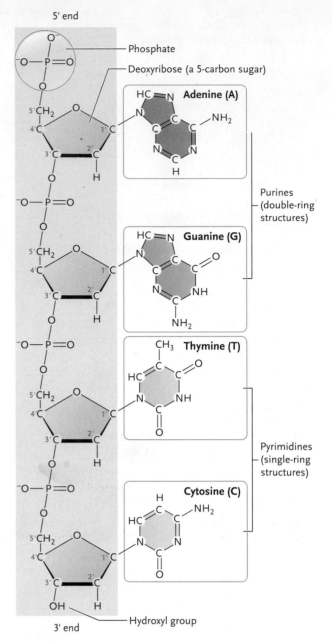

Figure 13.4

The four nucleotide subunits of DNA, linked into a polynucleotide chain. The sugar–phosphate backbone of the chain is highlighted in grey. The connection between adjacent deoxyribose sugars is a phosphodiester bond. The polynucleotide chain has polarity; at one end, the 5′ end, a phosphate group is bound to the 5′ carbon of a deoxyribose sugar, whereas at the other end, the 3′ end, a hydroxyl group is bound to the 3′ carbon of a deoxyribose sugar.

structure of DNA; instead, they used the research data of others for their analysis, relying heavily on data gathered by physicist Maurice H.F. Wilkins and research associate Rosalind Franklin **(Figure 13.5a),** at King's College, London. These researchers were using X-ray diffraction to study the structure of DNA **(Figure 13.5b).** In **X-ray diffraction,** an X-ray beam is directed at a molecule in the form of a regular solid, ideally in the form of a crystal. Within the crystal, regularly arranged rows and banks of atoms bend

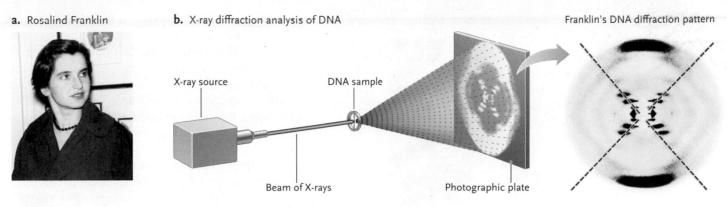

a. Rosalind Franklin

b. X-ray diffraction analysis of DNA

Franklin's DNA diffraction pattern

X-ray source

DNA sample

Beam of X-rays

Photographic plate

SPL/Photo Researchers, Inc.

Figure 13.5

X-ray diffraction analysis of DNA. **(a)** Rosalind Franklin. **(b)** The X-ray diffraction method to study DNA and the diffraction pattern Rosalind Franklin obtained. The X-shaped pattern of spots (dashed lines) was correctly interpreted by Franklin to indicate that DNA has a helical structure similar to a spiral staircase.

purine – purine ⇒ too wide

and reflect the X-rays into smaller beams that exit the crystal at definite angles determined by the arrangement of atoms in the crystal. If a photographic film is placed behind the crystal, the exiting beams produce a pattern of exposed spots. From that pattern, researchers can deduce the positions of the atoms in the crystal.

Wilkins and Franklin did not have DNA crystals with which to work, but they were able to obtain X-ray diffraction patterns from DNA molecules that had been pulled out into a fibre (see Figure 13.5). The patterns indicated that the DNA molecules within the fibre were cylindrical and about 2 nm in diameter. Separations between the spots showed that major patterns of atoms repeat at intervals of 0.34 and 3.4 nm within the DNA. Franklin correctly interpreted an X-shaped distribution of spots in the diffraction pattern (see dashed lines in Figure 13.5) to mean that DNA has a helical structure.

13.2b The New Model Proposed That Two Polynucleotide Chains Wind into a DNA Double Helix

Watson and Crick constructed scale models of the four DNA nucleotides and fitted them together in different ways until they arrived at an arrangement that satisfied both Wilkins' and Franklin's X-ray data and Chargaff's chemical analysis. Watson and Crick's trials led them to a double-stranded model for DNA structure in which two polynucleotide chains twist around each other in a right-handed way, like a double-spiral staircase **(Figure 13.6, p. 278).** They were the first to propose the famous double-helix model for DNA.

In the **double-helix model**, the two sugar–phosphate backbones are separated from each other by a regular distance. The bases extend into and fill this central space. A purine and a pyrimidine, if paired together, are exactly wide enough to fill the space between the backbone chains in the double helix. However, a purine–purine base pair is too wide to fit the space exactly, and a pyrimidine–pyrimidine pair is too narrow. From Chargaff's data, Watson and Crick proposed that the purine–pyrimidine base pairs in DNA are A-T and G-C pairs. That is, wherever an A occurs in one strand, a T must be opposite it in the other strand; wherever a G occurs in one strand, a C must be opposite it. This feature of DNA is called **complementary base pairing**, and one strand is said to be *complementary* to the other. The base pairs, which fit together like pieces of a jigsaw puzzle, are stabilized by hydrogen bonds—two between A and T and three between G and C (see Figure 13.6; hydrogen bonds are discussed in *The Chemical and Physical Foundations of Biology* pages). The hydrogen bonds between the paired bases, repeated along the double helix, hold the two strands together in the helix.

The base pairs lie in flat planes almost perpendicular to the long axis of the DNA molecule. In this state, each base pair occupies a length of 0.34 nm along the long axis of the double helix (see Figure 13.6). This spacing accounts for the repeating 0.34 nm pattern noted in the X-ray diffraction patterns. The larger 3.4 nm repeat pattern was interpreted to mean that each full turn of the double helix takes up 3.4 nm along the length of the molecule; therefore, 10 base pairs are packed into a full turn.

Watson and Crick also realized that the two strands of a double helix fit together in a stable chemical way only if they are **antiparallel**, that is, only if they run in opposite directions (see Figure 13.6, arrows). In other words, the *3′ end* of one strand is opposite the *5′ end* of the other strand. This antiparallel arrangement is highly significant for the process of replication, which is discussed in the next section.

As hereditary material, DNA must faithfully store and transmit genetic information for the entire life cycle of an organism. Watson and Crick recognized that this information is coded into the DNA by the particular

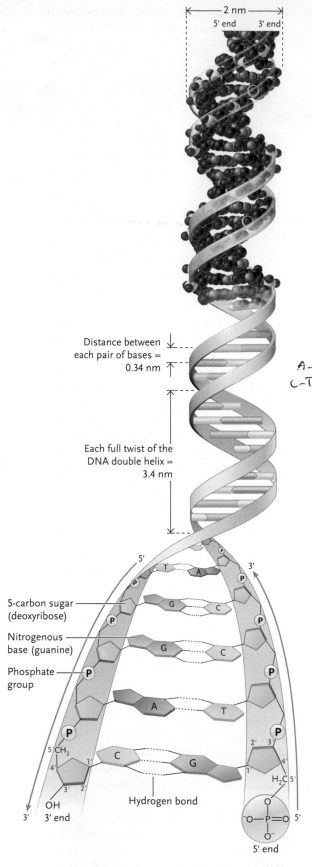

Distance between
each pair of bases =
0.34 nm

Each full twist of the
DNA double helix =
3.4 nm

5-carbon sugar
(deoxyribose)

Nitrogenous
base (guanine)

Phosphate
group

Hydrogen bond

Figure 13.6
DNA double helix. Arrows and labelling of the ends show that the two polynucleotide chains of the double helix are antiparallel—that is, they have opposite polarity in that they run in opposite directions. In the space-filling model at the top, the spaces occupied by atoms are indicated by spheres. There are 10 base pairs per turn of the helix; only 8 base pairs are visible because the other 2 are obscured where the backbones pass over each other.

sequence of the four nucleotides. Although only four different kinds of nucleotides exist, combining them in groups allows an essentially infinite number of different sequences to be "written," just as the 26 letters of the alphabet can be combined in groups to write a virtually unlimited number of words. Chapter 14 shows how taking the four nucleotides in groups of three forms enough words to spell out the structure of any conceivable protein.

Watson and Crick announced their model for DNA structure in a brief but monumental paper published in the journal *Nature* in 1953. Watson and Crick shared a Nobel Prize with Wilkins in 1962 for their discovery of the molecular structure of DNA. Rosalind Franklin might have been a candidate for a Nobel Prize had she not died of cancer at age 38 in 1958. (The Nobel Prize is given only to living investigators.) Unquestionably, Watson and Crick's discovery of DNA structure opened the way to molecular studies of genetics and heredity, leading to our modern understanding of gene structure and action at the molecular level.

A–G ⇒ purines
C–T ⇒ pyrimidines

STUDY BREAK

1. Which bases in DNA are purines? Which are pyrimidines?
2. What bonds form between complementary base pairs? Between a base and the deoxyribose sugar? a) hydrogen b) phosphodiester
3. Which features of the DNA molecule did Watson and Crick describe?

information is coded in DNA by 4 nucleotides

13.3 DNA Replication

Once they had discovered the structure of DNA, Watson and Crick realized immediately that complementary base pairing between the two strands could explain how DNA replicates **(Figure 13.7)**. They imagined that, for replication, the hydrogen bonds between the two strands break, and the two strands unwind and separate. Each strand then acts as a template for the synthesis of its partner strand. When replication is complete, there are two double helices, each of which has one strand derived from the parental DNA molecule base paired with a newly synthesized strand. Most important, each of the two new double helices has the identical base-pair sequence as the parental DNA molecule.

The model of replication Watson and Crick proposed is termed **semiconservative replication (Figure 13.8a, p. 280).** Other scientists proposed two other models for replication. In the *conservative replication model,* the two strands of the original molecule serve as templates for the two strands of a new

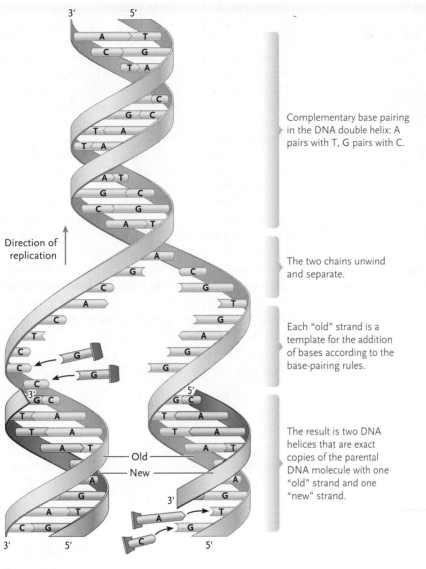

Complementary base pairing in the DNA double helix: A pairs with T, G pairs with C.

The two chains unwind and separate.

Each "old" strand is a template for the addition of bases according to the base-pairing rules.

The result is two DNA helices that are exact copies of the parental DNA molecule with one "old" strand and one "new" strand.

Direction of replication

Old
New

Figure 13.7

Watson and Crick's model for DNA replication. The original DNA molecule is shown in grey. A new polynucleotide chain (red) is assembled on each original chain as the two chains unwind. The template and complementary copy chains remain wound together when replication is complete, producing molecules that are half old and half new. The model is known as the semiconservative model for DNA replication.

DNA molecule and then rewind into an all "old" molecule **(Figure 13.8b)**. After the two complementary copies separate from their templates, they wind together into an all "new" molecule. In the *dispersive replication model,* neither parental strand is conserved, and both chains of each replicated molecule contain old and new segments **(Figure 13.8c)**.

13.3a Meselson and Stahl Showed that DNA Replication Is Semiconservative

A definitive experiment published in 1958 by Matthew Meselson and Franklin Stahl of the California Institute of Technology demonstrated that DNA replication is semiconservative **(Figure 13.9, p. 281)**. In their experiment, Meselson and Stahl had to be able to distinguish

parental DNA strands from newly synthesized DNA. To do this, they used a nonradioactive "heavy" nitrogen isotope to tag the parental DNA strands. The heavy isotope, ^{15}N, has one more **neutron** in its nucleus than the normal ^{13}N isotope. Molecules containing ^{15}N are measurably heavier (denser) than molecules of the same type containing ^{13}N.

As the first step in their experiment, Meselson and Stahl grew the bacterium *E. coli* in a culture medium containing the heavy ^{15}N isotope (see Figure 13.9, step 1). The heavy isotope was incorporated into the nitrogenous bases of DNA, resulting in all the DNA being labelled with ^{15}N. Then they transferred the bacteria to a culture medium containing the light ^{13}N isotope (step 2). All new DNA synthesized after the transfer contained the light isotope. Just before the transfer to the medium with the ^{13}N isotope, and after each round of replication following the transfer, they took a sample of the cells and extracted the DNA (step 3).

Meselson and Stahl then mixed the DNA samples with cesium chloride (CsCl) and centrifuged the mixture at very high speed (step 4). During the centrifugation, the CsCl forms a density gradient and DNA molecules move to a position in the gradient where their density matches that of the CsCl. Therefore, DNA of different densities is separated into bands, with the densest DNA settling closer to the bottom of the tube. In Figure 13.9, "Result" shows the outcome of these experiments, and "Conclusions" shows why the results were compatible with only the semiconservative replication model.

13.3b DNA Polymerases Are the Primary Enzymes of DNA Replication

During replication, complementary nucleotide chains are assembled from individual nucleotides by enzymes known as **DNA polymerases**. More than one kind of DNA polymerase is required for DNA replication in both eukaryotes and prokaryotes. *Nucleoside triphosphates* are substrates for the polymerization reaction catalyzed by

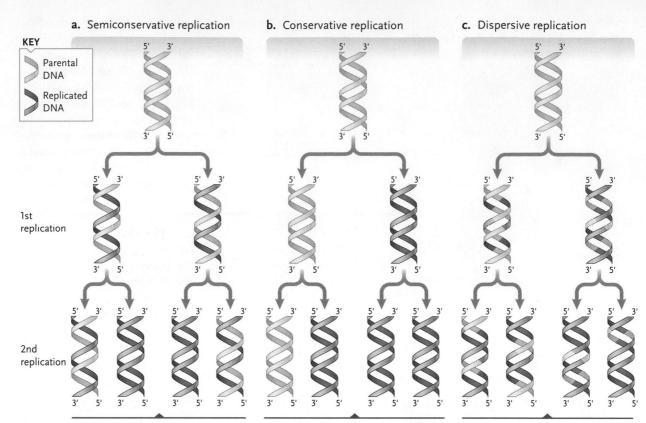

a. Semiconservative replication   b. Conservative replication   c. Dispersive replication

KEY

Parental DNA

Replicated DNA

1st replication

2nd replication

Figure 13.8
(a) Semiconservative, **(b)** conservative, and **(c)** dispersive models for DNA replication.

The two parental strands of DNA unwind, and each is a template for synthesis of a new strand. After replication has occurred, each double helix has one old strand paired with one new strand. This model was the one proposed by Watson and Crick themselves.

The parental strands of DNA unwind, and each is a template for synthesis of a new strand. After replication has occurred, the parental strands pair up again. Therefore, the two resulting double helices consist of one with two old strands, and the other with two new strands.

The original double helix splits into double-stranded segments onto which new double-stranded segments form. These newly formed sections somehow assemble into two double helices, both of which are a mixture of the original double-stranded DNA interspersed with new double-stranded DNA.

DNA polymerases **(Figure 13.10, p. 282)**. A nucleoside triphosphate is a nitrogenous base linked to a sugar, which is linked, in turn, to a chain of three phosphate groups. You have encountered a nucleoside triphosphate before, namely the adenosine triphosphate (ATP) produced in cellular respiration (see Chapter 6). The nucleoside triphosphates used in DNA replication differ from ATP by having the sugar deoxyribose rather than the sugar ribose. Because four different bases are found in DNA—adenine (A), guanine (G), cytosine (C), and thymine (T)—four different nucleoside triphosphates are used for DNA replication. By analogy with the ATP naming, the nucleoside triphosphates for DNA replication are given the short names dATP, dGTP, dCTP, and dTTP, where the "d" stands for "deoxyribose."

Figure 13.10 presents a section of a DNA polynucleotide chain being replicated to show how DNA polymerase catalyzes the assembly of a new DNA strand that is complementary to the template strand. To understand Figure 13.10, remember that the carbons in the deoxyriboses of nucleotides are numbered with primes. Each DNA strand has two distinct ends: the 5′ end has an exposed phosphate group attached to the 5′ carbon of the sugar, and the 3′ end has an exposed hydroxyl group attached to the 3′ carbon of the

sugar. As we learned earlier, because of the antiparallel nature of the DNA double helix, the 5′ end of one strand is opposite the 3′ end of the other.

Part of a template strand with two nucleotides of a new strand hydrogen bonded to it by complementary base pairing is shown in step 1 of Figure 13.10. One of the characteristics of DNA polymerase is that it can add a nucleotide *only to the 3′ end of an existing nucleotide chain.* The next template nucleotide has a T base. This means the DNA polymerase will bind a nucleoside triphosphate with an A base (dATP) from the surrounding solution (step 2). The enzyme then catalyzes the formation of the phosphodiester bond involving the 3′−OH group at the end of the existing chain and the innermost of the three phosphate groups of the dATP, releasing the other two phosphates as a pyrophosphate molecule (step 3). Hydrolysis of the bond between the two phosphates provides the energy for the formation of the new bond.

The DNA polymerase then moves to the next base on the DNA template, shown as guanine in step 3, binds a dCTP, and, using the reaction just described, catalyzes the formation of a phosphodiester bond, inserting the C nucleotide to the growing new strand. The process then continues, adding complementary nucleotides one by one to the growing DNA strand.

Figure 13.9
The Meselson and Stahl experiment demonstrating the semiconservative model to be correct.

QUESTION: Does DNA replicate semiconservatively?

EXPERIMENT: Matthew Meselson and Franklin Stahl proved that the semiconservative model of DNA replication is correct and that the conservative and dispersive models are incorrect.

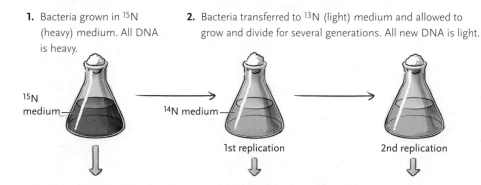

1. Bacteria grown in ¹⁵N (heavy) medium. All DNA is heavy.

2. Bacteria transferred to ¹³N (light) medium and allowed to grow and divide for several generations. All new DNA is light.

¹⁵N medium

¹⁴N medium

1st replication

2nd replication

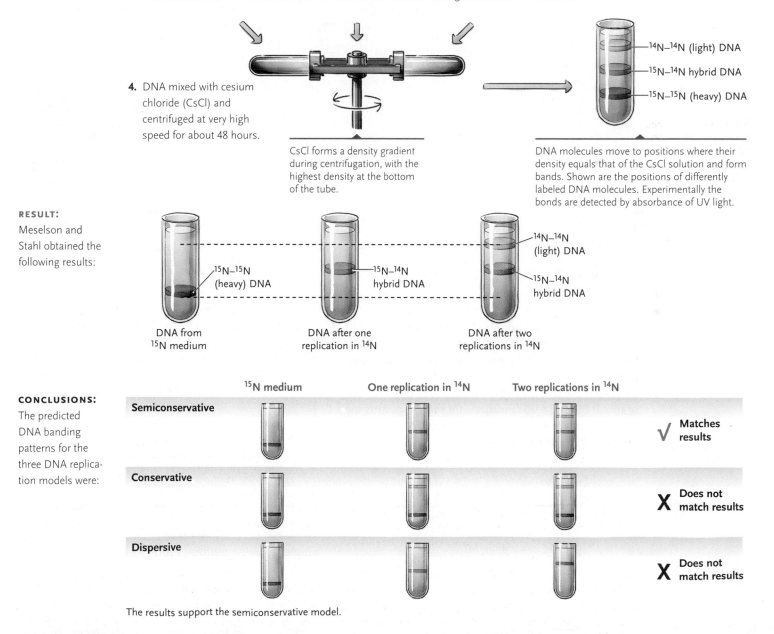

3. DNA extracted from bacteria cultured in ¹⁵N medium and after each generation in ¹³N medium.

4. DNA mixed with cesium chloride (CsCl) and centrifuged at very high speed for about 48 hours.

CsCl forms a density gradient during centrifugation, with the highest density at the bottom of the tube.

DNA molecules move to positions where their density equals that of the CsCl solution and form bands. Shown are the positions of differently labeled DNA molecules. Experimentally the bonds are detected by absorbance of UV light.

¹⁴N–¹⁴N (light) DNA
¹⁵N–¹⁴N hybrid DNA
¹⁵N–¹⁵N (heavy) DNA

RESULT:
Meselson and Stahl obtained the following results:

¹⁵N–¹⁵N (heavy) DNA

¹⁵N–¹⁴N hybrid DNA

¹⁴N–¹⁴N (light) DNA

¹⁵N–¹⁴N hybrid DNA

DNA from ¹⁵N medium

DNA after one replication in ¹⁴N

DNA after two replications in ¹⁴N

CONCLUSIONS:
The predicted DNA banding patterns for the three DNA replication models were:

	¹⁵N medium	One replication in ¹⁴N	Two replications in ¹⁴N	
Semiconservative				√ Matches results
Conservative				X Does not match results
Dispersive				X Does not match results

The results support the semiconservative model.

CHAPTER 13   DNA STRUCTURE, REPLICATION, AND ORGANIZATION

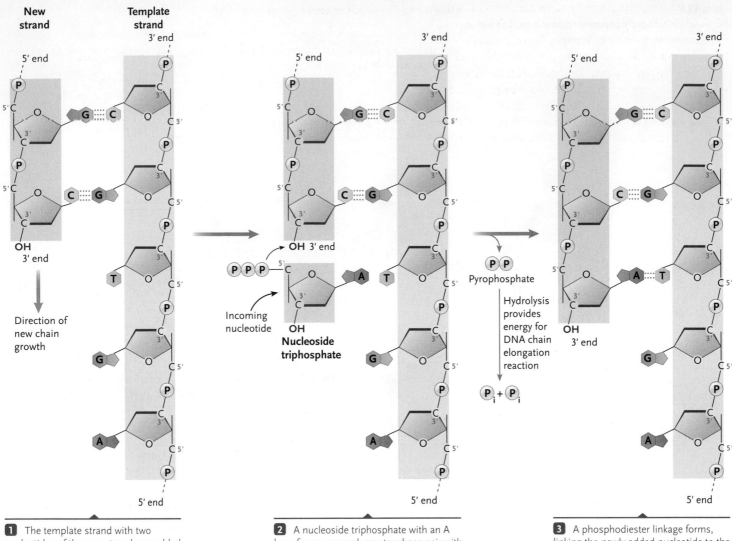

1 The template strand with two nucleotides of the new strand assembled.

2 A nucleoside triphosphate with an A base forms a complementary base pair with the next nucleotide of the template strand.

3 A phosphodiester linkage forms, linking the newly added nucleotide to the end of the primer, lengthening the strand by one.

Figure 13.10

Reactions assembling a complementary chain in the 5′→3′ direction on a template DNA strand, showing the phosphodiester linkage created when the DNA polymerase enzyme adds each nucleotide to the chain.

As a new DNA strand is assembled, a 3′−OH group is always exposed at its "newest" end; the "oldest" end of the new chain has an exposed 5′ triphosphate. DNA polymerases are therefore said to assemble nucleotide chains in the 5′→3′ direction. Because of the antiparallel nature of DNA, the template strand is "read" in the 3′→5′ direction for this new synthesis.

The key molecular events of DNA replication described in this section are as follows:

1. The two strands of the DNA molecule unwind for replication to occur.
2. Nucleotides are added only to an existing chain.
3. The overall direction of new synthesis is in the 5′→3′ direction, which is a direction antiparallel to that of the template strand.
4. Nucleotides enter into a newly synthesized chain according to the A-T and G-C complementary base-pairing rules.

The following sections describe how enzymes and other proteins conduct these molecular events.

13.3c Helicases Unwind DNA to Expose Template Strands for New DNA Synthesis

For replication to be semiconservative, the two strands of the parental DNA molecule must unwind and separate to expose template strands for new DNA synthesis during the replication process. The unwinding produces a Y-shaped structure called a **replication fork**, which consists of the two unwound template strands transitioning to double-helical DNA. An enzyme, **DNA helicase**, catalyzes the unwinding, which exposes both strands for the next steps in replication. The helicase uses the energy of ATP hydrolysis to unwind the DNA helix. The exposed single-stranded segments of DNA become coated with **single-stranded binding proteins**, which stabilize the DNA for the replication process. These proteins are displaced as the replication enzymes make the new polynucleotide chain on the template strands.

Let us consider a possible consequence of the unwinding of DNA by helicases. If the DNA is circular, as is the case for the genomes of most bacteria, unwinding the DNA will eventually cause the still-wound DNA ahead of the unwinding to become knotted. You can visualize this by making a small circular double helix with a pair of shoelaces. Now pick a place and pull apart the laces. You will see that the more you pull, the more the laces become overtwisted and strained on the other side of the circle. In the cell, the overtwisting and strain of DNA ahead of the replication fork during replication are avoided by the action of enzymes known as **topoisomerases**, which remove the overtwisting as it forms.

13.3d RNA Primers Provide the Starting Point for DNA Polymerase to Begin Synthesizing a New DNA Chain

DNA polymerases can add nucleotides only to the 3′ end of an existing strand. How, then, can a new strand begin since there is no existing strand in place? The answer lies in a short nucleotide chain called a **primer**, made of RNA instead of DNA. The primer, assembled by the enzyme **primase**, is laid down as the first series of nucleotides in a new DNA strand. RNA primers are removed and replaced with DNA later in replication.

13.3e One New DNA Strand Is Synthesized Continuously; the Other, Discontinuously

DNA polymerases assemble a new DNA strand on a template strand in the 5′→3′ direction. Because the two strands of a DNA molecule are antiparallel, only one of the template strands runs in a direction that allows DNA polymerase to make a 5′→3′ complementary copy in the direction of unwinding. That is, on this template strand (top strand in **Figure 13.11**), the new DNA strand is synthesized continuously in the direction of unwinding of the double helix. However, the other template strand (bottom strand in Figure 13.11) runs in the opposite direction; this means that DNA polymerase has to copy it in the direction opposite to the unwinding.

How is the new DNA strand made in the opposite direction to the unwinding? The polymerases make this strand in short lengths that are actually synthesized in the direction opposite to that of DNA unwinding (see Figure 13.11). The short lengths produced by this **discontinuous replication** are then covalently linked into a continuous polynucleotide chain. The short lengths are called *Okazaki fragments,* in honour of Reiji Okazaki, the Japanese scientist who first detected them. The new DNA strand assembled in the direction of DNA unwinding is called the **leading strand** of DNA replication; the strand assembled discontinuously in the opposite direction is called the **lagging strand**. The template strand for the leading strand is the *leading strand template,* and the template strand for the lagging strand is the *lagging strand template.*

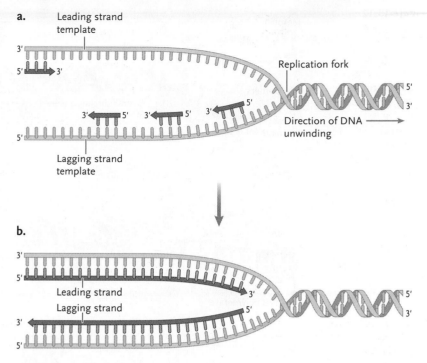

Figure 13.11

How antiparallel template strands are replicated at a fork. The template strand presented to DNA polymerase in the "wrong" 5′→3′ direction—the strand on the bottom in **(a)**—is copied in short lengths that run opposite to the direction of fork movement. The short lengths are then linked into a continuous chain **(b).** The overall effect is synthesis of both strands in the direction of fork movement.

13.3f Multiple Enzymes Coordinate Their Activities in DNA Replication

Helicase, primase, and DNA polymerase coordinate their activities with additional enzymes to replicate DNA. In the first step of the process, a helicase unwinds the template DNA to produce a replication fork (**Figure 13.12, p. 284,** step 1). Just behind the site of unwinding, primases lay down short RNA primers about 10 nucleotides in length. The primers are assembled in the 5′→3′ direction on both template chains—in the direction of unwinding on one chain and in the opposite direction on the other.

DNA polymerase then adds DNA nucleotides to the RNA primers (step 2). Helicase continues to unwind the DNA. Leading strand synthesis continues in the direction of unwinding, whereas on the lagging strand template, primase creates a new RNA primer and DNA polymerase adds DNA nucleotides to the new primer (step 3). When this second fragment reaches the primer of the first fragment, the DNA polymerase leaves and a different type of DNA polymerase binds. This polymerase removes the RNA primer on the first fragment, replacing the RNA nucleotides with DNA nucleotides (step 4). At this point, the two newly synthesized fragments are not covalently joined—they have a "nick" between them (see step 4). Another enzyme, **DNA ligase** (*ligare* = to tie), closes the nick,

Figure 13.12

Steps in DNA replication, including the activities of the helicase, primase, DNA polymerases, and DNA ligase taking part in the process. Primer synthesis, removal, gap filling, and nick sealing occur primarily in the lagging strand. The drawings simplify the process. In reality, the enzymes assemble at the fork, replicating both strands from that position as the template strands fold and pass through the assembly.

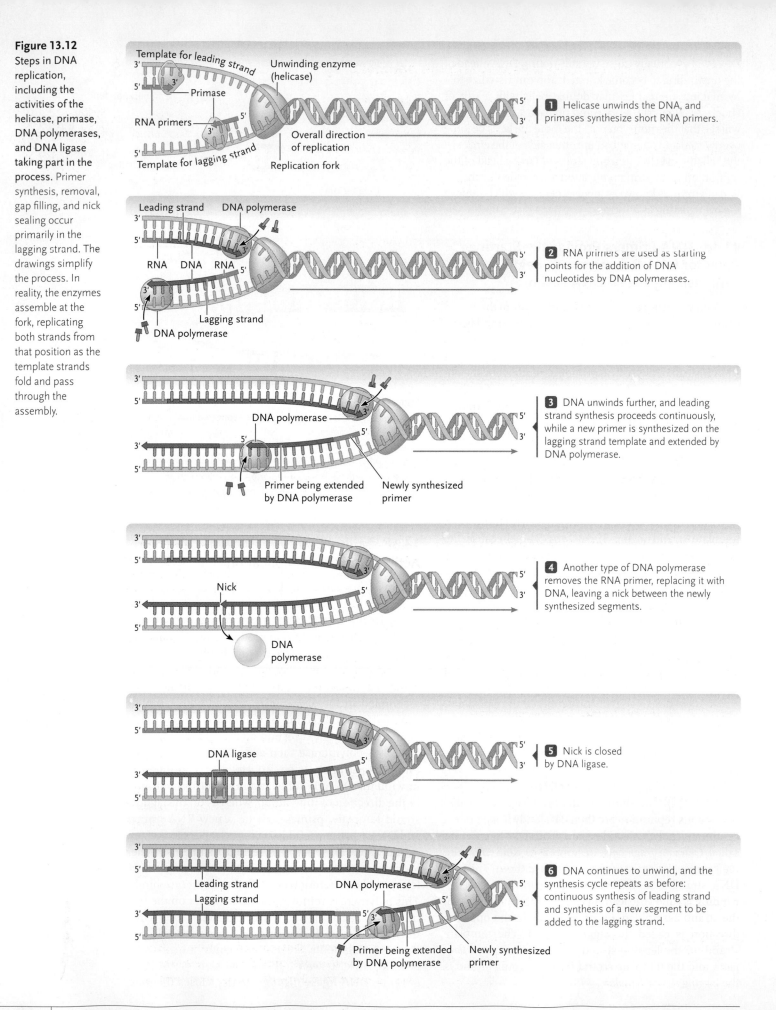

1 Helicase unwinds the DNA, and primases synthesize short RNA primers.

2 RNA primers are used as starting points for the addition of DNA nucleotides by DNA polymerases.

3 DNA unwinds further, and leading strand synthesis proceeds continuously, while a new primer is synthesized on the lagging strand template and extended by DNA polymerase.

4 Another type of DNA polymerase removes the RNA primer, replacing it with DNA, leaving a nick between the newly synthesized segments.

5 Nick is closed by DNA ligase.

6 DNA continues to unwind, and the synthesis cycle repeats as before: continuous synthesis of leading strand and synthesis of a new segment to be added to the lagging strand.

Acyclic Nucleoside Phosphonates as Antiviral Drugs

Viruses are obligate parasites that exploit the cellular machinery of infected host cells for replication and gene expression. Such intimate association with host biochemistry makes it difficult for scientists to find an exclusively viral "target" for antiviral drug binding.

However, the herpes viruses provide such a target when, once inside the nucleus of an infected cell, they transcribe a gene coding for their own distinctive DNA polymerase. This novel polymerase replicates viral DNA, drawing from the cellular pool of nucleotide triphosphates (see Figure 13.12).

It has been possible to selectively "poison" viral DNA replication with acyclic nucleoside phosphonates such as cidofovir, shown below, because they (1) are converted to their triphosphate form by infected cells, (2) are then selectively incorporated into viral DNA (instead of the normal nucleotides) by viral polymerase, and (3) block further DNA synthesis.

These drugs are part of a large class of compounds called base analogues that are incorporated into DNA by "mistake." Compare the structures below with those of the standard bases shown in Figure 13.4 and notice why these drugs are called "acyclic."

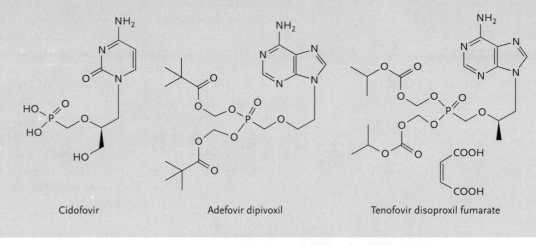

Cidofovir   Adefovir dipivoxil   Tenofovir disoproxil fumarate

joining the two fragments into one larger fragment (step 5). The replication process continues in the same way until the entire DNA molecule is copied (step 6). **Table 13.1** summarizes the activities of the major enzymes replicating DNA.

The entire replication mechanism, including the activities of the helicase, primase, DNA polymerases, DNA ligase, and other proteins involved in the process, advances at a rate of about 500 to 1000 nucleotides per second in prokaryotes and at a rate of about 50 to 100 per second in eukaryotes. The entire process is so rapid that the RNA primers and gaps left by discontinuous synthesis persist for only seconds or fractions of a second. Consequently, the replication enzymes operate only at the replication fork. A short distance behind the fork, the new DNA chains are fully continuous and wound with their template strands into complete DNA double helices. Each helix consists of one "old" and one "new" polynucleotide chain.

Researchers identified the enzymes that replicate DNA through experiments with a variety of prokaryotes and eukaryotes and with viruses that infect both types of cells. Experiments with the bacterium *E. coli* have provided the most complete information about DNA replication, particularly in the laboratory of Arthur Kornberg at Stanford University. Kornberg received a Nobel Prize in 1959 for his discovery of the mechanism for DNA synthesis.

Table 13.1	Major Enzymes of DNA Replication
Enzyme	**Activity**
Helicase	Unwinds DNA helix
Single-stranded binding proteins	Stabilize DNA in single-chain form
Primase	Assembles RNA primers
DNA polymerases	Assemble DNA chains on primers; replace primers while simultaneously replacing primer nucleotides with DNA nucleotides
DNA ligase	Seals nicks left after RNA primers replaced with DNA
Topoisomerases	Relieve overtwisting and strain of DNA ahead of replication fork (in circular DNA)

13.3g Telomerases Solve a Specialized Replication Problem at the Ends of Linear DNA Molecules

The priming mechanism outlined in Figure 13.12 leaves one major problem unsolved for linear chromosomes, such as those in eukaryotes. Think about replication

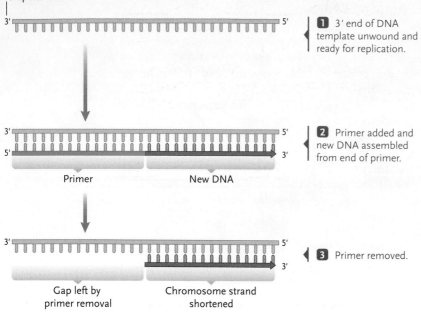

1 3' end of DNA template unwound and ready for replication.

2 Primer added and new DNA assembled from end of primer.

Primer   New DNA

3 Primer removed.

Gap left by primer removal   Chromosome strand shortened

Figure 13.13
How a gap is left by primer removal at the 5' end of a replicating linear DNA molecule.

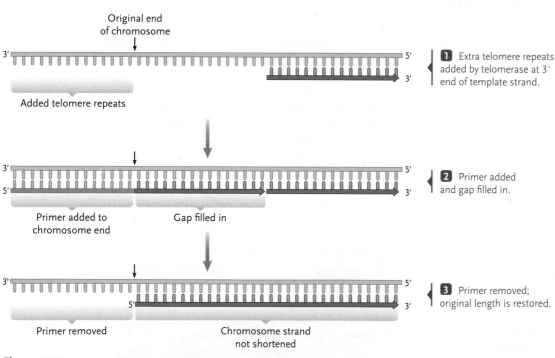

Original end of chromosome

1 Extra telomere repeats added by telomerase at 3' end of template strand.

Added telomere repeats

2 Primer added and gap filled in.

Primer added to chromosome end   Gap filled in

3 Primer removed; original length is restored.

Primer removed   Chromosome strand not shortened

Figure 13.14
How telomere repeats added to eukaryotic chromosomes prevent chromosome shortening.

that occurs at one end of a chromosome (**Figure 13.13, step 1**). To begin the new strand, an RNA primer is laid down opposite the end of the template strand and then a DNA polymerase adds new DNA nucleotides from the end of this primer (step 2). Once replication is under way, this first primer is removed, leaving a gap at the beginning (5') end of the new strand (as in step 3). It is important to understand why this gap is formed.

If you look at step 4 in Figure 13.12, you will see that the blue RNA is removed and replaced with red DNA just by elongating the 3' end of an Okazaki fragment. However, at the very end of a chromosome, no such fragment is available to be extended. Although it looks theoretically easy to repair the gap by extending the 5' end of the DNA, there are no polymerases known to have this ability. In a similar way, a gap is produced at the 5' end of the new strand made starting at the other end of the chromosome. Therefore, when these new, now shortened DNA strands are used as a template for the next round of DNA replication, the new chromosome will be shorter. Indeed, when most somatic cells go through the cell cycle, the chromosomes shorten with each division. Deletion of genes by such shortening would have serious, eventually lethal, consequences for the cell.

In most chromosomes, however, the genes are protected by a buffer of noncoding DNA. That is, at the ends of each **eukaryotic chromosome** are telomeres (*telo* = end; *mere* = segment). **Telomeres** are short sequences repeated hundreds to thousands of times, which do not code for proteins. In humans, the repeated sequence, the *telomere repeat*, is 5'-TTAGGG-3' on the leading template strand. With each replication, a fraction of the telomere repeats is lost, but the genes are unaffected. The buffering fails only when the entire telomere is lost.

The enzyme **telomerase** can maintain the buffer by adding telomere repeats to the chromosome ends. Discovered in 1985 by Elizabeth H. Blackburn and her graduate student Carol W. Greider at the University of California, Berkeley, telomerase adds additional telomere repeats to the end of the *template strand* before DNA replication begins (**see Figure 13.14, step 1**; compare with Figure 13.13, step 1). After the addition, the primer of the leading strand is laid down, using the newly added telomere repeats as the template. A DNA polymerase then extends the new DNA strand as usual (see Figure 13.14, step 2). The primer is removed, which still leaves an unfilled gap at the beginning of the leading chain (step 3). However, this gap is now out on the end of the chromosome, far from coding regions. The telomerase enzyme, which appears to be present in all eukaryotes, is an unusual enzyme that consists of protein subunits complexed with RNA; the

RNA part is the template for making the extra telomere repeats.

Telomerase is active in some cells but not in others. In particular, telomerase is active in sperm and eggs, which is necessary to maintain chromosome length from generation to generation. It is also active in the rapidly dividing cells of the early embryo. However, telomerase becomes inactive after a number of divisions, meaning that subsequent telomeres shorten as the cells continue to divide. As a result, a cell is capable of only a certain number of mitotic divisions before it stops dividing and dies. Could telomere shortening, then, contribute to the aging process in multicellular animals? Telomere shortening has indeed been linked to the aging process, but it is unknown whether it contributes to or is a result of aging. Some observations have made it difficult to draw firm conclusions on this issue. For example, humans, a long-lived species, have telomeres that are much shorter than mice, which live just a few years. Clearly, telomeres alone do not determine the life span of an organism.

An unexpected link between telomerases and cancer was found when investigators discovered that more than 90% of cancer cells have fully active telomerase enzymes, regardless of the type of body cell from which they are derived. Evidently, as body cells develop into cancer cells, their telomerases are reactivated, preserving chromosome length during the rapid divisions characteristic of cancer. A positive side of this discovery is that it may lead to an effective cancer treatment if a means can be found to switch off the telomerases in tumour cells. The chromosomes in the rapidly dividing cancer cells would then eventually shorten to the length at which they break down, leading to cell death and elimination of the tumour.

13.3h DNA Replication Begins at Replication Origins

Replication begins at sites called **replication origins.** Hundreds of replication origins may be present in the long chromosomes of eukaryotes. The origins are recognized by proteins that bind to the DNA and stimulate helicases to start the unwinding, followed by primer synthesis and DNA replication. In most cases, replication proceeds from both sides of a replication origin, producing two replication forks that move in opposite directions **(Figure 13.15).** (This means that the leading strands and lagging strands are reversed on the two sides.) The forks eventually meet along the chromosomes to produce fully replicated DNA molecules.

Normally, a replication origin is activated only once during the S phase of a eukaryotic cell cycle, so no portion of the DNA is replicated more than once.

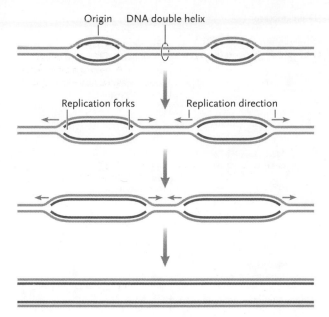

Figure 13.15
Replication from multiple origins in the chromosomes of eukaryotes.

STUDY BREAK

1. What is the importance of complementary base pairing to DNA replication?
2. Why is a primer needed for DNA replication on both strands?
3. Two DNA polymerases are used in DNA replication. What are their roles?
4. Why are telomeres important?

13.4 Mechanisms That Correct Replication Errors

DNA polymerases make very few errors as they assemble new nucleotide chains. Most of the mistakes that do occur, called **base-pair mismatches,** are corrected, either by a proofreading mechanism carried out during replication by the DNA polymerases themselves or by a DNA repair mechanism that corrects mismatched base pairs after replication is complete.

13.4a Proofreading Depends on the Ability of DNA Polymerases to Reverse and Remove Mismatched Bases

The **proofreading mechanism,** first proposed in 1972 by Arthur Kornberg and Douglas L. Brutlag of Stanford University, depends on the ability of DNA polymerases to back up and remove mispaired nucleotides from a DNA strand. Only when the most recently added base is correctly paired with its complementary base on the

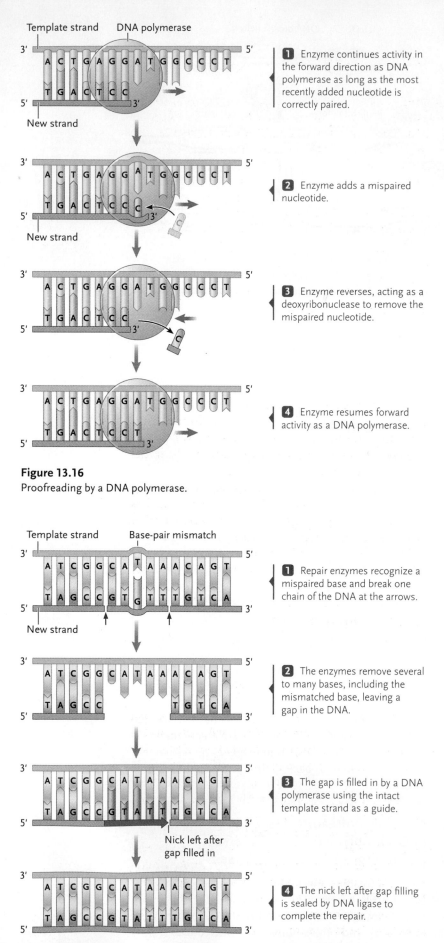

Figure 13.16
Proofreading by a DNA polymerase.

Enzyme continues activity in the forward direction as DNA polymerase as long as the most recently added nucleotide is correctly paired.

Enzyme adds a mispaired nucleotide.

Enzyme reverses, acting as a deoxyribonuclease to remove the mispaired nucleotide.

Enzyme resumes forward activity as a DNA polymerase.

Repair enzymes recognize a mispaired base and break one chain of the DNA at the arrows.

The enzymes remove several to many bases, including the mismatched base, leaving a gap in the DNA.

The gap is filled in by a DNA polymerase using the intact template strand as a guide.

The nick left after gap filling is sealed by DNA ligase to complete the repair.

Figure 13.17
Repair of mismatched bases in replicated DNA.

template strand can the DNA polymerases continue to add nucleotides to a growing chain. The correct pairs allow the fully stabilizing hydrogen bonds to form (**Figure 13.16,** step 1). If a newly added nucleotide is mismatched (step 2), the DNA polymerase reverses, using a built-in deoxyribonuclease to remove the newly added incorrect nucleotide (step 3). The enzyme resumes working forward, now inserting the correct nucleotide (step 4).

Several experiments have confirmed that the major DNA polymerases of replication can actually proofread their work. For example, when the primary DNA polymerase that replicates DNA in bacteria is intact, with its reverse activity working, its overall error rate is astonishingly low—only about 1 mispair survives in the DNA for every 1 million nucleotides assembled in the test tube. If the proofreading activity of the enzyme is experimentally inhibited, the error rate increases to about 1 mistake for every 1000 to 10 000 nucleotides assembled. Experiments with eukaryotes have yielded similar results.

13.4b DNA Repair Corrects Errors That Escape Proofreading

Any base-pair mismatches that remain after proofreading face still another round of correction by **DNA repair mechanisms**. These **mismatch repair** mechanisms increase the accuracy of DNA replication well beyond the one-in-a million errors that persist after proofreading. As noted earlier, the "correct" A-T and G-C base pairs fit together like pieces of a jigsaw puzzle, and their dimensions separate the sugar–phosphate backbone chains by a constant distance. Mispaired bases are too large or small to maintain the correct separation, and they cannot form the hydrogen bonds characteristic of the normal base pairs. As a result, base mismatches distort the structure of the DNA helix. These distortions provide recognition sites for the enzymes catalyzing mismatch repair.

The repair enzymes move along newly replicated DNA molecules, "scanning" the DNA for distortions in the newly synthesized nucleotide chain. If the enzymes encounter a distortion, they remove a portion of the new chain, including the mismatched nucleotides (**Figure 13.17,** step 1). The gap left by the removal (step 2) is then filled by a DNA polymerase, using the template strand as a guide (step 3). The repair is completed by a DNA ligase, which seals the nucleotide chain into a continuous DNA molecule (step 4).

The same repair mechanisms also detect and correct alterations in DNA caused by the damaging effects of chemicals and radiation, including the ultraviolet light in sunlight. Some idea of the importance of the repair mechanisms comes from the unfortunate plight of individuals with *xeroderma pigmentosum,* a hereditary disorder in which the repair mechanism is faulty. Because of the effects of unrepaired alterations in their DNA, skin cancer can develop quickly in these individuals if they are exposed to sunlight.

PEOPLE BEHIND BIOLOGY
Robert (Bob) Haynes, York University

In 1944, the Austrian physicist Erwin Schrödinger published *What Is Life?* This small book speculated about the theoretical nature of the genetic material and prompted several physicists to turn their creativity to solving fundamental problems in the field of biology.

Cross-fertilization of these scientific disciplines energized research into the molecular biology of the gene and, specifically through the career of Dr. Bob Haynes, provided pioneering insights into the ways in which cells suffer and respond to DNA damage. Subsequent research has revealed that a breakdown in repair of DNA damage has important implications for cancer, aging, certain genetic diseases, and exposure to physical and chemical mutagens.

Born in 1931, Dr. Haynes earned undergraduate and Ph.D. degrees in biophysics from the University of Western Ontario before working as a postdoctoral fellow in physics at St. Bartholomew's Hospital Medical College, University of London. He joined the Biophysics Departments of the University of Chicago and the University of California at Berkeley before returning to Canada in 1968 as chair of the Biology Department at York University in Toronto. Upon his death in 1998, Dr. Haynes was a fellow of the Royal Society of Canada and an officer of the Order of Canada in recognition of his broad contributions to research in environmental mutagenesis, international leadership, and science education.

Very few replication errors remain in DNA after proofreading and DNA repair. The errors that persist, although extremely rare, are a primary source of **mutations**, differences in DNA sequence that appear and remain in the replicated copies. When a mutation occurs in a gene, it can alter the property of the protein encoded by the gene, which, in turn, may alter how the organism functions. Hence, mutations are highly important to the evolutionary process because they are the ultimate source of the variability in offspring acted on by natural selection.

We now turn from DNA replication and error correction to the arrangements of DNA in eukaryotic and prokaryotic cells. These arrangements organize superstructures that fit the long DNA molecules into the microscopic dimensions of cells and also contribute to the regulation of DNA activity.

STUDY BREAK

Why is a proofreading mechanism important for DNA replication?

13.5 DNA Organization in Eukaryotes and Prokaryotes

Enzymatic proteins are the essential catalysts of every step in DNA replication. In addition, numerous proteins of other types organize the DNA in both eukaryotes and prokaryotes and control its function.

In eukaryotes, two major types of proteins, the histone and nonhistone proteins, are associated with DNA structure and regulation in the nucleus. These proteins are known collectively as the **chromosomal proteins** of eukaryotes. The complex of DNA and its associated proteins, termed **chromatin**, is the structural building block of a chromosome.

By comparison, the single DNA molecule of a prokaryotic cell is more simply organized and has fewer associated proteins. However, prokaryotic DNA is still associated with two classes of proteins with functions similar to those of the eukaryotic histones and nonhistones: one class that organizes the DNA structurally and one that regulates gene activity. We begin this section with the major DNA-associated proteins of eukaryotes.

13.5a Histones Pack Eukaryotic DNA at Successive Levels of Organization

The **histones** are a class of small, positively charged (basic) proteins that are complexed with DNA in the chromosomes of eukaryotes. (Most other cellular proteins are larger and are neutral or negatively charged.) The histones link to DNA by an attraction between their positive charges and the negatively charged phosphate groups of the DNA.

Five types of histones exist in most eukaryotic cells: H1, H2A, H2B, H3, and H4. The amino acid sequences of these proteins are highly similar among eukaryotes, suggesting that they perform the same functions in all eukaryotic organisms.

One function of histones is to pack DNA molecules into the narrow confines of the cell nucleus. For example, each human cell nucleus contains 2 metres of DNA. Combination with the histones compacts this length so much that it fits into nuclei that are only about 10 μm in diameter. Another function is the regulation of DNA activity.

Histones and DNA Packing.

The histones pack DNA at several levels of chromatin structure. In the most fundamental structure, called a **nucleosome**, two molecules each of H2A, H2B, H3, and H4 combine to form a bead-like, eight-protein **nucleosome core particle** around which DNA winds for almost two turns **(Figure 13.18)**. A short segment of DNA, the **linker**, extends between one nucleosome and the next. Under the electron microscope, this structure looks like beads on a string. The diameter of the beads (the nucleosomes) gives this structure its name—the **10 nm chromatin fibre** (see Figure 13.18).

Each nucleosome and linker includes about 200 base pairs of DNA. Nucleosomes compact DNA by a factor of about 7; that is, a length of DNA becomes about 7 times shorter when it is wrapped into nucleosomes.

Histones and Chromatin Fibres.

The fifth histone, H1, brings about the next level of chromatin packing. One H1 molecule binds both to the nucleosome at the point where the DNA enters and leaves the core particle and to the linker DNA. This binding causes the nucleosomes to package into a coiled structure 30 nm in diameter, called the **30 nm chromatin fibre** or **solenoid**, with about six nucleosomes per turn (see Figure 13.18).

The arrangement of DNA in nucleosomes and solenoids compacts the DNA and probably also protects it from chemical and mechanical damage. In the test tube, DNA wound into nucleosomes and chromatin fibres is much more resistant to attack by deoxyribonuclease (a DNA-digesting enzyme) than when it is not bound to histone proteins. Therefore, DNA must unwind almost entirely from solenoids and nucleosomes when it becomes active. When genes become active, however, their DNA becomes almost as susceptible to attack as naked DNA in the test tube.

Packing at Still Higher Levels: Euchromatin and Heterochromatin.

In interphase nuclei, chromatin fibres are loosely packed in some regions and densely packed in others. The loosely packed regions are known as **euchromatin** (*eu* = true, regular, or typical), and the densely packed regions are called **heterochromatin** (*hetero* = different). Chromatin fibres also fold and pack into the thick, rodlike chromosomes visible during mitosis and meiosis. Some experiments indicate that links formed between H1 histone molecules contribute to the packing of chromatin fibres, both into heterochromatin and into the chromosomes visible during nuclear division (see discussion in Section 9.2, as well as the more detailed discussion in Section 14.2). However, the exact mechanism for the more complex folding and packing is not known.

Several experiments indicate that heterochromatin represents large blocks of genes that have been turned off and placed in a compact storage form. For example, recall the process of X-chromosome inactivation in mammalian females (see Section 12.2). As one of the two X chromosomes becomes inactive in cells early in development, it packs down into a block of heterochromatin called the *Barr body*, which is large enough to see under the light microscope. These findings support the idea that, in addition to organizing nuclear DNA, histones play a role in regulating gene activity.

Figure 13.18
Levels of organization in eukaryotic chromatin and chromosomes.

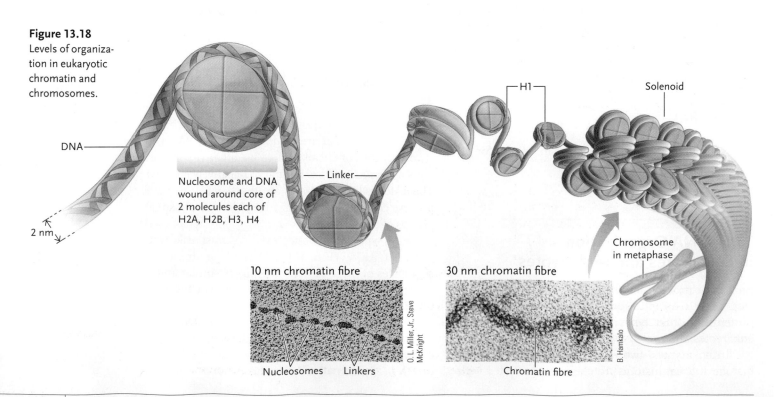

DNA

2 nm

Nucleosome and DNA wound around core of 2 molecules each of H2A, H2B, H3, H4

— Linker —

10 nm chromatin fibre

Nucleosomes   Linkers

O. L. Miller, Jr., Steve McKnight

H1

30 nm chromatin fibre

Chromatin fibre

B. Hamkalo

Solenoid

Chromosome in metaphase

13.5b Many Nonhistone Proteins Have Key Roles in the Regulation of Gene Expression

Nonhistone proteins are loosely defined as all the proteins associated with DNA that are not histones. Nonhistones vary widely in structure; most are negatively charged or neutral, but some are positively charged. They range in size from polypeptides smaller than histones to some of the largest cellular proteins.

Many nonhistone proteins help control the expression of individual genes. (The regulation of gene expression is the subject of Chapter 15.) For example, expression of a gene requires that the enzymes and proteins for that process be able to access the gene in the chromatin. If a gene is packed into heterochromatin, it is unavailable for activation. If the gene is in the more extended euchromatin, it is more accessible. Many nonhistone proteins affect gene accessibility by modifying histones to change how the histones associate with DNA in chromatin, either loosening or tightening the association. Other nonhistone proteins are regulatory proteins that activate or repress the expression of a gene. Yet others are components of the enzyme–protein complexes that are needed for the expression of any gene.

13.5c DNA Is Organized More Simply in Prokaryotes than in Eukaryotes

Several features of DNA organization in prokaryotes differ fundamentally from eukaryotic DNA. In contrast to the linear DNA in eukaryotes, the primary DNA molecule of most prokaryotic cells is circular, with only one copy per cell. In parallel with eukaryotic terminology, the DNA molecule is called a **bacterial chromosome.** The chromosome of the best-known bacterium, *E. coli*, includes about 1360 μm of DNA, which is equivalent to 4.6 million base pairs. There are exceptions: some bacteria have two or more different chromosomes in the cell, and some bacterial chromosomes are linear.

Replication begins from a single origin in the DNA circle, forming two forks that travel around the circle in opposite directions. Eventually, the forks meet at the opposite side from the origin to complete replication **(Figure 13.19).**

Inside prokaryotic cells, the DNA circle is packed and folded into an irregularly shaped mass called the **nucleoid** (shown in Figure 2.4). The DNA of the nucleoid is suspended directly in the cytoplasm with no surrounding membrane.

Many prokaryotic cells also contain other DNA molecules, called **plasmids**, in addition to the main chromosome of the nucleoid. Most plasmids are circular, although some are linear. Plasmids have replication origins and are duplicated and distributed to daughter cells together with the bacterial chromosome during cell division. Chapter 10 describes the process of conjugation, in which plasmids are replicated while being transferred from a donor cell to a recipient cell. The DNA is replicated by a mechanism called "rolling circle" replication, in which one strand of the plasmid is cut and travels into a recipient cell as a linear molecule; the other strand remains circular in the donor cell **(Figure 13.20, p. 292).** DNA replication restores both strands to double-strandedness, and the linear molecule recircularizes. Although rolling circle replication follows the usual rules of DNA replication, notice that the leading and lagging strand synthesis occur in separate cells rather than at one replication fork.

Although bacterial DNA is not organized into nucleosomes, there are positively charged proteins that combine with bacterial DNA. Some of these proteins help organize the DNA into loops, thereby providing some compaction of the molecule. Bacterial DNA also combines with many types of genetic regulatory proteins that have functions similar to those of the nonhistone proteins of eukaryotes (see Chapter 15).

With this description of prokaryotic DNA organization, our survey of DNA structure and its replication and organization is complete. The next chapter revisits the same structures and discusses how they function in the expression of information encoded in DNA.

STUDY BREAK

1. What is the structure of the nucleosome?
2. What is the role of histone H1 in eukaryotic chromosome structure?

Euk. DNA ⇒ linear
Prok. DNA ⇒ Circular.

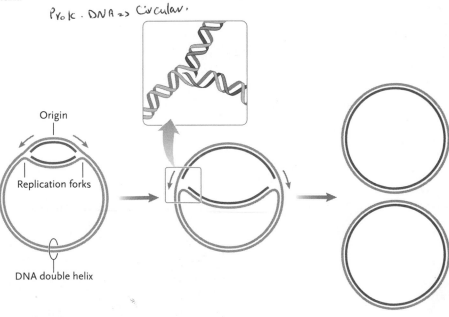

Origin

Replication forks

DNA double helix

Figure 13.19
Replication from a single origin in the DNA circle of prokaryotes.

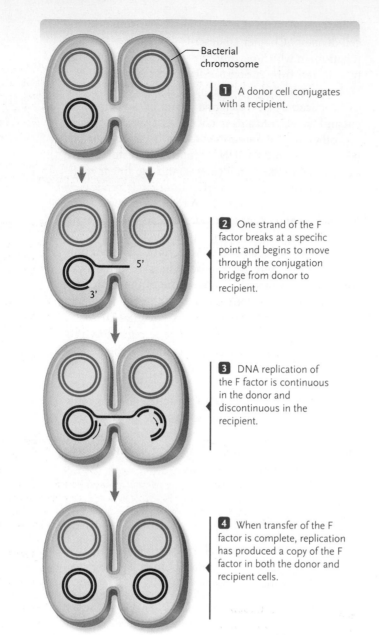

Bacterial chromosome

1 A donor cell conjugates with a recipient.

2 One strand of the F factor breaks at a specific point and begins to move through the conjugation bridge from donor to recipient.

5'

3'

3 DNA replication of the F factor is continuous in the donor and discontinuous in the recipient.

4 When transfer of the F factor is complete, replication has produced a copy of the F factor in both the donor and recipient cells.

Figure 13.20
Transfer of F factor by Rolling Circle Replication during conjugation. One of the two strands of the plasmid is nicked and the 5' end moves from the donor into a recipient cell. The remaining circular strand "rolls" like a tape dispenser. DNA synthesis is continuous in the donor cell and discontinuous in the recipient resulting in two complete plasmids

UNANSWERED QUESTIONS

In this chapter, we learned about the structure and replication of DNA, the key role of telomeres in maintaining the ends of chromosomes, and the packaging of DNA into chromosomes in eukaryotes.

Although research is ongoing in these areas, several big questions remain. For instance, the evolutionary relationship between DNA and RNA is intriguing. Why do all organisms have DNA as their genetic material? What does it mean that several types of viruses have RNA instead?

Chapter 9 described Hayflick factors that limit the life span of cells. Both DNA polymerase and telomerase influence cellular aging and senescence in ways that we are only beginning to understand.

Review

Go to CENGAGENOW™ at http://hed.nelson.com/ to access quizzing, animations, exercises, articles, and personalized homework help.

13.1 Establishing DNA as the Hereditary Molecule

- Griffith found that a substance derived from killed infective pneumonia bacteria could transform noninfective living pneumonia bacteria to the infective type (see Figure 13.2).

- Avery and his coworkers showed that DNA, not protein or RNA, was the molecule responsible for transforming pneumonia bacteria into the infective form.

- Hershey and Chase showed that the DNA of a phage, not the protein, enters bacterial cells to direct the life cycle of the virus. Taken together, the experiments of Griffith, Avery and his coworkers, and Hershey and Chase established that DNA is the hereditary molecule (see Figure 13.3).

13.2 DNA Structure

- Watson and Crick discovered that a DNA molecule consists of two polynucleotide chains twisted around each other into a right-handed double helix. Each nucleotide of the chains consists of deoxyribose, a phosphate group, and either adenine, thymine, guanine, or cytosine. The deoxyribose sugars are linked by phosphate groups to form an alternating sugar–phosphate backbone. The two strands are held together by adenine–thymine and guanine–cytosine base pairs. Each full turn of the double helix involves 10 base pairs (see Figures 13.4 and 13.6).

- The two strands of the DNA double helix are antiparallel.

13.3 DNA Replication

- DNA is duplicated by semiconservative replication, in which the two strands of a parental DNA molecule unwind and each serves as a template for the synthesis of a complementary copy (see Figures 13.7–13.9).

- DNA replication is catalyzed by several enzymes. Helicase unwinds the DNA; primase synthesizes an RNA primer used as a starting point for nucleotide assembly by DNA polymerases. DNA polymerases assemble nucleotides into a chain one at a time, in a sequence complementary to the sequence of bases in the template strand. After a DNA polymerase removes the primers and fills in the resulting gaps, DNA ligase closes the remaining single-chain nicks (see Figures 13.10 and 13.12).

- As the DNA helix unwinds, only one template strand runs in a direction allowing the new DNA strand to be made continuously in the direction of unwinding. The other template strand is copied in short lengths that run in the direction opposite to unwinding. The short lengths produced by this discontinuous replication are then linked into a continuous strand (see Figures 13.11 and 13.12).

- The ends of eukaryotic chromosomes consist of telomeres, short sequences repeated hundreds to thousands of times. These repeats provide a buffer against chromosome shortening during replication. Although most somatic cells show this chromosome shortening, some cell types do not because they have a telomerase enzyme that adds telomere repeats to the chromosome ends (see Figures 13.13 and 13.14).

- DNA synthesis begins at sites that act as replication origins and proceeds from the origins as two replication forks moving in opposite directions (see Figure 13.14).

13.4 Mechanisms That Correct Replication Errors

- In proofreading, the DNA polymerase reverses and removes the most recently added base if it is mispaired as a result of a replication error. The enzyme then resumes DNA synthesis in the forward direction (see Figure 13.16).

- In DNA mismatch repair, enzymes recognize distorted regions caused by mispaired base pairs and remove a section of DNA that includes the mispaired base from the newly synthesized nucleotide chain. A DNA polymerase then resynthesizes the section correctly, using the original template chain as a guide (see Figure 13.17).

13.5 DNA Organization in Eukaryotes and Prokaryotes

- Eukaryotic chromosomes consist of DNA complexed with histone and nonhistone proteins.

- In eukaryotic chromosomes, DNA is wrapped around a nucleosome consisting of two molecules each of histones H2A, H2B, H3, and H4. Linker DNA connects adjacent nucleosomes. The binding of histone H1 causes the nucleosomes to package into a coiled structure called a solenoid (see Figure 13.18).

- Chromatin is distributed between euchromatin, a loosely packed region in which genes are active in RNA transcription, and heterochromatin, densely packed masses in which the genes are inactive. Chromatin also folds and packs to form thick, rodlike chromosomes during nuclear division.

- Nonhistone proteins help control the expression of individual genes.

- The bacterial chromosome is a closed, circular molecule of DNA that is packed into the nucleoid region of the cell. Replication begins from a single origin and proceeds in both directions. Many bacteria also contain plasmids, which replicate independently of the host chromosome (see Figure 13.19).

- Bacterial DNA is organized into loops through interaction with proteins. Other proteins similar to eukaryotic nonhistones regulate gene activity in prokaryotes.

Questions

Self-Test Questions

1. Working on the Amazon River, a biologist isolated DNA from two unknown organisms, P and Q. He discovered that the adenine content of P was 15% and the cytosine content of Q was 42%. This means that
   a. the amount of guanine in P is 15%.
   b. the amount of guanine and cytosine combined in P is 70%.
   c. the amount of adenine in Q is 42%.
   d. the amount of thymine in Q is 21%.
   e. it takes more energy to unwind the DNA of P than the DNA of Q.

2. The Hershey and Chase experiment showed that viral
   a. ^{35}S entered bacterial cells.
   b. ^{32}P remained outside of bacterial cells.
   c. protein entered bacterial cells.
   d. DNA entered bacterial cells.
   e. DNA mutated in bacterial cells.

3. Pyrimidines include
   a. cytosine and thymine.
   b. adenine, cytosine, and guanine.
   c. adenine and thymine.
   d. cytosine and guanine.
   e. adenine and guanine.

4. Which of the following statements about DNA replication is *false*?
   a. Synthesis of the new DNA strand is from 3' to 5'.
   b. Synthesis of the new DNA strand is from 5' to 3'.
   c. DNA unwinds, primase adds RNA primer, and DNA polymerases synthesize the new strand and remove the RNA primer.
   d. Many initiation points exist in each eukaryotic chromosome.
   e. Okazaki fragments are synthesized in the opposite direction from the direction in which the replication fork moves.

5. Which of the following statements about DNA is *false*?
   a. Phosphate is linked to the 5' and 3' carbons of adjacent deoxyribose molecules.
   b. DNA is bidirectional in its synthesis.
   c. Each side of the helix is antiparallel to the other.
   d. The binding of adenine to thymine is through three hydrogen bonds.
   e. Avery identified DNA as the transforming factor in crosses between smooth and rough bacteria.

6. In the Meselson and Stahl experiment, the DNA in the parental generation was all ^{15}N^{15}N, and after one round of replication, the DNA was all ^{15}N^{13}N. What DNAs were seen after three rounds of replication, and in what ratio were they found?
   a. one ^{15}N^{13}N : one ^{13}N:^{13}N
   b. one ^{15}N^{13}N : two ^{13}N:^{13}N
   c. one ^{15}N^{13}N : three ^{13}N:^{13}N
   d. one ^{15}N^{13}N : four ^{13}N:^{13}N
   e. one ^{15}N^{13}N : seven ^{13}N:^{13}N

7. During replication, DNA is synthesized in a 5'$\rightarrow$3' direction. This implies that
   a. the template is read in a 5'$\rightarrow$3' direction.
   b. successive nucleotides are added to the 3'–OH end of the newly forming chain.
   c. because both strands are replicated nearly simultaneously, replication must be continuous on both.
   d. ligase unwinds DNA in a 5'$\rightarrow$3' direction.
   e. primase acts on the 3' end of the replicating strand.

8. Telomerase
   a. is active in cancer cells.
   b. is more active in adult than in embryonic cells.
   c. complexes with the ribosome to form telomeres.
   d. acts on unique genes called telomeres.
   e. shortens the ends of chromosomes.

9. Mismatch repair is the ability
   a. to seal Okazaki fragments with ligase into a continual DNA strand.
   b. of primase to remove the RNA primer and replace it with the correct DNA.
   c. of some enzymes to sense the insertion of an incorrect nucleotide, remove it, and use a DNA polymerase to insert the correct one.
   d. to correct mispaired chromosomes in prophase I of meiosis.
   e. to remove worn-out DNA by telomerase and replace it with newly synthesized nucleotides.

10. Prokaryotic DNA
    a. is surrounded by densely packed histones.
    b. has many sites for the initiation of DNA replication.
    c. has both strands synthesized in the same direction.
    d. is packaged as euchromatin and heterochromatin.
    e. is packaged as a large circular chromosome.

Questions for Discussion

1. Chargaff's data suggested that adenine pairs with thymine and guanine pairs with cytosine. What other data available to Watson and Crick suggested that adenine–guanine and cytosine–thymine pairs normally do not form?

2. Eukaryotic chromosomes can be labelled by exposing cells to radioactive thymidine during the S phase of interphase. If cells are exposed to radioactive thymidine during the S phase, would you expect both or only one of the sister chromatids of a duplicated chromosome to be labelled at metaphase of the following mitosis (see Section 9.2)?

3. If the cells in question 2 finish division and then enter another round of DNA replication in a medium that has been washed free of radioactive label, would you expect both or only one of the sister chromatids of a duplicated chromosome to be labelled at metaphase of the following mitosis?

4. During replication, an error uncorrected by proofreading or mismatch repair produces a DNA molecule with a base mismatch at the indicated position:

   AATTCCGACTCCTATGG
   TTAAGGTTGAGGATACC
   ↑

   The mismatch results in a mutation. This DNA molecule is received by one of the two daughter cells produced by mitosis. In the next round of replication and division, the mutation appears in only one of the two daughter cells. Develop a hypothesis to explain this observation.

5. Strains of bacteria that are resistant to an antibiotic sometimes appear spontaneously among other bacteria of the same type that are killed by the antibiotic. In view of the information in this chapter about DNA replication, what might account for the appearance of this resistance?

Transcription of a eukaryotic gene to produce messenger RNA (mRNA), a type of RNA that acts as a template for protein synthesis. The DNA of the gene unwinds from the nucleosome (left side) and is copied by an RNA polymerase (center) into mRNA (exiting the top).

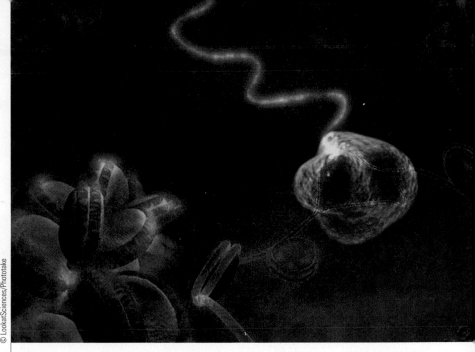

© LookatSciences/Phototake

14 Gene Structure and Expression

WHY IT MATTERS

The marine mussel *Mytilus* **(Figure 14.1, p. 296)** lives in one of the most demanding environments on the Earth—it clings permanently to rocks pounded by surf day in and day out, constantly in danger of being dashed to pieces or torn loose by foraging predators. The mussel is remarkably resistant to disturbance. If you try to pry one loose, you will find how difficult it is to tear the tough, elastic fibres that hold it fast. They are even hard to cut with a knife.

The fibres holding mussels to rocks are proteins secreted by the muscular foot of the animal. The proteins include keratin (an intermediate filament protein) and another resinous protein. Along with other proteins, they form a tough, adhesive material called byssus.

Byssus is one of the world's premier underwater adhesives. It fascinates biochemists, adhesive manufacturers, dentists, and surgeons looking for better ways to hold repaired body parts together. Genetic engineers are inserting segments of mussel deoxyribonucleic acid (DNA) into yeast cells, which reproduce in large numbers and serve as "factories" translating the mussel genes into proteins. Among the proteins produced may be those of byssus, allowing investigators to figure out how to use or imitate the mussel glue for human needs. This exciting

Figure 14.1
The marine mussel *Mytilus* and its natural habitat.

work, like the mussel's own byssus building, starts with one of life's universal truths: *Every protein is assembled on ribosomes according to instructions copied from genes coded in DNA.*

In this chapter, we trace the basic process that produces proteins in all organisms, beginning with the instructions encoded in DNA and leading through ribonucleic acid (RNA) to the sequence of amino acids in a protein. Many enzymes and other proteins are players as well as products in this story, as are several kinds of RNA and the cell's protein-making machines, the ribosomes. As your understanding of the fundamental elements of all protein production grows, be sure to notice the differences in the kinds of information coded in DNA, differences in the mechanisms in prokaryotes and eukaryotes, and differences in the structure of genes that code for protein versus those that code for RNA.

14.1 The Connection between DNA, RNA, and Protein

We know that genes encode proteins. In this section, you will learn how that connection was discovered. We also present an overview of the molecular steps needed to go from gene to protein: transcription and translation.

14.1a Genes Specify Either Protein or RNA Products

How do we know that genes encode—specify the amino acid sequence of—proteins? Two key pieces of research involving defects in metabolism illustrated this connection unequivocally. The first began in 1896 with Archibald Garrod, an English physician. He studied *alkaptonuria*, a human disease that does little harm but is detected easily by the fact that a patient's urine turns black in air. Garrod and William Bateson, a geneticist, studied families of patients with the disease and concluded that

it is an inherited trait. Garrod also found that people with alkaptonuria excrete a particular chemical in their urine. It is this chemical that turns black in air. Garrod concluded that normal people are able to metabolize the chemical, whereas people with alkaptonuria cannot. By 1908, Garrod had concluded that the disease was an inborn error of metabolism. He did not know it then, but the defect causing alkaptonuria is the result of an alteration of a gene that encodes an enzyme that metabolizes a key chemical. The altered gene causes a defect in the function of the enzyme, which leads to the phenotype of the disease. Garrod's work was the first to show a specific relationship between genes and metabolism.

In the second piece of research, George Beadle and Edward Tatum, working in the 1940s with the orange bread mould *Neurospora crassa*, collected data showing a direct relationship between genes and enzymes. Beadle and Tatum chose *Neurospora* for their work because it is a haploid fungus with simple nutritional needs. That is, wild-type *Neurospora*—the form of the mould found in nature—grows readily on a minimal medium (MM) consisting of a number of inorganic salts, sucrose, and a vitamin. The researchers reasoned that the fungus uses the simple chemicals in the medium to synthesize all of the more complex molecules needed for growth and reproduction, including amino acids for proteins and nucleotides for DNA and RNA.

Beadle and Tatum exposed spores of wild-type *Neurospora* to X-rays. X-rays are a mutagen, an agent that causes mutations. They found that some of the treated spores would not germinate and grow unless MM was supplemented with additional nutrients, such as amino acids or vitamins. Mutant strains that are unable to grow on MM are called auxotrophs (*auxo* = increased; *troph* = eater), or nutritional mutants. Beadle and Tatum hypothesized that each auxotrophic strain had a defect in a gene coding for an enzyme needed to synthesize a nutrient that now had to be added to the MM. The wild-type strain could make the nutrient for itself from raw materials in the MM, but the mutant strain could grow only if the researchers supplied the nutrient. By testing to see if each mutant strain would grow on MM supplemented with a given nutrient, Beadle and Tatum discovered which specific nutrient each mutant needed to grow and, therefore, which gene defect it had. For example, a mutant that required the addition of the amino acid arginine to grow had a defect in a gene for an enzyme involved in the synthesis of arginine. Such arginine auxotrophs are known as *arg* mutants. The assembly of arginine from raw materials is a multistep "assembly-line" process with a different enzyme catalyzing each step. Therefore, different *arg* mutants might differ in the particular enzyme that is defective and therefore in which step of the assembly pathway is blocked. (This is conceptually similar to Lederberg's work with auxotrophic bacteria described in Chapter 10.)

Beadle and Tatum determined where in the arginine synthesis pathway each of four mutants (*argE*, *argF*, *argG*, and *argH*) was blocked. They tested whether each mutant could grow on MM or on MM supplemented with either ornithine, citrulline, argininosuccinate—three compounds known to be involved in the synthesis of arginine—or arginine itself **(Figure 14.2, p. 298)**. None of the four mutants grew on MM, but, of course, they all grew on MM + arginine. Each of the *arg* mutants showed a different pattern of growth on the supplemented MM (see Figure 14.2). Beadle and Tatum deduced that the biosynthesis of arginine occurred in a number of steps, with each step controlled by a gene that encoded the enzyme for the step (see Figure 14.2, bottom). For example, the *argH* mutant grows on MM + arginine but not on MM + any of the other three compounds; this means that the mutant is blocked at the last step in the pathway, which produces arginine. Similarly, the *argG* mutant grows on MM + arginine or argininosuccinate but not on MM + any of the other supplements; this means that *argG* is blocked in the pathway before argininosuccinate is made (see Figure 14.2, bottom). With similar analysis, the researchers deduced the whole pathway from precursor to arginine and showed which gene encoded the enzyme that carried out each step. In sum, Beadle and Tatum had shown the direct relationship between genes and enzymes, which they put forward as the **one gene–one enzyme hypothesis**. Their experiment was a keystone in the development of molecular biology. As a result of their work, they were awarded a Nobel Prize in 1958.

It is important to understand that many proteins are not enzymes and many consist of more than one subunit, called a polypeptide. For instance, the protein hemoglobin is made up of four polypeptides, two each of an α subunit and a β subunit; this composition gives the protein its functional property of transporting oxygen rather than catalyzing a chemical reaction. Two different genes are needed to encode the hemoglobin protein: one for the α polypeptide and one for the β polypeptide. Beadle and Tatum's hypothesis was later restated as the **one gene–one polypeptide hypothesis**. It is important to keep the distinction between protein, the functional molecule, and polypeptide, the molecule encoded by a gene, clear as we discuss transcription and translation in the rest of this chapter.

14.1b The Pathway from Gene to Polypeptide Involves Transcription and Translation

The pathway from gene to polypeptide has two major steps, transcription and translation. **Transcription** is the mechanism by which the information encoded in DNA is made into a complementary RNA copy. It is called transcription because the information in one nucleic acid type is transferred to another nucleic acid type. **Translation** is the use of the information encoded in the RNA to assemble amino acids into a polypeptide. It is called translation because the information in a nucleic acid, in the form of nucleotides, is converted into a different kind of molecule—amino acids. In 1956, Francis Crick gave the name central dogma to the flow of information from DNA to RNA to protein.

In transcription, the enzyme RNA polymerase creates an RNA sequence that is complementary to the DNA sequence of a given gene. The process follows the same basic rules of complementary base pairing and nucleic acid chemistry that we first encountered in DNA replication (see Chapter 13). For each of the several thousand genes that will be appropriate to express in a given cell, one DNA strand or the other is the **template strand** and is read by the RNA polymerase. The RNA transcribed from a gene encoding a polypeptide is called **messenger RNA (mRNA)**.

In translation, an mRNA associates with a **ribosome**, a particle on which amino acids are linked into polypeptide chains. As the ribosome moves along the mRNA, the amino acids specified by the mRNA are joined one by one to form the polypeptide encoded by the gene.

The processes of transcription and translation are similar in prokaryotes and eukaryotes **(Figure 14.3, p. 299)**. One key difference is that whereas prokaryotes can transcribe and translate a given gene simultaneously, eukaryotes transcribe and process mRNA in the nucleus before exporting it to the cytoplasm for translation.

14.1c The Genetic Code Is Written in Three-Letter Words Using a Four-Letter Alphabet

Conceptually, the transcription of DNA into RNA is straightforward. The DNA "alphabet" consists of the four letters A, T, G, and C, representing the four

QUESTION: Do genes specify enzymes?

EXPERIMENT: Test *arg* mutants of the orange bread mold *Neurospora crassa* for growth on MM (minimal medium), MM + ornithine, MM + citrulline, MM + argininosuccinate, and MM + arginine. *Arg* mutants are unable to synthesize the amino acid arginine, which is essential for growth.

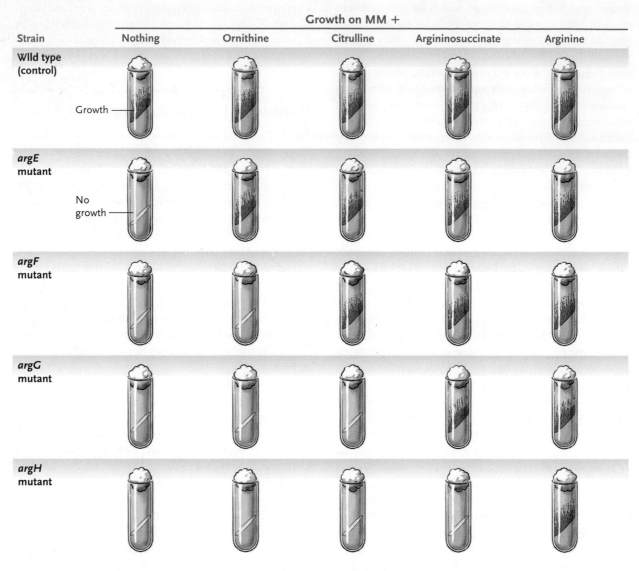

CONCLUSION: Arginine is synthesized in a biochemical pathway. Each step of the pathway is catalyzed by an enzyme, and each enzyme is encoded by a gene:

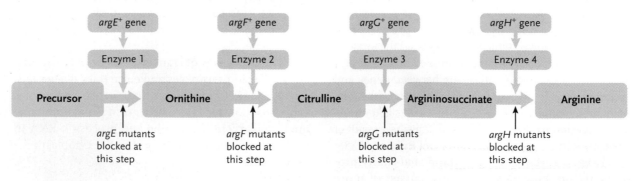

DNA nucleotide bases, adenine, thymine, guanine, and cytosine, and the RNA "alphabet" consists of the four letters A, U, G, and C, representing the four RNA bases, adenine, uracil, guanine, and cytosine. In other words, both nucleic acids share three of the four bases but differ in the other one: T in DNA is equivalent to U in RNA. But whereas there are 4 RNA bases, there are 20 amino acids. How is nucleotide information in an mRNA translated into the amino acid sequence of a polypeptide?

Breaking the Genetic Code. The nucleotide information that specifies the amino acid sequence of a polypeptide is called the **genetic code.** Scientists realized that the 4 bases in an mRNA (A, U, G, C) would have to be used in combinations of at least 3 to provide the capacity to code for 20 amino acids. One- and 2-letter words were eliminated because if the code used 1-letter words, only 4 different amino acids could be specified (that is, 4^1); if 2-letter words were used, only 16 different amino acids could be specified (that is, 4^2). But if the code used three-letter words, 64 different amino acids could be specified (that is, 4^3), more than enough to specify 20 amino acids. We know now that the genetic code is indeed a three-letter code; each three-letter word (triplet) is called a **codon. Figure 14.4,** illustrates the relationship between a gene, codons in an mRNA, and the amino acid sequence of a polypeptide. The three-letter codons in DNA are first transcribed into complementary three-letter RNA codons (the RNA complement to adenine [A] in the template strand is uracil [U] instead of thymine [T]). The template strand for a given gene is always read 3′ to 5′. For Gene *a* in Figure 14.4, the bottom strand is the template, and is therefore read left to right. However, the template for Gene b might be the top strand; RNA polymerase would then have to read right to left.

How do the codons correspond to the amino acids? Marshall Nirenberg and Philip Leder of the National Institutes of Health (NIH) established the identity of most of the codons in 1964. These researchers found that short, artificial mRNAs of codon length—three nucleotides—could bind to ribosomes in a test tube and cause a single **transfer RNA (tRNA)**, with its linked amino acid, to bind to the ribosome. (As we will discuss in Section 14.4, tRNAs are a special class of RNA molecules that bring amino acids to the ribosome for assembly into the polypeptide chain.) Nirenberg and Leder then made 64 of the short mRNAs, each consisting of a different, single codon. They added the mRNAs, one at a time, to a mixture in a test tube containing ribosomes and all the different tRNAs, each linked to its own amino acid. The idea was that, from the mixture of tRNAs, each single-codon mRNA would link to the tRNA carrying the amino acid corresponding to the codon. The experiment worked for 50 of the 64 codons, allowing those codons to be assigned to amino acids definitively.

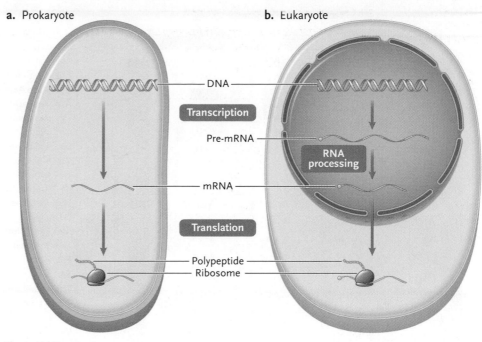

a. Prokaryote **b.** Eukaryote

DNA
Transcription
Pre-mRNA
RNA processing
mRNA
Translation
Polypeptide
Ribosome

Figure 14.3

Transcription and translation in **(a)** prokaryotes and **(b)** eukaryotes. In prokaryotes, RNA polymerase synthesizes an mRNA molecule that is ready for translation on ribosomes. In eukaryotes, RNA polymerase synthesizes a precursor–mRNA (pre-mRNA molecule) containing extra segments that are removed by RNA processing to produce a translatable mRNA. That mRNA exits the nucleus through a nuclear pore and is translated on ribosomes in the cytoplasm.

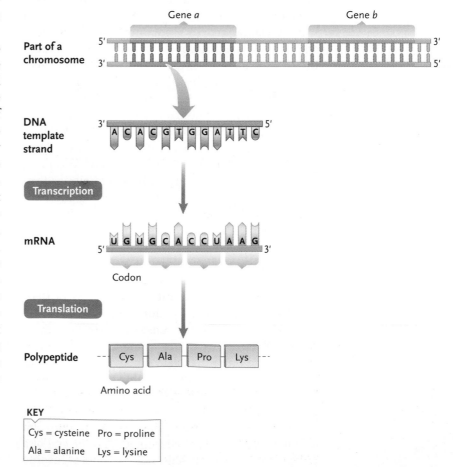

Gene *a*   Gene *b*

Part of a chromosome   5′ ... 3′   3′ ... 5′

DNA template strand   3′ A C A C G T G G A T T C 5′

Transcription

mRNA   5′ U G U G C A C C U A A G 3′

Codon

Translation

Polypeptide   Cys — Ala — Pro — Lys

Amino acid

KEY

Cys = cysteine	Pro = proline
Ala = alanine	Lys = lysine

Figure 14.4

Relationship between a gene, codons in an mRNA, and the amino acid sequence of a polypeptide.

Second base of codon

First base of codon	U	C	A	G	Third base of codon
U	UUU Phe	UCU Ser	UAU Tyr	UGU Cys	U
U	UUC Phe	UCC Ser	UAC Tyr	UGC Cys	C
U	UUA Leu	UCA Ser	UAA	UGA	A
U	UUG Leu	UCG Ser	UAG	UGG Trp	G
C	CUU Leu	CCU Pro	CAU His	CGU Arg	U
C	CUC Leu	CCC Pro	CAC His	CGC Arg	C
C	CUA Leu	CCA Pro	CAA Gln	CGA Arg	A
C	CUG Leu	CCG Pro	CAG Gln	CGG Arg	G
A	AUU Ile	ACU Thr	AAU Asn	AGU Ser	U
A	AUC Ile	ACC Thr	AAC Asn	AGC Ser	C
A	AUA Ile	ACA Thr	AAA Lys	AGA Arg	A
A	AUG Met	ACG Thr	AAG Lys	AGG Arg	G
G	GUU Val	GCU Ala	GAU Asp	GGU Gly	U
G	GUC Val	GCC Ala	GAC Asp	GGC Gly	C
G	GUA Val	GCA Ala	GAA Glu	GGA Gly	A
G	GUG Val	GCG Ala	GAG Glu	GGG Gly	G

KEY

- Ala = alanine
- Arg = arginine
- Asn = asparagine
- Asp = aspartic acid
- Cys = cysteine
- Gln = glutamine
- Glu = glutamic acid
- Gly = glycine
- His = histidine
- Ile = isoleucine
- Leu = leucine
- Lys = lysine
- Met = methionine
- Phe = phenylalanine
- Pro = proline
- Ser = serine
- Thr = threonine
- Trp = tryptophan
- Tyr = tyrosine
- Val = valine

Figure 14.5
The genetic code, written in the form in which the codons appear in mRNA. The AUG initiator codon, which codes for methionine, is shown in green; the three terminator codons are boxed in red.

Another approach, carried out in 1966 by H. Ghobind Khorana and his coworkers, used long, artificial mRNA molecules containing only one nucleotide repeated continuously or different nucleotides in repeating patterns. Each artificial mRNA was added to ribosomes in a test tube, and the sequence of amino acids in the polypeptide chain made by the ribosomes was analyzed. For example, an artificial mRNA containing only uracil nucleotides in the sequence UUUUUU . . . resulted in a polypeptide containing only the amino acid phenylalanine; they deduced that UUU must be the codon for phenylalanine. Khorana's approach, combined with the results of Nirenberg and Leder's experiments, identified the coding assignments of all the codons. Nirenberg and Khorana received a Nobel Prize in 1968 for solving the nucleic acid code.

Features of the Genetic Code. By convention, scientists write the codons in the 5′ → 3′ direction as they appear in mRNAs, substituting U for the T of DNA **(Figure 14.5).** Of the 64 codons, 61 specify amino acids. These are known as **sense codons**. One of these codons, AUG, specifies the amino acid methionine. It is the first codon translated in any mRNA in both prokaryotes and eukaryotes. In that position, AUG is called a **start** or **initiator codon.** The three codons that do not specify amino acids—UAA, UAG, and UGA—are **stop codons** (also called **nonsense** or **termination codons**) that act as "periods" indicating the end of a polypeptide-encoding sentence. When a ribosome reaches one of the stop codons, polypeptide synthesis stops and the new polypeptide chain is released from the ribosome.

Only two amino acids, methionine and tryptophan, are specified by a single codon. All the rest are represented by at least two, some by as many as six. In other words, there are many synonyms in the nucleic acid code, a feature known as **degeneracy** (or redundancy). For example, UGU and UGC both specify cysteine, whereas CCU, CCC, CCA, and CCG all specify proline.

Another feature of the genetic code is that it is **commaless**; that is, the words of the nucleic acid code are sequential, with no indicators such as commas or spaces to mark the end of one codon and the beginning of the next. Therefore, the code can be read correctly only by starting at the right place—at the first base of the first three-letter codon at the beginning of a coded message (the start codon)—and reading three nucleotides at a time. In other words, there is only one correct **reading frame** for each mRNA. For example, if you read the message SADMOMHASMOPCUTOFFBOYTOT three letters at a time, starting with the first letter of the first "codon," you would find that a mother reluctantly had her small child's hair cut. However, if you start incorrectly at the second letter of the first codon, you read the gibberish message ADM OMH ASM OPC UTO FFB OYT OT.

The code is also **universal**. With a few exceptions, the same codons specify the same amino acids in all living organisms, and also in viruses. The universality of the nucleic acid code indicates that it was established in its present form very early in the evolution of life and has remained virtually unchanged through billions of years of evolutionary history. Minor exceptions to the universality of the genetic code have been found in a few organisms, including yeast, some protozoans, a prokaryote, and in the genetic systems of mitochondria and chloroplasts.

Study Break

1. On the basis of their work with auxotrophic mutants of the fungus *Neurospora crassa,* Beadle and Tatum proposed the one gene–one enzyme hypothesis. Why was this hypothesis updated subsequently to the one gene–one polypeptide hypothesis?
2. Why is the sequence of bases different in the mRNA relative to the DNA of a given gene?

14.2 Transcription: DNA-Directed RNA Synthesis

Transcription is the process by which information coded in sequential DNA bases is transferred to a complementary RNA strand. Although certain aspects of this mechanism (**Figure 14.6, p. 302**) are similar to those of DNA replication (see Figure 13.11), it is important for you to understand how these processes are different. In transcription,

- in a given gene, only one of the two DNA nucleotide strands acts as a template for synthesis of a complementary copy, instead of both, as in replication.
- only a relatively small part of a DNA molecule—the sequence encoding a single gene—serves as a template, rather than all of both strands, as in DNA replication.
- **RNA polymerases** catalyze the assembly of nucleotides into an RNA strand, rather than the DNA polymerases that catalyze replication.
- the RNA molecules resulting from transcription are single polynucleotide chains, not double ones, as in DNA replication.

Although the mechanism of transcription is similar in prokaryotes and eukaryotes, watch for the important differences pointed out in this section.

14.2a RNA Polymerases Work Like DNA Polymerases but Require No Primer

Transcription begins as RNA polymerase binds to the DNA and unwinds it near the beginning of a gene (see Figure 14.6, steps 1 to 2). Unlike DNA polymerases, RNA polymerases can start the complementary copy with no need for a primer already in place (DNA primers are discussed in Section 14.3). Like DNA, RNA is made in the 5′ →3′ direction using the 3′ →5′ DNA strand as a template (step 3). Thus, we refer to the beginning of the RNA strand as the 5′ end and the other end as the 3′ end. The RNA polymerase continues adding nucleotides one at a time until the gene is transcribed completely. At this point, the newly synthesized RNA molecule and the enzyme are released from the DNA template (step 4).

14.2b Specific Sequences of Nucleotides in the DNA Indicate Where Transcription of a Gene Begins and Ends

An organism's genome contains a large number of genes. For example, scientists analyzing data from the human genome sequence suggest that between 20 000 and 25 000 protein-coding genes are needed to make a human. Transcription is the first step in a process whereby particular genes are expressed in any given cell at a given time. Some of those genes are protein-coding

genes that encode mRNAs to be translated; others are non–protein-coding genes that encode RNAs that are never translated, such as ribosomal RNAs (rRNAs), transfer RNAs (tRNAs), and small nuclear RNAs (snRNAs). The following sections describe the basic steps of transcription for protein-coding genes.

Organization of a Gene and the Steps of Transcription. Let us first outline the structure of a gene and how it is transcribed into an RNA (**Figure 14.7, p. 303**). At one end of a gene is a control sequence called a **promoter** (Figure 14.7, step 1). The part of the gene that is to be transcribed into RNA is called the **transcription unit.** To *initiate* transcription, RNA polymerase binds to the promoter, unwinds the DNA in that region, and starts synthesizing an RNA molecule at the transcription start point (step 2). As RNA polymerase moves along the DNA, unwinding it at the forward end of the enzyme, the new RNA molecule *elongates* as nucleotides are added one by one (step 3). The new RNA molecule winds temporarily with the template strand of the DNA into a hybrid RNA–DNA double helix. Beyond this short region of pairing, the growing RNA strand unwinds from the DNA and extends from the RNA polymerase as a single nucleotide chain. As the RNA polymerase passes, the DNA double helix reforms. Elongation of the RNA chain continues until the end of the transcription unit, at which point, RNA synthesis *terminates*, and the completed RNA transcript and RNA polymerase are released from the DNA (step 4).

Once an RNA polymerase molecule has started transcription and progressed past the beginning of a gene, another molecule of RNA polymerase may start creating another RNA as soon as there is room at the promoter. For most genes, there are many RNA polymerase molecules spaced closely along a gene, each making an RNA transcript.

The Promoter of Protein-Coding Genes and Transcription Initiation. The promoter specifies where on the DNA transcription begins. In prokaryotes, the promoters are immediately upstream of where transcription initiates. With the help of another protein, RNA polymerase recognizes key DNA sequences in the promoter, binds, and begins transcription of the mRNA. Since all the other types of genes in prokaryotes (for example, tRNA and rRNA genes) have similar promoters, the same RNA polymerase complex can transcribe them all.

In eukaryotes, there are different polymerases for transcribing different types of genes. RNA polymerase II transcribes protein-coding genes. RNA polymerases I and III transcribe genes for non-protein-coding RNAs. The promoters of protein-coding genes are immediately upstream of the transcription start point and are typically more complex than in prokaryotes. Other sequences further upstream of the gene regulate the rate of transcription (discussed in Chapter 15).

Figure 14.6

The overall mechanism of transcription, in which an RNA molecule is assembled on a DNA template. Note that only one of the two DNA strands is used as a template for synthesis of the complementary RNA transcript for any given gene.

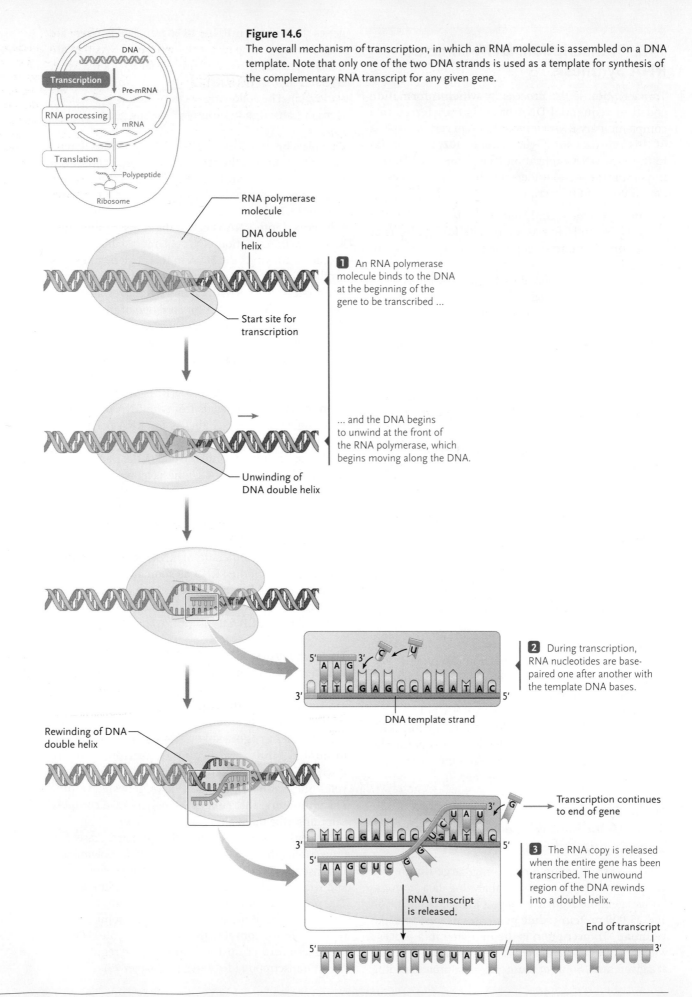

1 An RNA polymerase molecule binds to the DNA at the beginning of the gene to be transcribed ...

... and the DNA begins to unwind at the front of the RNA polymerase, which begins moving along the DNA.

2 During transcription, RNA nucleotides are base-paired one after another with the template DNA bases.

DNA template strand

Transcription continues to end of gene

3 The RNA copy is released when the entire gene has been transcribed. The unwound region of the DNA rewinds into a double helix.

RNA transcript is released.

End of transcript

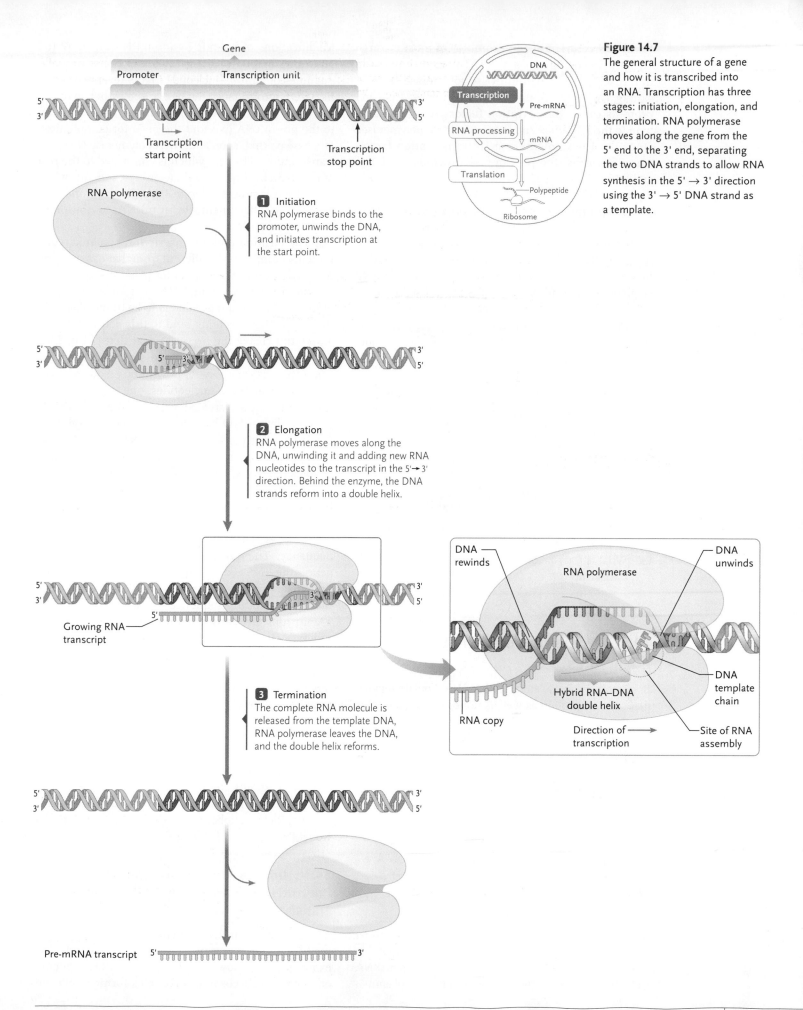

Gene

Promoter   Transcription unit

5'
3'

Transcription start point

Transcription stop point

RNA polymerase

1 Initiation
RNA polymerase binds to the promoter, unwinds the DNA, and initiates transcription at the start point.

5'
3'   5'   3'

2 Elongation
RNA polymerase moves along the DNA, unwinding it and adding new RNA nucleotides to the transcript in the 5'→3' direction. Behind the enzyme, the DNA strands reform into a double helix.

5'
3'   3'

Growing RNA transcript   5'

3 Termination
The complete RNA molecule is released from the template DNA, RNA polymerase leaves the DNA, and the double helix reforms.

5'
3'

Pre-mRNA transcript   5'   3'

DNA
Transcription
Pre-mRNA
RNA processing   mRNA
Translation
Polypeptide
Ribosome

Figure 14.7
The general structure of a gene and how it is transcribed into an RNA. Transcription has three stages: initiation, elongation, and termination. RNA polymerase moves along the gene from the 5' end to the 3' end, separating the two DNA strands to allow RNA synthesis in the 5' → 3' direction using the 3' → 5' DNA strand as a template.

DNA rewinds   DNA unwinds

RNA polymerase

Hybrid RNA–DNA double helix

DNA template chain

RNA copy   Direction of transcription   Site of RNA assembly

A key element of the promoter of most eukaryotic protein-coding genes, the **TATA box**, is important in transcription initiation. RNA polymerase II itself cannot recognize the promoter sequence. Instead, proteins called **transcription factors** recognize and bind to the TATA box and then recruit the polymerase. Once the RNA polymerase II–transcription factor complex forms, the polymerase unwinds the DNA and transcription begins.

Transcription Termination. In prokaryotes, there are two types of specific DNA sequences called **terminators** that signal the end of transcription of the gene. Both types of terminator sequences act *after they are transcribed*. In the first case, the terminator sequence on the mRNA base-pairs with itself to form a "hairpin." In the second case, a protein binds to the terminator sequence on the mRNA. Both of these mechanisms trigger the termination of transcription and the release of the RNA and RNA polymerase from the template. In eukaryotes, there are no equivalent "transcription terminator" sequences. Instead, the 3′ end of the mRNA is specified by a different process, which is discussed in the next section.

STUDY BREAK

1. If the DNA template strand has the sequence 3′-CAAATTGGCTTATTACCGGATG-5′, what would be the sequence of an RNA transcribed from it?
2. What is the role of the promoter in transcription?

14.3 Processing of mRNAs in Eukaryotes

Both prokaryotic and eukaryotic mRNAs contain regions that code for protein as well as noncoding regions that play key roles in the process of protein synthesis. In prokaryotic mRNAs, the coding region is flanked by untranslated ends, the 5′ untranslated region (5′ UTR) and a 3′ untranslated region (3′ UTR). The same elements are present in eukaryotic mRNAs along with additional noncoding elements. This section focuses particularly on the synthesis of mRNA in eukaryotes.

14.3a Eukaryotic Protein-Coding Genes Are Transcribed into Precursor-mRNAs that Are Modified in the Nucleus

A eukaryotic protein-coding gene is typically transcribed into a **precursor-mRNA (pre-mRNA)** that must be processed in the nucleus to produce translatable mRNA (see Figures 14.3 and 14.9). The mature mRNA exits the nucleus and is translated in the cytoplasm.

Modifications of Pre-mRNA and mRNA Ends. At the 5′ end of the pre-mRNA is the **5′ cap**, consisting of a guanine-containing nucleotide that is reversed so that its 3′-OH group faces the beginning rather than the end of the molecule. A capping enzyme adds the 5′ cap to the pre-mRNA (without the need for complementary base pairing) soon after RNA polymerase II begins transcription. The cap, which is connected to the rest of the chain by three phosphate groups, remains when pre-mRNA is processed to mRNA. The cap functions as the initial attachment site for mRNAs to ribosomes to allow translation.

The termination of transcription of a eukaryotic protein-coding gene is different from that of a prokaryotic gene in that there is no terminator sequence at the end of the gene in the DNA. Instead, at the 3′ end of the gene is a sequence that is to be transcribed into the pre-mRNA. Proteins bind to this *polyadenylation signal* and cleave the pre-mRNA at that point. This signals the RNA polymerase to stop transcription. Then the enzyme poly(A) polymerase adds a chain of 50 to 250 adenine nucleotides, one nucleotide at a time, to the newly created 3′ end of the pre-mRNA. No complementary base pairing with a template is needed for this particular type of RNA synthesis. The string of adenine nucleotides, called the **poly(A) tail**, enables the mRNA produced from the pre-mRNA to be translated efficiently and protects it from attack by RNA-digesting enzymes in the cytoplasm.

Sequences Interrupting the Protein-Coding Sequence. The transcription unit of a protein-coding gene—the RNA-coding sequence—also contains non–protein-coding sequences called **introns** that interrupt the protein-coding sequence (shown in **Figure 14.8**). The introns are transcribed into pre-mRNAs but are removed from pre-mRNAs during processing in the nucleus. The amino acid–coding sequences that are retained in finished mRNAs are called **exons**. The mechanisms by which introns originated in genes remain a mystery.

Introns were discovered by several methods, including direct comparisons between the nucleotide sequences of mature mRNAs and either pre-mRNAs or the genes encoding them. The majority of known eukaryotic genes contain at least one intron; some contain more than 60. The original discoverers of introns, Richard Roberts and Phillip Sharp, received a Nobel Prize in 1993 for their findings.

14.3b Introns Are Removed during Pre-mRNA Processing to Produce the Translatable mRNA

A process called **mRNA splicing**, which occurs in the nucleus, removes introns from pre-mRNAs and joins exons together. How does this occur? mRNA splicing occurs in a **spliceosome**, a complex formed between

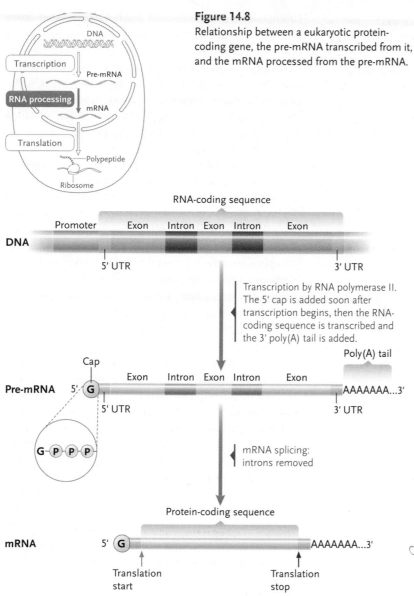

Figure 14.8
Relationship between a eukaryotic protein-coding gene, the pre-mRNA transcribed from it, and the mRNA processed from the pre-mRNA.

Transcription by RNA polymerase II. The 5' cap is added soon after transcription begins, then the RNA-coding sequence is transcribed and the 3' poly(A) tail is added.

mRNA splicing: introns removed

at the junction between the 3′ end of the intron and exon 2, releasing the intron and joining together the two exons (exon 1 and exon 2 in Figure 14.9). Because of the shape of the released intron, it is called a lariat structure. Enzymes degrade the intron, and the snRNPs are used in other mRNA splicing reactions. Researchers were surprised to discover that the catalytic activity in splicing resides not in the proteins but in the RNA component of spliceosomes. Some introns can even splice themselves! An RNA molecule that catalyzes a reaction like a protein enzyme is called a catalytic RNA or a **ribozyme** (ribonucleic acid enzyme).

The cutting and splicing are so exact that not a single base of an intron is retained in the finished mRNA, nor is a single base removed from the exons. Without this precision, removing introns would change the reading frame of the coding portion of the mRNA, producing gibberish from the point of a mistake onward.

14.3c Introns Contribute to Protein Variability

Introns seem wasteful in terms of the energy and raw materials required to replicate and transcribe them and the elaborate cellular machinery required to remove them during pre-mRNA processing. Why are they present in mRNA-encoding genes? Among a number of possibilities, introns may provide a selective advantage to organisms by increasing the coding capacity of existing genes through a process called alternative splicing and in a process generating new proteins by exon shuffling.

Alternative Splicing. The removal of introns from a given gene is not absolute. That is, in certain tissues, or under certain environmental conditions, exons may be joined in different combinations to produce different mRNAs from a single DNA gene sequence. The mechanism, called **alternative splicing**, greatly increases the number and variety of proteins encoded in the cell nucleus without increasing the size of the genome. For example, current data suggest that three-quarters of all human pre-mRNAs are subjected to alternative splicing.

the pre-mRNA and a handful of **small ribonucleoprotein particles** (snRNPs; pronounced "snurps") **(Figure 14.9, p. 306).** (Generally, a complex of RNA and proteins is called a ribonucleoprotein.) Located in the nucleus, each type of snRNP contains a relatively short RNA called a small nuclear RNA (snRNA) bound to a number of proteins.

The snRNPs bind in a particular order to an intron in the pre-mRNA. The first snRNPs are those with snRNAs that recognize and form complementary base pairs with mRNA sequences at the junctions of the intron and adjacent exons. Other snRNPs are then recruited, leading to looping out of the intron and bringing the two exon ends close together. At this point, the active spliceosome has been formed. The spliceosome cleaves the pre-mRNA at the junction between the 5′ end of the intron and the adjacent exon (exon 1 in Figure 14.9), and the intron loops back to bond with itself near the intron's 3′ end. The spliceosome then cleaves the pre-mRNA

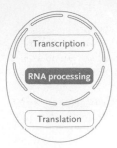

Pre-mRNA

5' end of pre-mRNA

Exon 1   Intron   Exon 2   3' end of pre-mRNA

snRNA Proteins

snRNPs

1 Segment of pre-mRNA with an intron

Active spliceosome

Several snRNPs

2 SnRNPs bind to the intron by recognizing its boundary sequences and loop the intron out, bringing the two exons close together. The active spliceosome has now formed.

3 The spliceosome cleaves the intron at its beginning. The intron folds back on and bonds to itself.

Degraded

Released intron in lariat structure

4 The spliceosome cleaves the intron at its end and splices together the two exons. The cleaved intron and snRNPs are released.

Reused

Released snRNPs

1   2

Figure 14.9
mRNA splicing—the removal of introns from pre-mRNA and joining of exons in the spliceosome.

In each case, the different mRNAs produced from the "parent" pre-mRNA are translated to produce a family of related proteins with various combinations of amino acid sequences derived from the exons. Each protein in the family, then, varies in its function. Alternative splicing helps us understand why humans with only about 25 000 genes can produce many more proteins. Ultimately, proteins direct an organism's functions.

Figure 14.10 shows an example of alternative splicing that occurs in mammals, including humans. The pre-mRNA transcript of the α-tropomyosin gene is alternatively spliced in various ways in different tissues—smooth muscle (e.g., muscles of the intestine and bladder), skeletal muscle (e.g., biceps, gluteus), fibroblast (connective tissue cell that makes collagen), liver, and brain—to produce different forms of the α-tropomyosin protein that are functionally optimized for each tissue type. Tropomyosins play a role in the regulation of cell contraction in muscle and non-muscle cells.

Figure 14.10 shows the alternative splicing of the α-tropomyosin pre-mRNA to the mRNAs found in smooth muscle and striated muscle. Exons 2 and 12 are found only in smooth muscle mRNA, whereas exons 3, 10, and 11 are exclusive to striated muscle mRNA. Different proteins are made in different tissues from the same DNA gene. Notice that alternative splicing causes us to further refine the "one gene–one polypeptide" idea to something like "one gene–one particular polypeptide under particular conditions."

Exon Shuffling. Another advantage provided by introns may come from the fact that intron–exon junctions often fall at points dividing major functional regions in encoded proteins, for example, genes for antibody proteins, hemoglobin blood proteins, and the peptide hormone insulin. The functional divisions may have allowed new proteins to evolve by exon shuffling, a process by which existing protein regions or domains, already selected for due to their functions, are mixed into novel combinations to create new proteins. Evolution of new proteins by this mechanism would produce changes much more quickly than by changes in individual amino acids at random points.

STUDY BREAK

1. What are the similarities and differences between pre-mRNAs and mRNAs?
2. What is the role of base pairing in mRNA splicing?
3. How is it possible for an organism to produce more proteins than it has genes for?

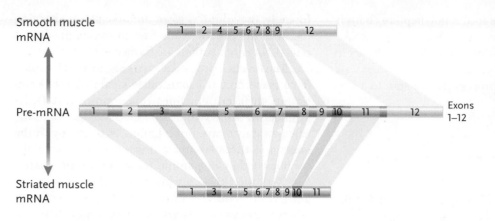

Smooth muscle mRNA

1 2 4 5 6 7 8 9 12

Pre-mRNA

1 2 3 4 5 6 7 8 9 10 11 12 | Exons 1–12

Striated muscle mRNA

1 3 4 5 6 7 8 9 10 11

Figure 14.10
Alternative splicing of the α-tropomyosin pre-mRNA to distinct mRNA forms found in smooth muscle and striated muscle. All of the introns are removed in both mRNA splicing pathways. However, to produce smooth muscle mRNA, "exons" 3, 10, and 11 are also removed; to produce the striated muscle mRNA, "exons" 2 and 12 are also removed.

14.4 Translation: mRNA-Directed Polypeptide Synthesis

Translation is the assembly of amino acids into polypeptides. In prokaryotes, translation takes place throughout the cell, whereas in eukaryotes, it occurs mostly in the cytoplasm, although, as we will see, a few specialized genes are transcribed and translated in mitochondria and chloroplasts.

Figure 14.11 (p. 309) summarizes the translation process. In prokaryotes, the mRNA produced by transcription is not confined within a nucleus and is therefore available immediately for translation. For eukaryotes, the mRNA produced by splicing of the pre-mRNA first exits the nucleus and then is translated in the cytoplasm. In translation, the mRNA associates with a ribosome and another type of RNA, transfer RNAs (tRNAs), brings amino acids to the complex to be joined one by one into the polypeptide chain. The

PEOPLE BEHIND BIOLOGY

Steve Zimmerly, University of Calgary

Dr. Steve Zimmerly and his colleagues think they know where introns came from.

Biology students (and researchers) often wonder about the origins of introns, and to investigate this question, Dr. Zimmerly collected and analyzed a large number of examples of a type of intron called "Group II" from plant organelles and bacteria. Group II introns have two fascinating abilities. First, they can splice themselves out of RNA without the need for proteins. Second, they are mobile; these elements can copy themselves and insert at a new location **(Figure 1)**.

The Zimmerly lab proposed a model for intron evolution that suggests the introns in nuclear genes of higher eukaryotes evolved from mobile Group II introns originating in prokaryotes. These Group II introns may have spread to eukaryotes at the time when their bacterial hosts were engulfed by eukaryotic cells to become endosymbiotic mitochondria and chloroplasts. Over evolutionary time, the nuclear introns lost their mobility and became dependent on spliceosomes for accurate splicing.

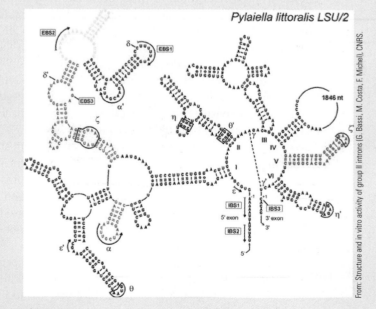

Figure 1
Sequence of a Group II intron showing extensive pairing with itself.

From: Structure and in vitro activity of group II introns (G. Bassi, M. Costa, F. Michell), CNRS.

sequence of amino acids in the polypeptide chain is determined by the sequence of codons in the mRNA.

We will start by learning about the key players in the process, the tRNAs and ribosomes, and then walk through the translation process from a start to a stop codon.

14.4a tRNAs Are Small RNAs of a Highly Distinctive Structure that Bring Amino Acids to the Ribosome

Transfer RNAs (tRNAs) bring amino acids to the ribosome for addition to the polypeptide chain.

tRNA Structure. tRNAs are small RNAs, about 75 to 90 nucleotides long (mRNAs are typically hundreds of nucleotides long), with a highly distinctive structure that accomplishes their role in translation **(Figure 14.12)**. All tRNAs can base-pair with themselves to wind into four double-helical segments, forming a cloverleaf pattern in two dimensions. At the tip of one of the double-helical segments is the **anticodon,** the three-nucleotide segment that pairs with a codon in mRNAs. At the other end of the cloverleaf is a double-helical segment that links to the amino acid corresponding to the anticodon. For example, a tRNA that is linked to serine (Ser) pairs with the codon 5′-AGU-3′ in mRNA (see Figure 14.12). The anticodon of the tRNA that pairs with this codon is 3′-UCA-5′. (The anticodon and codon pair in an antiparallel manner, as do the strands in DNA. We will write anticodons in the $5′ \rightarrow 3′$ direction to make it easy to see how they pair with codons normally written $5′ \rightarrow 3′$.)

The tRNA cloverleaf folds in three dimensions into the L-shaped structure shown in Figure 14.12b. The anticodon and the segment binding the amino acid are located at the opposite tips of the L.

Recall that 61 of the 64 codons of the genetic code specify an amino acid. Does this mean that 61 different tRNAs read the sense codons? The answer is no. Francis Crick's **wobble hypothesis** proposed that the complete set of 61 sense codons can be read by fewer than 61 distinct tRNAs because of the particular pairing properties of the bases in the anticodons. That is, the pairing of the anticodon with the first two nucleotides of the codon is always precise, but the anticodon has more flexibility in pairing with the third nucleotide of the codon. In many cases, the same tRNA's anticodon can read codons that have either U or C in the third position; for example, a tRNA carrying phenylalanine can read both codons UUU and UUC. Similarly, the same tRNA's anticodon can read two codons that have A or G in the third position; for example, a tRNA carrying glutamine can pair with both CAA and CAG codons.

Addition of Amino Acids to Their Corresponding tRNAs. The correct amino acid must be present on a tRNA if translation is to be accurate. The process of adding an amino acid to a tRNA is called **aminoacylation**

(literally, the addition of an amino acid) or **charging** (because the process adds free energy as the amino acid–tRNA combinations are formed).

The finished product of charging, a tRNA linked to its "correct" amino acid, is called an **aminoacyl–tRNA**. Twenty different enzymes called **aminoacyl–tRNA synthetases**—one synthetase for each of the 20 amino acids—catalyze aminoacylation. This energy in the aminoacyl–tRNA eventually drives the formation of the peptide bond linking amino acids during translation.

With the tRNAs attached to their corresponding amino acids, our attention moves to the ribosome, where the amino acids are removed from tRNAs and linked together into polypeptide chains.

14.4b Ribosomes Are rRNA–Protein Complexes that Work as Automated Protein Assembly Machines

Ribosomes are ribonucleoprotein particles that carry out protein synthesis by translating mRNA into chains of amino acids. Like some automated machines, such as those forming complicated metal parts by a series of machining steps, ribosomes use an information tape—an mRNA molecule—as the directions required to accomplish a task. For ribosomes, the task is joining amino acids in ordered sequences to make a polypeptide chain.

In prokaryotes, ribosomes carry out their assembly functions throughout the cell. In eukaryotes, ribosomes function in the cytoplasm, either suspended freely in the cytoplasmic solution or attached to the membranes of the endoplasmic reticulum (ER), the system of tubular or flattened sacs in the cytoplasm. Chloroplasts and mitochondria each have their own ribosomes in addition to those in the cytoplasm.

A finished ribosome is made up of two parts of dissimilar size, called the *large* and *small ribosomal subunits* **(Figure 14.13, p. 310).** Each subunit is made up of a combination of ribosomal RNA (rRNA) and ribosomal proteins.

Prokaryotic and eukaryotic ribosomes are similar in structure and function. However, the differences in their molecular structure, particularly in the ribosomal proteins, give them distinct properties. For example, the antibiotics streptomycin and erythromycin are effective antibacterial agents because they inhibit bacterial, but not eukaryotic, ribosomes.

To fulfill its role in translation, the ribosome has special binding sites active in bringing together mRNA with aminoacyl–tRNAs (see Figure 14.13 and refer also to Figure 14.11). One such site is where the mRNA threads through the ribosome. The **A site** (aminoacyl site) is where the incoming aminoacyl–tRNA (carrying the next amino acid to be added to the polypeptide chain) binds to the mRNA. The **P site** (peptidyl site) is where the tRNA carrying the growing polypeptide chain is bound. The **E site** (exit site) is where an exiting tRNA binds as it leaves the ribosome.

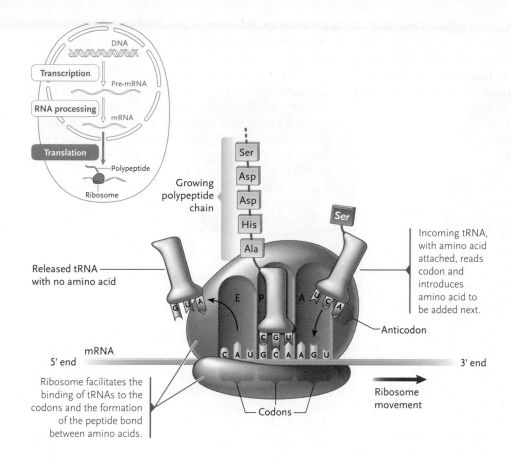

Figure 14.11

An overview of translation, in which ribosomes
assemble amino acids into a polypeptide chain. The
figure shows a ribosome in the process of translation. A tRNA molecule with an amino acid bound
to it is entering the ribosome on the right. The
anticodon on the tRNA will pair with the codon in
the mRNA. Its amino acid will then be added to the
growing polypeptide, which is currently attached to
the tRNA in the middle of the ribosome.

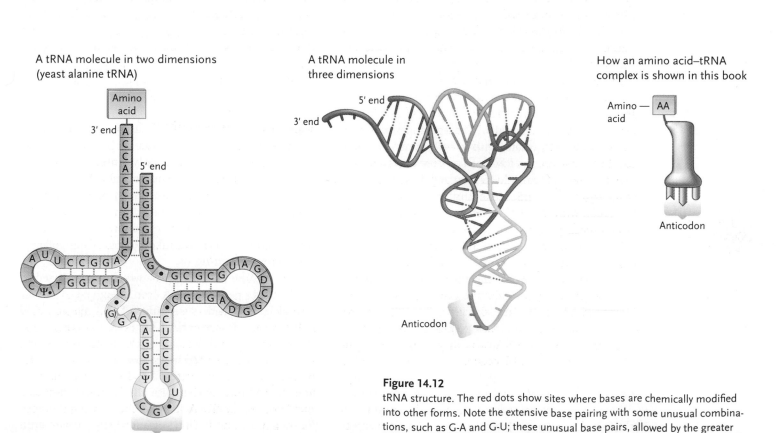

A tRNA molecule in two dimensions
(yeast alanine tRNA)

A tRNA molecule in
three dimensions

How an amino acid–tRNA
complex is shown in this book

Figure 14.12

tRNA structure. The red dots show sites where bases are chemically modified
into other forms. Note the extensive base pairing with some unusual combinations, such as G-A and G-U; these unusual base pairs, allowed by the greater
flexibility of short RNA chains, are common in tRNAs.

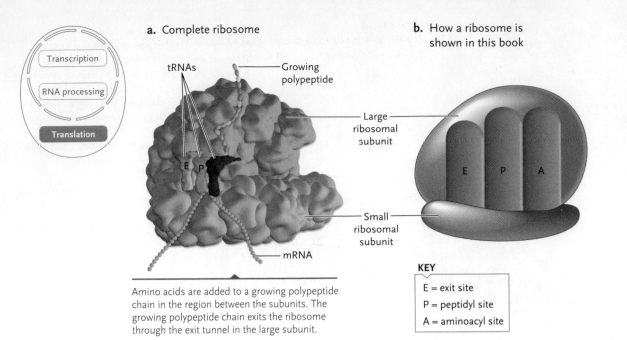

a. Complete ribosome

tRNAs

Growing polypeptide

Large ribosomal subunit

E P

Small ribosomal subunit

mRNA

Amino acids are added to a growing polypeptide chain in the region between the subunits. The growing polypeptide chain exits the ribosome through the exit tunnel in the large subunit.

b. How a ribosome is shown in this book

E P A

KEY

E = exit site
P = peptidyl site
A = aminoacyl site

Figure 14.13
Ribosome structure. **(a)** Computer model of a ribosome in the process of translation. **(b)** The ribosome as we will show it during translation. E = exit site, P = peptidyl site, and A = aminoacyl site.

Transcription

RNA processing

Translation

14.4c Translation Initiation Brings the Ribosomal Subunits, an mRNA, and the First Aminoacyl–tRNA Together

Translation is similar in prokaryotes and eukaryotes. In this section we present translation in a eukaryote but will point out along the way how it differs in prokaryotes.

There are three major stages of translation: initiation, elongation, and termination. Initiation involves the assembly of all the translation components on the start codon of the mRNA. Elongation involves reading the string of codons in the mRNA one at a time while assembling the specified amino acids into a polypeptide. Termination completes the translation process when the last amino acid has been added to the polypeptide.

In translation initiation, a large and small ribosomal subunit associates with an mRNA molecule and the first aminoacyl–tRNA of the new protein chain becomes bound to the AUG start codon **(Figure 14.14).** That aminoacyl–tRNA used for initiation is a specialized **initiator tRNA** with an anticodon to the methionine-specifying AUG start codon. Each step in translation initiation is aided by proteins called initiation factors.

In the first step of the initiation process, the initiator methionine–tRNA (Met–tRNA—anticodon 3′-UAC-5′) forms a complex with the small ribosomal subunit (see Figure 14.14, step 1). The complex binds to the mRNA at the 5′ cap and then moves along the mRNA—a process called *scanning*—until it reaches the first AUG codon (step 2). This is the start codon, and it is recognized by the Met–tRNA's anticodon. The large ribosomal subunit then binds, completing the ribosome (step 3). At the end of initiation, the initiator Met–tRNA is in the P site.

In prokaryotes, translation initiation is different: rather than scanning from the 5′ end of the mRNA, the rRNA of the ribosomal subunit finds the region with the start codon directly by base pairing with a specific **ribosome binding site** on the mRNA just upstream of the start codon. The large ribosomal subunit then binds to the small one to complete the ribosome.

After the initiator tRNA pairs with the AUG initiator codon, the subsequent stages of translation simply read the nucleotide bases three at a time on the mRNA. The initiator tRNA–AUG pairing thus establishes the correct reading frame—the series of codons for the polypeptide encoded by the mRNA.

14.4d Polypeptide Chains Grow during the Elongation Stage of Translation

The central reactions of translation take place in the elongation stage, which adds single amino acids sequentially to a growing polypeptide chain. The individual steps of elongation depend on the binding properties of P, A, and E sites of the ribosome. Protein elongation factors aid the elongation events.

The P site, with one exception, can only bind to a **peptidyl–tRNA**—a tRNA linked to a growing polypeptide chain containing two or more amino acids. The exception is the initiator tRNA, which is recognized by the P site as a peptidyl–tRNA even though it carries only a single amino acid, methionine. The A site can bind only to an aminoacyl–tRNA. The tRNA previously in the P site binds to the E site and then leaves the ribosome.

Figure 14.15 (p. 312) shows how the P, A, and E sites operate through the elongation cycle. We begin the cycle at the point when an initiator tRNA with its attached methionine is bound to the P site. The A site is empty. First, an aminoacyl–tRNA with an appropriate anticodon binds to the codon in the A site of the ribosome;

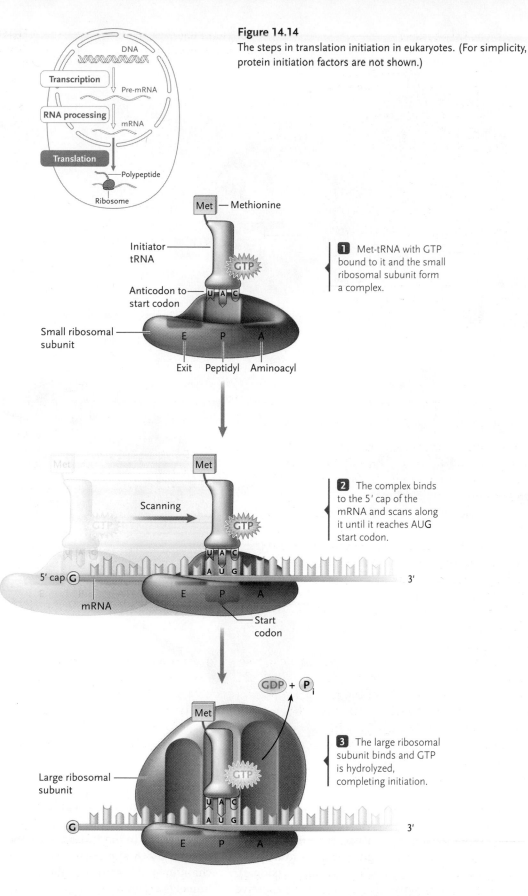

Figure 14.14
The steps in translation initiation in eukaryotes. (For simplicity, protein initiation factors are not shown.)

1 Met-tRNA with GTP bound to it and the small ribosomal subunit form a complex.

Met — Methionine

Initiator tRNA

Anticodon to start codon

Small ribosomal subunit

Exit   Peptidyl   Aminoacyl

E   P   A

2 The complex binds to the 5' cap of the mRNA and scans along it until it reaches AUG start codon.

Scanning

5' cap G

mRNA

Start codon

3 The large ribosomal subunit binds and GTP is hydrolyzed, completing initiation.

GDP + P$_i$

Large ribosomal subunit

guanosine triphosphate (GTP) is hydrolyzed to provide energy for this step (see **Figure 14.16, p. 314,** step 1).

Next, the amino acid (here, the initiator methionine) is cleaved from the tRNA in the P site and forms a peptide bond with the amino acid on the tRNA in the A site (step 2). **Peptidyl transferase** catalyzes this reaction. As we saw previously in the case of spliceosomes, catalytic activity of ribosomes resides in the rRNA component rather than the protein component, as was originally thought.

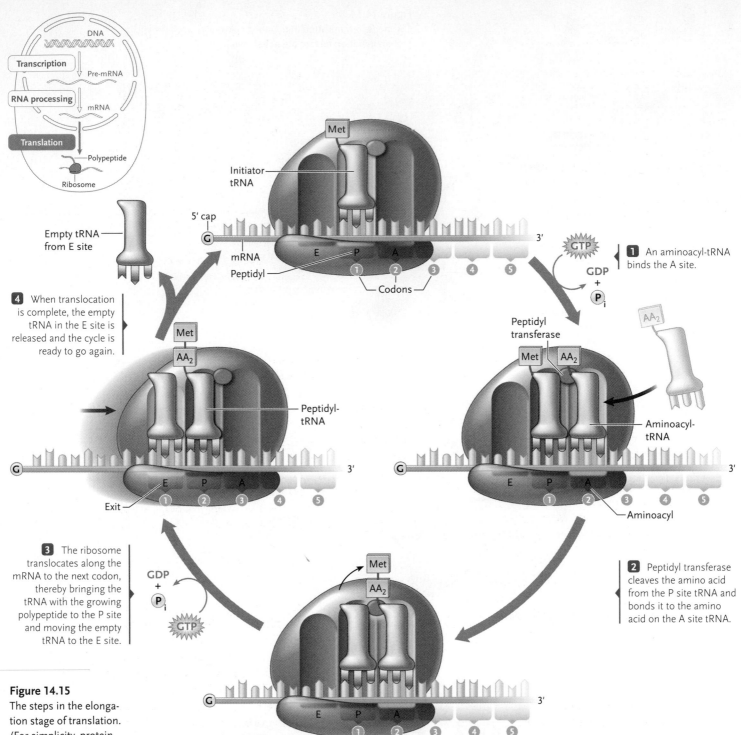

Figure 14.15
The steps in the elongation stage of translation. (For simplicity, protein elongation factors are not shown.)

Labels within the figure:

Transcription
DNA
Pre-mRNA
RNA processing
mRNA
Translation
Polypeptide
Ribosome

Met
Initiator tRNA
5' cap
Empty tRNA from E site
mRNA
Peptidyl
Codons
E P A
3'
G

GTP
GDP + P_i
1 An aminoacyl-tRNA binds the A site.

4 When translocation is complete, the empty tRNA in the E site is released and the cycle is ready to go again.

Met
AA_2
Peptidyl-tRNA
E P A
Exit
3'
G

Peptidyl transferase
Met AA_2
AA_2
Aminoacyl-tRNA
E P A
Aminoacyl
3'
G

3 The ribosome translocates along the mRNA to the next codon, thereby bringing the tRNA with the growing polypeptide to the P site and moving the empty tRNA to the E site.

GDP + P_i
GTP

Met
AA_2
E P A
3'
G

2 Peptidyl transferase cleaves the amino acid from the P site tRNA and bonds it to the amino acid on the A site tRNA.

At the end of the reaction, the (now) polypeptide chain is attached to the tRNA in the A site and an "empty" tRNA remains at the P site. Next, the ribosome moves—translocates—along the mRNA to the next codon, using energy from GTP hydrolysis (step 3). The two tRNAs remain bound to their respective codons, so this step positions the just-formed peptidyl–tRNA in the P site and generates a vacant A site. The empty tRNA that was in the P site moves to the E site, from where it is released from the ribosome (step 4). With the A site empty and a peptidyl–tRNA in the P site, the ribosome repeats the elongation cycle. In subsequent turns of the cycle, the growing polypeptide on the tRNA in the P site is transferred to the amino acid on the A site tRNA. The growing polypeptide chain extends from the ribosome through the exit tunnel (see Figure 14.13) as elongation continues.

Elongation is similar in prokaryotes and eukaryotes, with no substantive differences beyond being faster in prokaryotes. Each elongation cycle turns about 1 to 3 times per second in eukaryotes and 15 to 20 times per second in prokaryotes.

Amanitin

Alpha-amanitin is one of several potent toxins found in various species of the mushroom *Amanita* **(Figure 1)**. Although composed of many amino acid backbones linked in a ring, this interesting molecule is not a protein and is not produced by translation. In the laboratory, amanitin is a useful inhibitor of eukaryotic RNA polymerase. However, on the dinner table, amanitin is a powerful poison. People suffering from amanitin poisoning show extensive, and usually fatal, liver and kidney damage.

a.

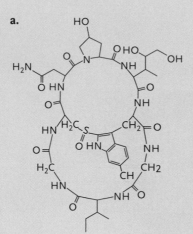

b.

Figure 1

(a) The very striking double circular structure of amanitin. **(b)** *Amanita phalloides.*

14.4e Termination Releases a Completed Polypeptide from the Ribosome

Translation switches from the elongation to the termination stage when the A site of a ribosome arrives at one of the stop codons (UAA, UAG, or UGA) on the mRNA (Figure 14.16, step 1). When a stop codon appears at the A site, a protein **release factor** (RF; also called a **termination factor**) binds at this site instead of an aminoacyl–tRNA (step 2). In response, the polypeptide chain is released from the tRNA at the P site as usual (step 3). However, because no amino acid is present at the A site, the freed polypeptide chain is released from the ribosome (step 4). At the same time, the ribosomal subunits separate and detach from the mRNA. The empty tRNA and the release factor are also released. Termination is the same in prokaryotes and eukaryotes.

14.4f Multiple Ribosomes Simultaneously Translate a Single mRNA

In the previous section describing transcription, we noted that several RNA polymerases can transcribe a gene at the same time; the same idea applies in translation. Once the first ribosome has begun translating, another one can assemble with an initiator tRNA as soon as there is room on the mRNA. Ribosomes continue to attach as translation continues and become spaced along the mRNA like beads on a string. The entire structure of an mRNA molecule and the multiple ribosomes attached to it is known as a **polysome** (a contraction of polyribosome; **Figure 14.17, p. 314**. Multiple ribosomes greatly increase the overall rate of polypeptide synthesis from a single mRNA.

In prokaryotes, the absence of a nuclear envelope allows transcription and translation to be tightly coupled. That is, as soon as the 5′ end of a new mRNA emerges from the RNA polymerase, ribosomal subunits may attach and initiate translation **(Figure 14.18, p. 314)**. In essence, the polysome forms while the mRNA is still being created. By the time the mRNA is completely transcribed, it is covered with ribosomes from end to end, each assembling a copy of the encoded polypeptide. Meanwhile, several other RNA polymerases have likely begun transcribing the same gene, each one trailing a collection of translating ribosomes. You can see that such a system allows prokaryotes to regulate the production of proteins very quickly in response to changing environmental conditions.

14.4g Newly Synthesized Polypeptides Are Processed and Folded into Finished Form

Most eukaryotic proteins are in an inactive, unfinished form when ribosomes release them. Processing reactions that convert the new proteins into finished form include the removal of amino acids from the ends or interior of the polypeptide chain and the addition of larger organic groups, including carbohydrate or lipid structures.

Proteins fold into their final three-dimensional shapes as the processing reactions take place. For many proteins, helper proteins called chaperones or chaperonins assist the folding process by combining with the folding protein, promoting "correct" three-dimensional structures, and inhibiting incorrect ones.

In some cases, the same initial polypeptide may be processed by alternative pathways that produce different mature polypeptides, usually by removing different, long stretches of amino acids from the interior of the polypeptide chain. Alternative processing is another mechanism, distinct from alternative splicing of mRNA, that increases the number of proteins encoded by a single gene.

Other proteins are processed into an initial, inactive form that is later activated at a particular time or location by removal of a covering segment of the

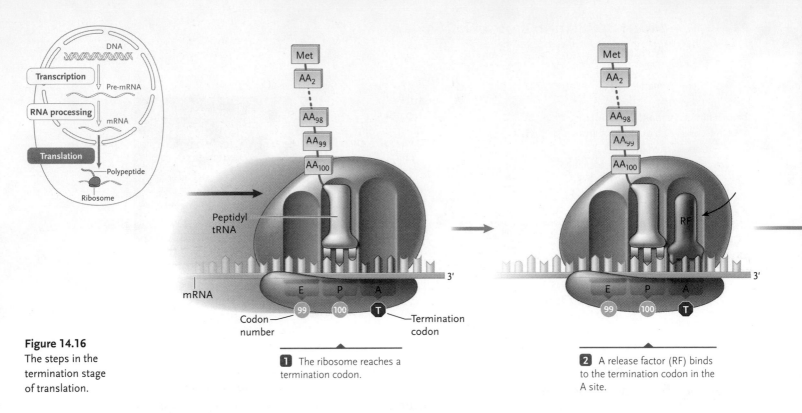

Figure 14.16
The steps in the termination stage of translation.

Peptidyl tRNA

mRNA

Codon number

Termination codon

1 The ribosome reaches a termination codon.

2 A release factor (RF) binds to the termination codon in the A site.

Figure 14.17
Polysomes, consisting of a series of ribosomes "reading" the same mRNA.

amino acid chain. The digestive enzyme pepsin, for example, is made by cells lining the stomach in an inactive form called **pepsinogen**. When the cells secrete pepsinogen into the stomach, the high acidity of that organ triggers removal of a segment of amino acids, thus converting the enzyme into the active form in which it rapidly degrades proteins in food particles. The initial production of the protein as inactive pepsinogen protects the cells that make it from having their proteins degraded by the enzyme.

14.4h Finished Proteins Contain Sorting Signals that Direct Them to Cellular Locations

Proteins are found in all parts of the eukaryotic cell, including the soluble cytoplasm, the nucleus, and the plasma membrane, as well as in the membranes or interior of various organelles; they are also transported to the cell exterior. How are newly synthesized proteins directed to these locations? Proteins that remain in the cytoplasmic solution, such as microtubule proteins or the enzymes used in glycolysis, have no signals; these proteins are made on ribosomes called free ribosomes that

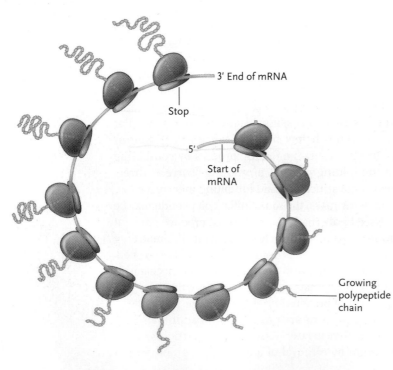

3' End of mRNA

Stop

5'

Start of mRNA

Growing polypeptide chain

mRNAs with attached ribosomes

Direction of translation

Direction of transcription

DNA

Courtesy Barbara A. Hamkalo

Figure 14.18
Simultaneous transcription and translation in progress in an electron microscope preparation extracted from *E. coli*, × 5 700 000. Courtesy of O.L. Miller Jr, Barbara A. Hamkalo, and C.A. Thomas Jr.

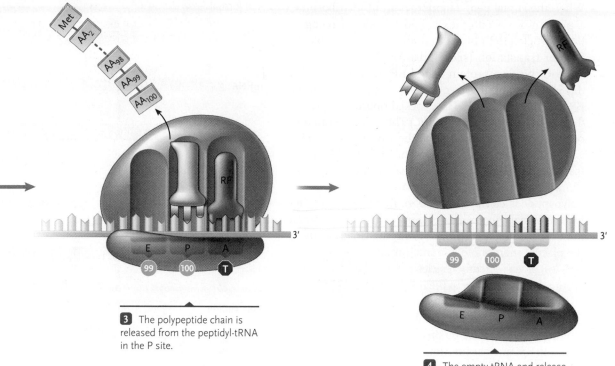

3 The polypeptide chain is released from the peptidyl-tRNA in the P site.

4 The empty tRNA and release factor are released, and the ribosomal subunits separate.

remain suspended in the cytosol. These proteins simply remain in the cytoplasmic solution as they are made.

For all other proteins, an amazing system of "address codes," written in the form of amino acid sequences, serves as sorting signals, directing the proteins to their cellular locations, or out of the cell. The signals are coded in the DNA, transcribed into mRNAs, and "printed" in proteins as they are made. The signals, first discovered by Günter Blobel and his coworkers, are recognized and bound by receptors in the locations to which the proteins are addressed. Blobel received a Nobel Prize in 1999 for his work with the mechanism sorting proteins in cells.

One major signal pathway sends proteins to the ER **(Figure 14.19)**. In these proteins, a short segment of amino acids called the **signal peptide** (or **signal sequence**) is in the first part of the polypeptide chain.

Figure 14.19
The signal mechanism directing proteins to the ER. The figure shows several ribosomes at different stages of translation of the mRNA.

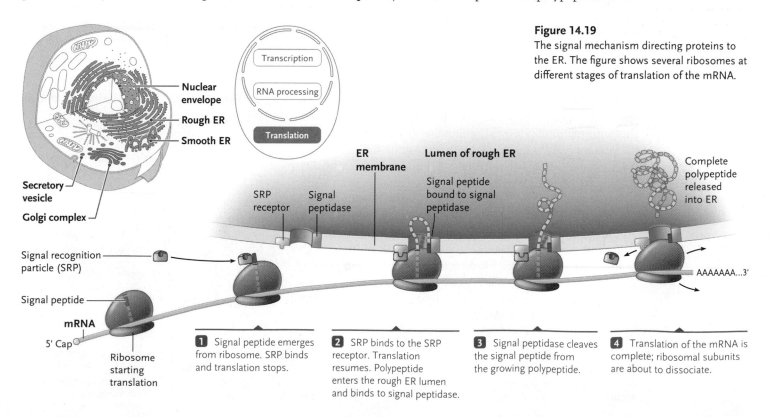

1 Signal peptide emerges from ribosome. SRP binds and translation stops.

2 SRP binds to the SRP receptor. Translation resumes. Polypeptide enters the rough ER lumen and binds to signal peptidase.

3 Signal peptidase cleaves the signal peptide from the growing polypeptide.

4 Translation of the mRNA is complete; ribosomal subunits are about to dissociate.

When the signal peptide emerges from the ribosome, a protein–RNA complex called the **signal recognition particle (SRP)** binds to it and temporarily blocks further translation (see Figure 14.19, step 1). Next, the SRP binds a protein in the ER membrane called the **SRP receptor**; this step "docks" the ribosome on the ER membrane (step 2). (The docked ribosomes give the the "roughness" to the rough ER.) The ribosome can now continue protein synthesis, and the growing polypeptide is pushed through the ER membrane into the ER lumen (see step 2). Here an enzyme, signal peptidase, removes the signal sequence (step 3), and synthesis of the polypeptide is completed (step 4). Depending on other built-in signals, the polypeptide may move to any part of the ER-based system (the ER itself, the Golgi complex, the plasma membrane, the nuclear envelope, secretory vesicles) or via secretory vesicles to the cell exterior (these destinations are shown in the inset to Figure 14.19).

Nuclear proteins include a signal bound by receptors in the pore complexes of the nuclear envelope. Once bound, they are pushed through the pore complex into the nuclear interior, in a process that requires adenosine triphosphate (ATP) energy. These proteins retain their signal because they need to reenter the nucleus each time the nuclear envelope is broken down and reforms during the cell division cycle.

Many proteins that are to become part of organelles, such as mitochondria, chloroplasts, or microbodies, are also made on free ribosomes. However, these proteins have signals that are bound by receptors in the organelle membranes, targeting them for entry into the organelles. Further signals on the proteins direct them to the different membranes or compartments inside the organelles.

The same basic system of sorting protein signals described above for eukaryotes also distributes proteins throughout prokaryotic cells, indicating that this mechanism probably evolved with the first cells. In prokaryotes, signals similar to the ER-directing signals of eukaryotes direct newly synthesized bacterial proteins to the plasma membrane (bacteria do not have ER membranes); further information built into the proteins keeps them in the plasma membrane or allows them to enter the cell wall or to be secreted outside the cell. Proteins without sorting signals remain in the cytoplasm.

Interestingly, prokaryotic and eukaryotic routing signals are interchangeable. That is, a prokaryotic signal peptide added to a polypeptide made in a eukaryotic cell routes the molecule to the ER membrane, and a eukaryotic ER-directing signal peptide grafted to a polypeptide made in a bacterial cell directs the molecule to the plasma membrane. The interchangeability of the bacterial and eukaryotic signal

Figure 14.20

Effects of mutations in protein-coding genes on the amino acid sequence of the encoded polypeptide.

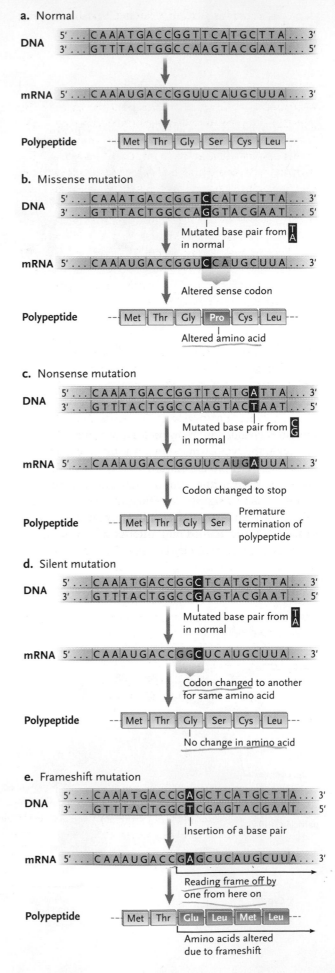

peptides provides further evidence that the sorting mechanism evolved early in the cells.

14.4i Base-Pair Mutations Can Affect Protein Structure and Function

Mutations are changes in the sequence of bases in the genetic material. How will mutations affect protein structure and function? It is hoped that your understanding of this chapter will lead you to respond, "It depends." For instance, let's consider several different mutations in the protein-coding region of a gene as shown in **Figure 14.20**. **Base-pair substitution mutations** involve a change of one particular base to another in the genetic material. This will change a base in a codon.

The normal (unmutated) DNA and amino acid sequences are shown in Figure 14.20a. If a mutation alters the codon to specify a different amino acid, then the resulting protein will have a different amino acid sequence. We call this a **missense mutation** because although an amino acid is placed in the polypeptide, it is the wrong one (see Figure 14.20b). Whether the polypeptide's function is altered significantly or not depends on which amino acid is changed and what it is changed to. A missense mutation in the gene for one of the two hemoglobin polypeptides **(Figure 14.21)** results in the genetic disease sickle cell anemia, described in Chapter 11.

A second type of base-pair substitution mutation is a **nonsense mutation** (see Figure 14.20c). In this case, the mutation changes a sense (amino acid–coding) codon to a nonsense (termination) codon in the mRNA. Translation of an mRNA containing a nonsense mutation results in a premature "stop" and a shorter-than-normal polypeptide. This polypeptide will likely be partially functional at best.

Because of the degeneracy of the genetic code, some base-pair substitution mutations do not alter the amino acid specified by the gene because the changed codon specifies the same amino acid as in the normal polypeptide. Such mutations are known as **silent mutations** (see Figure 14.20d).

If a single base pair is deleted or inserted in the coding region of a gene, the reading frame of the

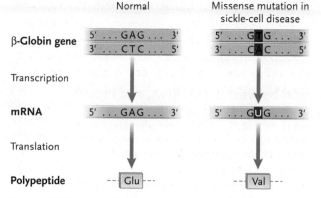

Figure 14.21

Missense mutation in a gene for one of the two polypeptides of hemoglobin that is the cause of sickle cell anemia.

resulting mRNA is altered. That is, after that point, the ribosome reads codons that are not the same as for the normal mRNA, typically producing a completely different amino acid sequence in the polypeptide from then on. This type of mutation is called a **frameshift mutation** (see Figure 14.20e; insertion mutation shown); the resulting polypeptide is usually nonfunctional because of the significantly altered amino acid sequence.

Both transcription and translation are steps in the process of gene expression, the realization of the gene's coded information in the makeup and activities of a cell. However, we will see in the next chapter that the flow of information is not one way; organisms and cells also exert control over how their genes are expressed.

STUDY BREAK

1. How does translation initiation occur in eukaryotes versus prokaryotes?
2. Distinguish between the E, P, and A sites of the ribosome.
3. How are proteins directed to different parts of a eukaryotic cell?

UNANSWERED QUESTIONS

The universality of the genetic code and the machinery that expresses it is a strikingly common feature of modern life. The same basic mechanism of transcription and translation is used by literally every cell on the planet to express its protein-coding genes. In spite of great progress in working out the specific functions of the multitude of components of the machinery, science is left with some big questions: Why is there only one system? How did it get started? What is the evolutionary origin and history of introns?

Review

Go to CENGAGENOW™ at http://hed.nelson.com/ to access quizzing, animations, exercises, articles, and personalized homework help.

14.1 The Connection between DNA, RNA, and Protein

- In their genetic experiments with *Neurospora crassa,* Beadle and Tatum found a direct correspondence between gene mutations and alterations of enzymes. Their one gene–one enzyme hypothesis is now restated as the one gene–one polypeptide hypothesis (Figure 14.2).

- The pathway from genes to proteins involves transcription then translation. In transcription, a sequence of nucleotides in DNA is copied into a complementary sequence in an RNA molecule. In translation, the sequence of nucleotides in an mRNA molecule specifies an amino acid sequence in a polypeptide (Figure 14.3).

- The genetic code is a triplet code. AUG at the beginning of a coded message establishes a reading frame for reading the codons three nucleotides at a time. The code is redundant: most of the amino acids are specified by more than one codon (Figures 14.4 and 14.5).

- The genetic code is essentially universal.

- Aside from genes that code for protein through translation of mRNA, other genes code directly for RNA products, such as tRNA, rRNA and snRNA, that are not translated.

14.2 Transcription: DNA-Directed RNA Synthesis

- Transcription is the process by which information coded in DNA is transferred to a complementary RNA copy (Figure 14.6).

- Transcription begins when an RNA polymerase binds to a promoter sequence in the DNA and starts synthesizing an RNA molecule. The enzyme then adds RNA nucleotides in sequence according to the DNA template. At the end of the transcribed sequence, the enzyme and the completed RNA transcript release from the DNA template. The mechanism of termination is different in eukaryotes and prokaryotes (Figure 14.7).

- In addition to sequences coding for amino acids, the DNA of protein-coding genes also contains several types of sequences that regulate transcription and translation.

14.3 Processing of mRNAs in Eukaryotes

- A gene encoding an mRNA molecule includes the promoter, which is recognized by the regulatory proteins and transcription factors that promote DNA unwinding and the initiation of transcription by an RNA polymerase. Transcription in eukaryotes produces a pre-mRNA molecule that consists of a 5′ cap, the 5′ untranslated region, interspersed exons (amino acid-coding segments) and introns, the 3′ untranslated region, and the 3′ poly(A) tail. All are copied from DNA except the 5′ cap and poly(A) tail, which are added during transcription (Figure 14.8).

- Introns in pre-mRNAs are removed to produce functional mRNAs by splicing. snRNPs bind to the introns, loop them out of the pre-mRNA, clip the intron at each exon boundary, and join the adjacent exons together (Figure 14.9).

- Many pre-mRNAs are subjected to alternative splicing, a process that joins exons in different combinations to produce different mRNAs encoded by the same gene. Translation of each mRNA produced in this way generates a protein with different function (Figure 14.10).

14.4 Translation: mRNA-Directed Polypeptide Synthesis

- Translation is the assembly of amino acids into polypeptides. Translation occurs on ribosomes. The P, A, and E sites of the ribosome are used for the stepwise addition of amino acids to the polypeptide as directed by the mRNA (Figures 14.11 and 14.14).

- Amino acids are brought to the ribosome attached to specific tRNAs. Amino acids are linked to their corresponding tRNAs by aminoacyl-tRNA synthetases. By matching amino acids with tRNAs, the reactions also provide the ultimate basis for the accuracy of translation (Figures 14.12 and 14.13).

- Translation proceeds through the stages of initiation, elongation, and termination. In initiation, a ribosome assembles with an mRNA molecule and an initiator methionine-tRNA. In elongation, amino acids linked to tRNAs add one at a time to the growing polypeptide chain. In termination, the new polypeptide is released from the ribosome and the ribosomal subunits separate from the mRNA (Figures 14.15–14.17).

- After they are synthesized on ribosomes, polypeptides are converted into finished form by processing reactions, which include removal of one or more amino acids from the protein chains, addition of organic groups, and folding guided by chaperones.

- Proteins are distributed in cells by means of signals spelled out by amino acid sequences (Figure 14.20).

- Base-pair substitution mutations alter the mRNA and can lead to changes in the amino acid sequence of the encoded polypeptide. A missense mutation changes one sense codon to one that specifies a different amino acid, a nonsense mutation changes a sense codon to a stop codon, and a silent mutation changes one sense codon to another sense codon that specifies the same amino acid. A base-pair insertion or deletion is a frameshift mutation that alters the reading frame beyond the point of the mutation, leading to a different amino acid sequence from then on in the polypeptide (Figures 14.21 and 14.22).

Questions

Self-Test Questions

1. Which statement about the following pathway is false?

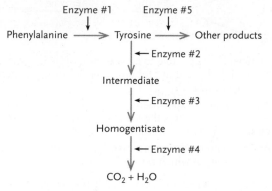

   a. A mutation for enzyme #1 causes phenylalanine to build up.
   b. A mutation for enzyme #2 prevents tyrosine from being synthesized.
   c. A mutation at enzyme #3 prevents homogentistate from being synthesized.
   d. A mutation for enzyme #2 could hide a mutation in enzyme #4.
   e. Each step in a pathway such as this is catalyzed by an enzyme, which is coded by a gene.

2. Eukaryotic mRNA:
   a. uses snRNPs to cut out introns and seal together translatable exons.
   b. uses a spliccosome mechanism made of DNA to recognize consensus regions to cut and splice.
   c. has a guanine cap on its 3′ end and a poly(A) tail on its 5′ end.
   d. is composed of adenine, thymine, guanine, and cytosine.
   e. codes the guanine cap and poly(A) tail from the DNA template.

3. A segment strand of DNA has a base sequence of 5′-GCATTAGAC-3′. What would be the sequence of an RNA molecule complementary to that sequence?
   a. 5′-GUCTAATGC-3′
   b. 5′-GCAUUAGAC-3′
   c. 5′-CGTAATCTG-3′
   d. 5′-GUCUAAUGC-3′
   e. 5′-CGUAAUCUG-3′

4. Which of the following statements about the initiation phase of translation is false?
   a. An initiation factor allows 5′ mRNA to attach to the small ribosomal subunit.
   b. Initiation factors complex with GTP to help Met-tRNA and AUG pair.
   c. mRNA attaches first to the small ribosomal subunit.
   d. GTP is synthesized.
   e. 3′-UAC-5′ on the tRNA binds 5′-AUG-3′ on mRNA.

5. Which of the following types of bonding DOES NOT involve complementary base pairing?
   a. codon to anticodon
   b. signal peptide to signal recognition particle
   c. RNA to RNA in hairpin transcription terminator
   d. DNA to RNA in transcription of snRNA gene
   e. rRNA to mRNA in prokaryotic translation initiation

6. Translation is in progress, with methionine bound to a tRNA in the P site, and a phenylalanine bound to a tRNA in the A site. The order of the next steps in the elongation cycle is:
   a. the ribosome translocates → a new aminoacyl-tRNA enters the A site → peptidyl transferase catalyzes a peptide bond between the two amino acids → empty tRNA is released from the ribosome.
   b. peptidyl transferase catalyzes a peptide bond between the two amino acids → a new aminoacyl-tRNA enters the A site → empty tRNA is released from the ribosome → the ribosome translocates.
   c. peptidyl transferase catalyzes a peptide bond between the two amino acids → empty tRNA is released from the ribosome → a new aminoacyl-tRNA enters the A site → the ribosome translocates.
   d. peptidyl transferase catalyzes a peptide bond between the two amino acids → the ribosome translocates → empty tRNA is released from the ribosome → a new aminoacyl-tRNA enters the A site.
   e. the ribosome translocates → peptidyl transferase catalyzes a peptide bond between the two amino acids → empty tRNA is released from the ribosome → a new aminoacyl-tRNA enters the A site.

7. Which of the following statements is false?
   a. GTP is an energy source during various stages of translation.
   b. In the ribosome, peptidyl transferase catalyses peptide bond formation between amino acids.
   c. When the mRNA code UAA reaches the ribosome, there is no tRNA to bind to it.
   d. A long polypeptide is cut off the tRNA in the A site so its Met amino acid links to the amino acid in the P site.
   e. Forty-two amino acids of a protein are encoded by 126 nucleotides of the mRNA.

8. Which item binds to SRP receptor and to the signal sequence to guide a newly synthesized protein to be secreted to its proper "channel"?
   a. ribosome
   b. signal recognition particle
   c. endoplasmic reticulum
   d. signal peptidase
   e. receptor protein

9. A part of an mRNA molecule with the sequence 5′-UGC GCA-3′ is being translated by a ribosome. The following activated tRNA molecules are available. Two of them can correctly bind the mRNA so that a dipeptide can form.

tRNA Anticodon	Amino Acid
3′-GGC-5′	Proline
3′-CGU-5′	Alanine
3′-UGC-5′	Threonine
3′-CCG-5′	Glycine
3′-ACG-5′	Cysteine
3′-CGG-5′	Alanine

   a. cysteine-alanine
   b. proline-cysteine
   c. glycine-cysteine
   d. alanine-alanine
   e. threonine-glycine

10. A missense mutation cannot be:
   a. the code for the sickle-cell gene.
   b. caused by a frameshift.
   c. the deletion of a base in a coding sequence.
   d. the addition of two bases in a coding sequence.
   e. the same as a silent mutation.

Questions for Discussion

1. Would you expect rRNA genes to have "start" codons? Why, or why not?

2. A mutation appears that alters an anticodon in a tRNA from AAU to AUU. What effect will this change have on protein synthesis in cells carrying this mutation?

3. The normal form of a gene contains the nucleotide sequence:

   5'-ATGCCCGCCTTTGCTACTTGGTAG-3'
   3'-TACGGGCGGAAACGATGAACCATC-5'

   When this gene is transcribed, the result is the following mRNA molecule:

   5'-AUGCCCGCCUUUGCUACUUGGUAG-3'

   In a mutated form of the gene, two extra base pairs (underlined) are inserted:

   5'-ATGCCCGCCTAATTGCTACTTGGTAG-3'
   3'-TACGGGCGGATTAACGATGAACCATC-5'

   What effect will this particular mutation have on the structure of the protein encoded in the gene?

4. A geneticist is attempting to isolate mutations in the genes for four enzymes acting in a metabolic pathway in the bacterium *Escherichia coli*. The end product *E* of the pathway is absolutely essential for life:

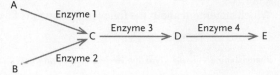

   The geneticist has been able to isolate mutations in the genes for enzymes 1 and 2, but not for enzymes 3 and 4. Develop a hypothesis to explain why.

5. How could you show experimentally that the genetic code is universal; namely, that it is the same in bacteria as it is in eukaryotes such as fungi, plants, and animals?

   How might the process of alternative splicing and exon shuffling affect the rate at which new proteins evolve?

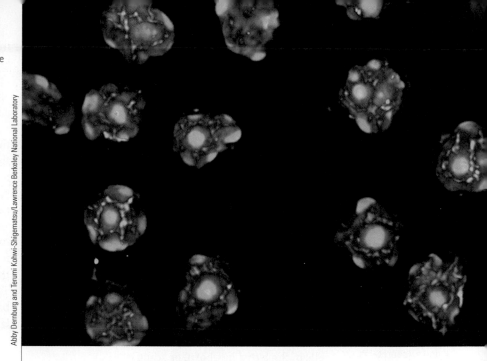

Chromatin remodelling proteins (gold) binding to chromatin (blue). Chromatin remodelling, a change in chromosome structure in the region of a gene, is a key step in the activation of genes in eukaryotes.

Abby Dernburg and Terumi Kohwi-Shigematsu/Lawrence Berkeley National Laboratory

15 Control of Gene Expression

WHY IT MATTERS

A human egg cell is almost completely inactive metabolically when it is released from the ovary. It remains quiescent as it begins its travel down a fallopian tube leading from the ovary to the uterus, carried along by movements of cilia lining the walls of the tube **(Figure 15.1, p. 322)**. It is here, in the fallopian tube, that egg and sperm cells meet and embryonic development begins. Within seconds after the cells unite, the fertilized egg breaks its quiescent state and begins a series of divisions that continues as the egg moves through the fallopian tube and enters the uterus. Subsequent divisions produce specialized cells that *differentiate* into the distinct types tailored for specific functions in the body, such as muscle cells and cells of the nervous system.

At first glance, you might think it most efficient for each differentiated cell type to retain only those genes needed to carry out its specific function; that is, liver cells might be expected to have a different collection of genes than bone cells. However, biochemical and cytogenetic analyses do not support this model and have, in fact, demonstrated that all nucleated cells of a developing embryo retain essentially the same set of genes that was created in the original single-celled zygote resulting from fertilization. Structural and functional differences in cell types

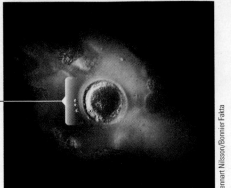

Figure 15.1
A human egg released from the ovary. The outer layer appearing light blue is a coat of polysaccharides and glycoproteins that surrounds the egg. Within the egg, genes and regulatory proteins are poised to enter the pathways initiating embryonic development.

result from the presence or absence of *the products resulting from expression of genes* rather than the actual genes themselves. The products of some genes, known as housekeeping genes, are expressed in nearly all cells, whereas the products of other genes may be found only in certain cell types under particular environmental conditions. For example, all cells contain genes coding for the enzymes needed for basic cellular metabolism (that is, the Krebs cycle), as well as genes coding for various hemoglobin polypeptides. While Krebs cycle gene products are found in all cells, particular hemoglobins are found only in those cells that give rise to red blood cells in the fetus, newborn, or adult.

What determines whether a gene product will be produced or not? The overall expression of a gene is subject to a number of fundamental mechanisms that provide fine-detail control over when, where, and how much a gene product is produced. The material in the previous chapter on transcription and translation hinted at these mechanisms. Usually, when we say that a gene is "turned on," we mean that it is being transcribed actively. Beyond transcription, the expression of gene products is subject to further controls affecting the processing of ribonucleic acid (RNA), possible translation into protein, and the activity and "life span" of the product itself. You saw in the previous chapter that transcription and translation are coincident in prokaryotes. This enables a rapid response to environmental conditions through regulation of transcription initiation. Eukaryotes, particularly multicellular organisms, exhibit both short-term response and long-term differentiation through a variety of mechanisms not used by prokaryotes.

In this chapter, we examine the mechanisms of **transcriptional regulation** and its fine-tuning by additional controls at the posttranscriptional, translational, and posttranslational levels. Our discussion begins with bacterial systems, where researchers first discovered a mechanism for transcriptional regulation, and then moves to eukaryotic systems, where the regulation of gene activity is more complicated. How genes regulate development is discussed in Chapters 30 and 39.

15.1 Regulation of Gene Expression in Prokaryotes

Transcription and translation are closely regulated in prokaryotes in ways that reflect prokaryotic life histories. Prokaryotes are relatively simple, single-celled organisms with generation times measured in minutes. Rather than the complex patterns of long-term cell differentiation and development typical of multicellular eukaryotes, prokaryotic cells typically undergo rapid and reversible alterations in biochemical pathways that allow them to adapt quickly to changes in their environment.

The bacterium *Escherichia coli,* for example, can find itself in the intestinal tract of a cow one minute and then in a treated municipal water supply soon after. Sugars such as lactose might be more available in the water environment, and genes coding for enzymes needed to metabolize this energy source need to be "turned on." Other nutrients, such as the amino acid tryptophan, may also be available in the water. Therefore, genes coding for enzymes needed to manufacture the amino acid "from scratch" need to be "turned off." The versatile and responsive control system allows the bacterium to make the most efficient use of the particular array of nutrients available at any given time.

15.1a The Operon Is a Unit of Transcription

When the environment in which a bacterium lives changes, some metabolic processes are stopped and others are started. Typically, this involves turning off the genes for the metabolic processes not needed and turning on the genes for the new metabolic processes. For each metabolic process, a few to many genes are involved, and the regulation of those genes must be coordinated. For example, three genes encode proteins for the metabolism of lactose by *E. coli*. In the absence of lactose, the three genes are not expressed, whereas in the presence of lactose, the genes are expressed. That is, the control of these genes is at the transcription level.

In 1961, François Jacob and Jacques Monod of the Pasteur Institute in Paris proposed the *operon model* for the control of the expression of genes for lactose metabolism in *E. coli*. Subsequently, data have shown the *operon model* to be widely applicable to the regulation of gene expression in bacteria and their viruses. Jacob and Monod received the Nobel Prize in 1965 for their explanation of bacterial operons and their regulation by repressors.

An **operon** is a cluster of prokaryotic genes and the DNA sequences involved in their regulation. The promoter, as we saw in the previous chapter, is a region where the RNA polymerase begins transcription. Each operon, which can contain several to many genes, is transcribed as a unit from the promoter into a single messenger RNA (mRNA), and as a result, the mRNA contains codes for several proteins. The cluster of genes transcribed into a single mRNA is called a **transcription unit**. A ribosome translates the mRNA from one end to the other, sequentially making each protein encoded in the mRNA. Typically, the proteins encoded by an operon catalyze steps in the same function, such as enzymes acting in sequence in a biochemical pathway.

The other regulatory DNA sequence in the operon is the **operator**, a short segment to which a regulatory protein binds. The regulatory protein is encoded by a gene separate from the operon that the protein controls. Some operons are controlled by a regulatory protein termed a **repressor,** which, when active, prevents the genes of the operon from being expressed. Other operons are controlled by a regulatory protein termed an *activator,* which, when active, stimulates the expression of genes.

Many operons are controlled by more than one regulatory mechanism, and a number of the repressors or activators control more than one operon. The result is a complex network of superimposed controls that provides regulation of transcription, allowing almost instantaneous responses to changing environmental conditions.

15.1b The *lac* Operon for Lactose Metabolism Is Transcribed When an Inducer Inactivates a Repressor

Jacob and Monod researched the genetic control of lactose metabolism in *E. coli*. Lactose is a sugar that, when metabolized, provides energy for the cell. Jacob and Monod used genetic and biochemical approaches to study the genetic control of lactose metabolism in *E. coli*. Their genetic studies showed that for lactose metabolism, three genes are involved: *lacZ, lacY,* and *lacA* **(Figure 15.2).** These three genes are adjacent to one another on the chromosome in the order Z-Y-A. The genes are transcribed as a unit into a single mRNA starting with the *lacZ* gene; the promoter for the transcription unit is upstream of *lacZ*. The *lacZ* gene encodes the enzyme β-galactosidase, which catalyzes the conversion of the disaccharide sugar, lactose, into the monosaccharide sugars, glucose and galactose. These sugars are then metabolized by other enzymes, producing energy for the cell. The *lacY* gene encodes a permease enzyme that transports lactose actively into the cell, and the *lacA* gene encodes a transacetylase enzyme, the function of which is unknown.

Jacob and Monod called the cluster of genes and adjacent sequences that control their expression the *lac* operon (see Figure 15.2). They coined the name *operon* from a key DNA sequence they discovered for regulating transcription of the operon—the **operator.** The operator was named because it controls the operation of the genes adjacent to it. For the *lac* operon, the operator is a short DNA sequence between the promoter and the *lacZ* gene.

These two investigators showed that the *lac* operon was controlled by a regulatory protein that they termed the *Lac repressor.* The Lac repressor is encoded by the regulatory gene *lacI,* which is nearby but separate from the *lac* operon (see Figure 15.2), and is synthesized in active form. When lactose is absent from the medium, active Lac repressor binds to the operator, thereby blocking the RNA polymerase from binding to the promoter; as a result, transcription cannot occur **(Figure 15.3a, p. 324).** Actually, the repressor occasionally falls off, allowing transcription to occur—but at a very slow rate, leading to just a few molecules of each encoded enzyme in the cell.

When lactose is added to the medium, the *lac* operon is turned on and all three enzymes are synthesized rapidly **(Figure 15.3b, p. 324).** How does this occur? Lactose enters the cell and the β-galactosidase molecules already present convert some of it to *allolactose,* an isomer of lactose. Allolactose is an **inducer** for the *lac* operon—the isomer turns on the three genes in the operon. Allolactose does this by binding to the Lac repressor, inactivating it by altering its shape so that it can no longer bind to the operator. With the repressor out of the way, RNA polymerase is then able to bind to the promoter, and it transcribes the three genes. The *lac* operon is called an **inducible operon** because an inducer molecule increases its expression.

When the lactose is used up, the regulatory system again switches the *lac* operon off. That is, the absence of lactose means that there are no allolactose inducer molecules to inactivate the repressor; the again-active repressor binds to the operator, blocking transcription of the

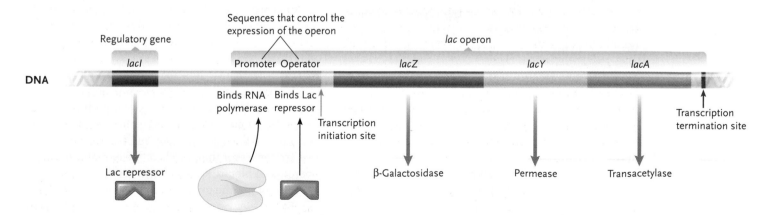

Figure 15.2

The *E. coli lac* operon. The *lacZ, lacY,* and *lacA* genes encode the enzymes taking part in lactose metabolism. The separate regulatory gene, *lacI,* encodes the Lac repressor, which plays a pivotal role in the control of the operon. The promoter binds RNA polymerase, and the operator binds activated Lac repressor. The transcription unit, which extends from the transcription initiation site to the transcription termination site, contains the genes.

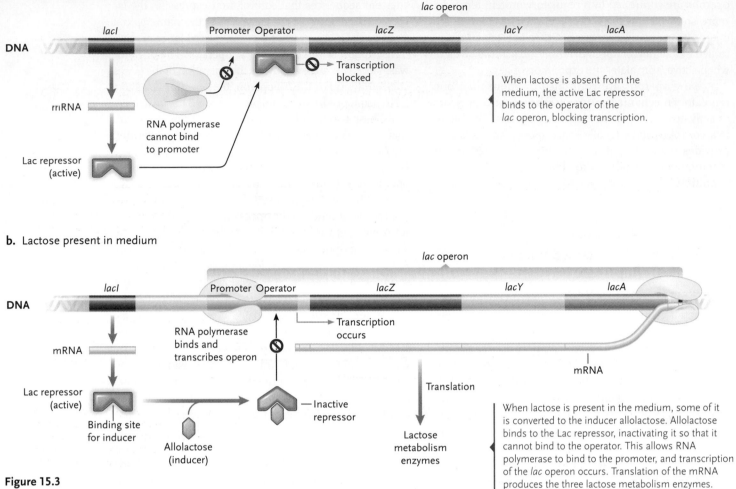

a. Lactose absent from medium

lac operon

lacI   Promoter Operator   *lacZ*   *lacY*   *lacA*

DNA

rrRNA

RNA polymerase cannot bind to promoter

Transcription blocked

Lac repressor (active)

When lactose is absent from the medium, the active Lac repressor binds to the operator of the *lac* operon, blocking transcription.

b. Lactose present in medium

lac operon

lacI   Promoter Operator   *lacZ*   *lacY*   *lacA*

DNA

mRNA

RNA polymerase binds and transcribes operon

Transcription occurs

mRNA

Lac repressor (active)

Binding site for inducer

Allolactose (inducer)

Inactive repressor

Translation

Lactose metabolism enzymes

When lactose is present in the medium, some of it is converted to the inducer allolactose. Allolactose binds to the Lac repressor, inactivating it so that it cannot bind to the operator. This allows RNA polymerase to bind to the promoter, and transcription of the *lac* operon occurs. Translation of the mRNA produces the three lactose metabolism enzymes.

Figure 15.3
Regulation of the inducible *lac* operon by the Lac repressor in the absence **(a)** and presence **(b)** of lactose.

operon. The controls are aided by the fact that bacterial mRNAs are very short-lived, about three minutes on average. This quick turnover permits the cytoplasm to be cleared quickly of the mRNAs transcribed from an operon. The enzymes themselves also have short lifetimes and are quickly degraded.

15.1c   Transcription of the *trp* Operon Genes for Tryptophan Biosynthesis Is Repressed When Tryptophan Activates a Repressor

Tryptophan is an amino acid that is used in the synthesis of proteins. If tryptophan is absent from the medium, *E. coli* must make it so that proteins can be synthesized. If tryptophan is present in the medium, then the cell will use that source rather than make its own.

Tryptophan biosynthesis also involves an operon, the *trp* operon **(Figure 15.4)**. The five genes in this operon, *trpA–trpE*, encode the enzymes for the steps in the tryptophan biosynthesis pathway. Upstream of the *trpE* gene are the operon's promoter and operator sequences. Expression of the *trp* operon is controlled by the Trp repressor, a regulatory protein encoded by the *trpR* gene, which is located elsewhere in the genome

(not nearby, as was the case for the repressor gene for the *lac* operon). In contrast to the Lac repressor, the Trp repressor is synthesized in an inactive form in which it cannot bind to the operator.

When tryptophan is absent from the medium and must be made by the cell, the *trp* operon genes are expressed (see **Figure 15.4a**). This is the default state: since the Trp repressor is inactive and cannot bind to the operator, RNA polymerase can bind to the promoter and transcribe the operon. The resulting mRNA is translated to produce the five tryptophan biosynthetic enzymes that catalyze the reactions for tryptophan synthesis.

If tryptophan is present, there is no need for the cell to make it, so the *trp* operon is shut off (see **Figure 15.4b**). This occurs because the tryptophan entering the cell binds to the Trp repressor and activates it. The active Trp repressor then binds to the operator of the *trp* operon and blocks RNA polymerase from binding to the promoter—the operon cannot be transcribed.

For the *trp* operon, then, the presence of tryptophan represses the expression of the tryptophan biosynthesis genes; hence, this operon is an example of a **repressible operon.** Here, tryptophan acts as a **corepressor,** a regulatory molecule that combines with a repressor to activate it and thus shut off the operon.

a. Tryptophan absent from medium

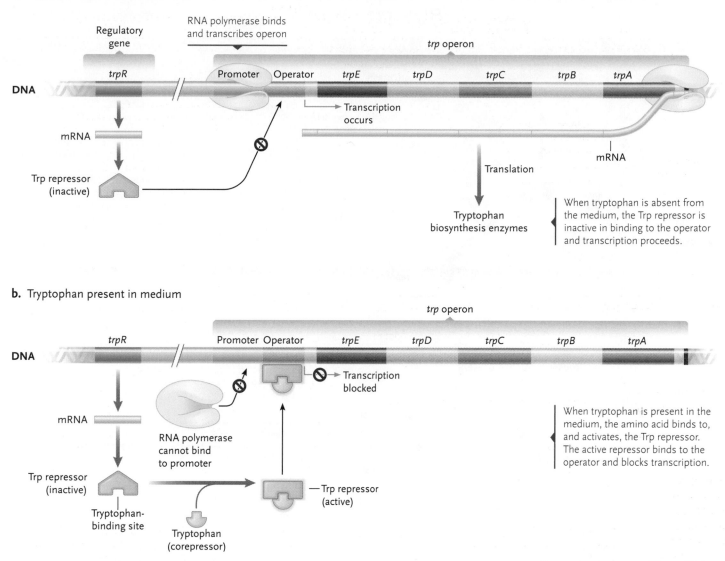

Regulatory gene

RNA polymerase binds and transcribes operon

trp operon

DNA — *trpR* | Promoter | Operator | *trpE* | *trpD* | *trpC* | *trpB* | *trpA*

mRNA

Trp repressor (inactive)

→ Transcription occurs

mRNA

Translation

Tryptophan biosynthesis enzymes

When tryptophan is absent from the medium, the Trp repressor is inactive in binding to the operator and transcription proceeds.

b. Tryptophan present in medium

trp operon

DNA — *trpR* | Promoter | Operator | *trpE* | *trpD* | *trpC* | *trpB* | *trpA*

mRNA

Trp repressor (inactive)

Tryptophan-binding site

RNA polymerase cannot bind to promoter

Transcription blocked

Trp repressor (active)

Tryptophan (corepressor)

When tryptophan is present in the medium, the amino acid binds to, and activates, the Trp repressor. The active repressor binds to the operator and blocks transcription.

Figure 15.4
Regulation of the repressible *trp* operon by the Trp repressor in the absence **(a)** and presence **(b)** of tryptophan.

To compare and contrast the two operons we have discussed: (1) In the *lac* operon, the repressor is synthesized in an active form. When the inducer (allolactose) is present, it binds to the repressor and inactivates it. The operon is then transcribed. (2) In the *trp* operon, the repressor is synthesized in an inactive form. When the corepressor (tryptophan) is present, it binds to the repressor and activates it. The active repressor blocks transcription of the operon.

Inducible and repressible operons illustrate two types of *negative gene regulation* because both are regulated by a repressor that turns off gene expression when it is in active form. Genes are expressed only when the repressor is in inactive form.

15.1d Transcription of the *lac* Operon Is Also Controlled by a Positive Regulatory System

Several years after Jacob and Monod proposed their operon model for the lactose metabolism genes, researchers found a *positive gene regulation* system that

also regulates the *lac* operon. This system ensures that the *lac* operon is transcribed if lactose is provided as an energy source, but not if glucose is present in addition to lactose. This is because glucose is a more efficient source of energy than is lactose. Glucose can be used directly in the glycolysis pathway to produce energy for the cell (see Chapter 6). Lactose, on the other hand, must first be converted into glucose and galactose, and the galactose then converted into glucose. These conversions require energy. Thus, the cell gains more by metabolizing glucose than lactose, or for that matter any other sugar.

Figure 15.5a (p. 326) shows the positive gene regulation system working when lactose is present and glucose is absent in the growth medium. In essence, this adds to the model shown earlier in Figure 15.3b. Lactose is metabolized to the inducer, allolactose, which binds to and inactivates the Lac repressor. RNA polymerase is then recruited to the promoter by active *CAP (catabolite activator protein)* at the *CAP site*, a DNA sequence immediately upstream of the promoter. CAP is an **activator**, a regulatory protein that stimulates gene

a. Lactose present; glucose low or absent

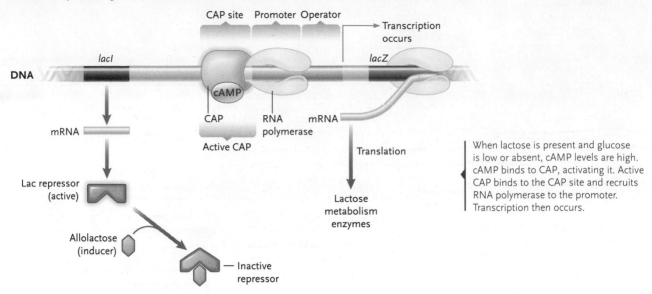

When lactose is present and glucose is low or absent, cAMP levels are high. cAMP binds to CAP, activating it. Active CAP binds to the CAP site and recruits RNA polymerase to the promoter. Transcription then occurs.

b. Lactose present; glucose present

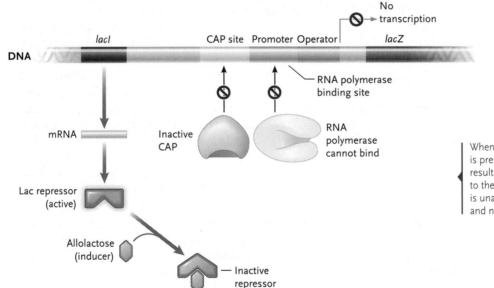

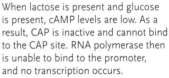

When lactose is present and glucose is present, cAMP levels are low. As a result, CAP is inactive and cannot bind to the CAP site. RNA polymerase then is unable to bind to the promoter, and no transcription occurs.

Figure 15.5

Positive regulation of the *lac* operon by the CAP activator. Other operons involved in the metabolism of various sugars are regulated in the same way.

expression. It is synthesized in *inactive* form and is activated when cyclic adenine monophosphate (cAMP) binds to it (cAMP is a nucleotide that plays a role in regulating cellular processes in both prokaryotes and eukaryotes; see Section 8.4). When glucose is absent from the medium, cAMP is abundant in the cell, so CAP is active under these conditions and can bind to the CAP site.

If both lactose and glucose are present in the medium, the *lac* operon is not transcribed (**Figure 15.5b**). Metabolism of the incoming glucose triggers a series of events leading to inactivation of adenylyl cyclase, the enzyme that catalyzes the synthesis of cAMP from ATP. The level of cAMP drops drastically, reaching a point where it is too low to activate CAP. Without active CAP bound to the CAP site, RNA polymerase is unable to bind

to the promoter, and the operon cannot be transcribed. In short, gene expression cannot be activated under these conditions. When glucose is depleted, the bacteria then shift to metabolizing lactose. Inactivation of adenylyl cyclase is reversed, cAMP levels rise again, and CAP is activated. The events of Figure 15.5a then occur.

The same positive gene regulation system using CAP and cAMP regulates a large number of other operons that control the metabolism of many sugars. In each case, the system functions so that glucose, if it is present in the growth medium, is metabolized first. This type of regulatory system, in which several operons are under the control of a common regulator, is called a regulon.

In sum, regulation of gene expression in prokaryotes occurs primarily at the transcription level. There are

AI-2

Bacterial cells can communicate with one another through the production and detection of molecules called autoinducers. When an autoinducer accumulates to high concentration in the local environment, it binds to membrane receptors that initiate a signal cascade, resulting in transcriptional activation of genes. This process, called quorum sensing, provides a mechanism for populations of cells to determine their density and thus coordinate gene expression as a community. For instance, although it is rather futile for an isolated single cell of *Vibrio harveyi* to express genes from its *lux* operon in order to bioluminesce, hundreds of millions of cells, all expressing *lux* genes, collectively produce biologically significant amounts of light. In a way, these populations of cells are behaving like multicellular organisms. Although various auto-inducers are known to mediate communication among members of the same species, a novel compound, called AI-2 **(Figure 1),** has been found to facilitate communication between members of *different* species. AI-2 is unlike any other known autoinducer and is particularly interesting in that it contains an atom of boron, an element whose function in biological systems has been quite mysterious.

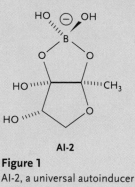

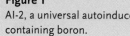

AI-2

Figure 1
AI-2, a universal autoinducer containing boron.

also some examples of regulation at the translation level. For example, some proteins can bind to the mRNAs that produce them and modulate their translation. This serves as a feedback mechanism to fine-tune the amounts of the proteins in the cell. In the remainder of the chapter, we discuss the regulation of gene expression in eukaryotes. You will see that regulation occurs at several points between the gene and the protein and that regulatory mechanisms are more complex than those in prokaryotes.

STUDY BREAK

1. Suppose the *lacI* gene is mutated so that the Lac repressor is not made. How does this mutation affect the regulation of the *lac* operon?
2. Answer the equivalent question for the *trp* operon: How would a mutation that prevents the Trp repressor from being made affect the regulation of the *trp* operon?

15.2 Regulation of Transcription in Eukaryotes

As you just learned, gene expression in prokaryotes is commonly regulated at the transcription level with genes organized in functional units called operons. The molecular mechanisms in operon function are a simple means of coordinating synthesis of proteins with related functions. In eukaryotes, the coordinated synthesis of proteins with related functions also occurs, but the genes involved are usually scattered around the genomes; that is, they are not organized into operons. Nonetheless, like operons, individual eukaryotic genes also consist of protein-coding sequences and adjacent regulatory sequences.

There are two general categories of eukaryotic gene regulation. Short-term regulation involves regulatory events in which gene sets are quickly turned on or off in response to changes in environmental or physiological conditions in the cell's or organism's environment. This type of regulation is most similar to prokaryotic gene regulation. Long-term gene regulation involves regulatory events required for an organism to develop and differentiate. Long-term gene regulation occurs in multicellular eukaryotes and not in simpler, unicellular eukaryotes. The mechanisms we discuss in this and the next section are applicable to both short-term and long-term regulation. The specific molecules and genes involved are different and, of course, so is the outcome to the cell or organism.

15.2a In Eukaryotes, Regulation of Gene Expression Occurs at Several Levels

The regulation of gene expression is more complicated in eukaryotes than in prokaryotes because eukaryotic cells are more complex, because the nuclear DNA is organized with histones into chromatin, and because multicellular eukaryotes produce large numbers and different types of cells. Further, the eukaryotic nuclear envelope separates the processes of transcription and translation, whereas in prokaryotes, translation can start on an mRNA that is still being made. Consequently, gene expression in eukaryotes is regulated at more levels. That is, there is transcriptional regulation, post-transcriptional regulation, translational regulation, and posttranslational regulation **(Figure 15.6, p. 328).** The most important of these is transcriptional regulation.

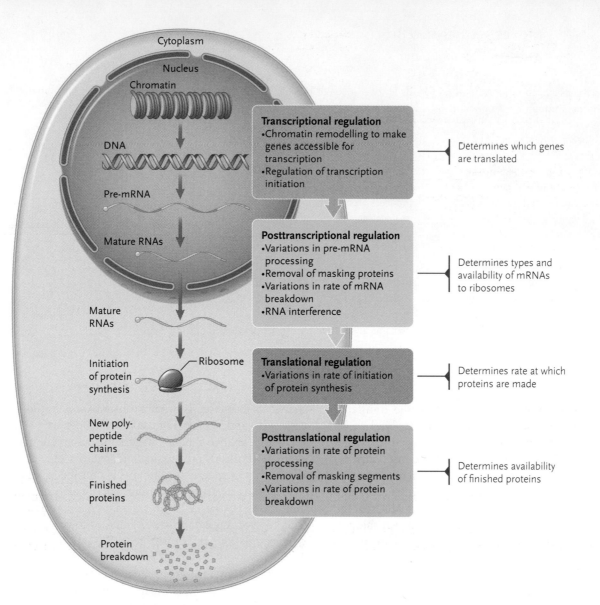

Cytoplasm

Nucleus

Chromatin

DNA

Pre-mRNA

Mature RNAs

Transcriptional regulation
•Chromatin remodelling to make genes accessible for transcription
•Regulation of transcription initiation

Determines which genes are translated

Posttranscriptional regulation
•Variations in pre-mRNA processing
•Removal of masking proteins
•Variations in rate of mRNA breakdown
•RNA interference

Determines types and availability of mRNAs to ribosomes

Mature RNAs

Initiation of protein synthesis — Ribosome

Translational regulation
•Variations in rate of initiation of protein synthesis

Determines rate at which proteins are made

New polypeptide chains

Posttranslational regulation
•Variations in rate of protein processing
•Removal of masking segments
•Variations in rate of protein breakdown

Determines availability of finished proteins

Finished proteins

Protein breakdown

Figure 15.6

Steps in transcriptional, posttranscriptional, translational, and posttranslational regulation of gene expression in eukaryotes.

15.2b Chromatin Structure Plays an Important Role in Whether a Gene Is Active or Inactive

Eukaryotic DNA is organized into chromatin by combination with histone proteins (discussed in Section 13.5). Recall that DNA is wrapped around a core of two molecules each made of histones H2A, H2B, H3, and H4, forming the nucleosome (see Figure 13.18). Higher levels of chromatin organization occur when histone H1 is linked to adjacent nucleosomes.

Genes in regions of the DNA that are tightly wound around histones in chromatin are inactive because their promoters are not accessible to the proteins that initiate transcription. Activating a gene involves changing the state of the chromatin so that the proteins that initiate transcription can bind to their promoters, a process called **chromatin remodelling.** In one type of chromatin remodelling, an activator binds to a regulatory sequence upstream of the gene's promoter and recruits a *remodelling complex,* a protein complex that displaces a nucleosome from the chromatin, exposing the promoter **(Figure 15.7).** In a second type of chromatin remodelling, an activator binds to a regulatory sequence upstream of the gene's promoter and recruits an enzyme that acetylates (adds acetyl groups: $CH_3CO—$) to histones in the nucleosome where the promoter is located. Acetylation causes the histones to loosen their association with DNA, and the promoter becomes accessible. This type of remodelling is reversed by deacetylation enzymes that remove the acetyl groups from the histones. Many activators use both of these chromatin remodelling mechanisms to regulate gene activity.

15.2c Regulation of Transcription Initiation Involves the Effects of Proteins Binding to a Gene's Promoter and Regulatory Sites

Chromatin remodelling is a crucial initial event in facilitating gene expression. Remodelling opens the way for transcription initiation to occur. Transcription initiation is the most important level at which the regulation of gene expression takes place.

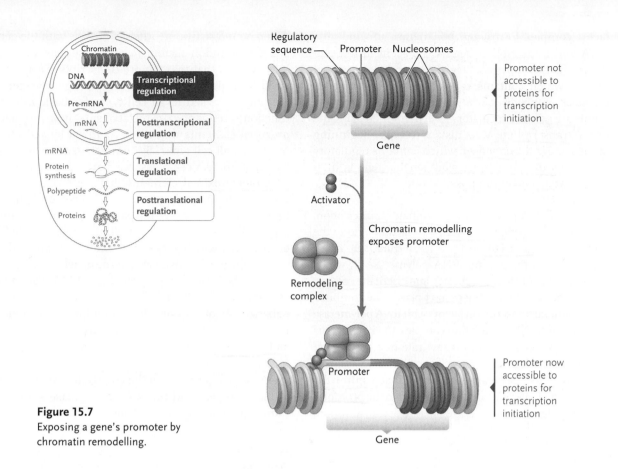

Figure 15.7
Exposing a gene's promoter by chromatin remodelling.

Organization of a Eukaryotic Protein-Coding Gene. Figure 15.8 shows a eukaryotic gene, emphasizing the regulatory sites involved in its expression. Immediately upstream of the transcription unit is the promoter, a short region often containing the TATA box. The TATA box plays an important role in transcription initiation. RNA polymerase II itself cannot recognize the promoter sequence. Instead, proteins called transcription factors recognize and bind to the TATA box and then recruit the polymerase. Once the RNA polymerase II–transcription

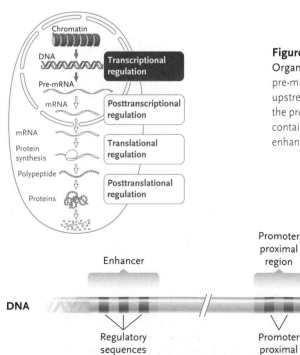

Figure 15.8
Organization of a eukaryotic gene. The transcription unit is the segment that is transcribed into the pre-mRNA; it contains the 5′ UTR (untranslated region), exons, introns, and 3′ UTR. Immediately upstream of the transcription unit is the promoter, which often contains the TATA box. Adjacent to the promoter and further upstream of the transcription unit is the promoter proximal region, which contains regulatory sequences called promoter proximal elements. More distant from the gene is the enhancer, which contains regulatory sequences that control the rate of transcription of the gene.

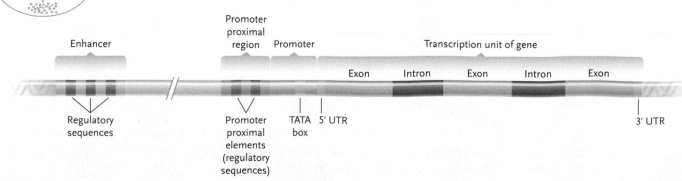

factor complex forms, the polymerase unwinds the DNA and transcription begins. Adjacent to the promoter, further upstream, is the **promoter proximal region**, which contains regulatory sequences called *promoter proximal elements*. Promoter proximal elements are part of a regulatory system for increasing the rate of transcription. More distant from the beginning of the gene is the **enhancer**, which contains regulatory sequences that determine whether the gene is transcribed at its maximum possible rate.

Activation of Transcription. To initiate transcription, proteins called **general transcription factors** bind to the promoter in the area of the TATA box **(Figure 15.9)**. These factors recruit the enzyme RNA polymerase II, which alone cannot bind to the promoter, and orient the enzyme to start transcription at the correct place. The combination of general transcription factors with RNA polymerase II is the **transcription initiation complex**. On its own, this complex brings about only a low rate of transcription initiation, which leads to just a few mRNA transcripts.

Activators—regulatory proteins that control the expression of one or more genes—bind to the promoter proximal elements to increase the rate of transcription.

When bound, activators interact directly with the general transcription factors to stimulate transcription initiation, so that many more transcripts are synthesized in a given time. Housekeeping genes—genes that are expressed in all cell types for basic cellular functions such as glucose metabolism—have promoter proximal elements that are recognized by activators present in all cell types. By contrast, genes expressed only in particular cell types or at particular times have promoter proximal elements that are recognized by activators found only in those cell types or at those times. Said another way, the particular set of activators present within a cell at a given time is responsible for determining which genes in that cell are expressed.

Events at the enhancer determine whether a gene is transcribed at its maximal rate **(Figure 15.10)**. Particular activators bind to the regulatory sequences within the enhancer. A **coactivator**, a large multiprotein complex, forms a bridge between the activators at the enhancer and the proteins at the promoter and promoter proximal region and causes the DNA to loop around on itself. The interactions between the coactivator, the proteins at the promoter, and the RNA polymerase stimulate transcription to its maximal rate.

Figure 15.9

Formation of the transcription complex on the promoter of a protein-coding gene by the combination of general transcription factors with RNA polymerase. The general transcription factors are needed for RNA polymerase to bind and initiate transcription at the correct place.

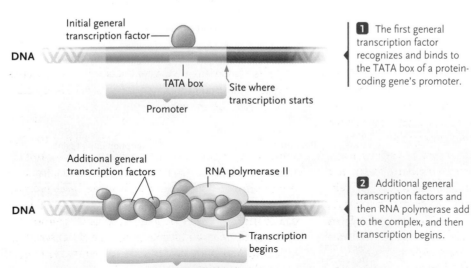

1 The first general transcription factor recognizes and binds to the TATA box of a protein-coding gene's promoter.

2 Additional general transcription factors and then RNA polymerase add to the complex, and then transcription begins.

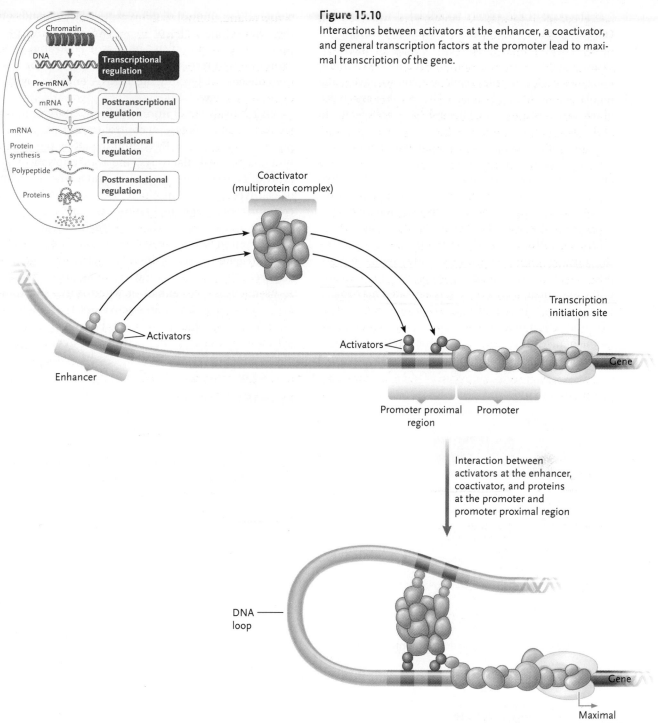

Figure 15.10

Interactions between activators at the enhancer, a coactivator, and general transcription factors at the promoter lead to maximal transcription of the gene.

Transcriptional regulation

Posttranscriptional regulation

Translational regulation

Posttranslational regulation

Chromatin

DNA

Pre-mRNA

mRNA

mRNA

Protein synthesis

Polypeptide

Proteins

Coactivator (multiprotein complex)

Transcription initiation site

Activators

Activators

Gene

Enhancer

Promoter proximal region

Promoter

Interaction between activators at the enhancer, coactivator, and proteins at the promoter and promoter proximal region

DNA loop

Gene

Maximal transcription

Repression of Transcription. In some genes, repressors oppose the effect of activators, thereby blocking or reducing the rate of transcription. The final rate of transcription then depends on the "battle" between the activation signal and the repression signal.

Repressors in eukaryotes work in various ways. Some repressors bind to the same regulatory sequence to which activators bind (often in the enhancer), thereby preventing activators from binding to that site. Other repressors bind to their own specific site in the DNA near where the activator binds and interact with the activator so that it cannot interact with the coactivator. Yet other repressors recruit histone deacetylation enzymes that modify histones, leading to chromatin compaction and making a gene's promoter inaccessible to the transcription machinery.

Combinatorial Gene Regulation. Let's review the key elements of regulation of transcription of a protein-coding gene. General transcription factors bind to certain promoter sequences such as the TATA box and recruit RNA polymerase II; this results in a basal level of transcription. Specific activators bind to promoter proximal elements and stimulate the rate of transcription initiation. Activators also bind to the enhancer to give maximal transcription of the gene.

How are these events coordinated in regulating gene expression? Characteristic of any given gene is the number and types of promoter proximal elements. In some genes, there may be only one regulatory element, but genes under complex regulatory control have many regulatory elements. Similarly, the number and types of regulatory sequences in the enhancer are specific to each gene.

Both promoter proximal regions and enhancers are important in regulating the transcription of a gene. Each different regulatory sequence in those two regions binds a specific regulatory protein. Since some regulatory proteins are activators and others are repressors, the overall effect of regulatory sequences on transcription depends on the particular proteins that bind to them. If activators bind to both the regulatory sequences in the promoter proximal region and to the enhancer, transcription is activated maximally, meaning a high rate of transcription and therefore the production of a high level of the mRNA encoded by the gene. But if a repressor binds to the enhancer and an activator binds to the promoter proximal

element, the amount of gene expression depends on the relative strengths of these two regulatory proteins. For example, if the repressor is strong, gene expression, in terms of the rate of transcription and the consequent level of the mRNA encoded by the gene, will be low.

A relatively small number of regulatory proteins (activators and repressors) control transcription of all protein-coding genes. By combining a few regulatory proteins in particular ways, the transcription of an array of genes can be controlled, and a large number of cell types can be specified. The process is called **combinatorial gene regulation.** Let us consider a theoretical example of two genes, each with activators already bound to the respective promoter proximal elements **(Figure 15.11).** Maximal transcription of gene *A* requires activators 2, 5, 7, and 8 binding to their regulatory sequences in the enhancer, whereas maximal transcription of gene *B* requires activators 1, 5, 8, and 11 binding to its enhancer. That is, both genes require activators 5 and 8 for full activation in combination with different other activators.

Figure 15.11

Combinatorial gene regulation. A relatively small number of regulatory proteins control transcription of all protein-coding genes. Different combinations of activators bind to enhancer regulatory sequences to control the rate of transcription of each gene.

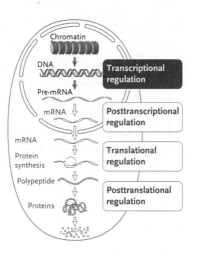

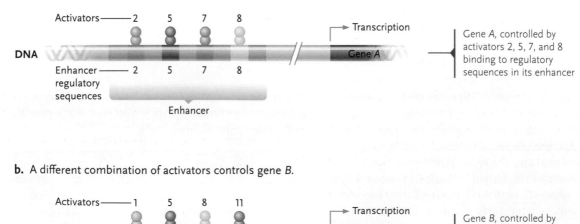

a. A unique combination of activators controls gene *A*.

Gene *A*, controlled by activators 2, 5, 7, and 8 binding to regulatory sequences in its enhancer

b. A different combination of activators controls gene *B*.

Gene *B*, controlled by activators 1, 5, 8, and 11 binding to regulatory sequences in its enhancer

This operating principle solves a basic dilemma in gene regulation—if each gene were regulated by a single, distinct protein, the number of genes encoding regulatory proteins would have to equal the number of genes to be regulated. Regulating the regulators would require another set of genes of equal number and so on until the coding capacity of any chromosome set, no matter how large, would be exhausted. But because different genes require different combinations of regulatory proteins, the number of genes encoding regulatory proteins can be much lower than the number of genes they control.

Coordinated Regulation of Transcription of Genes with Related Functions. In the discussion of prokaryotic operons, you learned that genes with related function are often clustered *and* they are transcribed from one promoter onto a single mRNA. That mRNA is translated from one end to the other to produce the several proteins encoded by the genes. There are no operons in eukaryotes, yet the transcription of genes with related functions is coordinated. How is this accomplished?

The answer is that all genes that are coordinately regulated have the same regulatory sequences associated with them. Therefore, with one signal, the transcription of all the genes can be controlled simultaneously. Let us consider an example of this: the control of gene expression by steroid hormones in mammals. A **hormone** is a molecule produced by one tissue and transported via the bloodstream to another specific tissue to alter its physiological activity. A **steroid** is a type of lipid derived from cholesterol. Examples of steroid hormones are testosterone and glucocorticoid. Testosterone regulates the expression of a large number of genes associated with the maintenance of primary and secondary male characteristics. Glucocorticoid, among other actions, regulates the expression of genes involved in the maintenance of the concentration of glucose and other fuel molecules in the blood.

A steroid hormone acts on specific target tissues in the body because only cells in those tissues have *steroid hormone receptors* in their cytoplasm that recognize and bind the hormone (see Chapter 8). The steroid hormone moves through the plasma membrane into the cytoplasm and the receptor binds to it **(Figure 15.12)**. The hormone–receptor complex then enters the nucleus and binds to specific regulatory sequences adjacent to the genes whose expression is controlled by the hormone. This binding activates transcription, and proteins encoded by the genes are made rapidly.

All genes regulated by a specific steroid hormone have the same DNA sequence to which the hormone–receptor complex binds. This sequence is called a **steroid hormone response element.** For example, all genes controlled by glucocorticoid have a glucocorticoid response element associated with them. Therefore, the release of glucocorticoid into the bloodstream coordinately activates the transcription of genes through that response element.

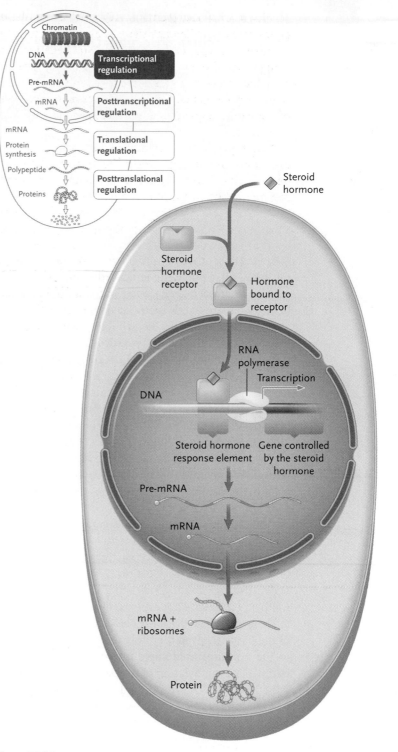

Figure 15.12

Steroid hormone regulation of gene expression. A steroid hormone enters the cell and forms a complex in the cytoplasm with a steroid hormone receptor that is specific to the hormone. Steroid hormone–receptor complexes migrate to the nucleus, bind to the steroid hormone response element next to each gene they control (one such gene is shown in the figure), and affect transcription of those genes.

15.2d Methylation of DNA Can Control Gene Transcription

DNA methylation, in which a methyl group ($-CH_3$) is added enzymatically to cytosine bases in the DNA, can also regulate transcription. Specifically, methylation of cytosines in promoters inhibits transcription and turns the genes off, a phenomenon called **silencing**.

For example, genes encoding the blood protein hemoglobin are highly methylated and inactive in most vertebrate body cells. In the cell lines giving rise to red blood cells, however, enzymes remove the methyl groups from the hemoglobin genes, which are then transcribed.

DNA methylation in some cases silences large blocks of genes, or even chromosomes. For example, in body cells of female placental mammals, including humans, one of the two X chromosomes packs tightly into a mass known as a Barr body, in which essentially all the genes of the X chromosome are turned off. As part of this general inactivation, which also includes chromatin modifications, cytosines in the DNA become methylated.

DNA methylation underlies **genomic imprinting**, in which methylation permanently silences transcription of either the inherited maternal or paternal allele of a particular gene (see Section 12.5). The methylation occurs during gametogenesis in a parent. An inherited methylated allele is not expressed—it is silenced. That allele is known as the *imprinted allele*. The expression of the gene involved therefore depends on expression of the nonimprinted allele inherited from the other parent. The methylation of the parental allele is maintained as the DNA is replicated, so that the silenced allele remains inactive in progeny cells. Some examples of genomic imprinting were presented in Section 12.5. In one of those examples, the mammalian *Igf2* (insulin growth factor 2) gene is inherited with the paternally derived allele nonmethylated and, therefore, active and with the maternally derived allele methylated and, therefore, silenced.

Once mRNAs are transcribed, further regulation occurs at each major step in the pathway from genes to proteins: during pre-mRNA processing and the movement of finished mRNAs to the cytoplasm (posttranslational regulation), during protein synthesis (translational regulation), and after translation is complete (posttranslational regulation). The next section describes the regulatory mechanisms operating at each of these steps.

STUDY BREAK

1. What is the role of histones in gene expression? How does acetylation of the histones affect gene expression?
2. What are the roles of general transcription factors, activators, and coactivators in transcription of a protein-coding gene?

15.3 Posttranscriptional, Translational, and Posttranslational Regulation

Transcriptional regulation determines which genes are copied into mRNAs. This basic level of regulation is fine-tuned by posttranscriptional, translational, and posttranslational controls, the subjects of this section (refer again to Figure 15.6).

15.3a Posttranscriptional Regulation Controls mRNA Availability

Posttranscriptional regulation directs translation by controlling the availability of mRNAs to ribosomes. The controls work by several mechanisms, including changes in pre-mRNA processing and the rate at which mRNAs are degraded.

Variations in Pre-mRNA Processing. In Chapter 14, we noted that mRNAs are transcribed initially as pre-mRNA molecules. These pre-mRNAs are processed to produce the finished mRNAs, which then enter protein synthesis. Variations in pre-mRNA processing can regulate *which* proteins are made in cells. As described in Section 14.3, pre-mRNAs can be processed by *alternative splicing*. Alternative splicing produces different mRNAs from the same pre-mRNA by removing different combinations of exons (the amino acid–coding segments) along with the introns (the noncoding spacers). The resulting mRNAs are translated to produce a family of related proteins with various combinations of amino acid sequences derived from the exons. Alternative splicing itself is under regulatory control. Regulatory proteins specific to the type of cell control which exons are removed from pre-mRNA molecules by binding to regulatory sequences within those molecules. The outcome of alternative splicing is that appropriate proteins within a family are synthesized in cell types or tissues in which they function optimally. Perhaps three-quarters of human genes are alternatively spliced at the pre-mRNA level.

Posttranscriptional Control by Masking Proteins. Some posttranscriptional controls operate by means of "masking" proteins that bind to mRNAs and make them unavailable for protein synthesis. These controls are important in many animal eggs, keeping mRNAs in an inactive form until the egg has been fertilized and embryonic development is under way. When an mRNA is to become active, other factors—other proteins, made as part of the developmental pathway—remove the masking proteins and allow the mRNA to enter protein synthesis.

Variations in the Rate of mRNA Breakdown. The rate at which eukaryotic mRNAs break down can also be controlled posttranscriptionally. The mechanism involves a regulatory molecule, such as a steroid hormone, directly or indirectly affecting the mRNA breakdown steps, either slowing or increasing the rate of those steps. For example, in the mammary gland of the rat, the mRNA for casein (a milk protein) has a half-life of about 5 hours (meaning that it takes 5 hours for half of the mRNA present at a given time to break down). The half-life of casein mRNA changes to about 92 hours if the peptide hormone prolactin is present. Prolactin is synthesized in the brain and in other tissues, including the breast. The most important effect of prolactin is to stimulate the **mammary glands** to produce milk (that is, it stimulates lactation). During milk production, a large amount of casein must be synthesized, and this is accomplished in part by radically decreasing the rate of breakdown of the casein mRNA.

Nucleotide sequences in the 5′ UTR (untranslated region; see Section 14.3) appear also to be important in determining mRNA half-life. If the 5′ UTR is transferred experimentally from one mRNA to another, the half-life of the receiving mRNA becomes the same as that of the donor mRNA. The controlling sequences in the 5′ UTR of an mRNA might be recognized by proteins that regulate its stability.

Regulation of Gene Expression by Small RNAs. The relatively recent discovery of *micro-RNAs* (miRNAs) has revolutionized our understanding of gene control. miRNAs are small, single-stranded RNAs found in organisms as diverse as worms, flies, plants, and mammals, where they regulate important processes such as development, growth, and behaviour. What are miRNAs and how do they work?

Each miRNA is encoded by a non-protein coding gene. Transcription of the gene produces an RNA that is the precursor to the miRNA **(Figure 15.13, p. 336).** The precursor RNA folds and base-pairs with itself, forming a stem-loop structure. An enzyme named Dicer cuts the stem-loop to produce a double-stranded RNA, about 21 to 22 base pairs long. A protein complex then binds to the double-stranded RNA and degrades one of the two RNA strands, leaving a small, single-stranded RNA—the miRNA. Still bound to the protein complex, the miRNA binds to any mRNA that has a complementary sequence. Gene expression is then silenced in one of two ways: either the proteins in the complex cleave the mRNA where the miRNA is bound to it, or the double-stranded segment formed between the miRNA and the mRNA blocks ribosomes from translating the mRNA.

Researchers think that there are 120 genes for miRNAs in worms and 250 genes in humans. Many of these miRNAs are expressed in developmentally regulated patterns. The targets of the miRNA's action are often mRNAs for regulatory proteins that control the development of the organism.

The phenomenon of silencing a gene posttranscriptionally by a small, single-stranded RNA that is complementary to part of an mRNA is termed **RNA interference (RNAi).** miRNAs are one class of single-stranded RNAs that cause RNAi; another class is known as **small interfering RNA (siRNA).** Whereas miRNA is produced from RNA that is encoded in the cell's genome, siRNA is produced from double-stranded RNA that is *not* encoded by nuclear genes. For example, the life cycle and replication of many viruses involves a double-stranded RNA stage. Viral double-stranded RNA enters the RNAi process as described for miRNAs: double-stranded RNA is cut by Dicer into short double-stranded RNA molecules, and then a protein complex binds to the molecules and degrades one of the RNA strands to produce siRNA. The protein complex is the same one that acts on the double-stranded RNA precursors of miRNAs. In the RNAi process, siRNA acts exactly like microRNA—mRNAs complementary to the siRNA are targeted and either they are degraded or their translation is blocked. In our viral example, the targeted mRNAs would be mRNAs for proteins needed for viral genome replication and the production of new virus particles.

Any gene can be silenced experimentally by RNAi. To silence a gene, researchers introduce a double-stranded RNA into a cell that can be processed by Dicer and the protein complex into an siRNA complementary to the mRNA transcribed from that gene. Indeed, RNAi has become a powerful new technique for silencing specific genes experimentally in a variety of organisms. Andrew Fire of the Massachusetts Institute of Technology and Craig Mello of Harvard University received a Nobel Prize in 2006 for their discovery of RNA interference.

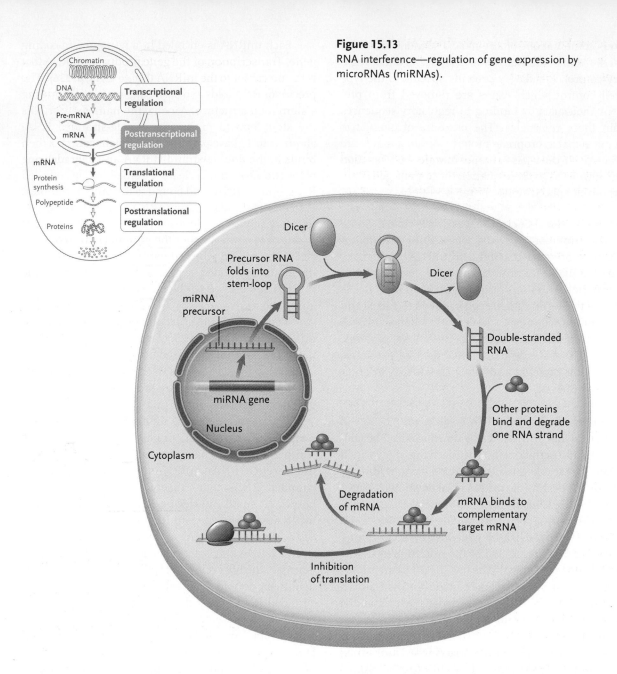

Within the figure:
Chromatin
DNA
Transcriptional regulation
Pre-mRNA
mRNA
Posttranscriptional regulation
mRNA
Protein synthesis
Translational regulation
Polypeptide
Posttranslational regulation
Proteins

Dicer
Precursor RNA folds into stem-loop
Dicer
miRNA precursor
Double-stranded RNA
miRNA gene
Nucleus
Other proteins bind and degrade one RNA strand
Cytoplasm
Degradation of mRNA
mRNA binds to complementary target mRNA
Inhibition of translation

15.3b Translational Regulation Controls the Rate of Protein Synthesis

At the next regulatory level, translational regulation controls the rate at which mRNAs are used in protein synthesis. Translational regulation occurs in essentially all cell types and species. For example, translational regulation is involved in cell cycle control in all eukaryotes and in many processes during development in multicellular eukaryotes, such as red blood **cell differentiation** in animals. Significantly, many viruses exploit translational regulation to control their infection of cells and to shut off the host cell's own genes.

Let us consider the general role of translational regulation in animal development. During early development of most animals, little transcription occurs. The changes in protein synthesis patterns seen in developing cell types and tissues instead derive from the activation, repression, or degradation of maternal mRNAs, the mRNAs that were present in the mother's egg before fertilization. One important mechanism for translational regulation involves adjusting the length of the poly(A) tail of the mRNA. (Recall from Section 14.3 that the poly(A) tail—a string of adenine-containing nucleotides—is added to the 3′ end of pre-mRNA and is retained on the mRNA produced from the pre-mRNA after introns are removed.) That is, enzymes can change the length of the poly(A) tail on an mRNA in the cytoplasm in either direction: by shortening it or lengthening it. Increases in poly(A) tail length result in increased translation; decreases in length result in decreased translation. For example, during embryogenesis (the formation of the embryo) of the fruit fly, *Drosophila,* key proteins are synthesized when the poly(A) tails on the mRNAs for those proteins are lengthened in a regulated way. Evidence for this came from experiments in which poly(A) tail lengthening was blocked; the result was that embryogenesis was inhibited. But although researchers know that the length of poly(A) tails is regulated in the cytoplasm, how this process occurs is not completely understood.

15.3c Posttranslational Regulation Controls the Availability of Functional Proteins

Posttranslational regulation controls the availability of functional proteins primarily in three ways: chemical modification, processing, and degradation. Chemical modification involves the addition or removal of chemical groups, which reversibly alters the activity of the protein. For example, you saw in Section 8.2 how the addition of phosphate groups to proteins involved in signal transduction pathways either stimulates or inhibits the activity of those proteins. Further, in Section 9.4, you learned how the addition of phosphate groups to target proteins plays a crucial role in regulating how a cell progresses through the cell division cycle. And in Section 15.2, you saw how acetylation of histones altered the properties of the nucleosome, loosening its association with DNA in chromatin.

In processing, proteins are synthesized as inactive precursors, which are converted to an active form under regulatory control. For example, you saw in Section 14.4 that the digestive enzyme pepsin is synthesized as pepsinogen, an inactive precursor that activates by removal of a segment of amino acids. Similarly, the glucose-regulating hormone insulin is synthesized as a precursor called proinsulin; processing of the precursor removes a central segment but leaves the insulin molecule, which consists of two polypeptide chains linked by disulphide bridges.

The rate of degradation of proteins is also under regulatory control. Some proteins in eukaryotic cells last for the lifetime of the individual, whereas others persist only for minutes. Proteins with relatively short cellular lives include many of the proteins regulating transcription. Typically, these short-lived proteins are marked for breakdown by enzymes that attach a "doom tag" consisting of a small protein called *ubiquitin* (**Figure 15.14,** step 1). The protein is given this name because it is indeed ubiquitous—present in almost the same form in essentially all eukaryotes. The ubiquitin tag labels the doomed proteins so that they are recognized and attacked by a *proteasome,* a large cytoplasmic complex of a number of different proteins (step 2). The proteasome unfolds the protein, and protein-digesting enzymes within the core digest the protein into small peptides. The peptides are released from the proteasome, and cytosolic enzymes further digest the peptides into individual amino acids, which are recycled for use in protein synthesis or oxidized as an energy source (step 3). The ubiquitin protein and proteasome are also recycled. Aaron Ciechanover and Avram Hershko, both of the Israel Institute of Technology, Haifa, Israel, and Irwin Rose of the University of California, Irvine, received a

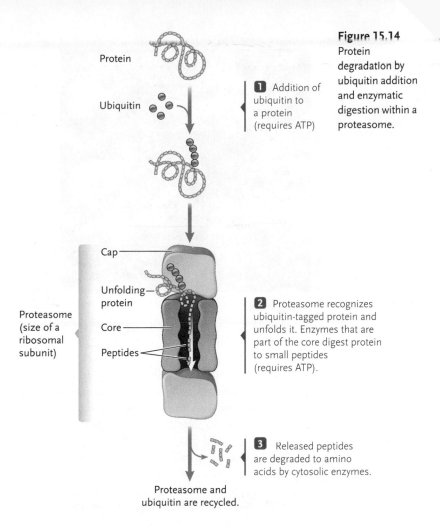

Figure 15.14
Protein degradation by ubiquitin addition and enzymatic digestion within a proteasome.

Protein

Ubiquitin

1 Addition of ubiquitin to a protein (requires ATP)

Cap

Unfolding protein

Proteasome (size of a ribosomal subunit)

Core

Peptides

2 Proteasome recognizes ubiquitin-tagged protein and unfolds it. Enzymes that are part of the core digest protein to small peptides (requires ATP).

3 Released peptides are degraded to amino acids by cytosolic enzymes.

Proteasome and ubiquitin are recycled.

Nobel Prize in 2004 for the discovery of ubiquitin-mediated protein degradation.

Control of protein breakdown is the last opportunity for control of gene expression. We now describe cancer, a disease in which the control of gene expression goes awry.

STUDY BREAK

1. How does a microRNA silence gene expression?
2. If the poly(A) tail on a mRNA was removed, what would likely be the effect on the translation of that mRNA?

15.4 The Loss of Regulatory Controls in Cancer

The cell division cycle of all eukaryotic cells from single-celled microorganisms to cells that are components of multicellular organisms is controlled by genes. The types of genes exerting this control are basically the same in terms of functions in all eukaryotes. Mutations in these genes can disrupt normal cell

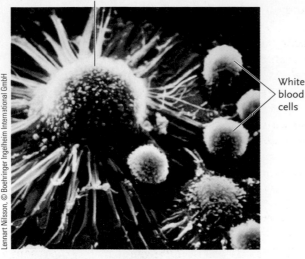

Cancer cell

White blood cells

Figure 15.15

A scanning electron micrograph of a cancer cell surrounded by several white blood cells.

growth and division. The effects of such mutations are more significant and profound in complex multicellular organisms. For example, occasionally, dividing and differentiating cells deviate from their normal genetic program and give rise to tissue masses called *tumours*. In other words, the cells lose their normal regulatory controls and revert partially or completely to an embryonic developmental state, in a process called *dedifferentiation*. If the deviant cells stay together in a single mass, the tumour is said to be *benign*. Benign tumours are usually not life threatening, and their surgical removal generally results in a complete cure. If the cells of a tumour invade and disrupt surrounding tissues, the tumour is said to be *malignant* and is called a cancer (**Figure 15.15** shows a cancer cell). Sometimes, cells from malignant tumours break off and move through the blood system or lymphatic system, forming new tumours at other locations in the body. The spreading of a malignant tumour is called *metastasis* (meaning "change of state"). Malignant tumours can result in debilitation and death in various ways, including damage to critical organs, metabolic problems, hemorrhage, and secondary malignancies. In some cases, malignant tumours can be eliminated from the body by surgery or destroyed by chemicals (*chemotherapy*) or radiation.

15.4a Most Cancers Are Caused by Genes That Have Lost Their Normal Controls

All the characteristics of cancer cells—dedifferentiation, uncontrolled division, and metastasis—reflect changes in gene activity. Many of the genes that become altered encode proteins that control the cell division cycle of normal cells. That is, healthy cells grow and divide only when the balance of stimulatory and inhibitory signals received from outside the cell favours cell division.

A cancer cell, by contrast, does not respond properly to the usual signals and divides without the usual constraints.

Two main types of genes commonly show altered activities as cells become cancerous. One class is the **proto-oncogenes** (*oncos* = bulk or mass), genes in normal cells that encode various kinds of proteins that stimulate cell division. In cancer cells, the proto-oncogenes are altered to become **oncogenes**, genes that stimulate the cell to progress to the cancerous state. Among the mechanisms that can convert proto-oncogenes to oncogenes:

- Mutations in a gene's promoter or other control sequences may disrupt normal regulatory controls, making the gene abnormally active. The mutations can occur spontaneously or be induced by radiation or by particular chemicals.
- Mutations in the coding segment of the gene may produce an altered form of the encoded protein that is abnormally active.
- Translocation, in which a segment of a chromosome breaks off and attaches to a different chromosome (discussed in Section 12.3), may move a gene that controls cell division to a new location near the promoter or enhancer sequence of a highly active gene, making the cell division gene overactive.
- Infecting viruses may introduce genes to regions in the chromosomes where the expression of the genes disrupts cell cycle control or alters regulatory proteins to turn genes on.

For example, translocation may affect *MYC*, a proto-oncogene controlling cell division. The activity of *MYC* is normally tightly regulated. However, *MYC* lies in a chromosome region that often breaks, causing a translocation that places *MYC* near the enhancer and promoter of a highly active antibody gene. The placement makes *MYC* continuously active, converting it into an oncogene that triggers rapid and uncontrolled cell division.

Several proto-oncogenes encode cell surface receptors that bind extracellular signal molecules such as peptide hormones or growth factors. In general, the oncogene forms of these receptors are continually activated, whether they are bound to the external signal molecule or not. As a result, the internal pathways they trigger, including those that cause cells to divide, are also continually active.

Another key group of proto-oncogenes encodes enzymes forming parts of the internal reaction pathways triggered by surface receptors (see Chapter 8). Most important are genes encoding the protein kinases, which regulate the activity of other proteins by adding phosphate groups to them. Some of the proteins phosphorylated by the protein kinases directly take part in gene regulation or initiation of

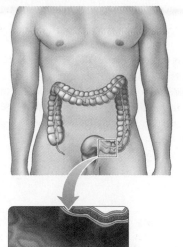

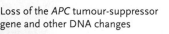

Normal
colon cells

↓ Loss of the *APC* tumour-suppressor
gene and other DNA changes

Small adenoma
(benign growth)

↓ *ras* oncogene activation; loss
of *DCC* tumour-suppressor gene

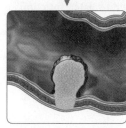

Large adenoma
(benign growth)

↓ Loss of *TP53* tumour-suppressor
gene and other mutations

Carcinoma (malignant
tumour with metastasis)

Figure 15.16
A multistep model for the development of a type of colorectal cancer.

cell division; others form parts of the cellular response pathways linked to surface receptors. The protein kinases encoded by the oncogene forms of the genes are continually active, constantly phosphorylating the control protein so that cell division continues at high and uncontrolled rates.

The other main class of genes that shows altered activity in cancer cells is the **tumour-suppressor genes**, which, in normal cells, encode proteins that inhibit cell division. Both alleles of a tumour-suppressor gene must be inactivated for inhibitory activity to be lost in cancer cells. The best known of these genes is *TP53*, so called because its encoded protein, p53, has a molecular weight of 53 000 **daltons**. Among other activities, normal p53 stops cell division by combining with and inhibiting cyclin-dependent protein kinases that trigger entry into critical stages of DNA replication and mitosis (discussed in Section 9.4). Without the normal form of the p53 protein, the cyclin-dependent protein kinases are continually active in triggering cell division. Inactive *TP53* genes are found in many types of cancers.

15.4b Cancer Develops Gradually by Multiple Steps

Cancer rarely develops by alteration of a single proto-oncogene to an oncogene, or inactivation of a single tumour-suppressor gene. Instead, in almost all cancers, successive alterations in several to many genes gradually accumulate to change normal cells into cancer cells. This is the *multistep progression of cancer* (**Figure 15.16**). The gradual nature of the process explains why smokers, for example, may not develop cancer until years after the first mutations caused by chemicals in tobacco smoke occur, soon after smoking begins. It also offers some hope to those who quit smoking, for stopping the exposure to the carcinogenic smoke may halt multistep progression before it reaches its deadly conclusion in cancer.

The ravages of cancer, probably more than any other example, bring home the critical extent to which humans and all other multicellular organisms depend on the mechanisms controlling gene expression to develop and live normally. In a sense, the most amazing thing about these control mechanisms is that, in spite of their complexity, they operate without failures throughout most of the lives of all eukaryotes.

STUDY BREAK

1. What is the normal function of a tumour-suppressor gene? How do mutations in tumour-suppressor genes contribute to the onset of cancer?
2. What is the normal function of a proto-oncogene? How can mutations in proto-oncogenes contribute to the onset of cancer?

Review

Go to CENGAGENOW" at http://hed.nelson.com/ to access quizzing, animations, exercises, articles, and personalized homework help.

15.1 Regulation of Gene Expression in Prokaryotes

- Transcriptional control in prokaryotes involves short-term changes that turn specific genes on or off in response to changes in environmental conditions. The changes in gene activity are controlled by regulatory proteins that recognize operators of operons (see Figure 15.2).

- Regulatory proteins may be repressors, which slow the rate of transcription of operons, or activators, which increase the rate of transcription.

- Some repressors are made in an active form, in which they bind to the operator of an operon and inhibit its transcription. Combination with an inducer blocks the activity of the repressor and allows the operon to be transcribed (see Figure 15.3). Loss of repressor activity results in constant transcription.

- Other repressors are made in an inactive form, in which they are unable to inhibit transcription of an operon unless they combine with a corepressor (see Figure 15.4).

- Activators typically are made in inactive form, in which they cannot bind to their binding site next to an operon. Combining with another molecule, often a nucleotide, converts the activator into the form in which it binds with its binding site and recruits RNA polymerase, thereby stimulating transcription of the operon (see Figure 15.5).

15.2 Regulation of Transcription in Eukaryotes

- Operons are not found in eukaryotes. Instead, genes that encode proteins with related functions typically are scattered through the genome, while being regulated in a coordinated manner.

- Two general types of gene regulation occur in eukaryotes. Short-term regulation involves relatively rapid changes in gene expression in response to changes in environmental or physiological conditions. Long-term regulation involves changes in gene expression associated with the development and differentiation of an organism.

- Gene expression in eukaryotes is regulated at the transcriptional level (where most regulation occurs) and at posttranscriptional, translational, and posttranslational levels (see Figure 15.6).

- Transcriptionally active genes have a looser chromatin structure than transcriptionally inactive genes. The change in chromatin structure that accompanies the activation of transcription of a gene involves chromatin remodelling—

specific histone modifications—particularly in the region of a gene's promoter (see Figure 15.7).

- Regulation of transcription initiation involves proteins binding to a gene's promoter and regulatory sites. At the promoter, general transcription factors bind and recruit RNA polymerase II, giving a very low level of transcription. Activator proteins bind to promoter proximal elements and increase the rate of transcription. Other activators bind to the enhancer and, through interaction with a coactivator, which binds also to the proteins at the promoter, greatly stimulate the rate of transcription (see Figures 15.8–15.10).

- The overall control of transcription of a gene depends on the particular regulatory proteins that bind to promoter proximal elements and enhancers. The regulatory proteins are cell type specific and may be activators or repressors. This gene regulation is achieved by a relatively low number of regulatory proteins, acting in various combinations (see Figure 15.11).

- The coordinated expression of genes with related functions is achieved by each of the related genes having the same regulatory sequences associated with them.

- Sections of chromosomes or whole chromosomes can be inactivated by DNA methylation, a phenomenon called silencing. DNA methylation is also involved in genomic imprinting, in which transcription of either the inherited maternal or paternal allele of a gene is inhibited permanently.

15.3 Posttranscriptional, Translational, and Posttranslational Regulation

- Posttranscriptional, translational, and posttranslational controls operate primarily to regulate the quantities of proteins synthesized in cells (see Figure 15.6).

- Posttranscriptional controls regulate pre-mRNA processing, mRNA availability for translation, and the rate at which mRNAs are degraded. In alternative splicing, different mRNAs are derived from the same pre-mRNA. In another process, small single-stranded RNAs complexed with proteins bind to mRNAs that have complementary sequences, and either the mRNA is cleaved or translation is blocked (see Figure 15.13).

- Translational regulation controls the rate at which mRNAs are used by ribosomes in protein synthesis.

- Posttranslational controls regulate the availability of functional proteins. Mechanisms of regulation include the alteration of protein activity by chemical modification, protein activation by processing of inactive precursors, and affecting the rate of degradation of a protein.

15.4 The Loss of Regulatory Controls in Cancer

- In cancer, cells partially or completely dedifferentiate, divide rapidly and uncontrollably, and break loose to form additional tumours in other parts of the body.
- Proto-oncogenes and tumour-suppressor genes typically are altered in cancer cells. Proto-oncogenes encode proteins that stimulate cell division. Their altered forms, oncogenes, are abnormally active. Tumour suppressor genes in their normal form encode proteins that inhibit cell division. Mutated forms of these genes lose this inhibitory activity.
- Most cancers develop by multistep progression involving the successive alteration of several to many genes (see Figure 15.16).

Questions

Self-Test Questions

1. The control of the delivery of mRNA to the cytoplasm is an example of
   a. translational regulation.
   b. posttranslational regulation.
   c. transcriptional regulation.
   d. posttranscriptional regulation.
   e. deoxyribonucleic regulation.

2. For the *E. coli lac* operon, when glucose is absent and lactose is added,
   a. allolactose binds to the operator.
   b. the *lac* gene cannot make Lac repressor protein.
   c. allolactose binds the Lac repressor protein to remove it from the operator.
   d. the genes *lacZ, lacY,* and *lacA* are turned off.
   e. β-galactosidase decreases in the cell.

3. For the *E. coli lac* operon, when lactose is present
   a. and glucose is absent, cAMP binds and activates catabolic activator protein (CAP).
   b. and glucose is absent, the level of cAMP decreases.
   c. activated CAP binds the repressor protein to remove it from the operator gene.
   d. the cell prefers lactose over glucose.
   e. RNA polymerase cannot bind to the promoter.

4. For the *trp* operon,
   a. tryptophan is an inducer.
   b. when end-product tryptophan binds to the Trp repressor, it stops transcription of the tryptophan biosynthesis genes.
   c. Trp repressor is synthesized in active form.
   d. low levels of tryptophan bind to the *trp* operator and block transcription of the tryptophan biosynthesis genes.
   e. high levels of tryptophan activate RNA polymerase and induce transcription.

5. Chromatin remodelling activates gene expression when it:
   a. allows proteins initiating transcription to disengage from the promoter.
   b. winds genes tightly around histones.
   c. deacetylates histones.
   d. inserts nucleosomes into chromatin.
   e. recruits a protein complex that displaces nucleosome from the promoter.

6. Which statement about activation of transcription is *not* correct?
   a. A transcription factor binds the TATA box.
   b. A coactivator called a mediator forms a bridge between the promoter and the gene to be transcribed.
   c. Transcription factors bind the promoter and RNA polymerase.
   d. Activators bind to the enhancer region on DNA.
   e. RNA is transcribed downstream from the promoter region.

7. Which of the following statements does not support the idea of combinatorial gene regulation?
   a. Promoter proximal regions and enhancers regulate transcription of genes.
   b. A few regulatory genes can control a large number of transcribable genes.
   c. If repressor binding to enhancer is strong, gene expression is reduced.
   d. Genes requiring complex regulation have a single regulatory element.
   e. The number and types of regulatory sequences in the enhancer vary with each gene.

8. Normal ears in a certain mammal are perky; mutants have droopy ears. In males of these mammals, the gene encoding perky ears is transcribed only from the female parent. This is because the gene from the male parent is silenced by methylation. If the maternal gene is mutated,
   a. male offspring have droopy ears.
   b. male offspring have perky ears.
   c. male offspring have one droopy ear and one perky ear.
   d. the genetic mechanism is called alternative splicing.
   e. this is an example of posttranscriptional regulation.

9. Which of the following statements does not describe microRNA?
   a. MicroRNA is encoded by non–protein-coding genes.
   b. MicroRNA has a precursor that is folded and then cut by a Dicer enzyme.
   c. MicroRNA is an example of a molecule that induces RNA interference or gene silencing.
   d. MicroRNA is synthesized *in vitro* but not *in vivo*.
   e. MicroRNA has a function similar to that of small interfering RNAs.

10. Which of the following is not a characteristic of cancer cells?
    a. proto-oncogenes converting to active oncogenes
    b. the position of the *MYC* gene near a repressor gene
    c. the mutation of the *TP53* gene
    d. their stepwise developmental stages
    e. amplification of growth factors and growth factor receptors

Questions for Discussion

1. In a mutant strain of *E. coli,* the CAP protein is unable to combine with its target region of the *lac* operon. How would you expect the mutation to affect transcription when cells of this strain are subjected to the following conditions?
   a. Lactose and glucose are both available.
   b. Lactose is available, but glucose is not.
   c. Both lactose and glucose are unavailable.

2. Duchenne muscular dystrophy, an inherited genetic disorder, affects boys almost exclusively. Early in childhood, muscle tissue begins to break down in affected individuals, who typically die in their teens or early twenties as a result of respiratory failure. Muscle samples from women who carry the mutation reveal some regions of degenerating muscle tissue adjacent to other regions that are normal. Develop a hypothesis explaining these observations.

3. Eukaryotic transcription is generally controlled by binding of regulatory proteins to DNA sequences rather than by modification of RNA polymerases. Develop a hypothesis explaining why this is so.

Protein microarray, a key tool of proteomics, the study of the complete set of proteins that can be expressed by an organism's genome. Each coloured dot is a protein, with a specific colour for each protein being studied.

Pasteka/SPL/Photo Researchers, Inc.

16 DNA Technologies and Genomics

WHY IT MATTERS

Imagine yourself as a member of the crew of *Sorcerer II,* a private yacht renovated by maverick biologist J. Craig Venter to serve as an oceanic survey laboratory. Several months out of Halifax, down the Atlantic coast of the United States, and through the Panama Canal into the Pacific, you are now threading among the famed Galapagos Islands. Of course, your mind wanders to the historic voyage of the H.M.S. *Beagle* that brought Charles Darwin to these same waters some 170 years ago. Darwin returned home with specimens of novel species and notebooks filled with the scientific observations, illustrations, and ideas that would revolutionize our understanding of biology; you will return home with frozen seawater samples containing billions of base pairs of DNA sequence that may well, once again, cause us to reconsider cherished beliefs.

Back on land, the DNA is isolated, broken into random fragments, and then sequenced by industrial sequencing robots. Computer programs compare the individual sequences, looking for novel genes and areas of overlap that will help reconstruct the entire genomes of previously unknown organisms and viruses. Analysis of the massive data set reveals a staggering degree of genetic diversity among the unicellular microorganisms in the marine environment; 400 new species are discovered. Scanning for potential protein-coding genes predicts hundreds of thousands of likely proteins, a surprising fraction of them unknown to science.

Venter's survey of genetic diversity in the ocean is an example of the emerging field of metagenomics, in which DNA from an entire community of organisms in a particular niche is harvested collectively, sequenced, and analyzed using some of the DNA technologies described in this chapter. This approach is significant because, until very recently, our understanding of the genetics of the microbial world was based almost exclusively on the very small proportion of species that can be cultivated in the laboratory. With the tools of modern metagenomics, we gain access to the genomes of a whole new world of previously inaccessible organisms.

Metagenomic studies targeted to microbial communities in such diverse environments as the termite gut, deep sea hydrothermal vents, glaciers, geysers, the bovine rumen, and desert soil will certainly identify tens of thousands of novel genes that code for enzymes that may have applications in industrial biofuel production, food processing, pollution control, and drug development. The use of such genes for practical purposes is called genetic engineering.

Genetic engineering is the latest addition to the broad area known as *biotechnology,* which is any technique applied to biological systems or living organisms to make or modify products or processes for a specific purpose. Thus, biotechnology includes manipulations that do not involve DNA technologies, such as the use of yeast to brew beer and bake bread, and the use of bacteria to make yogurt and cheese.

In this chapter, we focus on how biologists isolate genes and manipulate them for basic and **applied research.** You will learn about the basic DNA technologies and their applications to research in biology, to genetic engineering, and to the analysis of genomes. You will also learn about some of the risks and controversies surrounding genetic engineering and about some of the scientific, social, and ethical questions related to its application.

We begin our discussion with a description of methods used to obtain genes in large quantities, an essential step for their analysis or manipulation.

16.1 DNA Cloning

Remember from Chapter 10 that a *clone* is a line of genetically identical cells or individuals derived from a single ancestor. DNA cloning is a method for producing many copies of a piece of DNA; the piece of DNA is referred to as a "gene of interest", which is a gene that a researcher wants to study or manipulate. Scientists clone DNA for many reasons. For example, a researcher might be interested in how a particular human gene

functions. Each human cell contains only two copies of most genes, amounting to a very small fraction of the total amount of DNA in a diploid cell. In its natural state in the genome, then, the gene is extremely difficult to study. However, through DNA cloning, a researcher can produce a sample large enough for scientific experimentation.

Cloned genes are used in **basic research** to find out about their biological functions. For example, researchers can determine the DNA sequence of a cloned gene, giving them the ultimate information about its structure. Also, by manipulating the gene and inducing mutations in it, they can gain information about its function and about how its expression is regulated. Cloned genes can be expressed in bacteria, and the proteins encoded by the cloned genes can be produced in quantity and purified. Those proteins can be used in basic research, or, in the case of genes that encode proteins of pharmaceutical or clinical importance, they can be used in applied research.

An overview of one common method for cloning a gene of interest from a genome is shown in **Figure 16.1;** the method uses bacteria (commonly, *Escherichia coli*) and plasmids, the small circular DNA molecules that replicate separately from the bacterial chromosome (see Section 10.2). The researcher extracts DNA that contains a gene of interest from cells and cuts it into fragments. The fragments are inserted into plasmids producing *recombinant DNA molecules*—**recombinant DNA** is DNA from two or more different sources that are joined together. The recombinant plasmids are introduced into bacteria; each bacterium receives a different plasmid. The bacterium continues growing and dividing, and as it does, the plasmid continues to replicate. Through replication of the plasmid, amplification of the piece of DNA inserted into the plasmid occurs. The final step, then, is to identify the bacterium containing the plasmid with the gene of interest and isolate it for further study.

16.1a Bacterial Enzymes Called Restriction Endonucleases Form the Basis of DNA Cloning

The key to DNA cloning is the specific joining of two DNA molecules from different sources, such as a genomic DNA fragment and a bacterial plasmid (see Figure 16.1). This specific joining of DNA is made possible, in part, by bacterial enzymes called **restriction endonucleases** (also called **restriction enzymes**), discovered in the late 1960s. Restriction enzymes recognize short, specific DNA sequences called *restriction sites,* typically four to eight base pairs long, and cut the DNA at specific locations within those sequences. The DNA fragments produced by cutting a long DNA molecule with a restriction enzyme are known as **restriction fragments.**

The "restriction" in the name of the enzymes refers to their normal role inside bacteria, in which the enzymes defend against viral attack by breaking down (restricting) the DNA molecules of infecting viruses. The bacterium protects the restriction sites in its own DNA from cutting by modifying bases in those sites enzymatically, thereby blocking the action of its restriction enzyme.

Hundreds of different restriction enzymes have been identified, each one cutting DNA at a specific restriction site. As illustrated by the restriction site of *Eco*RI **(Figure 16.2, p. 346)**, most restriction sites are symmetrical in that the sequence of nucleotides read in the 5′→3′ direction on one strand is the same as the sequence read in the 5′→3′ direction on the complementary strand. The restriction enzymes most used in cloning—such as *Eco*RI—cleave the sugar–phosphate backbones of DNA to produce DNA fragments with single-stranded ends (step 1). The ends are called **sticky ends** because the short, single-stranded regions can form hydrogen bonds with complementary sticky ends on any other DNA molecules cut with the same enzyme. For example, step 2 shows the insertion of a DNA molecule with sticky ends produced by *Eco*RI between two other DNA molecules with the same sticky ends. The pairings leave nicks in the sugar–phosphate backbones of the DNA strands that are sealed by *DNA ligase,* an enzyme that has the same function in DNA replication (step 3; see Section 13.3). The result is DNA from two different sources joined together—a recombinant DNA molecule.

16.1b Bacterial Plasmids Illustrate the Use of Restriction Enzymes in Cloning

The bacterial plasmids used for cloning are examples of cloning vectors—DNA molecules into which a DNA fragment can be inserted to form a recombinant DNA molecule for cloning. Bacterial plasmid cloning vectors do not naturally occur in bacteria; they are plasmids modified to have special features. Commonly, plasmid cloning vectors are engineered to contain two genes that are useful in the final steps of a cloning experiment for identifying bacteria that have recombinant plasmids from those that do not. The *amp*^R gene encodes an enzyme that breaks down the antibiotic ampicillin; when the plasmid is introduced into *E. coli* and the *amp*^R gene is expressed, the bacteria become resistant to ampicillin. The *lacZ*^+ gene encodes β-galactosidase (recall the *lac* operon from Section 15.1), which hydrolyzes the sugar lactose, as well as a number of synthetic substrates. Restriction sites are located within

the *lacZ*^+ gene but do not alter the gene's function. For a given cloning experiment, one of these restriction sites is chosen.

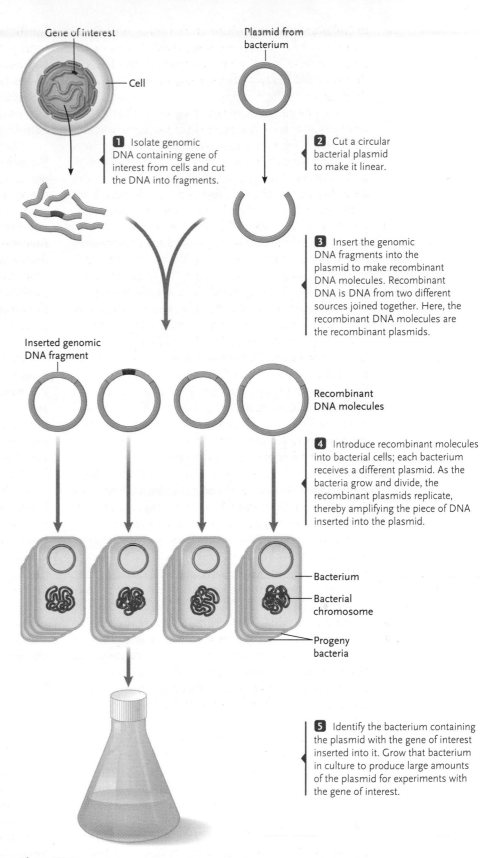

1 Isolate genomic DNA containing gene of interest from cells and cut the DNA into fragments.

2 Cut a circular bacterial plasmid to make it linear.

3 Insert the genomic DNA fragments into the plasmid to make recombinant DNA molecules. Recombinant DNA is DNA from two different sources joined together. Here, the recombinant DNA molecules are the recombinant plasmids.

4 Introduce recombinant molecules into bacterial cells; each bacterium receives a different plasmid. As the bacteria grow and divide, the recombinant plasmids replicate, thereby amplifying the piece of DNA inserted into the plasmid.

5 Identify the bacterium containing the plasmid with the gene of interest inserted into it. Grow that bacterium in culture to produce large amounts of the plasmid for experiments with the gene of interest.

Figure 16.1
Overview of cloning DNA fragments in a bacterial plasmid.

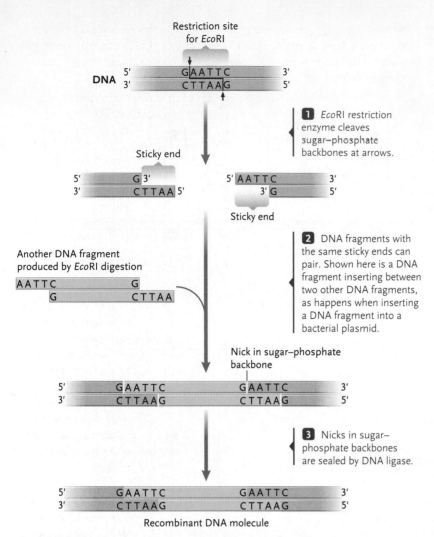

Restriction site
for *Eco*RI

DNA

5′ — G A A T T C — 3′
3′ — C T T A A G — 5′

1 *Eco*RI restriction enzyme cleaves sugar–phosphate backbones at arrows.

Sticky end

5′ — G — 3′
3′ — C T T A A — 5′

5′ — A A T T C — 3′
3′ — G — 5′

Sticky end

Another DNA fragment produced by *Eco*RI digestion

A A T T C   G
G   C T T A A

2 DNA fragments with the same sticky ends can pair. Shown here is a DNA fragment inserting between two other DNA fragments, as happens when inserting a DNA fragment into a bacterial plasmid.

Nick in sugar–phosphate backbone

5′ — G A A T T C   G A A T T C — 3′
3′ — C T T A A G   C T T A A G — 5′

3 Nicks in sugar–phosphate backbones are sealed by DNA ligase.

5′ — G A A T T C   G A A T T C — 3′
3′ — C T T A A G   C T T A A G — 5′

Recombinant DNA molecule

Figure 16.2
The restriction site for the restriction enzyme *Eco*RI, and the generation of a recombinant DNA molecule by complementary base pairing of DNA fragments produced by digestion with the same restriction enzyme.

Cloning a Gene of Interest. Figure 16.3 expands on the overview of Figure 16.1 to show the steps used to clone a gene of interest using a plasmid cloning vector and restriction enzymes. Genomic DNA isolated from the organism in which the gene is found is cut with a restriction enzyme, and a plasmid cloning vector is cut within the *lacZ*+ gene with the same restriction enzyme (steps 1 and 2). Mixing the DNA fragments and cut plasmid together with DNA ligase produces various joined molecules as the sticky ends pair and the enzyme seals them together. Some of these molecules are recombinant plasmids consisting of, in each case, a DNA fragment inserted into the plasmid cloning vector; others are nonrecombinant plasmids resulting from the cut plasmid resealed into a circle without an inserted fragment (step 3). In addition, ligase joins together pieces of genomic DNA with no plasmid involved. Only the recombinant plasmids are important in the cloning of the gene of interest; we sort out the other two undesired molecules in later steps.

Next, the DNA molecules are transformed—introduced—into ampicillin-sensitive, *lacZ*− *E. coli* (which cannot make β-galactosidase), and the transformed bacteria are spread on a plate of agar growth medium containing ampicillin and the β-galactosidase

substrate X-gal (steps 4 and 5). (Section 10.2 describes techniques for transformation of DNA into bacteria.) Only bacteria with a plasmid can grow and form colonies because expression of the plasmid's *amp*R gene makes the bacteria resistant to ampicillin (see Figure 16.3 results). Within each cell of a colony, the plasmids have replicated until a hundred or so are present.

The X-gal in the medium distinguishes between bacteria that have been transformed with recombinant plasmids and nonrecombinant plasmids by *blue-white screening* (see Figure 16.3, Interpreting the Results). If a colony produces β-galactosidase, it converts X-gal to a blue product and the colony turns blue, but if a colony does not produce the enzyme, X-gal is unchanged and the colony remains white. Colonies containing nonrecombinant plasmids have an intact *lacZ*+ gene, produce the enzyme, and turn blue. Colonies containing recombinant plasmids are white because those plasmids each contain a DNA fragment inserted into the *lacZ*+ gene, so they do not produce the enzyme. The white colonies are examined to find the one containing a recombinant plasmid with the gene of interest.

Two researchers, Paul Berg and Stanley Cohen, were prime movers in the development of DNA cloning techniques using restriction enzymes and bacterial plasmids. Berg and Cohen received a Nobel Prize in 1980 for their research, which pushed DNA technology to the forefront of biological investigations.

Identifying the Clone Containing the Gene of Interest. How is a clone containing the gene of interest identified among the population of clones? The gene of interest has a unique DNA sequence, which is the basis for one commonly used identification technique. In this technique, called **DNA hybridization**, the gene of interest is identified in the set of clones when it base-pairs with a short, single-stranded complementary DNA or RNA molecule called a *nucleic acid probe* (**Figure 16.4, p. 348**). The probe is typically labelled with a radioactive or a nonradioactive tag so investigators can detect it. In our example, if we know the sequence of part of the gene of interest, we can use that information to design and synthesize a nucleic acid probe. Or we can take advantage of DNA sequence similarities of evolutionarily related organisms. For instance, we could make a probe for a human gene based on the sequence of an equivalent mouse gene. Once a colony containing plasmids with the gene of interest has been identified, that colony can be used to produce large quantities of the cloned gene.

16.1c DNA Libraries Contain Collections of Cloned DNA Fragments

As you have seen, the starting point for cloning a gene of interest is a large set of plasmid clones carrying fragments representing all of the DNA of an organism's genome. A collection of clones that contains a copy of every DNA sequence in a genome is called a **genomic library.**

Figure 16.3
Cloning a gene of interest in a plasmid cloning vector.

PURPOSE: Cloning a gene produces many copies of a gene of interest that can be used, for example, to determine the DNA sequence of the gene, to manipulate the gene in basic research experiments, to understand its function, and to produce the protein encoded by the gene.

PROTOCOL:

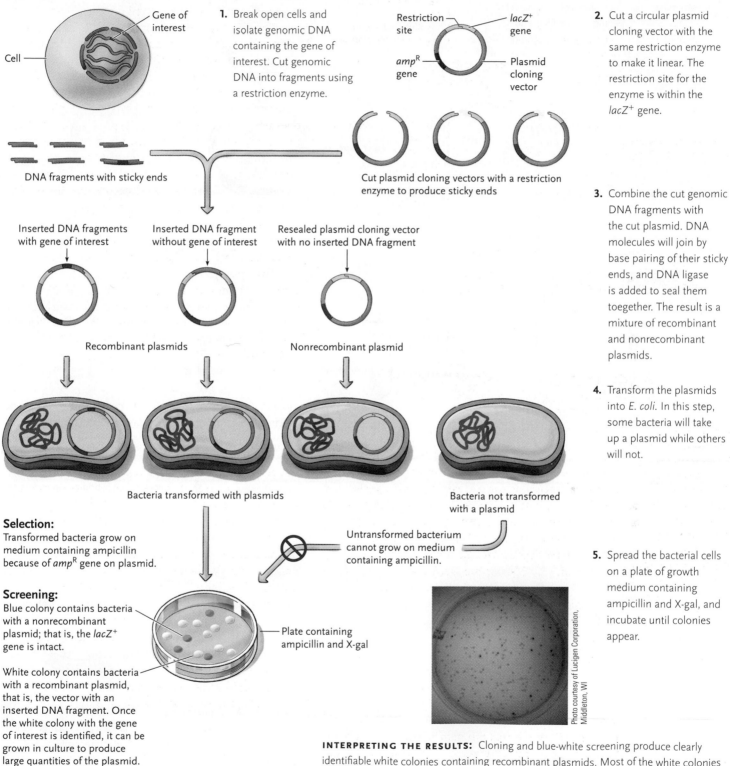

1. Break open cells and isolate genomic DNA containing the gene of interest. Cut genomic DNA into fragments using a restriction enzyme.

Gene of interest

Cell

DNA fragments with sticky ends

2. Cut a circular plasmid cloning vector with the same restriction enzyme to make it linear. The restriction site for the enzyme is within the *lacZ*+ gene.

Restriction site

lacZ+ gene

*amp*R gene

Plasmid cloning vector

Cut plasmid cloning vectors with a restriction enzyme to produce sticky ends

3. Combine the cut genomic DNA fragments with the cut plasmid. DNA molecules will join by base pairing of their sticky ends, and DNA ligase is added to seal them toegether. The result is a mixture of recombinant and nonrecombinant plasmids.

Inserted DNA fragments with gene of interest

Inserted DNA fragment without gene of interest

Resealed plasmid cloning vector with no inserted DNA fragment

Recombinant plasmids

Nonrecombinant plasmid

4. Transform the plasmids into *E. coli*. In this step, some bacteria will take up a plasmid while others will not.

Bacteria transformed with plasmids

Bacteria not transformed with a plasmid

Selection:
Transformed bacteria grow on medium containing ampicillin because of *amp*R gene on plasmid.

Untransformed bacterium cannot grow on medium containing ampicillin.

5. Spread the bacterial cells on a plate of growth medium containing ampicillin and X-gal, and incubate until colonies appear.

Screening:
Blue colony contains bacteria with a nonrecombinant plasmid; that is, the *lacZ*+ gene is intact.

Plate containing ampicillin and X-gal

White colony contains bacteria with a recombinant plasmid, that is, the vector with an inserted DNA fragment. Once the white colony with the gene of interest is identified, it can be grown in culture to produce large quantities of the plasmid.

Photo courtesy of Lucigen Corporation, Middleton, WI

INTERPRETING THE RESULTS: Cloning and blue-white screening produce clearly identifiable white colonies containing recombinant plasmids. Most of the white colonies will contain plasmids that do not contain the gene of interest. Further screening will be done to identify the particular white colony that contains a plasmid with the gene of interest (Figure 16.4). Once identified, the colony can be cultured to produce large quantities of the plasmid for analysis or manipulation of the gene.

Figure 16.4
DNA hybridization to identify a DNA sequence of interest.

PROTOCOL:

1. Prepare master plates of white colonies detected in the blue-white screening step of Figure 16.3. These colonies contain bacteria with recombinant plasmids. Hundreds or thousands of colonies can be screened for the gene of interest by using many master plates.

2. Lay a special filter paper on the plate to pick up some cells from each colony. This produces a replica of the colony pattern on the filter.

3. Treat the filter to break open the cells and to denature the released DNA to single strands. The single-stranded DNA sticks to the filter in the same position as the colony from which it was derived.

4. Add a labelled single-stranded probe (DNA or RNA) for the gene of interest and incubate. The label can be radioactive or nonradioactive. If a recombinant plasmid's inserted DNA fragment is complementary to the probe, the two will hybridize, that is, form base pairs. Wash off excess labelled probe.

5. Detect the hybridization event by looking for the labelled tag on the probe. If the probe was radioactively labelled, place the filter against photographic film. The decaying radioactive compound exposes the film, giving a dark spot when the film is developed. Correlate the position of any dark spot on the film to the original colony pattern on the master plate. Isolate the colony and use it to produce large quantities of the gene of interest.

PURPOSE: Hybridization with a specific DNA probe allows researchers to detect a specific DNA sequence, such as a gene, within a population of DNA molecules. Here, DNA hybridization is used to screen a collection of bacterial colonies to identify those containing a recombinant plasmid with a gene of interest.

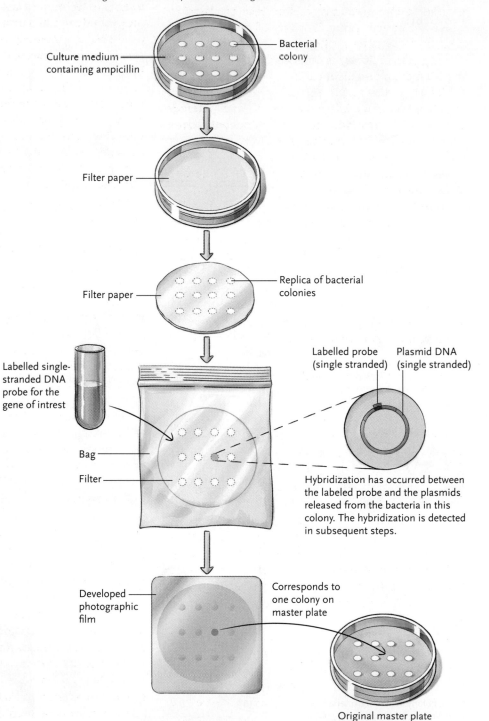

INTERPRETING THE RESULTS: DNA hybridization with a labelled probe enables a researcher to home in on a sequence of interest. If the probe is for a particular gene, it allows the specific identification of a colony containing bacteria with recombinant plasmids carrying that gene. The specificity of the method depends directly on the probe used. The same collection of bacterial clones can be used again and again to search for recombinant plasmids carrying different genes or different plasmids of interest simply by changing the probe used in the experiment.

A genomic library can be made using plasmid cloning vectors or any other kind of cloning vector. The number of clones in a genomic library increases with the size of the genome. For example, a yeast genomic library of plasmid clones consists of hundreds of plasmids, whereas a human genomic library of plasmid clones consists of thousands of plasmids.

A genomic library is a resource containing all of the DNA of an organism cut into pieces. Just as for a book library, where you can search through the same set of books on various occasions to find different passages of interest, you can search through the same genomic library on various occasions to find and isolate different genes or other DNA sequences.

Researchers also commonly use another kind of DNA library that is made starting with mRNA molecules isolated from a cell. To convert single-stranded mRNA to double-stranded DNA for cloning (RNA cannot be cloned), first they use the enzyme *reverse transcriptase* (made by retroviruses) to make a single-stranded DNA that is complementary to the mRNA. Then they degrade the mRNA strand with an enzyme and use DNA polymerase to make a second DNA strand that is complementary to the first. The result is **complementary DNA (cDNA)**. After adding restriction sites to each end, they insert the cDNA into a cloning vector as described for the genomic library. The entire collection of cloned cDNAs made from the mRNAs isolated from a cell is a **cDNA library**.

Not all genes are active in every cell. Therefore, a cDNA library is limited in that it includes copies of only the genes that were active in the cells used as the starting point for creation of the library. This limitation can be an advantage, however, in identifying genes active in one cell type and not another. cDNA libraries are useful, therefore, for providing clues to the changes in gene activity that are responsible for cell differentiation and specialization. An ingenious method for comparing the cDNA libraries produced by different cell types—the DNA chip—is described later in this chapter.

cDNA libraries provide a critical advantage to genetic engineers who wish to insert eukaryotic genes into bacteria, particularly when the bacteria are to be used as "factories" for making the protein encoded in the gene. The genes in eukaryotic nuclear DNA typically contain many *introns*, spacer sequences that interrupt the amino acid–coding sequence of a gene (see Section 14.3). Because bacterial DNA does not contain introns, bacteria are not equipped to process eukaryotic genes correctly. However, the cDNA copy of a eukaryotic mRNA already has the introns removed, so bacteria can transcribe and translate it accurately to make eukaryotic proteins.

Genomic and cDNA libraries both depend on cloning in a living cell to produce multiple copies of the DNA of interest. Next we look at a highly automated method of making copies of a targeted piece of DNA in a genome.

16.1d The Polymerase Chain Reaction (PCR) Amplifies DNA *In Vitro*

Producing multiple DNA copies by cloning requires a series of techniques and considerable time. A much more rapid process, **polymerase chain reaction (PCR)**, produces an extremely large number of copies of a specific DNA sequence from a DNA mixture without having to clone the sequence in a host organism. The process is called *amplification* because it increases the amount of DNA to the point where it can be analyzed or manipulated easily. Developed in 1983 by Kary B. Mullis and F. Faloona at Cetus Corporation (Emeryville, CA), PCR has become one of the most important tools in modern molecular biology, finding wide application in all areas of biology. Mullis received a Nobel Prize in 1993 for his role in the development of PCR.

How PCR is performed is shown in **Figure 16.5 (p. 350)**. PCR essentially is DNA replication, but a special case in which a DNA polymerase replicates just a portion of a DNA molecule rather than the whole molecule. PCR takes advantage of a characteristic common to all DNA polymerases: these enzymes add nucleotides only to the end of an existing chain called the *primer* (see Section 13.3). For replication to take place, a primer therefore must be in place, base-paired to the template chain at which replication is to begin. By cycling 20 to 30 times through a series of steps, PCR amplifies the target sequence, producing millions of copies.

Since the primers used in PCR are designed to bracket only the sequence of interest, the cycles replicate only this sequence from a mixture of essentially any DNA molecules. Thus, PCR not only finds the "needle in the haystack" among all the sequences in a mixture but also makes millions of copies of the "needle"—the DNA sequence of interest. Usually, no further purification of the amplified sequence is necessary.

The characteristics of PCR allow extremely small DNA samples to be amplified to concentrations high enough for analysis. PCR is used, for example, to produce enough DNA for analysis from the root of a single human hair, or from a small amount of blood, semen, or saliva, such as the traces left at the scene of a crime. It is also used to extract and multiply DNA sequences from skeletal remains; ancient sources such as mammoths, Neanderthals, and Egyptian mummies; and, in rare cases, amber-entombed fossils, fossil bones, and fossil plant remains.

A successful outcome of PCR is shown by analyzing a sample of the amplified DNA using **agarose gel electrophoresis** to see if the copies are the same length as the target **(Figure 16.6, p. 351)**. Gel electrophoresis is a technique by which DNA, RNA, or protein molecules are separated in a gel subjected to an electric field. The type of gel and the conditions used vary with the experiment, but in each case, the gel functions as a molecular sieve to separate the macromolecules based on size, electrical

Figure 16.5
The polymerase chain reaction (PCR).

PURPOSE: To amplify—produce large numbers of copies of—a target DNA sequence in the test tube without cloning.

PROTOCOL: A polymerase chain reaction mixture has four key elements: **(1)** the DNA with the target sequence to be amplified; **(2)** a pair of DNA primers, one complementary to one end of the target sequence and the other complementary to the other end of the target sequence; **(3)** the four nucleoside triphosphate precursors for DNA synthesis (dATP, dTTP, dGTP, and dCTP); and **(4)** DNA polymerase. Since PCR uses high temperatures for some of the steps, a heat-stable DNA polymerase is used, typically one isolated from a microorganism that grows in a high-temperature area such as a thermal pool or near a deep-sea vent.

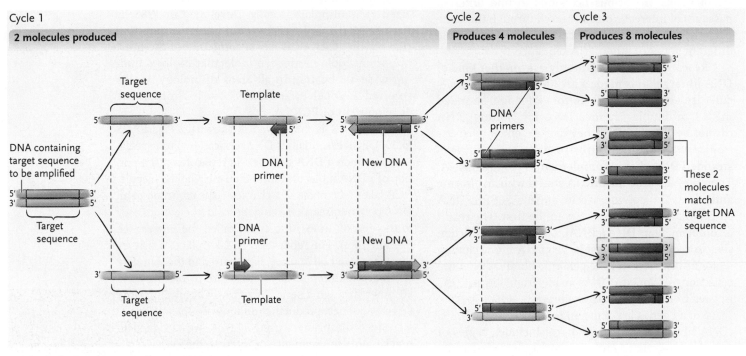

Cycle 1

2 molecules produced

Cycle 2

Produces 4 molecules

Cycle 3

Produces 8 molecules

1. Denaturation: Heat DNA containing target sequence to denature it to single strands.

2. Annealing: Cool the mixture to allow the two primers to anneal to their complementary sequences at the two ends of the target sequence.

3. Heat to the optimal temperature for DNA polymerase to extend the primers, using the four nucleoside triphosphate precursors to make complementary copies of the two template strands. This completes cycle 1 of PCR; the end result is two molecules.

4. Repeat the same steps of denaturation, annealing of primers, and extension in cycle 2, producing a total of four molecules.

5. Repeat the same steps in cycle 3, producing a total of eight molecules. Two of the eight match the exact length of the target DNA sequence (highlighted in yellow).

INTERPRETING THE RESULTS: After three cycles, PCR produces a pair of molecules matching the target sequence. Subsequent cycles amplify these molecules to the point where they outnumber all other molecules in the reaction by many orders of magnitude.

charge, or other properties. For separating large DNA molecules, such as those typically produced by PCR, a gel made of agarose, a natural molecule isolated from seaweed, is used because of its large pore size.

For PCR experiments, the size of the amplified DNA is determined by comparing the position of the DNA band with the positions of DNA fragments of known size separated on the gel at the same time. If that size matches the predicted size for the target DNA, PCR is deemed successful. In some cases, such as DNA from ancient sources, a size **prediction** may not be possible; in this case, agarose gel electrophoresis

Figure 16.6
Separation of DNA fragments by agarose gel electrophoresis.

PURPOSE: Gel electrophoresis separates DNA molecules, RNA molecules, or proteins according to their sizes, electrical charges, or other properties through a gel in an electric field. Different gel types and conditions are used for different molecules and types of applications. A common gel for separating large DNA fragments is made of agarose.

PROTOCOL:

1. Prepare a gel consisting of a thin slab of agarose and place it in a gel box in between two electrodes. The gel has wells for placing the DNA samples to be analyzed. Add buffer to cover the gel.

2. Load DNA sample solutions, such as PCR products, into wells of the gel, alongside a well loaded with marker DNA fragments of known sizes.

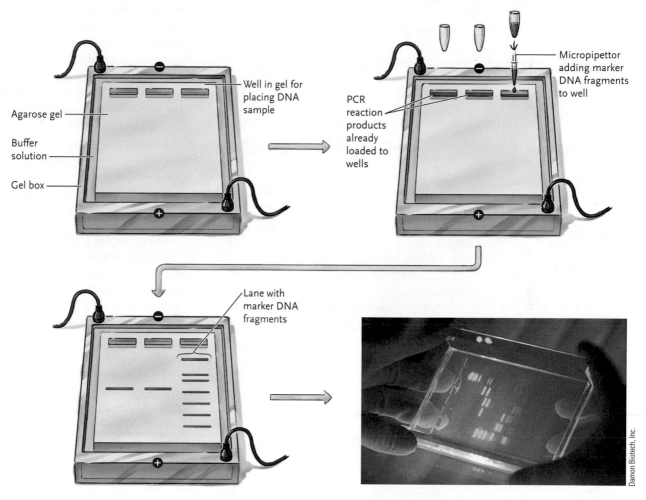

3. Apply an electric current to the gel; DNA fragments are negatively charged, so they migrate to the positive pole. Shorter DNA fragments migrate faster than longer DNA fragments. At the completion of the separation, DNA fragments of the same length have formed bands in the gel. At this point, the bands are invisible.

4. Stain the gel with a dye that binds to DNA. The dye fluoresces under UV light, enabling the DNA bands to be seen and photographed. An actual gel showing separated DNA bands stained and visualized this way is shown.

INTERPRETING THE RESULTS: Agarose gel electrophoresis separates DNA fragments according to their length. The lengths of the DNA fragments being analyzed are determined by measuring their migration distances and comparing those distances to a calibration curve of the migration distances of the marker bands, which have known length. For PCR, agarose gel electrophoresis shows whether DNA of the correct length was amplified. For restriction enzyme digests, this technique shows whether fragments are produced as expected.

analysis simply indicates whether there was DNA in the sample that could be amplified.

The advantages of PCR have made it the technique of choice for researchers, law enforcement agencies, and forensic specialists whose primary interest is in the amplification of specific DNA fragments up to a practical maximum of a few thousand base pairs. Cloning remains the technique of choice for amplification of longer fragments. The major limitation of PCR relates to the primers. To design a primer for PCR, the researcher must first have sequence information about the target DNA. By contrast, cloning can be used to amplify DNA of unknown sequence.

STUDY BREAK

1. What features do restriction enzymes have in common? How do they differ?
2. Plasmid cloning vectors are one type of cloning vector that can be used with *E. coli* as a host organism. What features of a plasmid cloning vector make it useful for constructing and cloning recombinant DNA molecules?
3. What is a cDNA library, and from what cellular material is it derived? How does a cDNA library differ from a genomic library?
4. What information and materials are needed to amplify a region of DNA using PCR?

16.2 Applications of DNA Technologies

The ability to clone pieces of DNA—genes, especially—and to amplify specific segments of DNA by PCR revolutionized biology. These and other DNA technologies are now used for research in all areas of biology, including cloning genes to determine their structure, function, and regulation of expression; manipulating genes to determine how their products function in cellular or developmental processes; and identifying differences in DNA sequences among individuals in ecological studies. The same DNA technologies also have practical applications, including medical and forensic detection, modification of animals and plants, and the manufacture of commercial products. In this section, case studies provide examples of how the techniques are used to answer questions and solve problems.

16.2a DNA Technologies Are Used in Molecular Testing for Many Human Genetic Diseases

Many human genetic diseases are caused by defects in enzymes or other proteins that result from mutations at the DNA level. Once scientists have identified the specific mutations responsible for human genetic diseases, they can often use DNA technologies to develop molecular tests for those diseases. One example is sickle cell disease (see *Why It Matters* in Chapter 11, Section 11.2, and Section 12.4). People with this disease are homozygous for a DNA mutation that affects hemoglobin, the oxygen-carrying molecule of the blood. Hemoglobin consists of two copies each of the α-globin and β-globin polypeptides. The mutation, which is in the β-globin gene, alters one amino acid in the polypeptide. As a consequence, the function of hemoglobin is significantly impaired in individuals homozygous for the mutation (who have sickle cell anemia) and mildly impaired in individuals heterozygous for the mutation (who have sickle cell trait).

The sickle cell mutation changes a restriction site in the DNA **(Figure 16.7).** Three restriction sites for *Mst*II are associated with the normal β-globin gene, two within the coding sequence of the gene and one upstream of the gene. The sickle cell mutation eliminates the middle site of the three. Cutting the β-globin gene with *Mst*II produces two DNA fragments from the normal gene and one fragment from the mutated gene (see Figure 16.7). Restriction enzyme–generated DNA fragments of different lengths from the same region of the genome such as in this example are known as **restriction fragment length polymorphisms** (RFLPs, pronounced "riff-lips").

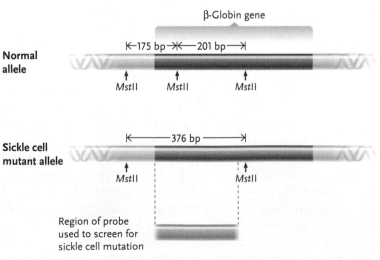

Figure 16.7
Restriction site differences between the normal and sickle cell mutant alleles of the β-globin gene. The figure shows a DNA segment that can be used as a probe to identify these alleles in subsequent analysis (see Figure 16.8).

Ethidium Bromide

Figure 16.6 shows an agarose gel containing DNA fragments separated by electrophoresis. The fragments appear orange because a stain has bound to the DNA and is fluorescing under ultraviolet light. The stain is ethidium bromide **(Figure 1)**. This relatively flat molecule slides neatly between the bases of DNA by a process called intercalation—hence, its usefulness as a stain. However, intercalation into DNA around replication forks can increase the frequency of addition/deletion mutations in cultured cells.

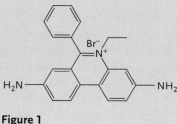

Figure 1
Ethidium bromide.

RFLPs typically are analyzed using **Southern blot analysis** (named after its inventor, researcher Edward Southern) **(Figure 16.8, p. 354)**. In this technique, genomic DNA is digested with a restriction enzyme, and the DNA fragments are separated using agarose gel electrophoresis. The fragments are then transferred—blotted—to a filter paper, and a labelled probe is used to identify a DNA sequence of interest from among the many thousands of fragments on the filter paper.

Analyzing DNA for the sickle cell mutation by *Mst*II digestion and Southern blot analysis is straightforward (see Figure 16.8). An individual with sickle cell disease will have one DNA band of 376 bp detected by the probe (lane A), a healthy individual will have two DNA bands of 175 and 201 bp (lane B), and an individual with sickle cell trait (heterozygous for normal and mutant alleles) will have three DNA bands of 376 bp (mutant allele) and 201 and 175 bp (normal allele) (lane C). The same probe detects all three RFLP fragments by binding to all or part of the sequence.

Restriction enzyme digestion and Southern blot analysis may be used to test for a number of other human genetic diseases, including phenylketonuria and Duchenne muscular dystrophy. In some cases, restriction enzyme digestion is combined with PCR for a quicker, easier analysis. The gene or region of the gene with the restriction enzyme variation is first amplified using PCR, and the amplified DNA is then cut with the diagnostic restriction enzyme. Amplification produces enough DNA so that separation by size on an agarose gel produces clearly visible bands, positioned according to fragment length. Researchers can then determine whether the fragment lengths match a normal or abnormal RFLP pattern. This method eliminates the need for a probe or for Southern blotting.

16.2b DNA Fingerprinting Is Used to Identify Human Individuals and Individuals of Other Species

Just as each human has a unique set of fingerprints, each also has unique combinations and variations of DNA sequences (with the exception of identical twins) known as *DNA fingerprints*. **DNA fingerprinting** is a technique used to distinguish between individuals of the same species using DNA samples. Invented by Sir Alec Jeffreys in 1985, DNA fingerprinting has become a mainstream technique for distinguishing human individuals, notably in forensics and paternity testing. Although the technique can be applied to all kinds of animals and plants, in this chapter we focus on humans.

DNA Fingerprinting Principles. In DNA fingerprinting, scientists use molecular techniques, most typically PCR, to analyze DNA variations at various loci in the genome. Several loci in noncoding regions of the genome are used for analysis. Each locus is an example of a *short tandem repeat* (STR) sequence, meaning that it has a short sequence of DNA repeated in series, with each repeat about 3 to 5 bp. Each locus has a different repeated sequence, and the number of repeats varies among individuals in a population. For example, one STR locus has the sequence AGAT repeated between 8 and 20 times. As a further source of variation, a given individual is either homozygous or heterozygous for an STR allele; perhaps you are homozygous for the 11-repeat allele or heterozygous for a 9-repeat allele and a 15-repeat allele. Likely your DNA fingerprint for this locus is different from most of the others in your class. Because each individual has an essentially unique combination of alleles (identical twins are the exception), analysis of multiple STR loci can discriminate between DNA of different individuals.

Figure 16.8
Southern blot analysis.

PURPOSE: The Southern blot technique allows researchers to identify DNA fragments of interest after separating DNA fragments on a gel. One application is to compare different samples of genomic DNA cut with a restriction enzyme to detect specific restriction fragment length polymorphisms. Here the technique is used to distinguish between individuals with sickle cell disease, individuals with sickle cell trait, and normal individuals.

PROTOCOL:

1. Isolate genomic DNA and digest with a restriction enzyme. Here, genomic DNA is isolated from three individuals: A, sickle cell disease (homozygous for the sickle cell mutant allele); B, normal (homozygous for the normal allele); and C, sickle cell trait (heterozygote for sickle cell mutant allele). Digest the DNA with *Mst*II.

2. Separate the DNA fragments by agarose gel electrophoresis. The thousands of differently sized DNA fragments generated results in a smear of DNA down the length of each lane in the gel, which can be seen after staining the DNA. (Gel electrophoresis and gel staining are shown in Figure 16.6).

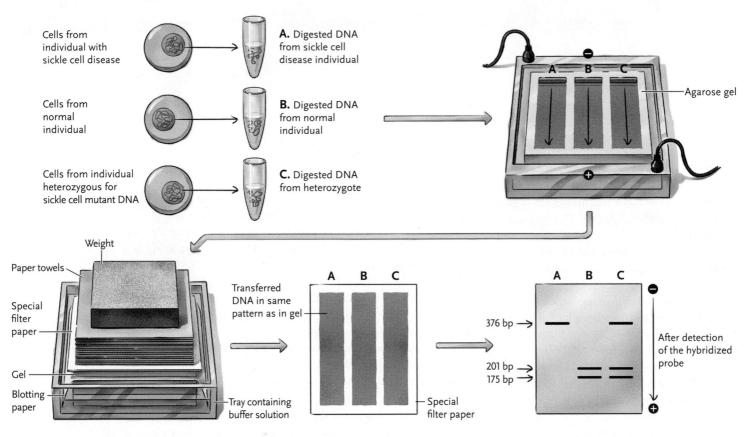

3. Hybridization with a labelled DNA probe to identify DNA fragments of interest cannot be done directly with an agarose gel. Edward Southern devised a method to transfer the DNA fragments from a gel to a special filter paper. First, treat the gel with a solution to denature the DNA to single strands. Next, place the gel on a piece of blotting paper with ends of the paper in the buffer solution and place the special filter paper on top of the gel. Capillary action wicks the buffer solution in the tray up the blotting paper, through the gel and special filter paper, and into the weighted stack of paper towels on top of the gel. The movement of the solution transfers—blots—the single-stranded DNA fragments to the filter paper, where they stick. The pattern of DNA fragments is the same as it was in the gel.

4. To home in on a particular region of the genome, use DNA hybridization with a labelled probe. That is, incubate a labelled, single-stranded probe with the filter and, after washing off excess probe, detect hybridization of the probe with DNA fragments on the filter. For a radioactive probe, the filter is placed against photographic film, which, after development will show a band or bands where the probe hybridized. In this experiment, the probe is a cloned piece of DNA from the area shown in Figure 16.7 that can bind to all three of the *Mst*II fragments of interest.

INTERPRETING THE RESULTS: The hybridization result indicates that the probe has identified a very specific DNA fragment or fragments in the digested genomic DNA. The RFLPs for the β-globin gene can be seen in Figure 16.7. DNA from the sickle cell disease individual cut with *Mst*II results in a single band of 376 bp detected by the probe, while DNA from the normal individual results in two bands of 201, and 175 bp. DNA from a sickle cell trait heterozygote results in three bands of 376 bp (from the sickle cell mutant allele), and 201 and 175 bp (the latter two from the normal allele). This type of analysis in general is useful for distinguishing normal and mutant alleles of genes where the mutation involved alters a restriction site.

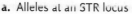

a. Alleles at an STR locus

STR locus

Left PCR primer →

DNA

9 repeats ← Right PCR primer

→

11 repeats ←

→

15 repeats ←

3 different alleles

b. DNA fingerprint analysis of the STR locus by PCR

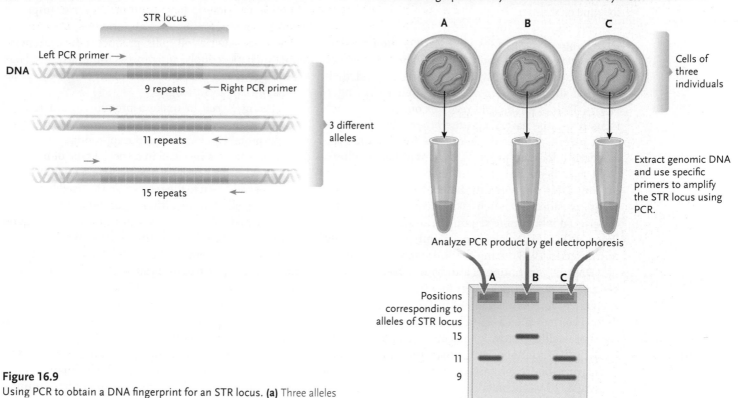

A B C

Cells of three individuals

Extract genomic DNA and use specific primers to amplify the STR locus using PCR.

Analyze PCR product by gel electrophoresis

A B C

Positions corresponding to alleles of STR locus

15

11

9

11,11 15,9 11,9

Figure 16.9

Using PCR to obtain a DNA fingerprint for an STR locus. **(a)** Three alleles of the STR locus with 9, 11, and 15 copies of the tandemly repeated sequence. The arrows indicate where left and right PCR primers can bind to amplify the STR locus. **(b)** DNA fingerprint analysis of the STR locus by PCR.

Figure 16.9 illustrates how PCR is used to obtain a DNA fingerprint for a theoretical STR locus with three alleles of 9, 11, and 15 tandem repeats (see Figure 16.9a). Using primers that flank the STR locus, the locus is amplified from genomic DNA using PCR, and the PCR products are analyzed by gel electrophoresis (see Figure 16.9b). The number of bands on the gel and the sizes of the DNA in the bands show the STR alleles that were amplified. One band indicates that the individual was homozygous for an STR allele with a particular number of repeats, whereas two bands indicate that the individual is heterozygous for two STR alleles with different numbers of repeats. In the result shown in Figure 16.9b, the A individual is homozygous for an 11-repeat allele (designated 11,11), B is heterozygous for a 15-repeat allele and a 9-repeat allele (15,9), and C is heterozygous for the 11-repeat allele and the 9-repeat allele (11,9).

DNA Fingerprinting in Forensics. DNA fingerprints are routinely used to identify criminals or eliminate innocent persons as suspects in legal proceedings. For example, a DNA fingerprint prepared from a hair found at the scene of a crime or from a semen sample might be compared with the DNA fingerprint of a suspect to link the suspect with the crime. Or a DNA fingerprint of blood found on a suspect's clothing or possessions might be compared with the DNA fingerprint

of a victim. Typically, the evidence is presented in terms of the probability that the particular DNA sample could have come from a random individual. Hence, the media report probability values, such as one in several million, or in several billion, that a person other than the accused could have left his or her DNA at the crime scene.

Although courts initially met with legal challenges to the admissibility of DNA fingerprints, experience has shown that they are highly dependable as a line of evidence if DNA samples are collected and prepared with care and if a sufficient number of polymorphic loci are examined. There is always concern, however, about the possibility of contamination of the sample with DNA from another source during the path from crime scene to forensic lab analysis. Moreover, in some cases, criminals themselves have planted fake DNA samples at crime scenes to confuse the investigation.

There are many examples of the use of DNA fingerprinting to identify a criminal. For example, in a case in England, the DNA fingerprints of more than 4000 men were made during an investigation of the rape and murder of two teenage girls. The results led to the release of a man wrongly imprisoned for the crimes and to the confession and conviction of the actual killer. And the application of DNA fingerprinting techniques to stored forensic samples has led to the release of a number of persons wrongly convicted for rape or murder.

DNA Fingerprinting in Testing Paternity and Establishing Ancestry. DNA fingerprints are also widely used as evidence of paternity because parents and their children share common alleles in their DNA fingerprints. That is, each child receives one allele of each locus from one parent and the other allele from the other parent. A comparison of DNA fingerprints for a number of loci can prove almost infallibly whether a child has been fathered or mothered by a given person. DNA fingerprints have also been used for other investigations, such as confirming that remains discovered in a remote region of Russia were actually those of Czar Nicholas II and members of his family, murdered in 1918 during the Russian revolution.

DNA fingerprinting is also widely used in studies of other organisms, including other animals, plants, and bacteria. Examples include testing for pathogenic *E. coli* in food sources such as hamburger meat, investigating cases of wildlife poaching, detecting genetically modified organisms among living organisms or in food, and comparing the DNA of ancient organisms with that of present-day descendants.

16.2c Genetic Engineering Uses DNA Technologies to Alter the Genes of a Cell or Organism

We have seen the many ways scientists use DNA technologies to ask and answer questions that were once completely inaccessible. Genetic engineering goes beyond gathering information; it is the use of DNA technologies to modify genes of a cell or organism. The goals of genetic engineering include using prokaryotes, fungi, animals, and plants as factories for the production of proteins needed in medicine and scientific research; correcting hereditary disorders; and improving animals and crop plants of agricultural importance. In many of these areas, genetic engineering has already been spectacularly successful. The successes and potential benefits of genetic engineering, however, are tempered by ethical and social concerns about its use, along with the fear that the methods may produce toxic or damaging foods or release dangerous and uncontrollable organisms to the environment.

Genetic engineering uses DNA technologies of the kind discussed already in this chapter. DNA—perhaps a modified gene—is introduced into target cells of an organism. Organisms that have undergone a gene transfer are called **transgenic**, meaning that they have been modified to contain genetic information—the *transgene*—from an external source.

The following sections discuss examples of applications of genetic engineering to bacteria, animals, and plants and assess major controversies arising from these projects.

Genetic Engineering of Bacteria to Produce Proteins. Transgenic bacteria have been made, for example, to make proteins for medical applications, break down toxic wastes such as oil spills, produce industrial chemicals such as alcohols, and process minerals. *E. coli* has been the organism of choice for many of these applications of DNA technologies.

Using *E. coli* to make a protein from a foreign source is conceptually straightforward. First, the gene for the protein is cloned from the appropriate organism. Then the gene is inserted in a special type of bacterial plasmid called an *expression vector*, which has a bacterial promoter adjacent to the restriction site used for inserting the gene. The resulting recombinant plasmid is transformed into *E. coli*, which transcribes the gene and translates the resulting mRNA to make the desired protein. The protein is either extracted from the bacterial cells and purified, or if the protein is secreted, it is purified from the culture medium.

For example, *E. coli* bacteria have been genetically engineered to make the human hormone insulin; the commercial product is called HUMULIN®. Insulin is required by persons with some forms of diabetes. Humulin is a perfect copy of the human insulin hormone. Many other proteins, including human growth hormone to treat human growth disorders, tissue plasminogen activator to dissolve blood clots that cause heart attacks, and a vaccine against hoof-and-mouth disease of cattle (a highly contagious and sometimes fatal viral disease), have been developed for commercial production in bacteria by similar methods.

Although they offer many benefits, genetically engineered bacteria pose the risk that they may be released accidentally into the environment, where any adverse effects are currently unknown. Scientists minimize the danger of accidental release by growing the bacteria in laboratories that follow appropriate biosafety protocols. In addition, the bacterial strains typically used are genetically modified so that they will not survive outside of the growth media used in the laboratory.

Genetic Engineering of Animals. Many animals, including fruit flies, fish, mice, pigs, sheep, goats, and cows, have been altered successfully by genetic engineering. There are many purposes for these alterations, including basic research, correcting genetic disorders in humans and other mammals, and producing pharmaceutically important proteins.

Genetic Engineering Methods for Animals. Several methods are used to introduce a gene of interest into animal cells. The gene may be introduced into *germline cells*, which develop into sperm or eggs and thus enable the introduced gene to be passed from generation to generation. Or, the gene may be introduced into *somatic* (body) *cells*, differentiated cells that are not part of lines producing sperm or eggs, in which case, the gene is not transmitted from generation to generation.

Germ-line cells of embryos are often used as targets for introducing genes, particularly in mammals (**Figure 16.10**). The treated cells are then cultured in quantity and reintroduced into early embryos. If the technique is successful, some of the introduced cells become founders of cell lines that develop into eggs or sperm with the desired genetic information integrated into their DNA. Individuals produced by crosses using the engineered eggs and sperm then contain the introduced sequences in all of their cells. Several genes have been introduced into the germ lines of mice by this approach, resulting in permanent, heritable changes in the engineered individuals.

A related technique involves introducing desired genes into *stem cells,* which are capable of differentiating into almost any adult cell type and tissue. Stem cells that have taken up the gene are then injected into an early embryo, where they differentiate into a variety of tissues along with cells of the embryo itself, including sperm and egg cells. Males and females are then bred, leading to offspring that are either homozygotes, containing two copies of the introduced gene, or heterozygotes, containing one introduced gene and one gene that was native to the embryo receiving the engineered stem cells.

Introduction of genes into stem cells has been performed mostly in mice. One of the highly useful results is the production of a "knockout mouse," a homozygous recessive that receives two copies of a gene altered to a nonfunctional state and thus has no functional copies. The effect of the missing gene on the knockout mouse is a clue to the normal function of the gene. In some cases, knockout mice are used to model human genetic diseases.

For introducing genes into somatic cells, typically somatic cells are removed from the body, cultured, and then transformed with DNA containing the transgene. The modified cells are then reintroduced into the body where the transgene functions. Because germ cells and their products are not involved, the transgene remains in the individual and is not passed to offspring.

Gene Therapy: Correcting Genetic Disorders. The path to **gene therapy**—correcting genetic disorders—in humans began with experiments using mice. In 1982, Richard Palmiter at the University of Washington, Ralph Brinster of the University of Pennsylvania, and their colleagues injected a growth hormone gene from rats into fertilized mouse eggs and implanted the eggs into a surrogate mother. She gave birth to some normal-sized mouse pups that grew faster than normal and became about twice the size of their normal litter mates. These *giant mice* (**Figure 16.11, p. 358**) attracted extensive media attention from around the world.

Figure 16.10
Introduction of genes into mouse embryos using embryonic germ-line cells.

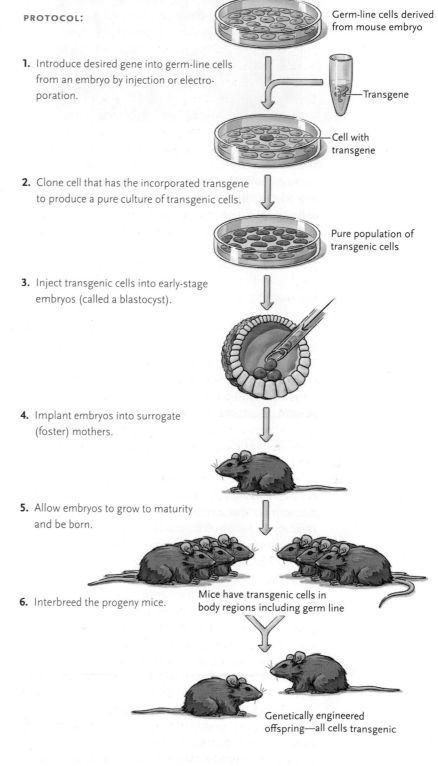

PURPOSE: To make a transgenic animal that can transmit the transgene to offspring. The embryonic germ-line cells that receive the transgene develop into the reproductive cells of the animal.

PROTOCOL:

Germ-line cells derived from mouse embryo

1. Introduce desired gene into germ-line cells from an embryo by injection or electroporation.

Transgene

Cell with transgene

2. Clone cell that has the incorporated transgene to produce a pure culture of transgenic cells.

Pure population of transgenic cells

3. Inject transgenic cells into early-stage embryos (called a blastocyst).

4. Implant embryos into surrogate (foster) mothers.

5. Allow embryos to grow to maturity and be born.

6. Interbreed the progeny mice.

Mice have transgenic cells in body regions including germ line

Genetically engineered offspring—all cells transgenic

INTERPRETING THE RESULTS: The result of the breeding is some offspring in which all cells are transgenic—a genetically engineered animal has been produced.

Figure 16.11
A genetically engineered giant mouse (right) produced by the introduction of a rat growth hormone gene into the animal. A mouse of normal size is on the left.

R. L. Brinster, R. E. Hammer, School of Veterinary Medicine, University of Pennsylvania

Palmiter and Brinster next attempted to cure a genetic disorder by gene therapy. In this experiment, they were able to correct a genetic growth hormone deficiency that produces dwarf mice. They introduced a normal copy of the growth hormone gene into fertilized eggs taken from mutant dwarf mice and implanted them into a surrogate mother. The transgenic mouse pups grew to slightly larger than normal, demonstrating that the genetic defect in those mice had been corrected.

This sort of experiment, in which a gene is introduced into germ-line cells of an animal to correct a genetic disorder, is **germ-line gene therapy.** For ethical reasons, germ-line gene therapy is not permitted with humans. Instead, humans are treated with **somatic gene therapy,** in which genes are introduced into somatic cells (as described in the previous section).

The first successful use of somatic gene therapy with a human subject who had a genetic disorder was carried out in the 1990s by W. French Anderson and his colleagues at the National Institutes of Health (NIH). The subject was a young girl with *adenosine deaminase deficiency (ADA)*. Without the adenosine deaminase enzyme, white blood cells cannot mature (see Chapter 44); without normally functioning white blood cells, the body's immune response is so deficient that most children with ADA die of infections before reaching puberty. The researchers successfully introduced a functional ADA gene into mature white blood cells isolated from the patient. Those cells were reintroduced into the girl, and expression of the ADA gene provided a temporary cure for her ADA deficiency. The cure was not permanent because mature white blood cells, produced by differentiation of stem cells in the bone marrow, are nondividing cells with a finite lifetime. Therefore, the somatic gene therapy procedure has to be repeated every few months. Indeed, the subject of this example still receives periodic gene therapy to maintain the necessary levels of the ADA enzyme in her blood. In addition, she receives direct doses of the normal enzyme.

Successful somatic gene therapy has also been achieved for sickle cell disease. In December 1998, a 13-year-old boy's bone marrow cells were replaced with stem cells from the umbilical cord of an unrelated infant. The hope was that the stem cells would produce healthy bone marrow cells, the source of blood cells. The procedure worked, and the patient has been declared cured of the disease.

However, despite enormous efforts, human somatic gene therapy has not been the panacea people expected. Relatively little progress has been made since the first gene therapy clinical trial for ADA deficiency was described, and, in fact, there have been major setbacks. In 1999, for example, a teenage patient in a somatic gene therapy trial died as a result of a severe immune response to the viral vector being used to introduce a normal gene to correct his genetic deficiency. Furthermore, some children in gene therapy trials involving the use of retrovirus vectors to introduce genes into blood stem cells have developed a leukemia-like condition. In short, somatic gene therapy is not yet an effective treatment for human genetic disease, even though the approach has been successful in a number of cases to correct models of human genetic disorders in experimental mammals. Although no commercial human gene therapy product has been approved for use, research and clinical trials continue as scientists try to circumvent the difficulties.

Turning Domestic Animals into Protein Factories. Another successful application of genetic engineering turns animals into pharmaceutical factories for the production of proteins required to treat human diseases or other medical conditions. Most of these *pharming* projects, as they are called, engineer the animals to produce the desired proteins in milk, making the production, extraction, and purification of the proteins harmless to the animals.

One of the first successful applications of this approach was carried out with sheep engineered to produce a protein required for normal blood clotting in humans. The protein, called a *clotting factor,* is deficient in persons with one form of hemophilia, who require frequent injections of the factor to avoid bleeding to death from even minor injuries. Using DNA cloning techniques, researchers joined the gene encoding the normal form of the clotting factor to the promoter sequences of the β-lactoglobin gene, which encodes a protein secreted in milk, and introduced it into fertilized eggs. Those cells were implanted into a surrogate mother, and the transgenic sheep born were allowed to mature. The β-lactoglobin promoter controlling the clotting factor gene became activated in mammary gland cells of females, resulting in the production of clotting factor. The clotting factor was then secreted into the milk. Production in the milk is harmless to the sheep and yields the protein in a form that can easily be obtained and purified.

Other similar projects are under development to produce particular proteins in transgenic mammals. These include a protein to treat cystic fibrosis, collagen to correct scars and wrinkles, human milk proteins to be added to infant formulas, and normal hemoglobin for use as an additive to blood transfusions.

Producing Animal Clones. Making transgenic mammals is expensive and inefficient. And because only one copy of the transgene typically becomes incorporated into the treated cell, not all progeny of a transgenic animal inherit that gene. Scientists reasoned that an alternative to breeding a valuable transgenic mammal to produce progeny with the transgene would be to clone the mammal. Each clone would be identical to the original, including the expression of the transgene. That this is possible was shown in 1997 when two Scottish scientists, Ian Wilmut and Keith H. S. Campbell of the Roslin Institute, Edinburgh, announced that they had successfully cloned a sheep from a single somatic cell derived from an adult sheep **(Figure 16.12)**—the first mammalian clone made. For their experiment, the researchers fused a diploid cell derived from the mammary gland of a 6-year-old adult sheep with an unfertilized egg cell from which the nucleus had been removed. Signals from the egg cytoplasm triggered DNA replication and cell division, producing a cluster of cells derived from the mammary gland cell. The cluster was implanted into the uterus of an adult female sheep, where it developed into an embryo that grew to full term and was delivered as an apparently normal lamb, named Dolly. Their cloning success rate, however, was very low—Dolly represents less than 0.4% of the transgenic cells they made. Dolly developed to sexual maturity and produced four normal offspring. She was euthanized at age 6 after contracting a fatal, virus-induced lung disease that her cloners believe was unrelated to the cloning.

After the successful cloning experiment producing Dolly, many additional mammals have been cloned, including mice, goats, pigs, monkeys, rabbits, dogs, a male calf appropriately named Gene, and a domestic cat called *CC* (for *Copy Cat*).

Cloning farm animals has been so successful that several commercial enterprises now provide cloned copies of champion animals. One example is a clone of an American Holstein cow, Zita, who was the U.S. national champion milk producer for many years. Animal breeders estimate that there are now more than 100 cloned animals on American farms, and breeders plan to produce entire herds if government approval is granted.

The cloning of domestic animals has its drawbacks. Many cloning attempts fail, leading to the death of the transplanted embryos. Cloned animals often suffer from health defects from conditions such as birth defects and poor lung development. Genes may be lost during the cloning process or may be expressed abnormally in the cloned animal. For example, molecular

PA News Photo Library/AP Wide World Photos

Figure 16.12
Dolly, the cloned sheep.

studies have shown that the expression of perhaps hundreds of genes in the genomes of clones is regulated abnormally.

Genetic Engineering of Plants. Genetic engineering of plants has led to increased resistance to pests and disease; greater tolerance to heat, drought, and salinity; greater crop yields; faster growth; and resistance to herbicides. Another aim is to produce seeds with higher levels of amino acids. The essential amino acid lysine, for example, is present only in limited quantities in cereal grains such as wheat, rice, oats, barley, and corn; the seeds of legumes such as beans, peas, lentils, soybeans, and peanuts are deficient in the essential amino acids methionine or cysteine. Increasing the amounts of the deficient amino acids in plant seeds by genetic engineering would greatly improve the diet of domestic animals and human populations that rely on seeds as a primary food source. Efforts are also under way to increase the content of vitamins and minerals in crop plants.

Other possibilities for plant genetic engineering include plant pharming to produce pharmaceutical products. Plants are ideal for this purpose because they are primary producers at the bottom rung of the **food chain** and can be grown in huge numbers with maximum conservation of the sun's energy captured in photosynthesis.

Some plants, such as *Arabidopsis,* tobacco, potato, cabbage, and carrot, have special advantages for genetic engineering because individual cells can be removed from an adult, altered by the introduction of a desired gene, and then grown in cultures into a multicellular mass of cloned cells called a *callus.* Subsequently, roots, stems, and leaves develop in the callus, forming a young plant that can then be grown in containers or fields by the usual methods. In the plant, each cell contains the introduced gene. The gametes produced by the transgenic plants can then be used in crosses to produce

Gall ⎯

Stephen Wolfe, Molecular and Cellular Biology

Figure 16.13
A crown gall tumour on the trunk of a California pepper tree. The tumour, stimulated by genes introduced from the bacterium *Rhizobium radiobacter*, is the bulbous, irregular growth extending from the trunk.

offspring, some of which will have the transgene, as in the similar experiments with animals.

Methods Used to Insert Genes into Plants. Genes are inserted into plant cells by several techniques. One commonly used method takes advantage of a natural process that causes crown gall disease, which is characterized by bulbous, irregular growths—tumours, essentially—that can develop at wound sites on the trunks and limbs of deciduous trees **(Figure 16.13)**. Crown gall disease is caused by the bacterium *Rhizobium radiobacter* (formerly *Agrobacterium tumefaciens*, recently reclassified on the basis of genome analysis). This bacterium contains a large, circular plasmid called the **Ti (tumour inducing) plasmid.** The interaction between the bacterium and the plant cell it infects stimulates the excision of a segment of the Ti plasmid called *T DNA* (for transforming DNA), which then integrates into the plant cell's genome. Genes on the T DNA are then expressed; the products stimulate the transformed cell to grow and divide and therefore to produce a tumour. The tumours provide essential nutrients for the bacterium. The Ti plasmid is used as a vector for making transgenic plants in much the same way as bacterial plasmids are used as vectors to introduce genes into bacteria **(Figure 16.14)**.

Successful Plant Genetic Engineering Projects. An early visual demonstration of the successful use of genetic engineering techniques to produce a transgenic plant is the glowing tobacco plant **(Figure 16.15, p. 362)**. The transgenic plant contained luciferase, the gene for the firefly enzyme. When the plant was soaked in the substrate for the enzyme, it became luminescent.

The most widespread application of genetic engineering of plants involves the production of transgenic crops. Thousands of such crops have been developed and field tested, and many have been approved for commercial use. If you analyze the processed plant-based foods at a national supermarket chain, you will likely find that at least two-thirds contain transgenic plants.

In many cases, plants are modified to make them resistant to insect pests, viruses, or herbicides. Crops modified for insect resistance include corn, cotton, and potatoes. The most common approach to making plants resistant to insects is to introduce the gene from the bacterium *Bacillus thuringiensis* that encodes the *Bt* toxin, an organic pesticide. This toxin has been used in powder form to kill insects in agriculture for many years, and now transgenic plants making their own *Bt* toxin are resistant to specific groups of insects that feed on them. Millions of acres of crop plants planted in the United States and Canada are *Bt*-engineered varieties.

Virus infections cause enormous crop losses worldwide. Transgenic crops that are virus-resistant would be highly valuable to the agricultural community. There is some promise in this area. By some unknown process, transgenic plants expressing certain viral proteins become resistant to infections by whole viruses that contain those same proteins. Two virus-resistant genetically modified crops made so far are papaya and squash.

Several crops have also been engineered to become resistant to herbicides. For example, *glyphosate* (commonly known by its brand name, Roundup) is a highly potent herbicide that is widely used in weed control. The herbicide works by inhibiting a particular enzyme in the chloroplast. Unfortunately, it also kills crops. But transgenic crops have been made in which a bacterial form of the chloroplast enzyme has been added to the plants. The bacteria-derived enzyme is not affected by Roundup, and farmers who use these herbicide-resistant crops can spray fields of crops to kill weeds without killing the crops. Now most of the corn, soybean, canola, and cotton plants grown in North America are the genetically engineered, glyphosate-resistant ("Roundup-ready") varieties.

Crop plants are also being engineered to alter their nutritional qualities. For example, a strain of rice plants has been produced with seeds rich in β-carotene, a precursor of vitamin A, as well as iron **(Figure 16.16, p. 362)**. The new rice, which is given a yellow or golden colour by the carotene, may provide improved nutrition for the billions of people who depend on rice as a diet staple. In particular, the rice may help improve the nutrition of children younger than age 5 in southeast Asia, 70% of whom suffer from impaired vision because of vitamin A deficiency.

Plant pharming is also an active area both in university research labs and at biotechnology companies. Plant pharming involves the engineering of transgenic plants to produce medically valuable products. The approach is one described earlier: the gene for the product is cloned into a cloning vector adjacent to a promoter, in this case one active in plants, and the recombinant DNA molecule is introduced into plants. Products under development include vaccines for various bacterial and viral diseases, protease inhibitors to treat or prevent virus infections, collagen to treat scars and wrinkles, and aprotinin to reduce bleeding and clotting during heart surgery.

In contrast to animal genetic engineering, genetically altered plants have been widely developed and appear to be here to stay as mainstays of agriculture. But, as the next section discusses, both animal and plant genetic engineering have not proceeded without concerns.

16.2d DNA Technologies and Genetic Engineering Are a Subject of Public Concern

When recombinant DNA technology was developed in the early 1970s, researchers quickly recognized that in addition to the many anticipated benefits, there might be deleterious outcomes. One key concern at the time was that a bacterium carrying a recombinant DNA molecule might escape into the environment. Perhaps it could transfer that molecule to other bacteria and produce new, potentially harmful, strains. To address these concerns, the U.S. scientists who developed the technology drew up safety guidelines for recombinant DNA research in the United States. Adopted by the NIH, the guidelines listed the precautions to be used in the laboratory when constructing recombinant DNA molecules and included the design and use of host organisms that could survive only in growth media in the laboratory. Since that time, countless thousands of experiments involving recombinant DNA molecules have been done in laboratories around the world. Those experiments have shown that recombinant DNA manipulations can be done safely. Over time, therefore, the recombinant DNA guidelines have become more relaxed. Nonetheless, stringent regulations still exist for certain areas of recombinant DNA research that pose significant risk, such as cloning genes from highly pathogenic bacteria or viruses, or gene therapy experiments. In essence, as the risk increases, the research facility must increase its security and must obtain more levels of approval by peer scientist groups.

Guidelines for genetic engineering also extend to research in several areas that have been the subject of public concern and debate. Although the public does not seem to be very concerned about genetically engineered microorganisms, for example, those cleaning up oil spills and hazardous chemicals, it is concerned about possible problems with **genetically modified organisms (GMOs)** used as food. A GMO is a transgenic organism; the majority of GMOs are crop plants. Issues are the safety of GMO-containing food and the possible adverse effects of the GMOs to the environment, such as by interbreeding with natural species or by harming beneficial insect species. For example, could introduced genes providing herbicide or insect resistance move from crop plants into related weed species through cross-pollination, producing "super weeds" that might be difficult or impossible to control? *Bt*-expressing corn was originally thought to have adverse effects on monarch butterflies who fed on the

Figure 16.14
Using the Ti plasmid of *Rhizobium radiobacter* to produce transgenic plants.

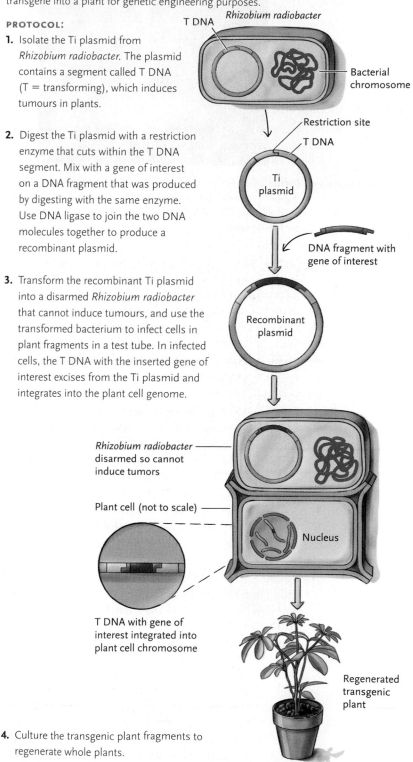

PURPOSE: To make transgenic plants. This technique is one way to introduce a transgene into a plant for genetic engineering purposes.

PROTOCOL:

1. Isolate the Ti plasmid from *Rhizobium radiobacter*. The plasmid contains a segment called T DNA (T = transforming), which induces tumours in plants.

2. Digest the Ti plasmid with a restriction enzyme that cuts within the T DNA segment. Mix with a gene of interest on a DNA fragment that was produced by digesting with the same enzyme. Use DNA ligase to join the two DNA molecules together to produce a recombinant plasmid.

3. Transform the recombinant Ti plasmid into a disarmed *Rhizobium radiobacter* that cannot induce tumours, and use the transformed bacterium to infect cells in plant fragments in a test tube. In infected cells, the T DNA with the inserted gene of interest excises from the Ti plasmid and integrates into the plant cell genome.

4. Culture the transgenic plant fragments to regenerate whole plants.

INTERPRETING THE RESULTS: The plant has been genetically engineered to contain a new gene. The transgenic plant will express a new trait based on that gene, perhaps resistance to an herbicide or the production of an insect toxin according to the goal of the experiment.

Figure 16.15
A genetically engineered tobacco plant, made capable of luminescence by the introduction of a firefly gene coding for the enzyme luciferase.

Kevin V. Wood

pollen. The most recent of a series of independent studies investigating this possibility has indicated that the risk to the butterflies is extremely low.

More broadly, different countries have reacted to GMOs in different ways. In Canada, transgenic crops are quite widely planted and harvested. Before commercialization, such GMOs are evaluated for potential risk by appropriate government regulatory agencies, including Health Canada, the Canadian Food Inspection Agency, and Environment Canada.

Political opposition to GMOs has been greater in Europe, dampening the use of transgenic crop plants in the fields and GMOs in food. In 1999, the European Union (EU) imposed a six-year moratorium on all GMOs, leading to a bitter dispute with the United States, Canada, and Argentina, the leading growers of transgenic crops. More recently, the EU has revised the GMO regulations in all member states. Basically, the EU has decided that using genetic engineering in agriculture and food production is permissible provided that the GMO or food containing it is safe for humans, animals, and the environment. All use of GMOs in the field or in food requires authorization following a careful review process.

Regular rice   Genetically engineered golden rice containing β-carotene

Dr. Jorge Mayer, Golden Rice Project

Figure 16.16
Rice genetically engineered to contain β-carotene.

On a global level, an international agreement, the **Cartagena Protocol on Biosafety**, "promotes biosafety by establishing practical rules and procedures for the safe transfer [between countries], handling and use of GMOs." Separate procedures have been set up for GMOs that are to be introduced into the environment and those that are to be used as food or feed or for processing. To date, several countries, mainly GMO exporters, have failed to ratify the protocol.

In sum, the use of DNA technologies in biotechnology has the potential for tremendous benefits to humankind. Such experimentation is not without risk, so for each experiment, researchers must assess that risk and make a judgment about whether to proceed and, if so, how to do so safely. Furthermore, agreed-upon guidelines and protocols should ensure a level of biosafety for researchers, consumers, politicians, and governments.

We now turn to the analysis of whole genomes.

STUDY BREAK

1. What are the principles of DNA fingerprinting?
2. What is a transgenic organism?
3. What is the difference between using germ-line cells and somatic cells for gene therapy?

16.3 Genome Analysis

The development of DNA technologies for analyzing genes and gene expression revolutionized experimental biology. DNA sequencing techniques (described in this section) have made it possible to analyze the sequences of cloned genes and genes amplified by PCR. Having the complete sequence of a gene aids researchers tremendously in unravelling how that gene functions. But a gene is only part of a genome. Researchers want to know about the organization of genes in a complete genome and how genes work together in networks to control life. Of particular interest, of course, is the human genome. The complete sequencing of the approximately 3 billion base-pair human genome—the Human Genome Project (HGP)—began in 1990. The task was completed in 2003 by an international consortium of researchers and by a private company, Celera Genomics. As part of the official HGP, for purposes of comparison, the genomes of several important model organisms commonly used in genetic studies were sequenced: *E. coli* (representing prokaryotes), the yeast *Saccharomyces cerevisiae* (representing single-celled eukaryotes), *Drosophila melanogaster* and *Caenorhabditis elegans* (the fruit fly and nematode worm, respectively, representing multicellular animals of moderate genome complexity), and *Mus musculus* (the house mouse, representing a mammal of genome complexity comparable to that of humans). In addition, the sequences of the genomes of many organisms beyond this list, including plants, have been completed or are in progress at this time. What researchers are learning from analyzing complete genomes is of enormous importance to our understanding of biology and the evolution of organisms.

16.3a DNA Sequencing Techniques Are Based on DNA Replication

DNA sequencing is the key technology for genome sequencing projects. DNA sequencing is also used on a smaller scale, for example, in determining the sequence of individual genes that have been cloned or amplified by PCR.

DNA sequencing was first developed in the late 1970s by Allan M. Maxam, a graduate student, and his mentor, Walter Gilbert of Harvard University; within a few years, another investigator, Frederick Sanger of Cambridge University, designed the method that is most used today. Gilbert and Sanger were awarded a Nobel Prize in 1980.

The Sanger method is based on the properties of nucleotides known as *dideoxyribonucleotides*—the method, therefore, is also called *dideoxy sequencing* **(Figure 16.17, p. 364).** Dideoxyribonucleotides have a single —H bound to the 3′ carbon of the deoxyribose sugar instead of the —OH normally appearing at this position in deoxyribonucleotides. DNA polymerases, the replication enzymes, recognize the dideoxyribonucleotides and place them in the DNA just as they do the normal deoxyribonucleotides. However, because a dideoxyribonucleotide has no 3′-OH group available for addition of the next base, replication of a nucleotide chain stops when one of these nucleotides is added to a growing nucleotide chain. (Remember from Section 13.3 that a 3′-OH group must be present at the growing end of a nucleotide chain for the next nucleotide to be added during DNA replication.) In a dideoxy sequencing reaction, researchers use a mixture of dideoxyribonucleotides and normal nucleotides, so that chain termination will occur randomly at each position where a particular nucleotide appears in the population of DNA molecules being replicated. Each chain-termination event generates a newly synthesized DNA strand that ends with the dideoxyribonucleotide; hence, for this particular strand, the base at the 3′ end is known, and because of base-pairing rules, the base on the template strand being sequenced is deduced. Once they know the base at the end of each terminated DNA strand, researchers can work out the complete sequence of the template DNA strand.

The dideoxy sequencing method can be used with any pure piece of DNA, such as a cloned DNA fragment or a fragment amplified by PCR. An unambiguous sequence of about 500 to 750 nucleotides can be obtained from each sequencing experiment.

16.3b Structural Genomics Determines the Complete DNA Sequence of Genomes

Genome analysis consists of two main areas: *structural genomics* and *functional genomics*. **Structural genomics** is the actual sequencing of genomes and the analysis of the nucleotide sequences to locate genes and other functionally important sequences within the genome. **Functional genomics** is the study of the functions of genes and of other parts of the genome. In the case of genes, this includes developing an understanding of the regulation of their expression, the proteins they encode, and the role played by the proteins in the organism's metabolic processes.

The most widely used method for sequencing a genome is the *whole-genome shotgun method* **(Figure 16.18, p. 365).** In this method, the entire genome is broken into thousands to millions of random, overlapping fragments, and each fragment is cloned and sequenced. The genome sequence then is assembled by computer on the basis of the sequence overlaps between fragments.

The first genome sequence reported, that of the bacterium *Haemophilus influenzae*, was determined using the whole-genome shotgun method by J. Craig Venter and his associates at Celera Genomics (the developers of the method). Originally, it was thought that the much larger genomes of eukaryotes would be too difficult to sequence using this method. But improvements in sequencing technologies and in the computer algorithms used to identify overlapping sequences have made it easier to assemble the segment sequences into the sequence of a whole genome. Whole-genome shotgun sequencing is now the method of choice for sequencing essentially any genome.

16.3c Functional Genomics Focuses on the Functions of Genes and Other Parts of the Genome

The genomes of a large number of viruses and more than 180 organisms have been sequenced, and those of more species are continually being added to the total. Among those already sequenced are the cytomegalovirus, bacteria including *E. coli*, various archaean species, and eukaryotes including the brewer's yeast *Saccharomyces cerevisiae*, the protozoan *Plasmodium falciparium* (the malarial parasite), the roundworm *Caenorhabditis elegans*, the plants *Arabidopsis thaliana* and rice, the fruit fly *Drosophila melanogaster*, the chicken, the mouse, the rat, the dog, the chimpanzee, and human. In fact, the entire diploid DNA sequence of two humans, J. Craig Venter and James Watson, has been determined.

Analysis of Genome Sequences. The complete genome sequence for an organism is basically a very long string of letters, which means little without further analysis.

Figure 16.17
Dideoxy (Sanger) method for sequencing DNA.

PURPOSE: Obtain the sequence of a piece of DNA, such as in gene sequencing or genome sequencing. The method is shown here with an automated sequencing system.

PROTOCOL:

1. A dideoxy sequencing reaction has the following components: the fragment of DNA to be sequenced (denatured to single strands); a DNA primer that will bind to the 3' end of the sequence to be determined; a mixture of the four deoxyribonucleotide precursors for DNA synthesis; and a mixture of the four dideoxyribonucleotides (dd) precursors, each labelled with a different fluorescent molecule, and DNA polymerase to catalyze the DNA synthesis reaction.

2. Synthesis of the new DNA strand is in the 5'→3' direction starting at the 3' end of the primer. New synthesis continues until a dideoxyribonucleotide is incorporated into the DNA instead of a normal deoxyribonucleotide. For a large population of template DNA strands, the dideoxy sequencing reaction produces a series of new strands, with lengths from one on up. At the 3' end of each new strand is the labelled dideoxyribonucleotide that terminated the synthesis.

3. The labelled strands produced by the reaction are separated by gel electrophoresis. The principle of separation is the same as for agarose gel electrophoresis described in Figure 16.8. But here it is necessary to discriminate between DNA strands that differ in length by one nucleotide, which agarose gels cannot do. In this case, therefore, a gel made of polyacrylamide is prepared in a capillary tube for separating the DNA fragments. As the bands of DNA fragments move near the bottom of the tube, a laser beam shining through the gel excites the fluorescent labels on each DNA fragment. The fluorescence is registered by a detector with the wavelength of the fluorescence indicating which of the four dideoxyribonucleotides is at the end of the fragment in each case.

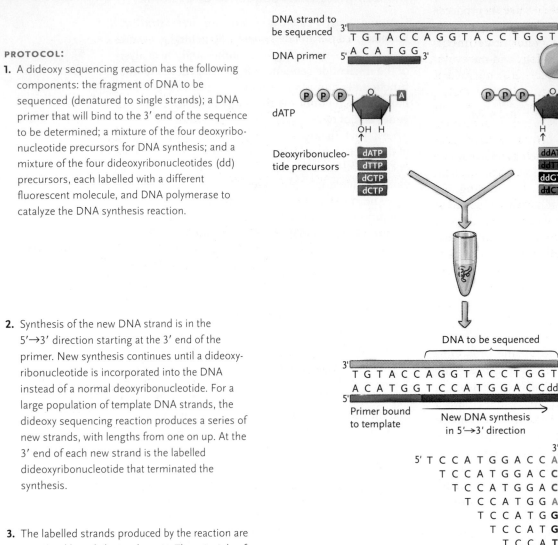

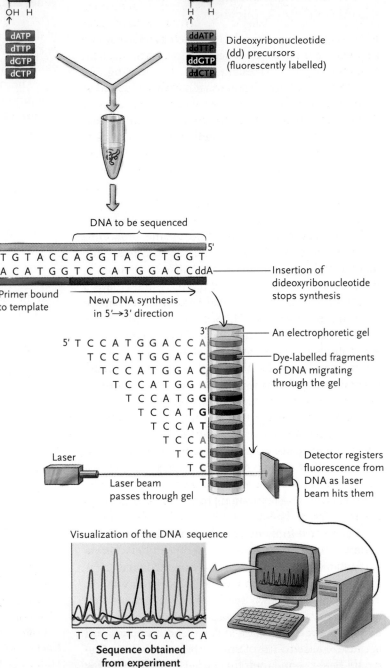

INTERPRETING THE RESULTS: The data from the laser system are sent to a computer that interprets which of the four possible fluorescent labels is at the end of each DNA strand. The results show the colours of the labels as the DNA bands passed the detector. They may be seen on the computer screen or in printouts. The sequence of the newly synthesized DNA, which is complementary to the template strand, is read from left (5') to right (3'). (The sequence shown here begins after the primer.)

Discovering the functions of genes and other parts of the genome is one important goal of this analysis. Most research is focused on the genes because they control the functions of cells and, therefore, of organisms. Functional genomics relies on laboratory experiments by molecular biologists and sophisticated computer analyses by researchers in the rapidly growing field of **bioinformatics**, which fuses biology with mathematics and computer science. Bioinformatics is used, for example, to find genes within a genomic sequence, align sequences in databases to determine the degree of matching, predict the structure and function of gene products, and postulate evolutionary relationships for sequences.

Protein-coding genes are of particular interest in genome analysis. Once a genome sequence is determined, researchers use computer algorithms to search both strands of the sequence for these genes. They identify possible protein-coding genes by searching for open reading frames, that is, a start codon (ATG, at the DNA level) in frame (separated by a multiple of three nucleotides) with one of the stop codons (TAG, TAA, or TGA at the DNA level). This process is easy for prokaryotic genomes, because the genes have no introns. In eukaryotic protein-coding genes, which typically have introns, more sophisticated algorithms are used to try to identify the junctions between exons and introns in scanning for open reading frames.

Each open reading frame found by computer analysis of a genome can be "translated" by computer to give the amino acid sequence of the protein it could encode. Researchers may then be able to assign a function to the open reading frame by performing a *sequence similarity search,* a computer-based comparison of a DNA or amino acid sequence with databases of sequences of known genes or proteins. That is, if an open reading frame or its protein product resembles those of a previously sequenced gene, the two genes are related in an evolutionary sense and are likely to have similar functions.

Many new features of genetic organization have been discovered, or previous conclusions reinforced, through the findings of genome sequencing. One of the more surprising discoveries is that the eukaryotic genomes sequenced to date contain large numbers of previously unknown genes, many more than scientists expected to find. In *Caenorhabditis,* for example, 12 000 of the 19 000 genes are of unknown function. Identifying these genes and their functions is one of the major challenges of contemporary molecular genetics.

Another revelation is the degree to which different organisms, some of them widely separated in evolutionary origins, contain similar genes. For example, even though the yeast *Saccharomyces* is a fungus separated from our species by millions of years of evolutionary history, about 2300 of its approximately 6000 genes are

Figure 16.18
Whole-genome shotgun sequencing.

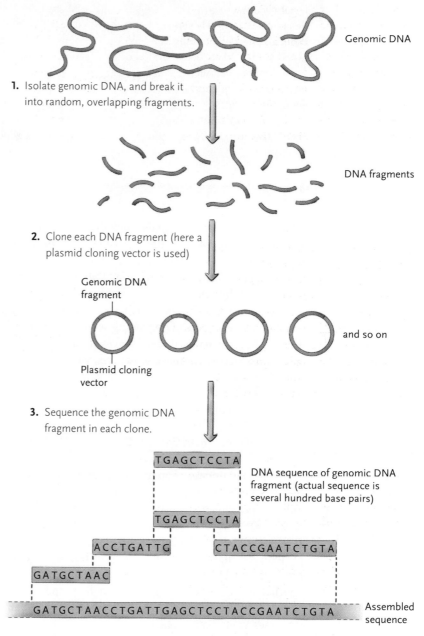

PURPOSE: Obtain the complete sequence of the genome of an organism.

PROTOCOL:

Genomic DNA

1. Isolate genomic DNA, and break it into random, overlapping fragments.

DNA fragments

2. Clone each DNA fragment (here a plasmid cloning vector is used)

Genomic DNA fragment

and so on

Plasmid cloning vector

3. Sequence the genomic DNA fragment in each clone.

TGAGCTCCTA

DNA sequence of genomic DNA fragment (actual sequence is several hundred base pairs)

TGAGCTCCTA

ACCTGATTG   CTACCGAATCTGTA

GATGCTAAC

GATGCTAACCTGATTGAGCTCCTACCGAATCTGTA   Assembled sequence

4. Enter the DNA sequences of the fragments into a computer program, to assemble overlapping sequences into the continuous sequences of each chromosome of the organism. This technique is analogous to taking 10 copies of a book that have been torn randomly into smaller sets of a few pages each and, by matching overlapping pages of the leaflets, assembling a complete copy of the book with the pages in the correct order.

INTERPRETING THE RESULTS: The method generates the complete sequence of the genome of an organism.

Michael Smith, University of British Columbia

The discipline of genetics was originally built on the study of rare, naturally occurring mutations. Researchers routinely screened thousands (or sometimes millions) of individuals to collect a handful of useful mutations. Agents that increased the frequency of mutations were often used, but they tended to be nonspecific, and the isolation of particular mutations in specific genes remained a lottery with unfavourable odds.

Michael Smith changed all of that in the late 1970s by demonstrating that *in vitro* DNA synthesis techniques could be used to create mutated sequences. This method of site-directed mutagenesis allowed specific mutations to be introduced into any given DNA sequence. For the first time, geneticists could create the exact changes they were interested in. Smith's work was recognized with the 1993 Nobel Prize in Chemistry.

In addition to his legacy as a scientist, Michael Smith was a generous philanthropist and a strong supporter of public education in science.

related to those of mammals, including many genes that control progress through the cell cycle. The similarities are so close that the yeast and human versions of many genes can be interchanged with little or no effect on cell functions in either organism.

The sequences also confirm that eukaryotic genomes contain large numbers of noncoding sequences, most of them in the form of repeated sequences of various lengths and numbers. Most of these sequences, which make up from about 25% to 50% of the total genomic DNA in different eukaryotic species, have no determined function at this point in time.

Features of the Human Genome Sequence. The human genome sequence consists of 3.2 *billion* base pairs. Until the genome was sequenced, researchers expected that human cells might contain as many as 100 000 different protein-coding genes. The best current estimate is 20 000 to 25 000 protein-coding genes. However, although the number of protein-coding genes is unexpectedly small, the total number of different proteins produced in humans is much greater and probably approaches the 100 000 figure originally proposed for genes. The additional proteins arise through such processes as alternative splicing during mRNA processing (see Section 14.3) and differences in protein processing (discussed further in the following sections).

All the protein-coding sequences occupy less than 2% of the human genome. Introns—the noncoding spacers in genes—occupy another 24% of the genome. The rest of the DNA, almost three-quarters of the genome, occupies the spaces between genes. Some of this intergenic DNA is functional and includes regulatory sequences such as promoters and enhancers, but much of it, more than 50% of the total genome, consists of repeated sequences that have no known function.

Completing the human genome sequence is only the beginning of human genomics. The next steps are to determine the functions of the unknown genes and of the sequence elements in intergenic regions. This *data mining*, as it is called, may answer fundamental questions about genome organization and the mechanisms controlling genes in development and cell differentiation. Genes related to human health and disease, including cancer, are of particular interest. The analysis of these disease-related genes may suggest methods to predict individual susceptibility to diseases and may possibly lead to means for their diagnosis and treatment.

On an even larger scale, the human genome is being compared with the genomes of other species to determine the molecular basis of differences in anatomy, physiology, and developmental patterns between species. Ultimately, species comparisons may reveal the mutational changes underlying the evolution of our species and many others. This area of genomics is known as *comparative genomics*.

There are bioethics issues concerning the human genome. To address those issues, the U.S. Department of Energy and the NIH have funded studies of the ethical, legal, and social issues surrounding the availability of genetic information from human genome research. The following are among the questions being looked at: Who should have access to personal genetic information, and how should it be used? To what extent should genetic information be private and confidential? How will genetic tests be evaluated and regulated? How can people be informed sufficiently about the genetic information from genomic analysis so that they can make informed personal medical choices? Does a set of genes predispose a person's behaviour, and can the person control that behaviour?

Studying Differential Gene Activity in Entire Genomes with DNA Microarrays. As part of genome research, investigators are interested in comparing which genes are active in different cell types of humans and other organisms, and tracking the changes in total gene activity in the same cell types as development progresses. In some cases, the researcher wants to know whether or not particular genes are being expressed, and in other cases how the level of expression varies in different circumstances. This research has been revolutionized by a technique using **DNA microarrays**. The microarrays are also called **DNA chips** for short because the techniques used to "print" the arrays resemble those used to lay out electronic circuits on a computer chip. The surface of a DNA chip is divided into a microscopic grid of about 60 000 spaces. On each space of the grid, a computerized system deposits a microscopic spot containing about 10 000 000 copies of a DNA probe about 20 nucleotides long.

Studies of gene activity using DNA microarrays involve comparing gene expression under a defined experimental condition with expression under a reference (control) condition. For instance, DNA microarrays can be used to answer basic biological questions, such as: How does gene expression change when a cell goes from a resting state (reference condition) to a dividing state (experimental condition). In other words: how is gene expression different in different stages of development? DNA microarrays can also be used to address many questions of medical significance, such as How are genes differentially expressed in normal cells and cells of various cancers? In these experiments, investigators might focus on which genes are active and inactive under the two conditions or on how the levels of expression of genes change under the two conditions.

Figure 16.19 (p. 368) shows how a DNA microarray is used to compare gene expression in normal cells and in cancer cells in humans. mRNAs are isolated from each cell type, and cDNAs are made from them, incorporating different fluorescent labels: green for one, red for the other. The two cDNAs are mixed and added to the DNA chip, where they hybridize with any complementary probes. A laser locates and quantifies the green and red fluorescence, enabling a researcher to see which genes are expressed in the cells and, for those that are expressed, to quantify differences in gene expression between the two cell types (see Interpreting the Results in Figure 16.19). The results can help researchers understand how the cancer develops and progresses.

DNA microarrays are also used to screen individuals for particular mutations. To detect mutations, the probes spotted onto the chip include probes for the normal sequence of the genes of interest along with probes for sequences of all known mutations. A fluorescent spot at a site on the chip printed with a probe for a given mutation immediately shows the presence of the mutation in the individual. Such a test is currently used to screen patients for whether they carry any one of a number of mutations of the *breast cancer 1* (*BRCA1*) gene known to be associated with the possible development of breast cancer.

16.3d Studying the Array of Expressed Proteins Is the Next Level of Genomic Analysis

Given that proteins are largely responsible for cell function, and therefore for all of an organism's functions, genome research also includes the analysis of the proteins that are encoded by a genome. The term **proteome** has been coined to refer to the complete set of proteins that can be expressed by an organism's genome. A *cellular proteome* is a subset of those proteins, the collection of proteins found in a particular cell type under a particular set of environmental conditions.

The study of the proteome is the field of **proteomics.** The number of possible proteins encoded by the genome is larger than the number of protein-coding genes in the genome, at least in eukaryotes. In eukaryotes, alternative splicing of gene transcripts and variation in protein processing means that expression of a gene may yield more than one protein product. Therefore, proteomics is a more challenging area of research than is genomics.

The two major immediate goals of proteomics are to determine (1) the number and structure of proteins in the proteome, and (2) the functional interactions between the proteins. The interactions are particularly important because they help us understand how proteins work together to determine the phenotype of the cell. For instance, if a particular set of interacting proteins characterized a lung tumour cell, then drugs could be developed that specifically target the interactions.

What are the tools of proteomics? For many years, it has been possible to separate and identify proteins by gel electrophoresis (using polyacrylamide to make the gels, the same material used for separating DNA fragments in DNA sequencing) or mass spectrometry. However, to study an entire cellular proteome, many more proteins must be analyzed simultaneously than is possible with either of those techniques. A big step in that direction is the development of **protein microarrays (protein chips)**, which are similar in concept to DNA microarrays. For example, one type of protein microarray involves binding antibodies prepared against different proteins to different locations on the protein chip. An antibody for a foreign substance, such as a protein, is generated by the immune system of an animal that has been injected with that substance. The antibody is isolated from the blood of that animal and can be used to bind specifically to the protein in experiments. Proteins are isolated from cells, labelled, and then pumped over the surface of the protein microarray. Each labelled protein binds to the antibody for that protein. After washing off excess proteins, the protein microarray is analyzed much as for DNA microarrays to determine where the proteins bound and to quantify that binding. With this technique, a researcher can quantify proteins in different cell types and different tissues. Researchers can also compare proteins under different conditions, such as during differentiation, or

Figure 16.19
DNA microarray analysis of gene expression levels.

PURPOSE: DNA microarrays can be used in various experiments, including comparing the levels of gene expression in two different tissues, as illustrated here. The power of the technique is that the entire set of genes in a genome can be analyzed simultaneously.

PROTOCOL:

Normal cells (reference) Cancer cells (experimental)

mRNA

cDNA

Each spot has a
different probe

1. Isolate mRNAs from a control cell type (here, normal cells) and an experimental cell type (here, cancer cells).

2. Prepare cDNA libraries from each mRNA sample. For the normal cell (control) library use nucleotides with a green fluorescent label, and for the cancer cell (experimental) library use nucleotides with a red fluorescent label.

3. Denature the cDNAs to single strands, mix them, and pump them across the surface of a DNA microarray containing a set of single-stranded probes representing every protein-coding gene in the human genome. The probes are spotted on the surface, with each spot containing a probe for a different gene. Allow the labelled cDNAs to hybridize with the gene probes on the surface of the chip, and then wash excess cDNAs off.

4. Locate and quantify the fluorescence of the labels on the hybridized cDNAs with a laser detection system.

Gene expressed
in both cell types

Gene expressed
in normal
cells only

Colored spots are
where labelled cDNAs
have hybridized

Gene expressed in
cancer cells only

Actual DNA microarray result

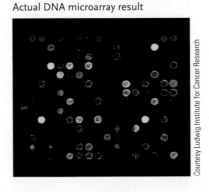

Courtesy Ludwig Institute for Cancer Research

INTERPRETING THE RESULTS: The coloured spots on the microarray indicate where the labelled cDNAs have bound to the gene probes attached to the chip and, therefore, which genes were active in normal and/or cancer cells. Moreover, we can quantify the gene expression in the two cell types by the colour detected. A purely green spot indicates the gene was active in the normal cell, but not in the cancer cell. A purely red spot indicates the gene was active in the cancer cell, but not in the normal cell. A yellow spot indicates the gene was equally active in the two cell types, and other colours tell us the relative levels of gene expression in the two cell types. For this particular experiment, we would be able to see how many genes have altered expression in the cancer cells, and exactly how their expression was changed.

with and without a particular disease condition, or with and without a particular drug treatment. In the future, we can expect protein arrays to become routine for studying cellular proteomes.

Overall, taking an "omics" approach to biology—considering all of the genes, or all of the proteins, or all of the mRNA, or all of the interactions between these components in a system—reveals a picture of complexity that was only glimpsed through past studies of each isolated component. This more holistic understanding extends beyond individual cells or organisms to consider relationships to the populations, communities, and ecosystems in which they reside.

STUDY BREAK

1. How are possible protein-coding genes identified in a genome sequence of a bacterium? Of a mammal?
2. What are the steps in whole-genome shotgun cloning?

UNANSWERED QUESTIONS

This chapter leaves us with two big questions.

First, how much diversity is out there?
Metagenomic studies increase the number of known genes by leaps and bounds each year. Will we ever know them all? Leaving aside genes, will we ever even find all of the different organisms and viruses on the planet?

Second, how can this diversity be used to our benefit?
In just over 50 years since the structure of DNA was published by Watson and Crick, scientists have learned to cut it, paste it, amplify it, sequence it, and synthesize it "from scratch." These technologies enable the creation of "custom-designed" organisms with novel qualities or abilities. The challenge will be in determining how to effectively apply these tools toward some of the significant problems facing the world in the coming years.

Review

Go to CENGAGENOW™ at http://hed.nelson.com/ to access quizzing, animations, exercises, articles, and personalized homework help.

16.1 DNA Cloning

- Producing multiple copies of genes by cloning is a common first step for studying the structure and function of genes or for manipulating genes. Cloning involves cutting genomic DNA and a cloning vector with the same restriction enzyme, joining the fragments to produce recombinant plasmids, and introducing those plasmids into a living cell such as a bacterium, where replication of the plasmid takes place (see Figures 16.1–16.3).

- A clone containing a gene of interest may be identified among a population of clones by using DNA hybridization with a labelled nucleic acid probe (see Figure 16.4).

- A genomic library is a collection of clones that contains a copy of every DNA sequence in the genome. A cDNA (complementary DNA) library is the entire collection of cloned cDNAs made from the mRNAs isolated from a cell. A cDNA library contains only sequences from the genes that are active in the cell when the mRNAs are isolated.

- PCR amplifies a specific target sequence in DNA, such as a gene, defined by a pair of primers. PCR increases DNA quantities by successive cycles of denaturing the template DNA, annealing the primers, and extending the primers in a DNA synthesis reaction catalyzed by DNA polymerase; with each cycle, the amount of DNA doubles (see Figure 18.5).

16.2 Applications of DNA Technologies

- Recombinant DNA and PCR techniques are used in DNA molecular testing for human genetic disease mutations. One approach exploits restriction site differences between normal and mutant alleles of a gene that create restriction fragment length polymorphisms (RFLPs) detectable by DNA hybridization with a labelled nucleic acid probe (see Figures 16.7 and 16.8).

- Human DNA fingerprints are produced from a number of loci in the genome characterized by tandemly repeated sequences that vary in number in all individuals (except identical twins). To produce a fingerprint, the PCR is used to amplify the region of genomic DNA for each locus, and the lengths of the PCR products indicate the alleles an individual has for the repeated sequences at each locus. DNA fingerprints are widely used to establish paternity, ancestry, or criminal guilt (see Figure 16.9).

- Genetic engineering is the introduction of new genes or genetic information to alter the genetic makeup of humans, other animals, plants, and microorganisms such as bacteria and yeast. Genetic engineering primarily aims to correct hereditary defects, improve domestic animals and crop plants, and provide proteins for medicine, research, and other applications (see Figures 16.10, 16.11, and 16.14).

- Genetic engineering has enormous potential for research and applications in medicine, agriculture, and industry. Potential risks include unintended damage to living organisms or the environment.

16.3 Genome Analysis

- Genome analysis consists of two main areas: structural genomics, the sequencing of genomes and the identification of the genes the sequences contain, and functional genomics, the study of the function of genes and other parts of the genome.

- Sequencing a genome involves a replication reaction with a DNA template, a DNA primer, the four normal deoxyribonucleotides, and a mixture of four dideoxyribonucleotides, each labelled with a different fluorescent tag, and DNA polymerase. Replication stops at any place in the sequence in which a dideoxyribonucleotide is substituted for the normal deoxyribonucleotide. The lengths of the terminated DNA chains and the label on them indicate the overall sequence of the DNA chain being sequenced (see Figure 16.17).

- The whole-genome shotgun method of sequencing a genome involves breaking up the entire genome into random, overlapping fragments, cloning each fragment, determining the sequence of the fragment in each clone, and using computer algorithms to assemble overlapping sequences into the sequence of the complete genome (see Figure 16.18).

- Once a gene is sequenced, the sequence of the protein encoded in a prokaryotic gene can be deduced by reading the coding portion of the gene three nucleotides at a time, starting at the AUG codon that indicates the beginning of a coding sequence.

- Complete genome sequences have been obtained for many viruses, a large number of prokaryotes, and many eukaryotes, including the human. The sequences have revealed that all eukaryotes share related gene sequences, and they have also revealed a significant proportion of genes whose functions are not presently known.

- Having the complete genome of an organism makes it possible to study the expression of all of the genes in the genome simultaneously, including comparing gene expression in two different cell types. The DNA microarray (or DNA chip) is typically used for the comparison; this technique can provide information about which genes are active in the two cell types, as well as relative levels of expression of those genes (see Figure 16.19).

- Proteomics is the study of the complete set of proteins in an organism or in a particular cell type. Protein numbers, protein structure, and protein interactions are all topics of proteomics.

- Systems biology combines data derived from genomics, proteomics, and other sources of information. Using sophisticated quantitative analysis, it seeks to model the total array of interactions responsible for an organism's form and function.

Questions

Self-Test Questions

1. Using cDNA is associated with which of the following?
   a. Introns can be identified and sequenced by this method.
   b. It measures both active and inactive DNA.
   c. Promoter regions can be identified by this method.
   d. One can identify start and stop regions by this method.
   e. One can identify active mRNA and make a complementary DNA sequence to the mRNA.

2. Restriction endonucleases, ligases, plasmids, viral or yeast vectors, electrophoretic gels, and a bacterial gene resistant to an antibiotic are all required for:
   a. dideoxyribonucleotide analysis.
   b. PCR.
   c. DNA cloning.
   d. DNA fingerprinting.
   e. DNA sequencing.

3. The PCR technique is distinguished from other processes discussed in this chapter by the use of:
   a. primers.
   b. DNA.
   c. RNA.
   d. Taq polymerase.
   e. the four nucleoside triphosphates.

4. Restriction fragment length polymorphisms:
   a. are produced by reaction with restriction endonucleases and are detected by Southern blot analysis.
   b. are of the same length for mutant and normal β-globin alleles.
   c. determine the sequence of bases in a DNA fragment.
   d. have in their middle short fragments of DNA that are palindromic.
   e. are used as vectors.

5. DNA fingerprinting:
   a. compares one stretch of the same DNA between two or more people.
   b. measures different lengths of DNA from many repeating noncoding regions for comparison between two or more people.
   c. requires the largest DNA lengths to run the greatest distance on a gel.
   d. requires amplification after the gels are run.
   e. can easily differentiate DNA between identical twins.

6. Dolly, a sheep, was an example of reproductive (germ line) cloning. Required to perform this process was:
   a. implantation of uterine cells from one strain into the mammary gland of another.
   b. the fusion of the mammary cell from one strain with an enucleated egg of another strain.
   c. the fusion of an egg from one strain with the egg of a different strain.
   d. the fusion of an embryonic diploid cell with an adult haploid cell.
   e. the fusion of two nucleated mammary cells from two different strains.

7. Which of the following statements is NOT true for somatic cell gene therapy?
   a. White blood cells can be used.
   b. Somatic cells are cultured, and the desired DNA is introduced into them.
   c. Cells with the introduced DNA are returned to the body.
   d. The technique is still very experimental.
   e. The inserted genes are passed on to the offspring.

8. The sequence of the human genome
   a. was obtained by sequencing overlapping DNA fragments.
   b. revealed far more genes than expected.
   c. revealed 3 trillion base pairs.
   d. used techniques not applicable to mapping other species.
   e. revealed 250 000 protein-coding genes.

9. Sanger's DNA sequencing technique:
   a. uses dideoxyribonucleotides to make new full-length strands of DNA.
   b. is based on cellular transcription.
   c. requires an RNA template, an RNA primer, RNA polymerase, reverse transcriptase, and the dideoxyribonucleotides, ddATP, ddUTP, ddCTP, and ddGTP.
   d. places the RNA template to be sequenced on a gel and then adds the other ingredients from (c).
   e. is based on DNA replication.

10. A microarray could be used to
    a. sequence DNA from several chromosomes in one individual.
    b. synthesize multiple copies of DNA from several sources.
    c. propagate human germ-line cells for cloning.
    d. compare coding DNA from a patient's normal lung cells with coding DNA from his cancerous lung cells.
    e. determine proteins that are expressed under certain environmental conditions.

Questions for Discussion

1. Do you think that genetic engineering is worth the risk? Who do you think should decide whether genetic engineering experiments and projects should be carried out: scientists, judges, politicians?

2. Do you think that human germ-line cells should be modified by genetic engineering to cure birth defects? To increase intelligence or beauty?

3. Write a paragraph supporting genetic engineering and one arguing against it. Which argument carries more weight, in your opinion?

4. What should juries know to interpret DNA evidence? Why might juries sometimes ignore DNA evidence?

5. A forensic scientist obtained a small DNA sample from a crime scene. To examine the sample, he increased its quantity by PCR. He estimated that there were 50 000 copies of the DNA in his original sample. Derive a simple formula and calculate the number of copies he will have after 15 cycles of PCR.

6. A market puts out a bin of tomatoes that have outstanding colour, flavour, and texture. A sign posted above them identifies them as genetically engineered produce. Most shoppers pick unmodified tomatoes in an adjacent bin, even though they are pale, mealy, and nearly tasteless. Which tomatoes would you pick? Why?

7. Suppose a biotechnology company has developed a GMO, a transgenic plant that expresses *Bt* toxin. The company sells its seeds to a farmer under the condition that the farmer may plant the seed, but not collect seed from the plants that grow and use it to produce crops in the subsequent season. The seeds are expensive, and the farmer buys seeds from the company only once. How could the company show experimentally that the farmer has violated the agreement and is using seeds collected from the first crop to grow the next crop?

The Chemical and Physical Foundations of Biology

Measurement and Scale

The SI System of Measurement

The International System of Units is the most widely used system of measurement in the world. Its abbreviation, *SI,* is from the French Système International d'Unités. It was adopted by the eleventh General Conference of Weights and Measures in 1960 and represents the latest modification of the metric system, which was first implemented by the French National Assembly in 1790.

The SI system uses seven base units, each of which measures or describes a different kind of physical quantity. Each unit is strictly defined, although the defintions have been modified (and made more accurate) over time. As an example, the metre was originally defined by the French Academy of Sciences as the length between two marks on a platinum–iridium bar, which was designed to represent 1/10 000 000 of the distance from the equator to the North Pole through Paris. This definition was changed in 1983 by the International Bureau of Weights and Measures as the distance travelled by light in absolute vacuum in 1/299 792 458 of a second.

The SI system also uses a series of prefix names and prefix symbols to form the names and symbols of the decimal multiples of the base SI units. Note that the base unit for mass is the kilogram, not the gram. One kg = 10^3 g. This list has been extended several times: prefixes now range from yotta, at 10^{24} (one septillion), to yocto, at 10^{-24} (one septillionth).

Factor	Prefix	Symbol	Factor	Prefix	Symbol
10^{24}	yotta	Y	10^{-1}	deci	d
10^{21}	zetta	Z	10^{-2}	centi	c
10^{18}	exa	E	10^{-3}	milli	m
10^{15}	peta	P	10^{-6}	micro	μ
10^{12}	tera	T	10^{-9}	nano	n
10^9	giga	G	10^{-12}	pico	p
10^6	mega	M	10^{-15}	femto	f
10^3	kilo	k	10^{-18}	atto	a
10^2	hecto	h	10^{-21}	zepto	z
10^1	deca	da	10^{-24}	yocto	y

The Seven Base Units of the SI System

Name	Symbol	Quantity
metre	m	length
kilogram	kg	mass
second	s	time
ampere	A	electric current
kelvin	K	temperature
mole	mol	amount of substance
candela	cd	luminous intensity

Derived SI Units

Several other units have been derived from combinations of the seven base units of measure. Three of the more common concern units of force (newton), pressure (pascal), and energy or heat (joule). The measurement of temperature in degrees Celsius is also considered a derived unit, even though one Celsius degree is the same size as one kelvin. However, 0°C = 273.16 K (note that no degree symbol is used when expressing temperature in kelvin).

Name	Symbol	Quantity	Expression
newton	N	force	$m \cdot kg \cdot s^{-2}$
pascal	Pa	pressure	$N \cdot m^{-2}$
joule	J	energy and work	$N \cdot m$

Non-SI Units in Common Usage

A number of units not derived from the base SI units are accepted for use with SI units.

Name	Symbol	Value in SI Units
minute	min	60 s
hour	h	3600 s
day	d	86 400 s
litre	L	$1 dm^3 = 10^{-3} m^3$
ångström	Å	10^{-10} m
calorie, a measure of food energy*	cal	4.184 J
unified atomic mass unit or Dalton**	u or Da	$\sim 1.66054 \times 10^{-24}$ kg

*One food calorie = 1 Cal = 1000 cal
**Value determined experimentally to be one-twelfth of the mass of an unbound atom of carbon-12.

Why Everyone Should Use SI Units

In December 1998, NASA launched the Mars Climate Orbiter on a mission to study the Martian weather and climate. As it approached Mars, the spacecraft received instructions from flight control on Earth to fire thruster engines to enter into a proper orbit about 140 to 150 km above the Martian surface. However, as it approached the planet, a navigation error caused the spacecraft to descend into an orbit of only 57 km above the surface. The spacecraft was soon destroyed by the heat caused by atmospheric friction.

The review of the incident found that the root cause was a mix-up between the use of SI units and an older system of measure, imperial units (e.g., inches, feet, and pounds). More specifically, the software that was used to control the thruster engines of the spacecraft from the ground was written using the imperial unit of force, the pound-force, whereas onboard the spacecraft, information was interpreted in terms of newtons, the metric unit of force. Since 1 pound-force equals about 4.45 newtons, instructions from the ground were thus multiplied by 4.45.

The total cost of the mission was approximately $327 million.

Scale in Biology

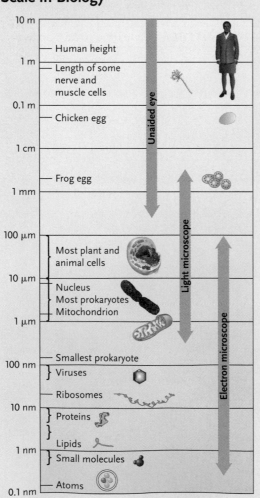

The Organization of Matter

Any substance in the universe that has mass and occupies space is defined as **matter.** The basic scientific concepts that explain how matter is organized in biological systems are no different from those for nonliving forms of matter. Living organisms are built from the same chemistry building blocks as nonliving systems and abide by the same laws of chemistry. Because of this, a basic understanding of these chemistry principles is important for our understanding of how biological systems operate.

Elements and Compounds

All matter in the universe—anything that occupies space and has mass—is composed of elements. An element is a pure substance that cannot be broken down into simpler substances by ordinary chemical or physical techniques. Ninety-two different elements occur naturally on Earth, and more than 15 artificial elements have been synthesized in the laboratory.

Living organisms are composed of about 25 elements, with only 4—carbon, hydrogen, oxygen, and nitrogen—accounting for more than 96% of the weight of living organisms. Seven other elements—calcium, phosphorus, potassium, sulphur, sodium, chlorine, and magnesium—contribute most of the remaining 4%. Nine additional elements occur in organisms in quantities so small (<0.01%) that they are known as **trace elements.** The proportions by mass of different elements differ markedly in seawater, the human body, a fruit, and Earth's crust.

Molecules whose component atoms are different (such as carbon dioxide) are called compounds. The chemical and physical properties of compounds are typically distinct from those of their atoms or elements. For example, we all know that water is a liquid at room temperature. We also know that water does not burn. However, the properties of the individual elements of water—hydrogen and oxygen—are quite different. Hydrogen and oxygen are gases at room temperature, and both are highly reactive.

Atoms combined chemically in fixed numbers and ratios form the molecules of living and nonliving matter. For example, the oxygen we breathe is a molecule formed from the chemical combination of two oxygen atoms; a molecule of the carbon dioxide that we exhale contains one carbon atom and two oxygen atoms. Because carbon dioxide is a molecule consisting of different elements, it is referred to as a compound.

Percentage Composition

Seawater		Human		Pumpkin		Earth's crust	
Oxygen	88.3	Oxygen	65.0	Oxygen	85.0	Oxygen	46.6
Hydrogen	11.0	Carbon	18.5	Hydrogen	10.7	Silicon	27.7
Chlorine	1.9	Hydrogen	9.5	Carbon	3.3	Aluminum	8.1
Sodium	1.1	Nitrogen	3.3	Potassium	0.34	Iron	5.0
Magnesium	0.1	Calcium	2.0	Nitrogen	0.16	Calcium	3.6
Sulphur	0.09	Phosphorus	1.1	Phosphorus	0.05	Sodium	2.8
Potassium	0.04	Potassium	0.35	Calcium	0.02	Potassium	2.6
Calcium	0.04	Sulphur	0.25	Magnesium	0.01	Magnesium	2.1
Carbon	0.003	Sodium	0.15	Iron	0.008	Other elements	1.5
Silicon	0.0029	Chlorine	0.15	Sodium	0.001		
Nitrogen	0.0015	Magnesium	0.05	Zinc	0.0002		
Strontium	0.0008	Iron	0.004	Copper	0.0001		
		Iodine	0.0004				

Steve Lissau/Rainbow

Jack Carey

Atomic Structure

Elements are composed of individual atoms—the smallest units that retain the chemical and physical properties of an element. Any given element has only one type of atom that is identified by a standard one- or two-letter symbol. The element carbon is identified by the single letter C, which stands for both the carbon atom and the element.

Each atom consists of an **atomic nucleus**, surrounded by one or more smaller, fast-moving particles called electrons. All atomic nuclei contain one

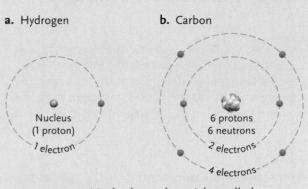

a. Hydrogen

Nucleus
(1 proton)

1 electron

b. Carbon

6 protons
6 neutrons

2 electrons

4 electrons

Atomic Number and Mass Number of the Most Common Elements in Living Organisms			
Element	Symbol	Atomic Number	Mass Number of the Most Common Form
Hydrogen	H	1	1
Carbon	C	6	12
Nitrogen	N	7	14
Oxygen	O	8	16
Sodium	Na	11	23
Magnesium	Mg	12	24
Phosphorus	P	15	31
Sulphur	S	16	32
Chlorine	Cl	17	35
Potassium	K	19	39
Calcium	Ca	20	40
Iron	Fe	26	56
Iodine	I	53	127

or more positively charged particles called protons. The number of protons in the nucleus of each kind of atom is referred to as the **atomic number**. This number does not vary and thus specifically identifies the atom. The smallest atom, hydrogen, has a single proton in its nucleus, so its atomic number is 1. The heaviest naturally occurring atom, uranium, has 92 protons in its nucleus and therefore has an atomic number of 92. Similarly, carbon with six protons, nitrogen with seven protons, and oxygen with eight protons have atomic numbers of 6, 7, and 8, respectively.

With one exception, the nuclei of all atoms also contain uncharged particles called neutrons, which occur in variable numbers approximately equal to the number of protons. The single exception is the most common form of hydrogen, which has a nucleus that contains only a single proton.

A neutron and a proton have almost the same mass, about 1.66×10^{-24} grams (g). This mass is defined as a standard unit, the dalton. Atoms are assigned a **mass number** based on the total number of protons and neutrons in the atomic nucleus. Electrons are ignored in determinations of atomic mass because the mass of an electron is very small.

Isotopes

All atoms of a specific element have the same number of protons, but they may differ in the number of neutrons. These distinct forms of the atoms of an element that have the same atomic number but have different atomic masses are called isotopes.

The nuclei of some isotopes are unstable and break down, or *decay,* giving off particles of matter and energy that can be detected as radioactivity. The decay transforms the unstable, radioactive isotope—called a **radioisotope**—into an atom of another element. The decay continues at a steady, clocklike rate, with a constant proportion of the radioisotope breaking down at any instant. The rate of decay is not affected by chem-

ical reactions or environmental conditions such as temperature or pressure. For example, the carbon isotope ^{14}C is unstable and undergoes radioactive decay in which one of its neutrons splits into a proton and an electron. The electron is ejected from the nucleus, but the proton is retained, giving a new total of seven protons and seven neutrons, which is characteristic of the most common form of nitrogen. Thus, the decay transforms the carbon atom into an atom of nitrogen.

Because unstable isotopes decay at a clocklike rate, they can be used to estimate the age of organic material, rocks, or fossils that contain them. These techniques have been vital in dating animal remains and tracing evolutionary lineages. Isotopes are also

continued on next page

Isotopes of hydrogen

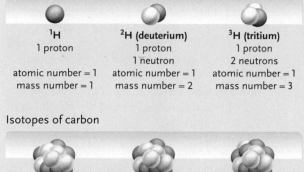

¹H	²H (deuterium)	³H (tritium)
1 proton	1 proton	1 proton
	1 neutron	2 neutrons
atomic number = 1	atomic number = 1	atomic number = 1
mass number = 1	mass number = 2	mass number = 3

Isotopes of carbon

¹²C	¹³C	¹⁴C
6 protons	6 protons	6 protons
6 neutrons	7 neutrons	8 neutrons
atomic number = 6	atomic number = 6	atomic number = 6
mass number = 12	mass number = 13	mass number = 14

used in biological research as tracers to label molecules so that they can be tracked as they pass through biochemical reactions. Radioactive isotopes of carbon (^{14}C), phosphorus (^{32}P), and sulphur (^{35}S) can be traced easily by their radioactivity. A number of stable, nonradioactive isotopes, such as ^{15}N, can be detected by their mass differences and have also proved valuable as **tracers** in biological experiments.

Electrons and Electron Orbitals

In an atom, the number of electrons is equal to the number of protons in the nucleus. As they carry a negative charge that is exactly equal and opposite to the positive charge of the proton the total structure of an atom is electrically neutral. Electrons move around the atomic nucleus in a specific region called an **orbital**. An orbital is essentially the region of space where the electron "lives" most of the time. Although either one or two electrons may occupy an orbital, the most stable and balanced condition occurs when an orbital contains a pair of electrons. Orbitals are grouped into what are called energy levels or energy shells. These shells are numbered 1, 2, 3, and so on, to indicate their relative distance from the nucleus. The lowest energy level of an atom, the one nearest the nucleus, may be occupied by a maximum of two electrons in a single orbital. The second and third shells can hold a maximum of eight electrons each.

The first shell consists of a single spherical orbital, the 1s orbital. Hydrogen and helium, for example, consist of only a 1s orbital, containing one or two electrons, respectively. The second shell, if present, consists of the 2s orbital and three 2p orbitals. Collectively, the second shell holds a maximum of eight electrons. Neon is the element formed when both the first and the second shell contain a full complement of electrons. Neon is very stable, as explained in the next box.

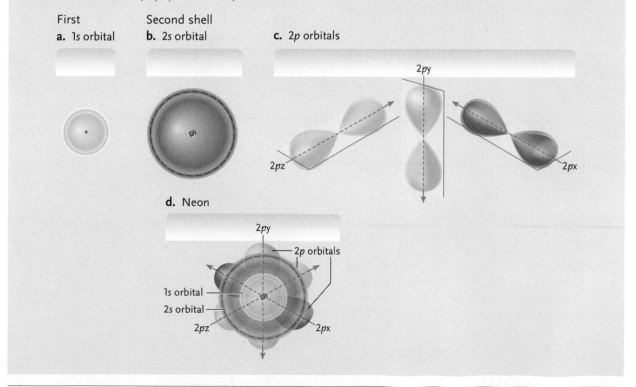

First
a. 1s orbital

Second shell
b. 2s orbital

c. 2p orbitals

2py

2pz

2px

d. Neon

2py

2p orbitals

1s orbital

2s orbital

2pz

2px

THE CHEMICAL AND PHYSICAL FOUNDATIONS OF BIOLOGY

Valence Electrons

The electrons in an atom's outermost energy level are known as **valence electrons**. Atoms in which the outermost energy level is not completely filled with electrons tend to be chemically reactive; those with a completely filled outermost energy level are non-reactive, or inert. For example, hydrogen has a single, unpaired electron in its outermost and only energy level, and it is highly reactive; helium has two valence electrons filling its single orbital and is unreactive (stable), or inert. For atoms with two or more energy levels, only those with unfilled outer energy levels are reactive. Those with eight electrons completely filling the four orbitals of the outer energy levels, such as neon and argon, are stable and chemically unreactive.

Because an unfilled electron shell is less stable than a filled one, atoms with an incomplete outer shell have a strong tendency to interact with other atoms in a way that causes them to either gain or lose enough electrons to achieve a completed outermost shell. All elements commonly found in living organisms have unfilled outermost shells (red in the picture here) and can thus participate in chemical reactions with other atoms. By comparison, some elements that have only filled shells (yellow are shown here) are chemically unreactive and are not found in living systems.

Atoms with outer energy levels that contain electrons near the stable numbers tend to gain or lose electrons to reach the stable configuration. For example, sodium has two electrons in its first energy level, eight in the second, and one in the third and outermost level. The outermost electron is readily lost to another atom, giving the sodium atom a stable second energy level (now the outermost level) with eight electrons. Chlorine, with seven electrons in its outermost energy level, tends to take up an electron from another atom to attain the stable number of eight electrons.

Atoms that differ from the stable configuration by more than one or two electrons tend to attain stability by *sharing* electrons in joint orbitals with other atoms rather than by gaining or losing electrons completely. Among the atoms that form biological molecules, electron sharing is most characteristic of carbon, which has four electrons in its outer energy level and thus falls at the midpoint between the tendency to gain or lose electrons. Oxygen, with six electrons in its outer level, and nitrogen, with five electrons in its outer level, also share electrons readily. Hydrogen may either share or lose its single electron. The relative tendency to gain, share, or lose valence electrons underlies the chemical bonds and forces that hold the atoms of molecules together.

Atomic number →

	Element	I	II	III	IV
1	Hydrogen	○			
2	Helium	○○			
6	Carbon	○○	○○○○		
7	Nitrogen	○○	○○○○○		
8	Oxygen	○○	○○○○○○		
10	Neon	○○	○○○○○○○○		
11	Sodium	○○	○○○○○○○○	○	
12	Magnesium	○○	○○○○○○○○	○○	
15	Phosphorus	○○	○○○○○○○○	○○○○○	
16	Sulphur	○○	○○○○○○○○	○○○○○○	
17	Chlorine	○○	○○○○○○○○	○○○○○○○	
18	Argon	○○	○○○○○○○○	○○○○○○○○	
19	Potassium	○○	○○○○○○○○	○○○○○○○○	○
20	Calcium	○○	○○○○○○○○	○○○○○○○○	○○

Electron shell — columns I, II, III, IV

Chemical Bonds

Atoms of the inert elements, such as helium, neon, or argon, occur naturally in uncombined forms, but atoms of reactive elements tend to combine into molecules by forming **chemical bonds**. Four types of chemical linkages are important in biological molecules: ionic bonds, covalent bonds, hydrogen bonds, and **van der Waals** forces. Because of their importance in hydrogen bonding, polar molecules are also discussed here.

Ionic Bonds

Ionic bonds form between atoms that gain or lose valence electrons completely. A sodium atom (Na) readily loses a single electron to achieve a stable outer energy level, and chlorine (Cl) readily gains an electron. After the transfer, the sodium atom, now with 11 protons and 10 electrons, carries a single positive charge. The chlorine atom, now with 17 protons and 18 electrons, carries a single negative charge. In this charged condition, the atoms are called ions: sodium with a positive charge is a cation, whereas chloride with a negative charge is the anion.

Ionic bonds are common among the forces that hold ions, atoms, and molecules together because these bonds have three key features:

- they exert an attractive force over greater distances than any other chemical bond
- their attractive force extends in all directions
- they vary in strength depending on the presence of other charged substances

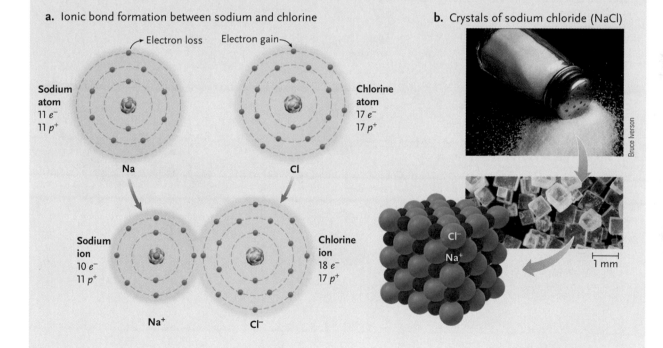

a. Ionic bond formation between sodium and chlorine

Electron loss
Electron gain

Sodium atom
11 e^-
11 p^+

Na

Chlorine atom
17 e^-
17 p^+

Cl

Sodium ion
10 e^-
11 p^+

Na$^+$

Chlorine ion
18 e^-
17 p^+

Cl$^-$

b. Crystals of sodium chloride (NaCl)

Bruce Iverson

Cl$^-$
Na$^+$

1 mm

Covalent Bonds

Covalent bonds form when atoms share a pair of valence electrons rather than gaining or losing them. The formation of molecular hydrogen, H_2, by two hydrogen atoms is the simplest example of the sharing mechanism. If two hydrogen atoms collide, the single electron of each atom may join in a new, combined two-electron orbital that surrounds both nuclei. The two electrons fill the orbital; thus, the hydrogen atoms tend to remain linked stably together. The linkage formed by the shared orbital is a covalent bond.

In molecular diagrams, a covalent bond is represented by a pair of dots or a single line, designating the pair of shared electrons. For example, in H_2, the molecule is represented as H:H or H–H.

Unlike ionic bonds, which extend their attractive force in all directions, the shared orbitals that form covalent bonds extend between atoms at discrete angles and directions, giving covalently bound molecules distinct, three-dimensional forms. For biological molecules such as proteins, which are composed of amino acids linked together by covalent bonds, the three-dimensional form imparted by the bonds is critical to the molecule's overall function.

Carbon has four unpaired outer electrons and typically forms four covalent bonds to complete its outermost energy level. An example is methane, CH_4, the main component of natural gas. The four covalent bonds formed by the carbon atom are fixed at an angle of 109.5° from each other, forming a tetrahedron. The tetrahedral arrangement of the bonds allows carbon atoms to link extensively to each other in chains and rings in both branched and unbranched forms. Such structures form the backbones of an almost unlimited variety of molecules. Carbon can also form double bonds, in which two carbon atoms share two pairs of electrons, and triple bonds, in which two carbon atoms share three pairs of electrons.

Oxygen, hydrogen, nitrogen, and sulphur also have electrons that readily form covalent linkages, and they commonly combine with carbon in biological molecules. In these linkages, oxygen typically forms two covalent bonds; hydrogen, one; nitrogen, three; and sulphur, two.

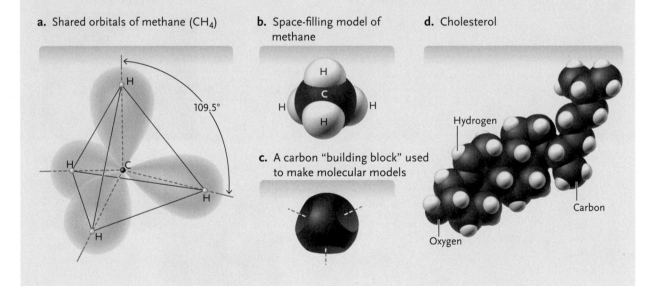

a. Shared orbitals of methane (CH_4)

109.5°

b. Space-filling model of methane

c. A carbon "building block" used to make molecular models

d. Cholesterol

Hydrogen

Carbon

Oxygen

Polar Molecules

Although all covalent bonds involve the sharing of valence electrons, they differ widely in the degree of sharing. Electronegativity is the measure of an atom's attraction for the electrons it shares in a covalent bond with another atom. The more electronegative an atom is, the more strongly it attracts shared electrons. Among atoms, electronegativity increases as the number of protons in the nucleus increases and as the distance between the electrons and the nucleus increases. This unequal sharing of electrons between two atoms that differ in their electronegativity results in a **polar covalent bond**.

The atom that attracts the electron(s) more strongly carries a partial negative charge, which results in the other atom carrying a partial positive charge. The atoms carrying partial charges may give the whole molecule partially positive and negative ends; in other words, the molecule is *polar*.

continued on next page

For example, the oxygen atom in water forms polar covalent bonds with two hydrogen atoms. Because the oxygen nucleus with its eight protons attracts electrons much more strongly than the

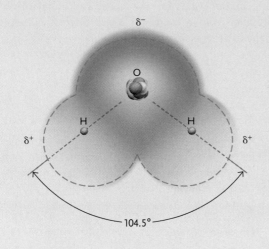

hydrogen nuclei do, the bonds are strongly polar. In addition, the water molecule is asymmetrical, with the oxygen atom located on one side and the hydrogen atoms on the other. This arrangement gives the entire molecule an unequal charge distribution, with the hydrogen end partially positive and the oxygen end partially negative, making water molecules strongly polar. Although less so than oxygen, sulphur and nitrogen are also electronegative, giving rise to polar bonds with hydrogen.

Polar molecules attract and align themselves with other polar molecules and with charged ions and molecules and tend to exclude nonpolar molecules. Polar molecules that associate readily with water because it is strongly polar are identified as hydrophilic (*hydro* = water; *philic* = preferring). Nonpolar substances that are excluded by water and other polar molecules (such as oils) are identified as hydrophobic (*phobic* = avoiding).

Hydrogen Bonding

When hydrogen atoms are made partially positive by sharing electrons unequally with oxygen, nitrogen, or sulphur, they may be attracted to nearby oxygen, nitrogen, or sulphur atoms made partially negative by unequal electron sharing in a different covalent bond. This attractive force is the hydrogen bond, illustrated by a dotted line in structural diagrams of molecules. Hydrogen bonds may form between atoms in the same or different molecules.

Individual hydrogen bonds are weak compared with ionic and covalent bonds. However, large biological molecules may offer many opportunities for hydrogen bonding, both within and between molecules. When numerous, hydrogen bonds are collectively strong and lend stability to the three-dimensional structure of molecules such as proteins. Hydrogen bonds between water molecules are responsible for many of the properties that make water uniquely important to life.

The weak attractive force of hydrogen bonds makes them much easier to break than covalent and ionic bonds, particularly when elevated temperature increases the movements of molecules. Hydrogen bonds begin to break extensively as temperatures rise above 45°C and become practically nonexistent at 100°C.

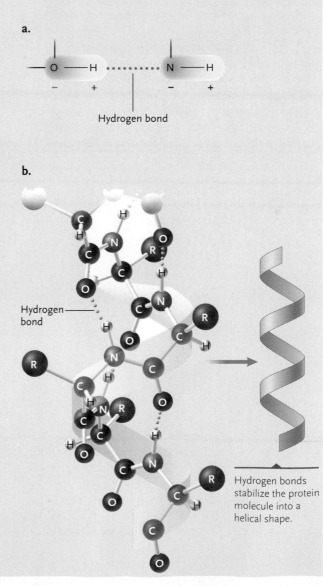

a.

Hydrogen bond

b.

Hydrogen bond

Hydrogen bonds stabilize the protein molecule into a helical shape.

van der Waals Forces

van der Waals forces are even weaker than hydrogen bonds. These forces develop between nonpolar molecules or regions of molecules when, through their constant motion, electrons accumulate by chance in one part of a molecule or another. This process leads to zones of positive and negative charge, making the molecule polar. If they are oriented in the right way, the polar parts of the molecules are attracted electrically to one another and cause the molecules to stick together briefly. Although an individual bond formed with van der Waals forces is weak and transient, the formation of many bonds of this type can stabilize the shape of a large molecule, such as a protein.

Chemical Reactions

Chemical reactions occur when atoms or molecules interact to form new chemical bonds or break old ones. As a result of bond formation or breakage, atoms are added to or removed from molecules or the linkages of atoms in molecules are rearranged. When any of these alterations occur, molecules change from one type to another, usually with different chemical and physical properties. In biological systems, chemical reactions are accelerated by *enzymes*. Enzymes typically are proteins (see Chapter 4 for a more detailed discussion of enzymes).

The atoms or molecules entering a chemical reaction are called the reactants, and those leaving a reaction are the products. A chemical reaction is written with an arrow showing the direction of the reaction; reactants are placed to the left of the arrow and products to the right. Both reactants and products are usually written in chemical shorthand as formulas.

For example, the overall reaction of photosynthesis, in which carbon dioxide and water are combined to produce sugars and oxygen (see Chapter 9), is written as follows:

$$\underset{\text{carbon dioxide}}{6CO_2} + \underset{\text{water}}{6H_2O} \rightarrow \underset{\text{a sugar}}{C_6H_{12}O_6} + \underset{\text{molecular oxygen}}{6O_2}$$

The number in front of each formula indicates the number of molecules of that type among the reactants and products (the number 1 is not written). Notice that there are as many atoms of each element on the left of the arrow as there are on the right, even though the products are different from the reactants. This balance reflects the fact that in chemical reactions, atoms may be rearranged but are not created or destroyed. Chemical reactions written in balanced form are known as chemical equations.

Water

All living organisms contain water, and many kinds of organisms live directly in water. Even those that live in dry environments contain water in all their structures—different organisms range from 50% to more than 95% water by weight. The water inside organisms is crucial for life: it is required for many important biochemical reactions and plays major roles in maintaining the shape and organization of cells and tissues.

Hydrogen Bonds and the Properties of Water

The properties of water molecules that make them so important to life depend to a great extent on their polar structure and their ability to link to each other by hydrogen bonds (see PP3). Hydrogen bonds form readily between water molecules in both liquid water and ice. In liquid water, each water molecule establishes an average of 3.4 hydrogen bonds with its neighbours, forming an arrangement known as the water lattice. In liquid water, the hydrogen bonds that hold the lattice together constantly break and reform, allowing the water molecules to break loose from the lattice, slip past one another, and reform the lattice in new positions.

In ice, the **water lattice** is a rigid, crystalline structure in which each water molecule forms four hydrogen bonds with neighbouring molecules. The rigid ice lattice spaces the water molecules farther apart than the water lattice. Because of this greater spacing, water has the unusual property of being about 10% less dense when solid than when liquid. Imagine what Earth would be like if ice sank to the bottom, as most solids do.

a. Hydrogen-bond lattice of liquid water

KEY

b. Hydrogen-bond lattice of ice

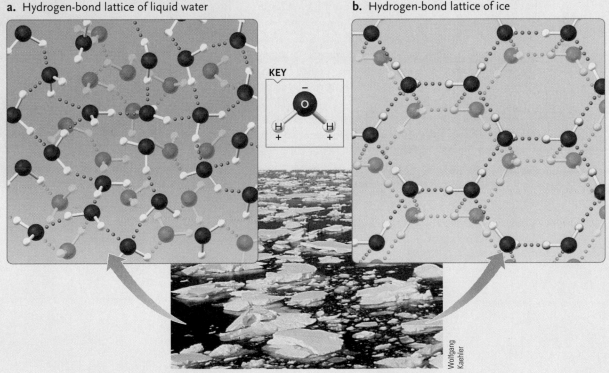

Wolfgang Kaehler

Specific Heat Capacity, Cohesion, and Surface Tension of Water

As a result of its stabilizing hydrogen-bond lattice, water has a relatively high specific heat capacity—that is, the amount of heat required to increase the temperature of a given quantity of water. As heat flows into water, much of it is absorbed in the breakage of hydrogen bonds. As a result, the temperature of water, reflected in the average motion of its molecules, increases relatively slowly as heat is added. As a result, relatively high temperatures and the addition of considerable heat are required to break enough hydrogen bonds to make water boil. The high boiling point maintains water as a liquid over the wide temperature range of 0° to 100°C. Compared to water, H_2S, which has a comparable molecular structure, is a gas at room temperature and has a melting point of -85°C and a boiling point of -60°C, a range of only 25 degrees. Without its hydrogen-bond lattice, water would boil at -81°C. If this were the case, most of the water on Earth would be in gaseous form and life as described in this book could not exist.

The hydrogen-bond lattice of water results in water molecules staying together, a phenomenon that is referred to as cohesion. For example, in land plants, cohesion holds water molecules in unbroken columns in the microscopic conducting tubes that extend from the roots to the highest leaves. As water evaporates from the leaves, water molecules in the columns, held together by cohesion, move upward through the tubes to replace the lost water.

Related to cohesion is **surface tension**, which is a measure of how difficult it is to stretch or break the surface of a liquid. The water molecules at surfaces facing air can form hydrogen bonds with water molecules beside and below them but not on the sides

that face the air. This unbalanced bonding produces a force that places the surface water molecules under tension, making them more resistant to separation than the underlying water molecules. This force is strong enough to allow small insects such as water striders to walk on water.

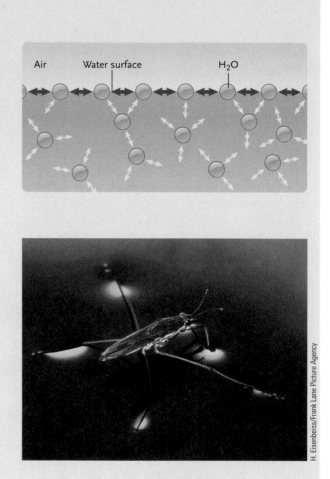

H. Eisenbeiss/Frank Lane Picture Agency

Aqueous Solutions

Because water molecules are small and strongly polar, they readily surround other polar and charged molecules and ions. The surface coat, called a hydration shell, reduces the attraction between the molecules or ions and promotes their separation and entry into a solution, where they are suspended individually, surrounded by water molecules. Once in solution, the hydration shell prevents the polar molecules or ions from reassociating. In such an aqueous solution, water is called the *solvent,* and the molecules of a substance dissolved in water are called the *solute.*

Sodium chloride (salt) dissolves in water because water molecules quickly form **hydration layers** around the Na^+ and Cl^+ ions in the salt crystals, reducing the attraction between the ions so much that they separate from the crystal and enter the surrounding water lattice as individual ions. In much the same way, hydration shells surround macromolecules such as nucleic acids and proteins, reducing their electrostatic interaction with other molecules.

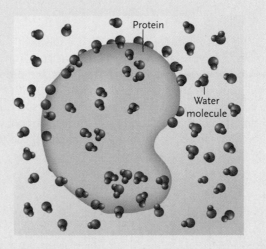

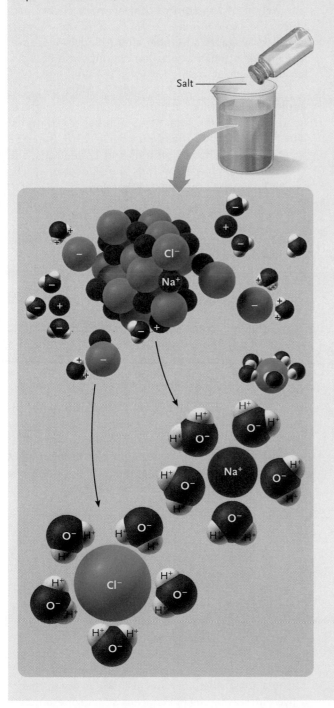

Determining Solute Concentration

In the cell, chemical reactions depend on solutes dissolved in aqueous solutions. To understand these reactions, you need to know the number of atoms and molecules involved. **Concentration** is the number of molecules or ions of a substance in a unit volume of space, such as a millilitre (mL) or litre (L). The number of molecules or ions in a unit volume cannot be counted directly, but it can be calculated indirectly by using the mass number of atoms as the starting point.

The mass number of an atom is equivalent to the number of protons and neutrons in its nucleus. From the mass number, and the fact that neutrons and protons weigh approximately the same (that is, 1.66×10^{-24} g), you can calculate the weight of an atom of any substance. For an atom of the most common form of carbon, with six protons and six neutrons in its nucleus, the total weight is

$$12 \times (1.66 \times 10^{-24} \text{ g}) = 1.992 \times 10^{-23} \text{ g}$$

For an oxygen atom, with eight protons and eight neutrons in its nucleus, the total weight is

$$16 \times (1.66 \times 10^{-24} \text{ g}) = 2.656 \times 10^{-23} \text{ g}$$

Dividing the total weight of a sample of an element by the weight of a single atom gives the number of atoms in the sample. Suppose you have a carbon sample that weighs 12 g—a weight in grams equal to the atom's mass number. (A weight in grams equal to the mass number is known as the **atomic weight** of an element.) Dividing 12 g by the weight of one carbon atom gives

$$\frac{12}{(1.992 \times 10^{23} \text{g})} = 6.02 \times 10^{23} \text{ atoms}$$

If you divide the atomic weight of oxygen (16 g) by the weight of one oxygen atom, you get the same result:

$$\frac{16}{(2.656 \times 10^{23} \text{ g})} = 6.02 \times 10^{23} \text{ atoms}$$

In fact, dividing the atomic weight of any element by the weight of an atom of that element always produces the same number: 6.022×10^{23}. This number is called **Avogadro's number** after Amedeo Avogadro, the nineteenth-century Italian chemist who first discovered the relationship.

The same relationship holds for molecules. The **molecular weight** of any molecule is the weight in grams equal to the total mass number of its atoms. For NaCl, the total mass number is $23 + 35 = 58$ (a sodium atom has 11 protons and 12 neutrons, and a chlorine atom has 17 protons and 18 neutrons). The weight of an NaCl molecule is therefore

$$58 \times (1.66 \times 10^{-24} \text{ g}) = 9.628 \times 10^{-23} \text{ g}$$

Dividing a molecular weight of NaCl (58 g) by the weight of a single NaCl molecule gives

$$\frac{58}{(9.628 \times 10^{23} \text{g})} = 6.02 \times 10^{23} \text{ molecules}$$

When concentrations are described, the atomic weight of an element or the molecular weight of a compound—the amount that contains 6.02×10^{23} atoms or molecules—is known as a **mole** (abbreviated **mol**). The number of moles of a substance dissolved in 1 L of solution is known as the **molarity** (abbreviated **M**) of the solution. This relationship is highly useful in chemistry and biology because we know that two solutions with the same volume and molarity but composed of different substances will contain the same number of molecules of the substances.

Water Ionization and pH

The most critical property of water that is unrelated to its hydrogen-bond lattice is its ability to separate or dissociate. This occurs when a hydrogen atom that is involved in a hydrogen bond between two water molecules moves from one molecule to the other. What actually leaves is a proton (H^+); the electron is left behind. This proton switch results in the formation of a hydroxide ion (OH^-) and a hydronium ion (H_3O^+). It is convention to simply use H^+ (the hydrogen ion) to denote the hydronium ion. The proportion of water molecules that dissociates to release hydrogen and hydroxide ions is small. However, because of the dissociation, water always contains some H^+ and OH^- ions.

In pure water, the concentrations of H^+ and OH^- ions are equal. However, adding other substances may alter the relative concentrations of H^+ and OH^-, making them unequal. Some substances, called **acids**, are proton donors that release hydrogen ions (and anions) when they are dissolved in water, effectively increasing the H^+ concentration. For example,

continued on next page

hydrochloric acid (HCl) dissociates into H^+ and Cl^- when dissolved in water:

$$HCl \rightarrow H^+ + Cl^-$$

Other substances, called **bases**, are proton acceptors that reduce the H^+ concentration of a solution. Most bases dissociate in water into hydroxide ions (OH^-) and cations. The hydroxide ion can act as a base by accepting a proton (H^+) to produce water. For example, sodium hydroxide (NaOH) separates into Na^+ and OH^- ions when dissolved in water:

$$NaOH \rightarrow Na^+ + OH^-$$

The excess OH^- combines with H^+ to produce water:

$$OH^- + H^+ \rightarrow H_2O$$

thereby reducing the H^+ concentration. Basic solutions are also called *alkaline* solutions.

Other bases do not dissociate to produce hydroxide ions directly. For example, ammonia (NH_3), a poisonous gas, acts as a base when dissolved in water, directly accepting a proton from water, producing an ammonium ion, and releasing a hydroxide ion:

$$NH_3 + H_2O \rightarrow NH_4^+ + OH^-$$

The concentration of H^+ ions compared with the concentration of OH^- ions in an aqueous solution determines the acidity of the solution. Scientists measure acidity using a numerical scale from 0 to 14, called the pH scale. Because the number of H^+ ions in solution increases exponentially as the acidity increases, the scale is based on logarithms of this number to make the values manageable:

$$pH = -\log_{10}[H^+]$$

In this formula, the brackets indicate concentration in moles per litre. The negative of the logarithm is used to give a positive number for the pH value. For example, in a water solution that is *neutral*—neither acidic nor basic—the concentration of *both* H^+ and OH^- ions is 1×10^{-7} M (0.000 000 1 M). The $\log_{10}$ of 1×10^{-7} is -7. The negative of the logarithm -7 is 7. Thus, a neutral water solution with an H^+ concentration of 1×10^{-7} M has a pH of 7. *Acidic* solutions have pH values less than 7, with pH 0 being the value for the highly acidic 1 M hydrochloric acid (HCl); *basic* solutions have pH values greater than 7, with pH 14 being the value for the highly basic 1 M sodium hydroxide (NaOH). Each whole number on the pH scale represents a value 10 times greater or less than the next number.

Acidity is important to cells because even small changes, on the order of 0.1 or even 0.01 pH unit, can drastically affect biological reactions. In large part, a small change in pH can cause structural changes in proteins that can damage or destroy the proteins' function. Consequently, all living organisms have elaborate systems that control their internal acidity by regulating H^+ concentration near the neutral value of pH 7.

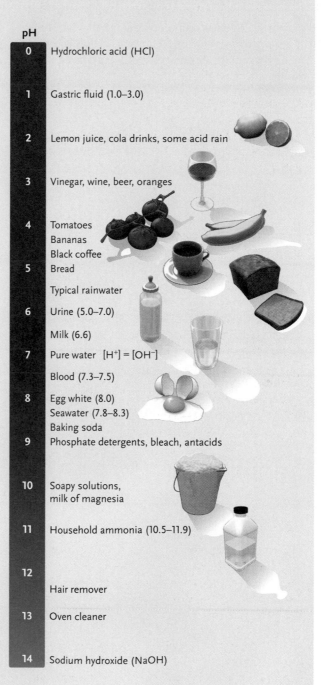

pH	
0	Hydrochloric acid (HCl)
1	Gastric fluid (1.0–3.0)
2	Lemon juice, cola drinks, some acid rain
3	Vinegar, wine, beer, oranges
4	Tomatoes
	Bananas
	Black coffee
5	Bread
	Typical rainwater
6	Urine (5.0–7.0)
	Milk (6.6)
7	Pure water $[H^+] = [OH^-]$
	Blood (7.3–7.5)
8	Egg white (8.0)
	Seawater (7.8–8.3)
	Baking soda
9	Phosphate detergents, bleach, antacids
10	Soapy solutions, milk of magnesia
11	Household ammonia (10.5–11.9)
12	
	Hair remover
13	Oven cleaner
14	Sodium hydroxide (NaOH)

Buffers Help Keep pH under Control

Living organisms control the internal pH of their cells with **buffers**, substances that compensate for pH changes by absorbing or releasing hydrogen ions. When hydrogen ions are released in excess by biological reactions, buffers combine with them and remove them from the solution; if the concentration of hydrogen ions decreases, buffers release H^+ to restore the balance. Most buffers are weak acids, weak bases, or combinations of these substances that dissociate reversibly in water solutions to release or absorb H^+ or OH^-. (Weak acids, such as acetic acid, or weak bases, such as ammonia, release relatively few H^+ or OH^- ions in an aqueous solution, whereas strong acids or bases dissociate extensively. HCl is a strong acid; NaOH is a strong base.)

The buffering mechanism that maintains blood pH near neutral values is a good example. In humans and many other animals, blood pH is buffered by a chemical system based on carbonic acid (H_2CO_3), a weak acid. In water solutions, carbonic acid dissociates readily into bicarbonate ions (HCO_3^-) and H^+:

$$H_2CO_3 \rightarrow HCO_3^- + H^+$$

The reaction is reversible. If hydrogen ions are present in excess, the reaction is pushed to the left—the excess H^+ ions combine with bicarbonate ions to form H_2CO_3. If the H^+ concentration declines below normal levels, the reaction is pushed to the right—H_2CO_3 dissociates into HCO_3^- and H^+, restoring the H^+ concentration. The back-and-forth adjustments of the buffer system help keep human blood close to its normal pH of 7.4.

Carbon Compounds

Carbon Bonding

Compounds that contain carbon form the structures of living organisms and take part in all biological reactions as well as serving as energy sources. Collectively, molecules based on carbon are known as organic molecules. All other substances, that is, those without carbon atoms in their structures, are inorganic molecules. A few of the smallest carbon-containing molecules that occur in the environment as minerals or atmospheric gases, such as $CaCO_3$ and CO_2, are also considered inorganic molecules.

Carbon's central role in life's molecules arises from its bonding properties: it can assemble into an astounding variety of chain and ring structures that form the backbones of all biological molecules. The reason for this is that carbon has four unpaired outer electrons that it readily shares to complete its outermost energy level, forming four covalent bonds. With different combinations of single, double, and even triple bonds, an almost limitless array of molecules is possible. Carbon atoms bond covalently to each other and to other atoms, chiefly hydrogen, oxygen, nitrogen, and sulphur, in molecular structures that range in size from a few to thousands or even millions of atoms. Molecules consisting of carbon linked only to hydrogen atoms are called **hydrocarbons** (*hydro-* refers to hydrogen, not water). The simplest hydrocarbon, CH_4 (methane), consists of a single carbon atom bonded to four hydrogen atoms. Removing one hydrogen from methane leaves a methyl group, which occurs in many biological molecules:

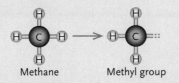

| Methane | Methyl group |

Now imagine bonding two methyl groups together. Removing a hydrogen atom from the resulting structure, ethane, produces an ethyl group:

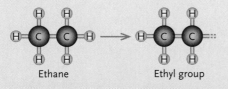

| Ethane | Ethyl group |

Repeating this process builds a linear hydrocarbon chain:

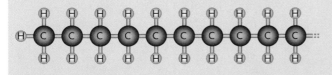

Branches can be added to produce a branched hydrocarbon chain:

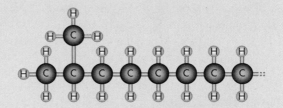

A chain can loop back on itself to form a ring. For example, cyclohexane, C_6H_{12}, has single covalent bonds between each pair of carbon atoms and two hydrogen atoms attached to each carbon atom:

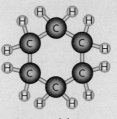

C_6H_{12}, cyclohexane

Hydrocarbons gain added complexity when neighbouring carbon atoms form double or triple bonds. Because each carbon atom can form a maximum of four bonds, the number of hydrogen atoms in a molecule decreases as the number of bonds between any two carbon atoms increases:

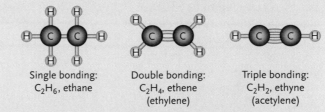

| Single bonding: C_2H_6, ethane | Double bonding: C_2H_4, ethene (ethylene) | Triple bonding: C_2H_2, ethyne (acetylene) |

Double bonds between carbon atoms are also found in carbon rings:

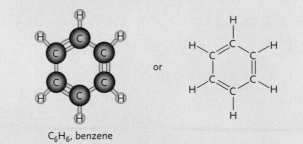

or

C_6H_6, benzene

We will also use this depiction of a carbon ring in figures:

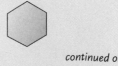

continued on next page

Many carbon rings can join together to produce larger molecules, as in the string of sugar molecules that makes up a polysaccharide chain:

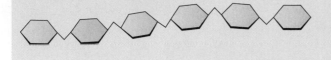

There is almost no limit to the number of different hydrocarbon structures that carbon and hydrogen can form. However, the molecules of living systems typically contain other elements in addition to carbon and hydrogen. These other elements confer functional properties on organic molecules, producing the four major classes of organic molecules—*carbohydrates*, *lipids*, *proteins*, and *nucleic acids*.

Functional Groups

Carbohydrates, lipids, proteins, and nucleic acids are synthesized and degraded in living organisms through interactions between small, reactive groups of atoms attached to the organic molecules. The atoms in these reactive groups, called functional groups, occur in positions in which their covalent bonds are more readily broken or rearranged than the bonds in other parts of the molecules.

The functional groups that enter most frequently into biological reactions are the *hydroxyl, carbonyl, carboxyl, amino, phosphate,* and *sulfhydryl* groups. The unconnected covalent bonds written to the left of each structure link these functional groups to other atoms in biological molecules, usually carbon atoms. A double bond, such as that in the **carbonyl group**, indicates that two pairs of electrons are shared between the carbon and oxygen atoms.

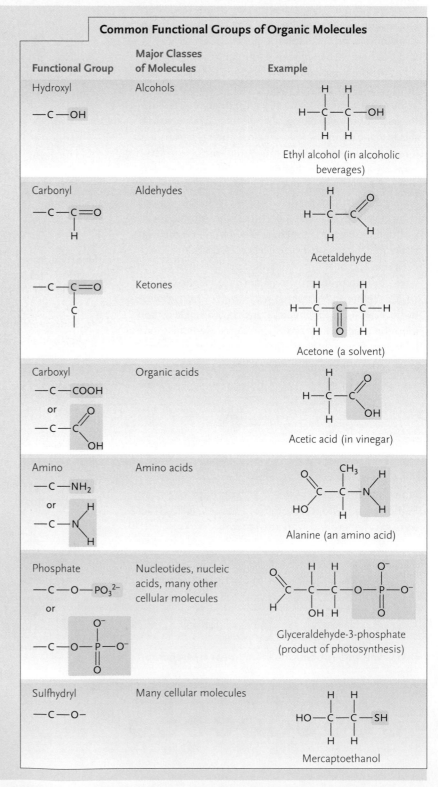

Common Functional Groups of Organic Molecules

Functional Group	Major Classes of Molecules	Example
Hydroxyl	Alcohols	Ethyl alcohol (in alcoholic beverages)
Carbonyl	Aldehydes	Acetaldehyde
	Ketones	Acetone (a solvent)
Carboxyl	Organic acids	Acetic acid (in vinegar)
Amino	Amino acids	Alanine (an amino acid)
Phosphate	Nucleotides, nucleic acids, many other cellular molecules	Glyceraldehyde-3-phosphate (product of photosynthesis)
Sulfhydryl	Many cellular molecules	Mercaptoethanol

Dehydration and Hydrolysis Reactions

In many of the reactions that involve functional groups, the components of a water molecule, —H and —OH, are removed from or added to the groups as they interact. When the components of a water molecule are *removed* during a reaction, usually as part of the assembly of a larger molecule from smaller subunits, the reaction is called a dehydration synthesis reaction or **condensation reaction**. For example, this type of reaction occurs when individual sugar molecules combine to form a starch molecule. In hydrolysis, the reverse reaction, the components of a water molecule are *added* to functional groups as molecules are broken into smaller subunits. For example, the breakdown of a protein molecule into individual amino acids occurs by hydrolysis.

a. Dehydration synthesis reactions

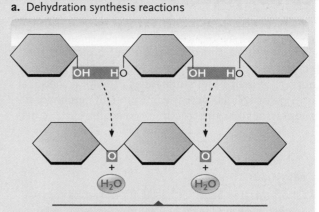

The components of a water molecule are removed as subunits join into a larger molecule.

b. Hydrolysis

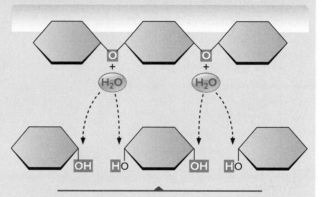

The components of a water molecule are added as molecules are split into smaller subunits.

Carbohydrates

Carbohydrates, the most abundant biological molecules, serve many functions. Together with fats, they act as the major fuel substances providing chemical energy for cellular activities. Chains of carbohydrate subunits also form structural molecules such as cellulose, one of the primary constituents of plant cell walls. Carbohydrates get their name because they contain carbon, hydrogen, and oxygen atoms, with the approximate ratio of the atoms being 1 carbon: 2 hydrogens:1 oxygen (CH_2O).

Monosaccharides

Carbohydrates occur either as monosaccharides or as chains of monosaccharide units linked together. Monosaccharides are soluble in water, and most have a distinctly sweet taste. Of the monosaccharides, those that contain three carbons (*trioses*), five carbons (*pentoses*), and six carbons (*hexoses*) are most common in living organisms. All monosaccharides can occur in the linear form, where each carbon atom in the chain except one has both an —H and an —OH group attached to it.

Monosaccharides with five or more carbons can fold back on themselves to assume a ring form. Folding into a ring occurs through a reaction between two functional groups in the same monosaccharide, as occurs in glucose. The ring form of most five- and six-carbon sugars is much more common in cells than the linear form.

When glucose forms into a ring, two alternative arrangements are possible (α-glucose and β-glucose) that differ in the arrangements of the —OH group bound to the carbon at position 1. These two different forms of glucose are called **isomers**, which are discussed below.

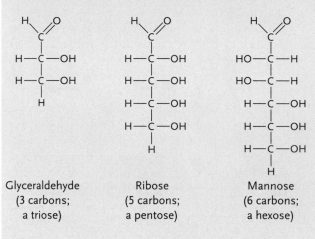

Glyceraldehyde
(3 carbons;
a triose)

Ribose
(5 carbons;
a pentose)

Mannose
(6 carbons;
a hexose)

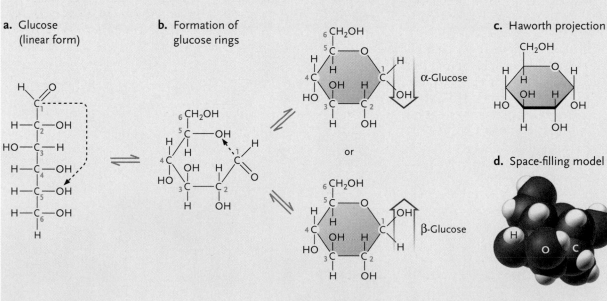

a. Glucose
   (linear form)

b. Formation of
   glucose rings

α-Glucose

or

β-Glucose

c. Haworth projection

d. Space-filling model

Isomers of the Monosaccharides

Typically, one or more of the carbon atoms in a monosaccharide links to four different atoms or chemical groups. Carbons linked in this way are called *asymmetrical* carbons; they have important effects on the structure of a monosaccharide because they can take either of two fixed positions with respect to other carbons in a carbon chain. For example, the middle carbon of the three-carbon sugar glyceraldehyde is asymmetrical because it shares electrons in covalent bonds with four different atoms or groups: —H, —OH, —CHO, and —CH$_2$OH. The —H and —OH groups can take either of two positions, with the —OH extending to either the left or the right of the carbon chain relative to the —CHO and —CH$_2$OH groups:

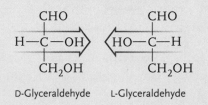

D-Glyceraldehyde   L-Glyceraldehyde

Note that the two forms of glyceraldehyde have the same chemical formula, C$_3$H$_6$O$_3$. The difference between the two forms is similar to the difference between your two hands. Although both hands have four fingers and a thumb, they are not identical; rather, they are mirror images of each other. That is, when you hold your right hand in front of a mirror, the reflection looks like your left hand and vice versa.

Two or more molecules with the same chemical formula but different molecular structures are called isomers. Isomers that are mirror images of each other, like the two forms of glyceraldehyde, are called enantiomers, or optical isomers. One of the enantiomers—the one in which the hydroxyl group extends to the left in the view just shown—is called the l-form (*laevus* = left). The other enantiomer, in which the —OH extends to the right, is called the d-form (*dexter* = right). The difference between l- and d-enantiomers is critical to biological function. Typically, one of the two forms enters much more readily into cellular reactions; just as your left hand does not fit readily into a right-hand glove, enzymes (proteins that accelerate chemical reactions in living organisms)

fit best to one of the two forms of an enantiomer. For example, most of the enzymes that catalyze the biochemical reactions of monosaccharides react more rapidly with the d-form, making this form much more common among cellular carbohydrates than l-forms. Many other kinds of biological molecules besides carbohydrates form enantiomers; an example is the amino acids.

In the ring form of many five- or six-carbon monosaccharides, including glucose, the carbon at the 1 position of the ring is asymmetrical because its four bonds link to different groups of atoms. This asymmetry allows monosaccharides such as glucose to exist as two different **enantiomers**. The glucose enantiomer with an —OH group pointing below the plane of the ring is known as *alpha-glucose*, or *α-glucose*; the enantiomer with an —OH group pointing above the plane of the ring is known as *beta-glucose*, or *β-glucose*. Other five- and six-carbon monosaccharide rings have similar α- and β-configurations.

The α- and β-rings of monosaccharides can give the polysaccharides assembled from them vastly different chemical properties. For example, starches, which are assembled from α-glucose units, are biologically reactive polysaccharides easily digested by animals; cellulose, which is assembled from β-glucose units, is relatively unreactive and, for most animals, completely indigestible.

Another form of isomerism is found in monosaccharides, as well as in other molecules. Two molecules with the same chemical formula but atoms that are arranged in different ways are called structural isomers. The sugars glucose and fructose are examples of **structural isomers**.

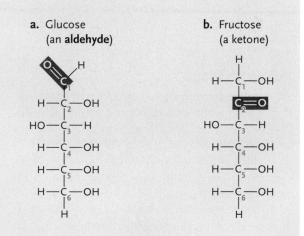

a. Glucose (an **aldehyde**)

b. Fructose (a ketone)

Disaccharides

Disaccharides typically are assembled from two monosaccharides linked together by a dehydration synthesis reaction. For example, the disaccharide maltose is formed by the linkage of two α-glucose molecules with oxygen as a bridge between the number 1 carbon of the first glucose unit and the 4 carbon of the second glucose unit. Bonds of this type, which commonly link monosaccharides into chains, are known as glycosidic bonds. A glycosidic bond between a 1 carbon and a 4 carbon is written in chemical shorthand as a 1→4 linkage. Linkages such as 1→2, 1→3, and 1→6 are also common in carbohydrate chains. The linkages are designated as α or β depending on the orientation of the —OH group at the 1 carbon that forms the bond. In maltose, the —OH group is in the α position. Therefore, the link between the two glucose subunits of maltose is written as an α(1→4) linkage. Maltose, sucrose, and lactose are common disaccharides.

a. Formation of maltose

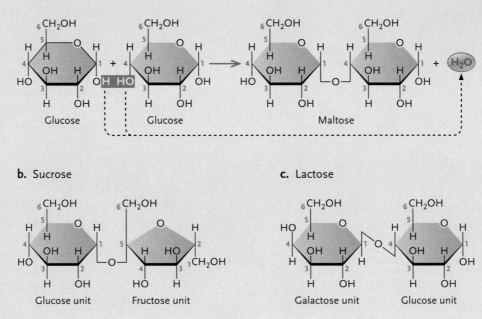

b. Sucrose   **c.** Lactose

Polysaccharides

Polysaccharides are longer chains formed by the end-to-end linking of monosaccharides through dehydration synthesis reactions. A polysaccharide is a type of macromolecule, which is a very large molecule assembled by the covalent linkage of smaller subunit molecules. The subunit for a polysaccharide is the monosaccharide.

The dehydration synthesis reactions that assemble polysaccharides from monosaccharides are examples of polymerization, in which identical or nearly identical subunits, called the monomers of the reaction, join like links in a chain to form a larger molecule called a polymer. Linkage of a relatively small number of nonidentical subunits can create highly diverse and varied biological molecules. Many kinds of polymers are found in cells, not just polysaccharides. DNA is a primary example of a highly diverse polymer assembled from various sequences of only four different types of monomers.

The most common polysaccharides—the plant starches, glycogen, and cellulose—are all assembled from hundreds or thousands of glucose units. Other polysaccharides are built up from a variety of different sugar units. Polysaccharides may be linear, unbranched molecules, or they may contain one or more branches in which side chains of sugar units are attached to a main chain.

continued on next page

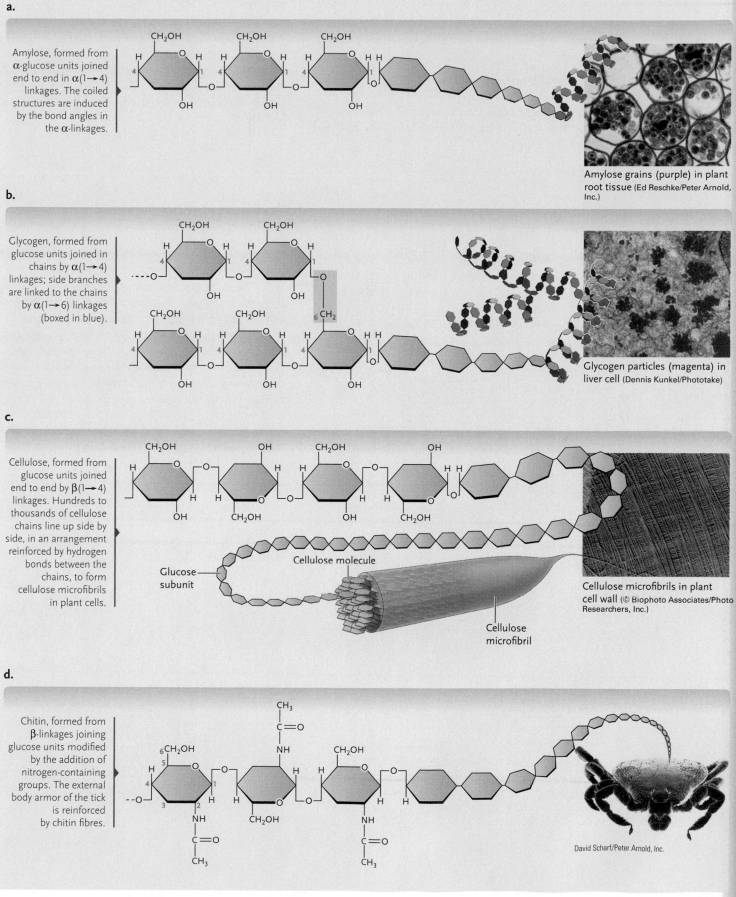

a.

Amylose, formed from α-glucose units joined end to end in α(1→4) linkages. The coiled structures are induced by the bond angles in the α-linkages.

CH_2OH

CH_2OH

CH_2OH

Amylose grains (purple) in plant root tissue (Ed Reschke/Peter Arnold, Inc.)

b.

Glycogen, formed from glucose units joined in chains by α(1→4) linkages; side branches are linked to the chains by α(1→6) linkages (boxed in blue).

CH_2OH

CH_2OH

CH_2OH

CH_2OH

CH_2OH

$6 CH_2$

Glycogen particles (magenta) in liver cell (Dennis Kunkel/Phototake)

c.

Cellulose, formed from glucose units joined end to end by β(1→4) linkages. Hundreds to thousands of cellulose chains line up side by side, in an arrangement reinforced by hydrogen bonds between the chains, to form cellulose microfibrils in plant cells.

CH_2OH

OH

CH_2OH

OH

CH_2OH

CH_2OH

OH

CH_2OH

Glucose subunit

Cellulose molecule

Cellulose microfibril

Cellulose microfibrils in plant cell wall (© Biophoto Associates/Photo Researchers, Inc.)

d.

Chitin, formed from β-linkages joining glucose units modified by the addition of nitrogen-containing groups. The external body armor of the tick is reinforced by chitin fibres.

CH_3

$C=O$

NH

$6 CH_2OH$

CH_2OH

CH_2OH

NH

$C=O$

CH_3

NH

$C=O$

CH_3

David Scharf/Peter Arnold, Inc.

Proteins

Proteins perform many vital functions in living organisms:

- Structural proteins provide much of the supporting framework of cells
- Enzymes accelerate the rate of cellular reactions.
- Motile proteins impart movement to cells and cellular structures.
- Transport proteins transport substances across biological membranes.
- Proteins serve as recognition and receptor molecules at cell surfaces.
- Proteins regulate the activity of other proteins and DNA.

Amino Acids

All proteins are polymers of amino acids. Amino acids share a similar structure with a central carbon atom attached to an amino group ($-NH_2$), a carboxyl group ($-COOH$), and a hydrogen atom:

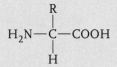

The remaining bond of the central carbon is linked to 1 of 19 different side groups represented by the R, ranging from a single hydrogen atom to complex carbon chains or rings. The one exception to this organization is the amino acid proline, which has a ring structure that includes the central carbon atom. Differences in the side groups give the amino acids their individual properties. Some side groups are polar and some are nonpolar; among the polar side groups, some carry a positive or negative charge and some act as acids or bases. Many of the side groups contain reactive functional groups, such as $-NH_2$, $-OH$, $-COOH$, or $-SH$, which may interact with atoms located elsewhere in the same protein or with molecules and ions outside the protein.

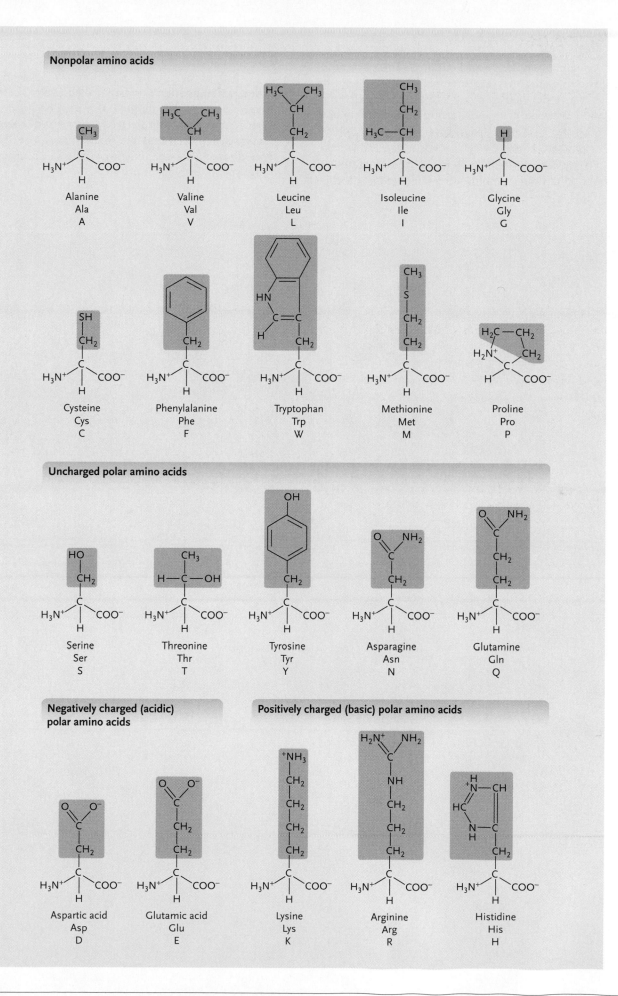

Nonpolar amino acids

Alanine
Ala
A

Valine
Val
V

Leucine
Leu
L

Isoleucine
Ile
I

Glycine
Gly
G

Cysteine
Cys
C

Phenylalanine
Phe
F

Tryptophan
Trp
W

Methionine
Met
M

Proline
Pro
P

Uncharged polar amino acids

Serine
Ser
S

Threonine
Thr
T

Tyrosine
Tyr
Y

Asparagine
Asn
N

Glutamine
Gln
Q

Negatively charged (acidic) polar amino acids

Aspartic acid
Asp
D

Glutamic acid
Glu
E

Positively charged (basic) polar amino acids

Lysine
Lys
K

Arginine
Arg
R

Histidine
His
H

Peptides

Covalent bonds link amino acids into chains of subunits that make proteins. The link, a peptide bond, is formed by a dehydration synthesis reaction between the —NH$_2$ group of one amino acid and the —COOH group of a second. An amino acid chain always has an —NH$_2$ group at one end, called the **N-terminal end**, and a —COOH group at the other end, called the **C-terminal end**. In cells, amino acids are added only to the —COOH end of the growing peptide strand.

The chain or polymer of amino acids formed by sequential peptide bonds is called a peptide. A *polypeptide* is usually defined as a peptide greater than 50 amino acids in length. A protein is one or more polypeptides that are folded into a precise three-dimensional shape. Only after this occurs is the polypeptide able to function.

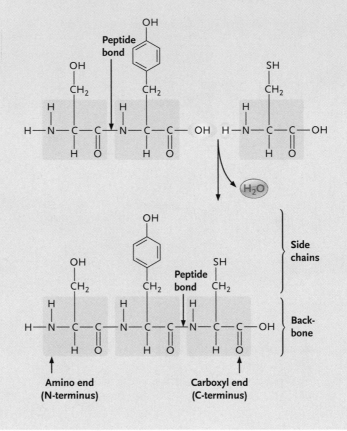

Protein Structure

Proteins potentially have four levels of structure, with each level imparting different characteristics and degrees of complexity to the molecule.

Primary Structure

The primary structure of a protein is the linear sequence of its amino acids. The types of amino acids and their order underlie all other higher levels of structure. Changing even a single amino acid of the primary structure alters the secondary, tertiary, and **quaternary structures** to at least some degree and, by so doing, can alter or even destroy the biological function of that protein.

Secondary Structure

Most proteins have portions that repeatedly coil or fold into patterns that contribute to the overall shape of a protein. This **secondary structure** is the result of hydrogen bonding among molecules of the amino acid backbone. Specifically, hydrogen bonding occurs between the electronegative nitrogen and oxygen atoms and the hydrogen atoms. Two highly regular secondary structures are the alpha helix (right) and the beta pleated sheet (below). A **beta sheet** is formed by side-by-side alignment of two amino acid chains. The arrows point in the direction of the C-terminal end of the amino acid chain.

H_3N^+ —| Phe | Val | Asn | Gln | His | Leu | Cys | Gly | Ala |— COO^-

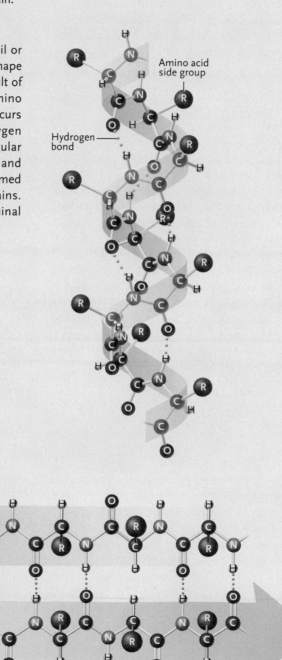

Amino acid side group

Hydrogen bond

Hydrogen bond

continued on next page

Tertiary Structure

Whereas the secondary structure of a protein is the result of interactions among molecules of the backbone, the overall shape of a protein is due to a range of bonding interactions among the amino acid R-groups. These include (1) ionic bonds, (2) hydrogen bonds, (3) hydrophobic interactions, and (4) disulphide bridges. The specific bonding arrangements between R groups give rise to a protein's distinctive three-dimensional shape, or *conformation*. This final conformation displays limited shape changes, a feature that is critical to the function of certain proteins, especially enzymes. Extreme conditions (temperature, pH, etc.) can unfold a protein from its conformation, causing denaturation, a loss of both the structure and the function of the protein.

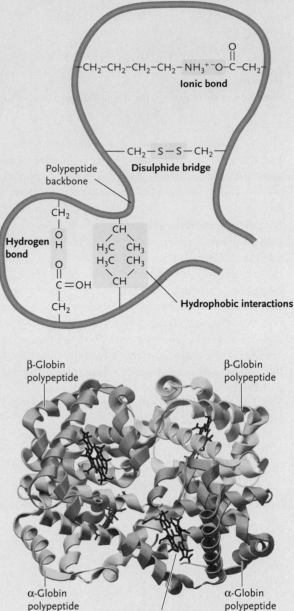

Quaternary Structure

Some proteins are composed of two or more polypeptides that come together to form the functional protein. This quaternary structure is a level of organization that exists in many proteins, such as hemoglobin, which comprises four individual folded polypeptides. The same bonds and forces that fold single amino acid chains into **tertiary structures**—including hydrogen bonds, polar and nonpolar attractions, and **disulphide linkages**—also hold the multiple polypeptide chains together. The hemoglobin molecule (left) displays quaternary structure as it is composed of four polypeptides.

Prosthetic Groups

Besides properly folded peptides, many proteins require nonprotein components called prosthetic groups in order to function. A good example is hemoglobin, the major protein involved in O_2 transport in vertebrates. The four globin proteins do not bind the oxygen; rather, the oxygen is bound to molecules called *heme*, one per protein molecule, which bind specifically to the proteins. Chlorophyll is a prosthetic group of many proteins of the photosynthetic apparatus, and many enzymes require metal-containing prosthetic groups in order to function.

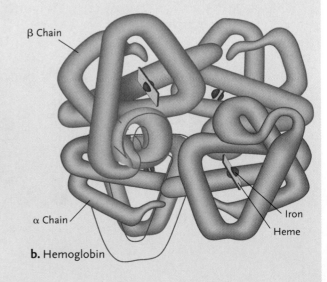

b. Hemoglobin

Nucleic Acids

Two types of nucleic acids exist: DNA and RNA. Deoxyribonucleic acid (DNA) stores the hereditary information responsible for inherited traits in all eukaryotes and prokaryotes and in many viruses. Ribonucleic acid (RNA) is the hereditary molecule of some viruses. Types of RNA are found in all organisms:

- Messenger RNA carries the instructions for assembling proteins from DNA to the ribosomes, the organelles that assemble proteins.
- Ribosomal RNA forms part of ribosomes.
- Transfer RNA brings amino acids to the ribosome for their assembly into proteins.

Nucleotides

All nucleic acids are polymers of nucleotides. A nucleotide consists of three parts linked together by covalent bonds: (1) a nitrogenous base formed from rings of carbon and nitrogen atoms; (2) a five-carbon, ring-shaped sugar; and (3) one to three phosphate groups.

In nucleotides, the nitrogenous bases link covalently to a five-carbon sugar, either **deoxyribose** or **ribose**. The carbons of the two sugars are numbered with a prime symbol—1′, 2′, 3′, 4′, and 5′. The prime symbols are added to distinguish the carbons in the sugars from those in the nitrogenous bases, which are written without primes. The two sugars differ only in the chemical group bound to the 2′ carbon: deoxyribose has an —H at this position, and ribose has an —OH group.

The two types of nitrogenous bases are pyrimidines, with one carbon–nitrogen ring, and purines, with two rings. Three pyrimidine bases—uracil (U), thymine (T), and cytosine (C)—and two purine bases—adenine (A) and guanine (G)—form parts of nucleic acids in cells.

All nucleic acids are polymers of nucleotides. A nucleotide consists of three parts linked together by covalent bonds:

a. Overall structural plan of a nucleotide

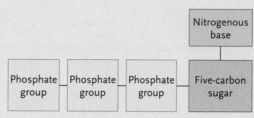

b. Chemical structures of nucleotides

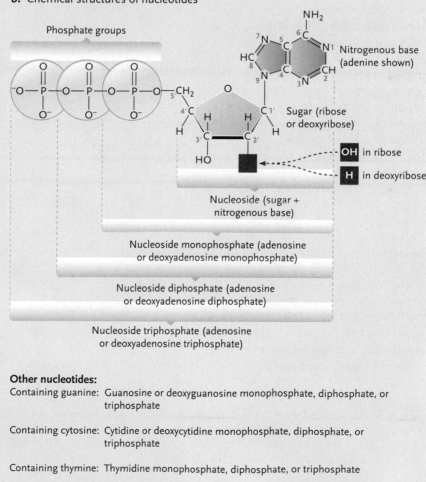

Other nucleotides:

Containing guanine: Guanosine or deoxyguanosine monophosphate, diphosphate, or triphosphate

Containing cytosine: Cytidine or deoxycytidine monophosphate, diphosphate, or triphosphate

Containing thymine: Thymidine monophosphate, diphosphate, or triphosphate

Containing uracil: Uridine monophosphate, diphosphate, or triphosphate

continued on next page

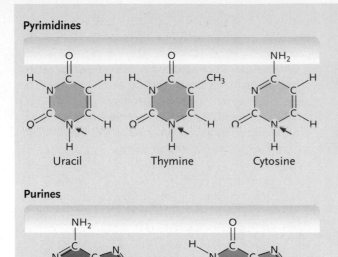

Pyrimidines

Uracil Thymine Cytosine

Purines

Adenine Guanine

Nucleotides perform many functions in cells in addition to serving as the building blocks of nucleic acids. Two nucleotides in particular, adenosine triphosphate (ATP) and guanosine triphosphate (GTP), are the primary molecules that transport chemical energy from one reaction system to another; the same nucleotides function to regulate and adjust cellular activity.

DNA and RNA Structure

DNA and RNA consist of chains of nucleotides—*polynucleotide chains*—with one nucleotide linked to the next by a single bridging phosphate group between the 5′ carbon of one sugar and the 3′ carbon of the next sugar in line. This linkage is called a *phosphodiester bond*. This arrangement of alternating sugar and phosphate groups forms the backbone of a nucleic acid chain. The nitrogenous bases of the nucleotides project from this backbone.

Each nucleotide of a DNA chain contains deoxyribose, a phosphate group, and one of the four bases A, T, G, or C. Each nucleotide of an RNA chain contains ribose, a phosphate, and one of the four bases A, U, G, or C.

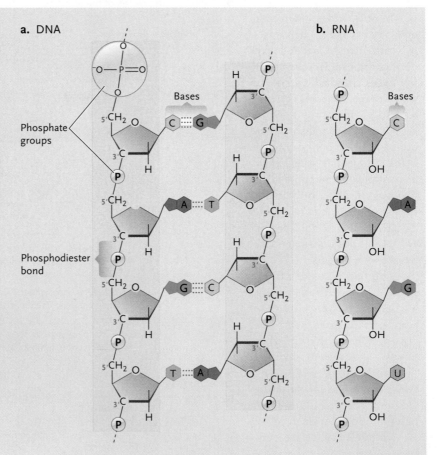

a. DNA

b. RNA

Bases

Phosphate groups

Phosphodiester bond

Bases

The DNA Double Helix

In cells, DNA takes the form of a double helix: two nucleotide chains wrapped around each other in a spiral that resembles a twisted ladder. The sides of the ladder are the sugar–phosphate backbones of the two chains, which twist around each other in a right-handed direction to form the double helix. The rungs of the ladder are the nitrogenous bases, which extend inward from the sugars toward the centre of the helix. Each rung consists of a pair of nitrogenous bases held in a flat plane roughly perpendicular to the long axis of the helix. The two nucleotide chains of a DNA double helix are held together primarily by hydrogen bonds between the base pairs. Slightly more than 10 base pairs are packed into each turn of the double helix. A DNA double-helix molecule is also referred to as double-stranded DNA.

The space separating the sugar–phosphate backbones of a DNA double helix is just wide enough to accommodate a base pair that consists of one purine and one pyrimidine. Purine–purine base pairs are too wide and pyrimidine–pyrimidine pairs are too narrow to fit this space exactly. More specifically, of the possible purine–pyrimidine pairs, only two combinations, adenine with thymine and guanine with cytosine, can form stable hydrogen bonds so that the base pair fits precisely within the double helix. An adenine–thymine (A-T) pair forms two stabilizing hydrogen bonds; a guanine–cytosine (G-C) pair forms three.

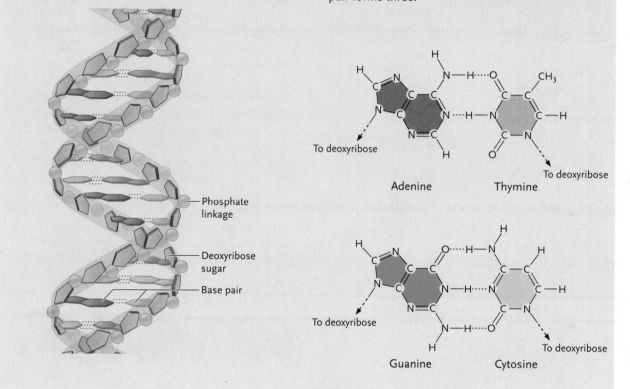

Lipids

Lipids are a diverse group of water-insoluble, primarily nonpolar biological molecules composed mostly of hydrogen and carbon (hydrocarbons). The term lipid is a catch-all word for a range of nonpolar molecules. They are not large enough to be considered true macromolecules and, unlike nucleic acids and proteins, are not considered polymers of defined monomeric subunits. As a result of their nonpolar character, lipids typically dissolve much more readily in nonpolar solvents, such as acetone and chloroform, than in water. Their insolubility in water underlies their ability to form cell membranes. In addition, some lipids are stored and used in cells as an energy source. Other lipids serve as hormones that regulate cellular activities. Lipids in living organisms can be grouped into one of three categories—fats, phospholipids, and steroids.

Isoprenes and Fatty Acids

The structural backbone of all lipids is derived from one of two hydrocarbon molecules: isoprene or fatty acids. Isoprenes are five-carbon molecules that when linked together can form long hydrocarbon chains. Isoprenes are the structural unit in steroids and a number of phospholipids. A fatty acid consists of a single hydrocarbon chain with a carboxyl group (—COOH) linked at one end. The carboxyl group gives the fatty acid its acidic properties. The fatty acids in living organisms contain four or more carbons in their hydrocarbon chain, with the most common forms having even-numbered chains of 14 to 22 carbons. As their chain length increases, fatty acids become progressively less water soluble and more solid.

If the hydrocarbon chain of a fatty acid binds the maximum possible number of hydrogen atoms, so that only single bonds link the carbon atoms, the fatty acid is said to be saturated with hydrogen atoms. If one or more double bonds link the carbons, reducing the number of bound hydrogen atoms, the fatty acid is unsaturated. Fatty acids with one double bond are **monounsaturated**; those with more than one double bond are **polyunsaturated**. Unlike saturated fatty acids, the presence of double bonds imparts a "kink" in the molecule.

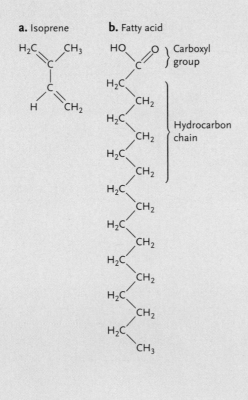

a. Isoprene **b.** Fatty acid

Carboxyl group

Hydrocarbon chain

c. Stearic acid, $CH_3(CH_2)_{16}COOH$

d. Oleic acid, $CH_3(CH_2)_7CH{=}CH(CH_2)_7COOH$

Fats

A fat consists of three fatty acid chains linked to a single molecule of glycerol. Because of this, fats are also often referred to as triacylglycerols or triglycerides. The three fatty acids linked to the glycerol may be different or the same. Different organisms usually have distinctive combinations of fatty acids in their triglycerides. As with individual fatty acids, triglycerides generally become less fluid as the length of their fatty acid chains increases; those with shorter chains remain liquid as **oils** at biological temperatures, and those with longer chains solidify.

Triglycerides are used widely as stored energy in animals. Gram for gram, they yield more than twice as much energy as carbohydrates. Therefore, fats are an excellent source of energy in the diet. Storing the equivalent amount of energy as carbohydrates rather than fats would add more than 100 pounds to the weight of an average man or woman. A layer of fatty tissue just under the skin also serves as an insulating blanket in humans, other mammals, and birds. Triglycerides secreted from special glands in waterfowl and other birds help make feathers water repellent.

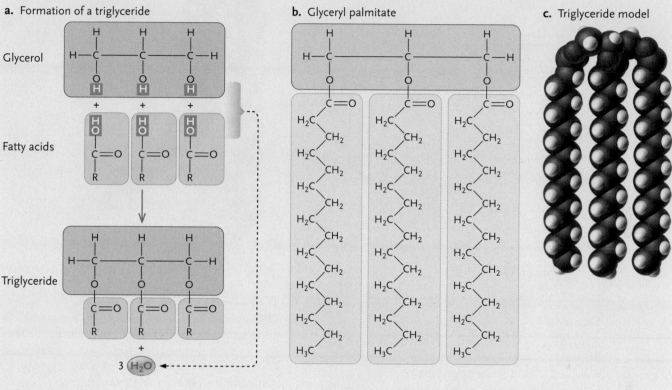

a. Formation of a triglyceride

Glycerol

Fatty acids

Triglyceride

3 H_2O

b. Glyceryl palmitate

c. Triglyceride model

Phospholipids

Phosphate-containing lipids called phospholipids are the primary lipids of cell membranes. In the most common phospholipids, glycerol forms the backbone for the molecule as in triglycerides, but only two of its binding sites are linked to fatty acids. The third site is linked to a polar phosphate group, which also binds to another polar unit. Thus, a phospholipid contains two hydrophobic fatty acids at one end, attached to a hydrophilic polar group, often called the head group. Molecules that contain both hydrophobic and hydrophilic regions are called amphipathic molecules.

continued on next page

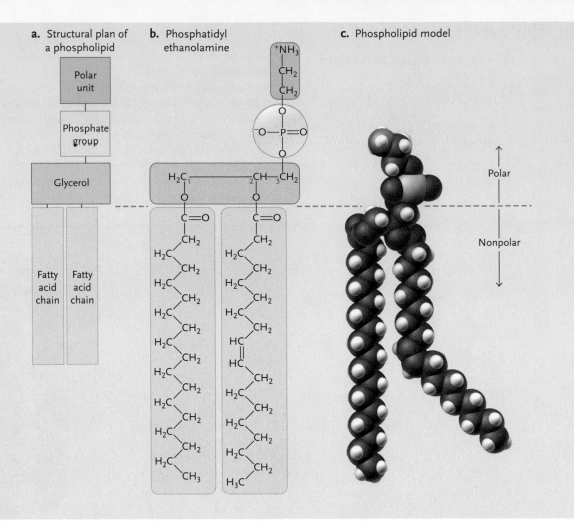

a. Structural plan of a phospholipid

b. Phosphatidyl ethanolamine

c. Phospholipid model

Polar unit

Phosphate group

Glycerol

Fatty acid chain | Fatty acid chain

Polar

Nonpolar

Steroids

Steroids are a group of lipids with structures based on a framework of four carbon rings that are derived from iso-prene units. Small differences in the side groups attached to the rings distinguish one steroid from another. The most abundant steroids, the sterols, have a single polar —OH group linked to one end of the ring framework and a complex, nonpolar hydrocarbon chain at the other end.

Although sterols are almost completely hydrophobic, the single hydroxyl group gives one end of the molecules a slightly polar, hydrophilic character. As a result, sterols also have dual solubility properties and, like phospholipids, tend to assume positions that satisfy these properties.

Cholesterol is an important component of the plasma membrane surrounding animal cells; similar sterols, called phytosterols, occur in plant cell membranes.

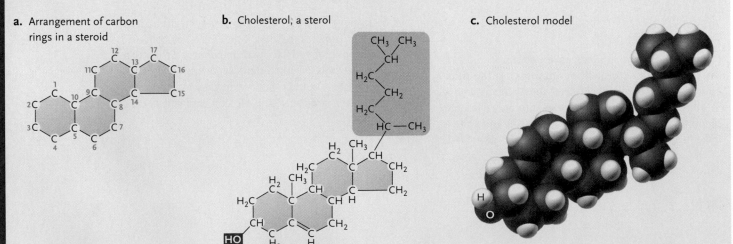

a. Arrangement of carbon rings in a steroid

b. Cholesterol, a sterol

c. Cholesterol model

Model Research Organisms

Certain species or groups of organisms have become favourite subjects for laboratory and field studies because their characteristics make them relatively easy research subjects. In most cases, such **model organisms** became popular because they have rapid development, short life cycles, and small adult size. Thus, researchers can rear and house large numbers of them in the laboratory. Also, as fuller portraits of their genetics and other aspects of their biology emerge, their appeal as research subjects tends to grow because biologists have a better understanding of the biological context within which specific processes occur. Because the fundamental elements of biochemistry, development, and evolution are common to all organisms, research on these small and often simple model organisms provides insights into biological processes that operate in and among larger and more complex organisms.

As a cautionary note, you should also be aware that the very characteristics that make model organisms valuable for research may make them poor representatives of other organisms in that group. Thus, specific findings from *Drosophila* or *Caenorhabditis elegans* may not be generally applicable to other insects or nematodes, respectively. The use of model organisms only, to the exclusion of others, may obscure the richness of biological diversity.

Escherichia coli

We probably know more about *Escherichia coli* than any other organism. For example, microbiologists have deciphered the complete DNA sequence of the genome of a standard laboratory strain of *E. coli*, including the sequence of the approximately 4400 genes in its genome. The functions of about one-third of these genes are still unidentified; however, *E. coli* got its start in laboratory research because of the ease with which it can be grown in cultures. Because *E. coli* cells divide about every 20 minutes under optimal conditions, a clone of 1 billion cells can be grown in a matter of hours in only 10 mL of culture medium. The same amount of medium can accommodate as many as 10 billion cells before the growth rate begins to slow. *E. coli* strains can be grown in the laboratory with minimal equipment, requiring little more than culture vessels in an incubator held at 37°C.

The study of naturally occurring plasmids in *E. coli* and of enzymes that cut DNA at specific sequences eventually resulted in the development of recombinant DNA techniques—procedures to combine DNA from different sources. Today, **E. coli** is used extensively for creating such molecules and for amplifying (cloning) them once they are made. In essence, the biotechnology industry has its foundation in molecular genetics studies of *E. coli*. Large-scale *E. coli* cultures are widely used as "factories" for the production of desired proteins. For example, the human insulin hormone, required for treatment of certain forms of diabetes, can be produced by *E. coli* factories.

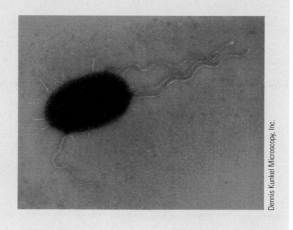

Dennis Kunkel Microscopy, Inc.

Saccharomyces cerevisiae

Commonly known as baker's yeast or brewer's yeast, *Saccharomyces cerevisiae* was probably the first microorganism to have been domesticated by humans—a beer-brewing vessel is basically a *Saccharomyces* culture. Favourite strains of baker's and brewer's yeasts have been kept in continuous cultures for centuries. The yeast has also been widely used in scientific research; its microscopic size and relatively short generation time make it easy and inexpensive to culture in large numbers in the laboratory.

The complete DNA sequence of *S. cerevisiae*, which includes more than 12 million base pairs that encode about 6000 genes, was the first eukaryotic genome to be determined. Plasmids, extrachromosomal segments of DNA, have been produced that are used to introduce genes into yeast cells. Using plasmids, researchers can experimentally alter any of the yeast genes to test their functions and can introduce genes or DNA samples from other organisms for testing or cloning. These genetic engineering studies have demonstrated that many mammalian genes can replace yeast genes when introduced into the fungi, confirming their close relationships, even though mammals and fungi are separated by millions of years of evolution. *S. cerevisiae* has been so important to genetic studies in eukaryotes that it is often called the eukaryotic *E. coli*. Research with another yeast, *Schizosaccharomyces pombe*, has been similarly productive, particularly in studies of genes that control the cell cycle.

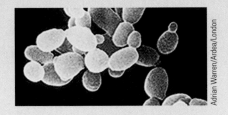

Adrian Warren/Ardea/London

Drosophila melanogaster

The unobtrusive little fruit fly that appears seemingly from nowhere when rotting fruit or a fermented beverage is around is one of the mainstays of genetic research. It was first described in 1830 by C. F. Fallén, who named it *Drosophila,* meaning "dew lover." The species identifier became *melanogaster,* which means "black belly." The great geneticist Thomas Hunt Morgan began to culture *D. melanogaster* in 1909 in the famous "Fly Room" at Columbia University. Many important discoveries in genetics were made in the Fly Room, including sex-linked genes and sex linkage and the first chromosome map. The subsequent development of methods to induce mutations in *Drosophila* led, through studies of the mutants produced, to many other discoveries that collectively established or confirmed essentially all the major principles and conclusions of eukaryotic genetics.

One reason for the success of *D. melanogaster* as a subject for genetics research is the ease of culturing it. It is grown usually at 25°C in small bottles stopped with a cotton or plastic foam wad and about one-third filled with a fermenting medium that contains water, cornmeal, agar, molasses, and yeast. The several hundred eggs laid by each adult female hatch rapidly and progress through larval and pupal stages to produce adult flies in about 10 days. These are ready to breed within 10 to 12 hours. Males and females can be identified easily with the unaided eye.

Many types of mutations produce morphological differences, such as changes in eye colour, wing shape, or the numbers and shapes of bristles, which can be seen with the unaided eye or under a low-power binocular microscope. The salivary gland cells of the fly larvae have giant chromosomes that are so large that differences can be observed directly with the light microscope. The availability of a wide range of mutants, comprehensive linkage maps of each of its chromosomes, and the ability to manipulate genes readily by molecular techniques made the fruit fly genome one of the first to be sequenced. The sequencing of *Drosophila*'s genome was completed in 2001; it has approximately 14 000 genes in its 165 million-base-pair genome. (A database of the *Drosophila* genome is available at http://flybase.bio .indiana.edu.) Importantly, the relationship between fruit fly and human genes is close, to the point that many human disease genes have counterparts in the fruit fly genome. This similarity enables the fly genes to be studied as models of human disease genes to understand better the functions of those genes and how alterations in them can lead to disease.

The analysis of fruit fly embryonic development has also contributed significantly to the understanding of development in humans. For example, experiments on mutants that affect fly development have provided insights into the genetic basis of many human birth defects. Before making a career as an environmentalist, Dr. David Suzuki studied temperature-sensitive neurological mutants at the University of British Columbia.

Herman Eisenbeiss/Photo Researchers, Inc.

Caenorhabditis elegans

Researchers studying the tiny, free-living nematode *C. elegans* have made many advances in molecular genetics, animal development, and neurobiology. It is so popular as a model research organism that most workers simply refer to it as "the worm." Several attributes make *C. elegans* a model research organism. The adult is about 1 mm long and thrives on cultures of *E. coli* or other bacteria; thus, thousands can be raised in a culture dish. It completes its life cycle from egg to reproductive adult within three days at room temperature. Furthermore, stock cultures can be kept alive indefinitely by freezing them in liquid nitrogen or in an ultra-cold freezer (−80°C). Researchers can therefore store new mutants for later research without having to clean, feed, and maintain active cultures. Best of all, the worm is anatomically simple; an adult contains just 959 cells (excluding the gonads). Having a fixed cell number is relatively uncommon among animals, and developmental biologists have made good use of this trait. The eggs, juveniles, and adults of the worm are completely transparent, and researchers can observe cell divisions and cell movements in living animals with straightforward microscopy techniques. There is no need to kill, fix, and stain specimens for study. And virtually every cell in the worm's body is accessible for manipulation by laser microsurgery, microinjection, and similar approaches.

The genome of *C. elegans*, which was sequenced in 1998, is also simple, consisting of 100 million base pairs organized into roughly 17 000 genes on 6 pairs of chromosomes. The genome, which is about the same size as 1 human chromosome, specifies the amino acid sequences of about 10 000 protein molecules—far fewer than are found in more complex animals.

The knowledge gained from research on *C. elegans* is highly relevant to studies of larger and more complex organisms, including vertebrates. Recent research demonstrates some striking similarities among nematodes, fruit flies, and mice in the genetic control of development; in some of the proteins that govern important events such as cell death; and in the molecular signals used for cell-to-cell communication. Using a relatively simple model such as *C. elegans*, researchers can answer research questions more quickly and more efficiently than they could if they studied larger and more complex animals.

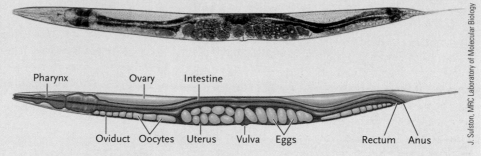

Pharynx Ovary Intestine

Oviduct Oocytes Uterus Vulva Eggs Rectum Anus

J. Sulston, MRC Laboratory of Molecular Biology

Arabidopsis thaliana

For plant geneticists, the little white-flowered thale cress, *Arabidopsis thaliana,* has attributes that make it a prime subject for genetic research. A tiny member of the mustard family, *Arabidopsis* is revealing answers to some of the biggest questions in plant development and physiology. Each plant grows only a few centimetres tall, so little laboratory space is required to house a large population. As long as *Arabidopsis* is provided with damp soil containing basic nutrients, it grows easily and rapidly in artificial light. Seeds grow to mature plants in just over a month and then flower and reproduce themselves in another three to four weeks. This permits investigators to perform desired genetic crosses and obtain large numbers of offspring with known, desired genotypes with relative ease.

The *Arabidopsis* genome was the first complete plant genome to be sequenced. Researchers have identified approximately 28 000 genes arranged on 5 pairs of chromosomes. The genome contains relatively little repetitive DNA, so it is fairly easy to isolate *Arabidopsis* genes, which can then be cloned using genetic engineering techniques. Cloned genes are inserted into bacterial plasmids, and the recombinant plasmids are transferred to the bacterial species *Agrobacterium tumefaciens,* which readily infects *Arabidopsis* cells. Amplified by the bacteria, the genes and their protein products can be sequenced or studied in other ways. Typically, researchers use chemical mutagens or recombinant bacteria to introduce changes in the *Arabidopsis* genome.

Courtesy of the Arabidopsis Information Resource, 2005.

continued on next page

Arabidopsis mutants are also being used to probe fundamental questions such as how plant cells respond to gravity and the role of pigments called phytochromes in plant responses to light. An ambitious, multinational research effort called the 2010 Project aims to determine the functions of all *Arabidopsis* genes by 2010. In Canada, major projects are under way at the University of Toronto, the University of British Columbia, the National Research Council Plant Biotechnology Research Institute, and Agriculture Canada. The Arabidopsis Information Resource (TAIR) recently estimated the percentages of *A. thaliana* genes in different functional categories. The goal of Project 2010 is to create a comprehensive genetic portrait of a flowering plant—how each gene affects the functioning of not only individual cells but also the plant as a whole.

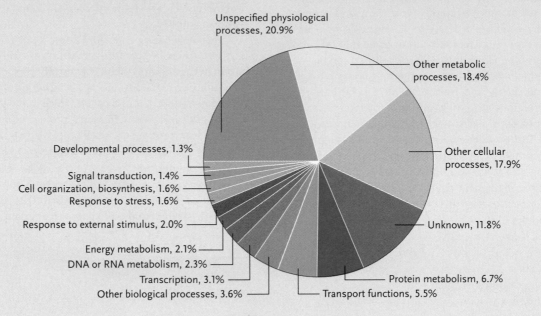

Unspecified physiological processes, 20.9%

Other metabolic processes, 18.4%

Other cellular processes, 17.9%

Unknown, 11.8%

Protein metabolism, 6.7%

Transport functions, 5.5%

Other biological processes, 3.6%

Transcription, 3.1%

DNA or RNA metabolism, 2.3%

Energy metabolism, 2.1%

Response to external stimulus, 2.0%

Response to stress, 1.6%

Cell organization, biosynthesis, 1.6%

Signal transduction, 1.4%

Developmental processes, 1.3%

Danio rerio

The zebrafish (*Danio rerio*) is a small (3 cm) freshwater fish that gets its name from the black and white stripes running along its body. Native to India, it has spread around the world as a favourite aquarium fish. Beginning about 30 years ago, it began to be used in scientific laboratories as a model vertebrate organism for studying the roles of genes in development. Its use is now so widespread that it has been dubbed the "vertebrate fruit fly."

The zebrafish brings many advantages as a model research organism. It can be maintained easily in an ordinary aquarium on a simple diet. Although its generation time is relatively long (3 months for the zebrafish compared with 6 weeks for the mouse), a female zebrafish produces about 200 offspring at a time, compared with an average of 10 for the mouse. Embryonic development of the zebrafish takes place in eggs released to the outside by the female. The embryos develop rapidly, taking only three days from egg laying to hatching. Best of all, the eggs and embryos are transparent, providing an open window that allows researchers to observe developmental stages directly, with little or no disturbance to the embryo. Observational conditions are so favourable that the origin and fate of each cell can be traced from the fertilized egg to the hatchling. Individual nerve cells can be traced, for example, as they grow and make connections in the brain, spinal cord, and peripheral body regions. Removing or transplanting cells and tissues is also relatively easy. Biochemical and molecular studies can be carried out by techniques ranging from the simple addition of reactants to the water surrounding the embryos to injection of chemicals into individual cells.

The advantages of working with the zebrafish have spurred efforts to investigate its genetics, with particular interest in genes that regulate embryonic development. This work has already identified mutants of more than 2000 genes, including more than 400 genes that influence development. Most of the mechanisms controlled by the developmental genes resemble their counterparts in humans and other mammals. Developmental and physiological studies have revealed functions of some zebrafish genes that were previously unknown for their mammalian equivalents.

David M. Parichy

Mus musculus

The "wee, sleekit, cow'rin', tim'rous beastie," as the poet Robert Burns called the mouse (*Mus musculus*), has a much larger stature among scientists. The mouse and its cells have been used to great advantage as models for research on mammalian developmental genetics, immunology, and cancer. The availability of the mouse as a research tool enables scientists to carry out mammalian experiments that would not be practical or ethical with humans. Its small size makes the mouse relatively inexpensive and easy to maintain in the laboratory, and its short generation time, compared with most other mammals, allows genetic crosses to be carried out within a reasonable time span. Mice can be mated when they are 10 weeks old; in 18 to 22 days, the female gives birth to a litter of 5 to 10 offspring. A female may be rebred a little more than a day after giving birth.

Mice have a long and highly productive history as experimental animals. Gregor Mendel, the founder of genetics, is known to have kept mice as part of his studies. Toward the end of the nineteenth century, August Weissmann helped disprove an early evolutionary hypothesis, the inheritance of acquired characters, by cutting off the tails of mice for 22 successive generations and finding that it had no effect on tail length. The first example of a lethal allele was also found in mice, and pioneering experiments on the transplantation of tissues between individuals were conducted with mice. During the 1920s, Fred Griffith laid the groundwork for the research showing that DNA is the hereditary molecule in his work with pneumonia-causing bacteria in mice.

More recently, genetic experiments with mice have revealed more than 500 mutants that cause hereditary diseases, immunological defects, and cancer in mammals, including humans. The mouse has also been the mammal of choice for experiments that introduce and modify genes through genetic engineering. One of the most spectacular results of this research was the production of giant mice by introducing a human growth hormone gene into a line of dwarfed mice that were deficient for this hormone. Genetic engineering has also produced "knockout" mice, in which a gene of interest is completely nonfunctional. The effects of this lack of function often help investigators determine the role of the normal form of the gene. Some knockout mice are defective in genes homologous to human genes that cause serious diseases, such as cystic fibrosis, so researchers can study the disease in mice with the goal of developing cures or therapies.

The revelations in developmental genetics from studies with the mouse have been of great interest and importance in their own right. In 2002, the sequence of the mouse genome was reported. This sequence is enabling researchers to refine and expand their use of the mouse as a model organism for studies of mammalian biology and mammalian diseases. More and more, as we find that much of what applies to the mouse also applies to humans, the findings in mice have shed new light on human development and opened pathways to the possible cures of human genetic diseases.

© Peter Skinner/Photo Researchers, Inc.

Anolis Lizards of the Caribbean

The lizard genus *Anolis* has been a model system for studies in ecology and evolutionary biology since the 1960s, when Ernest E. Williams of Harvard University's Museum of Comparative Zoology first began studying it. With more than 400 known species—and new ones being described all the time—*Anolis* is one of the most diverse vertebrate genera known. Most anoles are less than 10 cm long, not including the tail, and many occur at high densities, making it easy to collect a lot of data in a relatively short time. Male anoles defend territories, and their displays make them conspicuous even in dense forests.

Anolis species are widely distributed in South America and Central America, but nearly 40% occupy Caribbean islands. The number of species on an island is generally proportional to the island's size. Cuba, the largest island, has more than 50 species, whereas small islands have just one or two. Studies by Williams and others suggest that the anoles on some large islands are the products of independent adaptive radiations. Eight of the 10 *Anolis* species now found on Puerto Rico probably evolved on that island from a common ancestor. Similarly, the seven *Anolis* species on Jamaica shared a common ancestor, which was different from the ancestor of the Puerto Rican species. The anole faunas on Cuba and Hispaniola are the products of several independent radiations on each island. Williams discovered that these independent radiations had produced similar-looking species on different islands. He developed the concept of the *ecomorph*, a group of species that have similar morphological, behavioural, and ecological characteristics even though they are not closely related within the genus. Williams named the ecomorphs after the vegetation that they commonly used. For example, grass anoles are small, slender species that usually perch on low, thin vegetation. Trunk-ground anoles have chunky bodies and large heads, and they perch low on tree trunks, frequently jumping to the ground to feed. Although the grass anoles or the trunk-ground anoles on different islands are similar in many ways, they are not closely related to each other. Their resemblances are the products of convergent evolution.

A. cooki

A. poncensis

Manuel Leal, Duke University

Manuel Leal, Duke University

Sunny lowlands · Shaded uplands

A. cuvieri
A. occultus
A. stratulus · A. evermanni
Desert habitats
A. cristatellus
A. cooki
A. gundlachi
A. pulchellus
A. krugi
A. poncensis

A. gundlachi

Manuel Leal, Duke University

A. krugi

Manuel Leal, Duke University

Chapter 1

1. e 2. d 3. b 4. a 5. e 6. d 7. e 8. d 9. d 10. e

Chapter 2

1. c 2. b 3. c 4. e 5. e 6. e 7. d 8. b 9. e 10. b

Chapter 3

1. c 2. c 3. b 4. a 5. b 6. b 7. b 8. e 9. e 10. c

Chapter 4

1. e 2. d 3. d 4. d 5. d 6. c 7. e 8. c 9. d 10. e

Chapter 5

1. d 2. a 3. e 4. d 5. d 6. e 7. c 8. b 9. a 10. c

Chapter 6

1. c 2. d 3. c 4. d 5. e 6. b 7. c 8. d 9. d 10. e

Chapter 7

1. e 2. c 3. a 4. b 5. e 6. b 7. c 8. e 9. c 10. b

Chapter 8

1. b 2. d 3. c 4. c 5. e

Chapter 9

1. c 2. b 3. d 4. b 5. b 6. d 7. a 8. b 9. b 10. c

Chapter 10

1. a 2. c 3. d 4. a 5. e 6. b 7. d 8. c 9. b 10. b 11. a 12. d 13. b

Chapter 11

1. (a) The CC parent produces all C gametes, and the Cc parent produces $1/2$ C and $1/2$ c gametes. All offspring would have coloured seeds—half homozygous CC and half heterozygous Cc. (b) Both parents produce $1/2$ C and $1/2$ c gametes. Of the offspring, three-fourths would have coloured seeds ($1/4$ CC + $1/2$ Cc) and one-fourth would have colourless seeds ($1/4$ cc). (c) The Cc parent produces $1/2$ C gametes and $1/2$ c gametes, and the cc parent produces all c gametes. Half of the offspring are coloured ($1/2$ Cc) and half are colourless ($1/2$ cc).

2. The genotypes of the parents are Tt and tt.

3. The taster parents could have a nontaster child, but nontaster parents are not expected to have a child who can taste PTC. The chance that they might have a taster child is 3/4. The chance of a nontaster child being born to the taster couple would be 1/4. Because each combination of gametes is an independent event, the chance of the couple having a second child, or any child, who cannot taste PTC is expected to be 1/4.

4. (a) All A B. (b) $1/2$ A B + $1/2$ a B. (c) $1/2$ A b + $1/2$ a b. (d) $1/4$ A B + $1/4$ A b + $1/4$ a B + $1/4$ a b.

5. (a) All Aa BB. (b) $1/4$ AA BB + $1/4$ AA Bb + $1/4$ Aa BB + $1/4$ Aa Bb. (c) $1/4$ Aa Bb _ $1/4$ Aa bb + $1/4$ aa Bb + $1/4$ aa bb. (d) $1/4$ Aa Bb + $1/8$ AA Bb + $1/8$ Aa BB + $1/8$ Aa bb + $1/8$ aa Bb + $1/16$ AA BB + $1/16$ AA bb + $1/16$ aa BB + $1/16$ aa bb.

6. (a) All A B C. (b) $1/2$ A B c + $1/2$ a B c. (c) $1/4$ A B C + $1/4$ A B c + $1/4$ a B C + $1/4$ a B c. (d) $1/8$ A B C + $1/8$ A B c + $1/8$ A b C + $1/8$ A b c + $1/8$ a B C + $1/8$ a B c + $1/8$ a b C + $1/8$ a b c.

7. Because the man can produce only 1 type of allele for each of the 10 genes, he can produce only 1 type of sperm cell with respect to these genes. The woman can produce 2 types of alleles for each of her 2 heterozygous genes, so she can produce $2 \times 2 = 4$ different types of eggs with respect to the 10 genes. In general, as the number of heterozygous genes increases, the number of possible types of gametes increases as 2^n, where n = the number of heterozygous genes.

8. Use a standard testcross; that is, cross the guinea pig with rough, black fur with a double recessive individual, rr bb (smooth, white fur). If your animal is homozygous RR BB, you would expect all the offspring to have rough, black fur.

9. One gene probably controls pod colour. One allele, for green pods, is dominant; the other allele, for yellow pods, is recessive.

10. The cross $RR \times Rr$ will produce $1/2$ RR and $1/2$ Rr offspring. The cross $Rr \times Rr$ will produce $1/4$ RR, $1/2$ Rr, and $1/4$ rr as combinations of alleles. However, the $1/4$ rr combination is lethal, so it does not appear among the offspring. Therefore, the offspring will be born with only two types, RR and Rr, with twice as many Rr as rr in a 1:2 ratio (or $1/3$ RR + $2/3$ Rr).

11. The parental cross is GG TT $RR \times gg$ tt rr. All offspring of this cross are expected to be tall plants with green pods and round seeds, or Gg Tt Rr. When crossed, this heterozygous F1 generation is expected to produce eight different

phenotypes among the offspring: green-tall-round, green-dwarf-round, yellow-tall-round, green-tall-wrinkled, yellow-dwarf-round, green-dwarf-wrinkled, yellow-tall-wrinkled, yellow-dwarf-wrinkled, in a 27:9:9:9:3:3:3:1 ratio.

12. The genotypes are: bird 1, *Ff Pp*; bird 2, *FF PP*; bird 3, *Ff PP*; bird 4, *Ff Pp*.

13. Yes, it can be determined that the child is not hers, because the father must be AB to have both an A and B child with a type O wife; none of the woman's children could have type O blood with an AB father.

14. The cross is expected to produce white, tabby, and black kittens in a 12:3:1 ratio.

15. The mother is homozygous recessive for both genes, and the father must be heterozygous for both genes. The child is homozygous recessive for both genes. The chance of having a child with normal hands is 1/2, and that of having a child with woolly hair is 1/2. Using the product rule of probability, the probability of having a child with normal hands and woolly hair is $1/2 \times 1/2 = 1/4$.

Chapter 12

1. All sons will be colour-blind, but none of the daughters will be. However, all daughters will be heterozygous carriers of the trait.

2. The chance that her son will be colour-blind is 1/2, regardless of whether she marries a normal or colour-blind male.

3. All these questions can be answered from the pedigree. Polydactyly is caused by a dominant allele, and the trait is not sex linked. The genotypes of each person are:

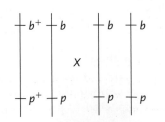

4. The sequence of the genes is ADBC.

5. Let the allele for wild-type gray body colour = b^+, and the allele for black body = b. Let the allele for wild-type red eye colour = p^+, and the allele for purple eyes = p. Then the parents are:

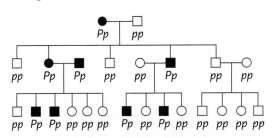

The F$_1$ flies with black bodies and red eyes are:

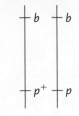

and the flies with gray bodies and purple eyes are:

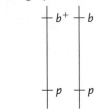

6. The genes are linked by their presence on the same chromosome (an autosome), but they are not sex linked. Because the F$_1$ females must have produced 600 gametes to give these 600 progeny, and because 42 + 30 of these were recombinant, the percentage of recombinant gametes is 72/600, or 12%, which implies that 12 map units separate the two genes.

7. Because this trait is probably carried on the Y chromosome, which a man transmits to all his sons, all will have hairy ears. None of the daughters will have hairy ears because they do not have a Y chromosome.

8. You might suspect that a recessive allele is sex linked and is carried on one of the two X chromosomes of the female parent in the cross. When present on the single X of the male (or if present on both Xs of a female) the gene is lethal.

Chapter 13

1. b 2. d 3. a 4. a 5. d 6. c 7. b 8. a 9. c 10. b

Chapter 14

1. b 2. a 3. e 4. d 5. b 6. c 7. d 8. b 9. a 10. e

Chapter 15

1. d 2. c 3. a 4. b 5. e 6. b 7. d 8. a 9. d 10. b

Chapter 16

1. e 2. c 3. d 4. a 5. b 6. b 7. e 8. a 9. e 10. d

Glossary

3′ end The end of a polynucleotide chain at which a hydroxyl group is bonded to the 3 carbon of a deoxyribose sugar.

5′ cap In eukaryotes, a guanine-containing nucleotide attached in a reverse orientation to the 5′ end of pre-mRNA and retained in the mRNA produced from it. The 5′ cap on an mRNA is the site where ribosomes attach to initiate translation.

5′ end The end of a polynucleotide chain at which a phosphate group is bound to the 5 carbon of a deoxyribose sugar.

10-nm chromatin fibre The most fundamental level of chromatin packing of a eukaryotic chromosome in which DNA winds for almost two turns around an eight-protein nucleosome core particle to form a nucleosome and linker DNA extends between adjacent nucleosomes. The result is a beads-on-a-string type of structure with a 10 nm diameter.

30-nm chromatin fibre Level of chromatin packing of a eukaryotic chromosome in which histone H1 binds to the 10-nm chromatin fibre, causing it to package into a coiled structure about 30 nm in diameter and with about six nucleosomes per turn. Also referred to as a *solenoid*.

A site The site where the incoming amino-acyl-tRNA carrying the next amino acid to be added to the polypeptide chain binds to the mRNA.

abiotic Nonbiological, often in reference to physical factors in the environment.

absorption spectrum Curve representing the amount of light absorbed at each wavelength.

acid Proton donor that releases H (and anions) when dissolved in water.

acidity The concentration of H in a water solution, compared with the concentration of OH^-.

action spectrum Graph produced by plotting the effectiveness of light at each wavelength in driving photosynthesis.

activation energy The initial input of energy required to start a reaction.

activator A regulatory protein that controls the expression of one or more genes.

active site The region of an enzyme that recognizes and combines with a substrate molecule.

active transport The mechanism by which ions and molecules move against the concentration gradient across a membrane, from the side with the lower concentration to the side with the higher concentration.

adaptive radiation A cluster of closely related species that are each adaptively specialized to a specific habitat or food source.

adaptive zone A part of a habitat that may be occupied by a group of species exploiting the same resources in a similar manner.

adenine A purine that base-pairs with either thymine in DNA or uracil in RNA.

adiabatic cooling A decrease in temperature without the actual loss of heat energy, occurring in air masses that expand as they rise in the atmosphere.

agarose gel electrophoresis Technique by which DNA, RNA, or molecules are separated in a gel subjected to an electric field.

alcohol A molecule of the form R—OH in which R is a chain of one or more carbon atoms, each of which is linked to hydrogen atoms.

alcoholic fermentation Reaction in which pyruvate is converted into ethyl alcohol and CO_2 in a two-step series that also converts NADH into NAD^+.

aldehyde Molecule in which the carbonyl group is linked to a carbon atom at the end of a carbon chain, along with a hydrogen atom.

allele One of two or more versions of a gene.

allosteric activator Molecule that converts an enzyme with an allosteric site, a regulatory site outside the active site, from the inactive form to the active form.

allosteric inhibitor Molecule that converts an enzyme with an allosteric site, a regulatory site outside the active site, from the active form to the inactive form.

allosteric regulation Specialized control mechanism for enzymes with an allosteric site, a regulatory site outside the active site, that may either slow or accelerate activity depending on the enzyme.

allosteric site A regulatory site outside the active site.

alternative hypothesis An explanation of an observed phenomenon that is different from the explanation being tested.

alternative splicing Mechanism that joins exons in different combinations to produce different mRNAs from a single gene.

amino acid A molecule that contains both an amino and a carboxyl group.

amino group Group that acts as an organic base, consisting of a nitrogen atom bonded on one side to two hydrogen atoms and on the other side to a carbon chain.

aminoacylation The process of adding an amino acid to a tRNA. Also referred to as *charging*.

aminoacyl–tRNA A tRNA linked to its "correct" amino acid, which is the finished product of charging.

aminoacyl–tRNA synthetase An enzyme that catalyzes aminoacylation.

amniocentesis Technique of prenatal diagnosis in which cells are obtained from the amniotic fluid.

amphipathic Contains a region that is hydrophobic and a region that is hydrophilic.

anabolic pathway Type of metabolic pathway in which energy is consumed to build complicated molecules from simpler ones; often called a biosynthetic pathway.

anabolic reaction Metabolic reaction that requires energy to assemble simple substances into more complex molecules.

anaerobe An organism that does not require oxygen to live.

anaphase The phase of mitosis during which the spindle separates sister chromatids and pulls them to opposite spindle poles.

aneuploid An individual with extra or missing chromosomes.

angiotensin A peptide hormone that raises blood pressure quickly by constricting arterioles in most parts of the body; it also stimulates release of the steroid hormone aldosterone.

antenna A chemosensory appendage attached to the head of some adult arthropods.

antenna complex (light-harvesting complex) In photosystems, the sites at which light is absorbed and converted into chemical energy during photosynthesis, an aggregate of many chlorophyll pigments and a number of carotenoid pigments that serves as the primary site of absorbing light energy in the form of photons.

anther The pollen-bearing part of a stamen.

antibiotic A natural or synthetic substance that kills or inhibits the growth of bacteria and other microorganisms.

antibody A highly specific soluble protein molecule that circulates in the blood and lymph, recognizing and binding to antigens and clearing them from the body.

anticodon The three-nucleotide segment in tRNAs that pairs with a codon in mRNAs.

antiparallel Strands of DNA that run in opposite directions.

antiport A secondary active transport mechanism in which a molecule moves through a membrane channel into a cell and powers the active transport of a second molecule out of the cell. Also referred to as *exchange diffusion*.

apoptosis Programmed cell death.

applied research Research conducted with the goal of solving specific practical problems.

aster Radiating array produced as microtubules extending from the centrosomes of cells grow in length and extent.

atmosphere The component of the biosphere that includes the gases and airborne particles enveloping the planet.

atom The smallest unit that retains the chemical and physical properties of an element.

atomic nucleus The nucleus of an atom, containing protons and neutrons.

atomic number The number of protons in the nucleus of an atom.

atomic weight The weight of an element in grams, equal to the mass number.

ATP (adenosine triphosphate) The primary agent that couples exergonic and endergonic reactions.

ATP cycle Continued breakdown and resynthesis of ATP.

ATP synthase A membrane-spanning protein complex that couples the energetically favourable transport of protons across a membrane to the synthesis of ATP.

autosomal dominant inheritance Pattern in which the allele that causes a trait is dominant, and only homozygous recessives are unaffected.

autosomal recessive inheritance Pattern in which individuals with a trait are homozygous for a recessive allele.

autosome Chromosome other than a sex chromosome.

autotroph An organism that produces its own food using CO_2 and other simple inorganic compounds from its environment and energy from the sun or from oxidation of inorganic substances.

auxotrophs Mutant strains that are unable to synthesize amino acids.

Avogadro's number The number 6.022×10^{23}, derived by dividing the atomic weight of any element by the weight of an atom of that element.

bacillus (plural, bacilli) A cylindrical or rod-shaped prokaryote.

bacterial chromosome DNA molecule in bacteria in which hereditary information is encoded.

bacteriophage A virus that infects bacteria. Also referred to as a *phage*.

Barr body The inactive, condensed X chromosome seen in the nucleus of female mammals.

base Proton acceptor that reduces the H concentration of a solution.

base-pair mismatch An error in the assembly of a new nucleotide chain in which bases other than the correct ones pair together.

base-pair substitution mutation A particular mutation involving a change from one base pair to another in DNA.

basic research Research conducted to search for explanations about natural phenomena to satisfy curiosity and advance collective knowledge of living systems.

beta (β) sheet A type of primary structure in a polypeptide in which the amino acid chain zigzags in a flat plane to form a beta strand, and beta strands then align side by side in the same or opposite direction.

bilayer A membrane with two molecular layers.

binary fission Prokaryotic cell division—splitting or dividing into two parts.

biodiversity The richness of living systems as reflected in genetic variability within and among species, the number of species living on Earth, and the variety of communities and ecosystems.

bioinformatics Field that fuses biology with mathematics and computer science that is used for the analysis of genome sequences.

bioluminescent An organism that glows or releases a flash of light, particularly when disturbed.

biome A large-scale vegetation type and its associated microorganisms, fungi, and animals.

biosphere All regions of Earth's crust, waters, and atmosphere that sustain life.

biotechnology The manipulation of living organisms to produce useful products.

biotic Biological, often in reference to living components of the environment.

blending theory of inheritance Theory suggesting that hereditary traits blend evenly in offspring through mixing of the blood of the two parents.

blood A fluid connective tissue composed of blood cells suspended in a fluid extracellular matrix, plasma.

brain A single, organized collection of nervous tissue in an organism's head that forms the control centre of the nervous system and major sensory structures.

breathing The exchange of gases with the respiratory medium by animals.

buffer Substance that compensates for pH changes by absorbing or releasing H^+.

bulk-phase endocytosis Mechanism by which extracellular water is taken into a cell together with any molecules that happen to be in solution in the water. Also referred to as *pinocytosis*.

C4 cycle A reaction series that allows CO_2 to be fixed by a carboxylase that is unaffected by high oxygen concentrations.

Ca²⁺ pump (calcium pump) Pump that pushes Ca^{2+} from the cytoplasm to the cell exterior and from the cytosol into the vesicles of the endoplasmic reticulum.

calorie (cal) The amount of heat required to raise 1 g of water by 1°C, known as a "small" calorie; when capitalized, a unit equal to 1000 small calories.

Calvin cycle *See* light-independent reaction.

CAM plant A C_4 plant that runs the Calvin and C_4 cycles at different times to circumvent photorespiration. CAM stands for "crassulacean acid metabolism."

capsule An external layer of sticky or slimy polysaccharides coating the cell wall in many prokaryotes.

carbonyl group The reactive part of aldehydes and ketones, consisting of an oxygen atom linked to a carbon atom by a double bond.

carboxyl group The characteristic functional group of organic acids, formed by the combination of carbonyl and hydroxyl groups.

carotenoid Molecule of yellow-orange pigment by which light is absorbed in photosynthesis.

carrier An individual who carries a mutant allele and could pass it on to offspring but does not display its symptoms.

carrier protein Transport protein that binds a specific single solute and transports it across the lipid bilayer.

Cartagena Protocol on Biosafety An international agreement that promotes biosafety as it relates to genetically modified organisms.

caspase A protease involved in programmed cell death.

catabolic pathway Type of metabolic pathway in which energy is released by the breakdown of complex molecules to simpler compounds.

catabolic reaction Cellular reaction that breaks down complex molecules such as sugar to make their energy available for cellular work.

catalyst Substance with the ability to accelerate a spontaneous reaction without being changed by the reaction.

cation A positively charged ion.

cDNA library The entire collection of cloned cDNAs made from the mRNAs isolated from a cell.

cell Smallest unit with the capacity to live and reproduce.

cell adhesion protein Protein that binds cells together by recognizing and binding receptors or chemical groups on other cells or on the extracellular matrix.

cell culture A living cell grown in a laboratory vessel.

cell cycle The sequence of events during which a cell experiences a period of growth followed by nuclear division and cytokinesis.

cell differentiation A process in which changes in gene expression establish cells with specialized structure and function.

cell junction Junction that seals the spaces between cells and provides direct communication between cells.

cell plate In cytokinesis in plants, a new cell wall that forms between the daughter nuclei and grows laterally until it divides the cytoplasm.

cell theory Three generalizations yielded by microscopic observations: all organisms are composed of one or more cells; the cell is the smallest unit that has the properties of life; and cells arise only from the growth and division of preexisting cells.

cell wall A rigid external layer of material surrounding the plasma membrane of cells in plants, fungi, bacteria, and some protists, providing cell protection and support.

cellular respiration The process by which energy-rich molecules are broken down to produce energy in the form of ATP.

cellular senescence Loss of proliferative ability over time.

centimorgan *See* map unit.

central nervous system (CNS) One of the two major divisions of the nervous system containing the brain and spinal cord.

centriole A cylindrical structure consisting of nine triplets of microtubules in the centrosomes of most animal cells.

centromere A specialized chromosomal region that connects sister chromatids and attaches them to the mitotic spindle.

centrosome (cell centre) The main microtubule organizing centre of a cell, which organizes the microtubule cytoskeleton during interphase and positions many of the cytoplasmic organelles.

channel protein Transport protein that forms a hydrophilic channel in a cell membrane through which water, ions, or other molecules can pass, depending on the protein.

character A heritable characteristic.

charging *See* aminoacylation.

checkpoint Internal control of the cell cycle that prevents a critical phase from beginning until the previous phase is complete.

chemical bond Link formed when atoms of reactive elements combine into molecules.

chemical equation A chemical reaction written in balanced form.

chemical reaction A reaction that occurs when atoms or molecules interact to form new chemical bonds or break old ones.

chemical signal Any secretion from one cell type that can alter the behaviour of a different cell that bears a receptor for it; a means of cell communication.

chemiosmosis Ability of cells to use the proton-motive force to do work.

chemotroph An organism that obtains energy by oxidizing inorganic or organic substances.

chiasmata *See* crossover.

chlorophyll Molecule of green pigment that absorbs photons of light in photosynthesis.

chloroplast The site of photosynthesis in plant cells.

cholesterol The predominant sterol of animal cell membranes.

chorionic villus sampling Technique of prenatal diagnosis in which cells are obtained from portions of the placenta that develop from tissues of the embryo.

chromatin The structural building block of a chromosome, which includes the complex of DNA and its associated proteins.

chromatin remodelling Process in which the state of the chromatin is changed so that the proteins that initiate transcription can bind to their promoters.

chromosomal protein The histone and nonhistone protein associated with DNA structure and regulation in the nucleus.

chromosome The nuclear unit of genetic information, consisting of a DNA molecule and associated proteins.

chromosome segregation The equal distribution of daughter chromosomes to each of the two cells that result from cell division.

chromosome theory of inheritance The principle that genes and their alleles are carried on the chromosomes.

cilium Motile structure, extending from a cell surface, that moves a cell through fluid or fluid over a cell.

cisternae (singular, cisterna) Membranous channels and vesicles that make up the endoplasmic reticulum.

citric acid cycle Series of reactions in which acetyl groups are oxidized completely to carbon dioxide and some ATP molecules are synthesized. Also referred to as *Krebs cycle* and *tricarboxylic acid cycle*.

clathrin The network of proteins that coat and reinforce the cytoplasmic surface of cell membranes.

climate The weather conditions prevailing over an extended period of time.

clone An individual genetically identical to an original cell from which it descended.

CO_2 fixation Process in which electrons are used as a source of energy to convert inorganic CO_2 to an organic form.

coactivator (mediator) In eukaryotes, a large multiprotein complex that bridges between activators at an enhancer and proteins at the promoter and promoter proximal region to stimulate transcription.

coated pit A depression in the plasma membrane that contains receptors for macromolecules to be taken up by endocytosis.

codominance Condition in which alleles have approximately equal effects in individuals, making the alleles equally detectable in heterozygotes.

codon Each three-letter word (triplet) of the genetic code.

coenzymes Organic cofactors that include complex chemical groups of various kinds.

cofactor An inorganic or organic nonprotein group that is necessary for catalysis to take place.

combinatorial gene regulation The combining of a few regulatory proteins in particular ways so that the transcription of a wide array of genes can be controlled and a large number of cell types can be specified.

commaless The sequential nature of the words of the nucleic acid code, with no indicators such as commas or spaces to mark the end of one codon and the beginning of the next.

community Populations of all species that occupy the same area.

competitive inhibition Inhibition of an enzyme reaction by an inhibitor molecule that resembles the normal substrate closely enough so that it fits into the active site of the enzyme.

complementary base pairing Feature of DNA in which the specific purine–pyrimidine base pairs A–T (adenine–thymine) and G–C (guanine–cytosine) occur to bridge the two sugar–phosphate backbones.

complementary DNA (cDNA) A DNA molecule that is complementary to an mRNA molecule, synthesized by reverse transcriptase.

compound A molecule whose component atoms are different.

concentration The number of molecules or ions of a substance in a unit volume of space.

concentration gradient The concentration difference that drives diffusion.

condensation reaction Reaction during which the components of a water molecule are removed, usually as part of the assembly of a larger molecule from smaller subunits. Also referred to as *dehydration synthesis reaction*.

conformation The overall three-dimensional shape of a protein.

conformational change Alteration in the three-dimensional shape of a protein.

conjugation In bacteria, the process by which a copy of part of the DNA of a donor cell moves through the cytoplasmic bridge into the recipient cell where genetic recombination can occur. In ciliate protozoans, a process of sexual reproduction in which individuals of the same species temporarily couple and exchange genetic material.

consumer An organism that consumes other organisms in a community or ecosystem.

contact inhibition The inhibition of movement or proliferation of normal cells that results from cell–cell contact.

continental climate Climate not moderated by the distant ocean.

core The nucleic acid centre of a virus in the free form.

corepressor In the regulation of gene expression in bacteria, a regulatory molecule that combines with a repressor to activate it and shut off an operon.

cornea The transparent layer that forms the front wall of the eye, covering the iris.

cotransport *See* symport.

coupled reaction Reaction that occurs when an exergonic reaction is joined to an endergonic reaction, producing an overall reaction that is exergonic.

covalent bond Bond formed by electron sharing between atoms.

crassulacean acid metabolism (CAM) A biochemical variation of photosynthesis that was discovered in a member of the plant family Crassulaceae. Carbon dioxide is taken up and stored during the night to allow the stomata to remain closed during the daytime, decreasing water loss.

crossing-over The recombination process in meiosis, in which chromatids exchange segments.

crossover Site of recombination during meiosis. Also referred to as a *chiasmata*.

cross-pollination Fertilization of one plant by a different plant.

cross-talk Interaction by which cell signalling pathways communicate with one another to integrate their responses to cellular signals.

C-terminal end The end of an amino acid chain with a —COO group.

cyclic AMP (cAMP) In particular signal transduction pathways, a second messenger that activates protein kinases, which elicit the cellular response by adding phosphate groups to specific target proteins. cAMP functions in one of two major G protein–coupled receptor–response pathways.

cyclic electron transport An electron transport pathway associated with photosystem I in photosynthesis that produces ATP without the synthesis of NADPH.

cyclin In eukaryotes, protein that regulates the activity of CDK (cyclin-dependent kinase) and controls progression through the cell cycle.

cyclin-dependent kinase (CDK) A protein kinase that controls the cell cycle in eukaryotes.

cytochrome Protein with a heme prosthetic group that contains an iron atom.

cytokinesis Division of the cytoplasm into two daughter cells following the nuclear division stage of mitosis.

cytoplasm All parts of the cell that surround the central nuclear or nucleoid region.

cytoplasmic inheritance Pattern in which inheritance follows that of genes in the cytoplasmic organelles, mitochondria, or chloroplasts.

cytoplasmic streaming Intracellular movement of cytoplasm.

cytosine A pyrimidine that base-pairs with guanine in nucleic acids.

cytoskeleton The interconnected system of protein fibres and tubes that extends throughout the cytoplasm of a eukaryotic cell.

cytosol Aqueous solution in the cytoplasm containing ions and various organic molecules.

dalton A standard unit of mass, about 1.66×10^{24} grams.

decomposer A small organism, such as a bacterium or fungus, that feeds on the remains of dead organisms, breaking down complex biological molecules or structures into simpler raw materials.

degeneracy (redundancy) The feature of the genetic code in which, with two exceptions, more than one codon represents each amino acid.

dehydration synthesis reaction *See* condensation reaction.

deletion Chromosomal alteration that occurs if a broken segment is lost from a chromosome.

denaturation A loss of both the structure and function of a protein due to extreme conditions that unfold it from its conformation.

deoxyribonucleic acid (DNA) The large, double-stranded, helical molecule that contains the genetic material of all living organisms.

deoxyribose A five-carbon sugar to which the nitrogenous bases in nucleotides of DNA link covalently.

derivative One of the daughter cells produced when a plant cell divides; it typically divides once or twice and then enters on the path to differentiation.

desaturases A group of enzymes that synthesize unsaturated fatty acids.

desert A sparsely vegetated biome that forms where rainfall averages less than 25 cm per year.

development A series of programmed changes encoded in DNA, through which a fertilized egg divides into many cells that ultimately are transformed into an adult, which is itself capable of reproduction.

diacylglycerol (DAG) In particular, signal transduction pathways, a second messenger that activates protein kinases, which elicit the cellular response by adding phosphate groups to specific target proteins. DAG is involved in one of two major G protein–coupled receptor–response pathways.

diatom Photosynthetic single-celled organisms with a glassy silica shell; also called bacillariophytes.

diffusion The net movement of ions or molecules from a region of higher concentration to a region of lower concentration.

dihybrid A zygote produced from a cross that involves two characters.

dihybrid cross A cross between two individuals that are heterozygous for two pairs of alleles.

diploid An organism or cell with two copies of each type of chromosome in its nucleus.

discontinuous replication Replication in which a DNA strand is formed in short lengths that are synthesized in the direction opposite of DNA unwinding.

disulphide linkage Linkage that occurs when two sulfhydryl groups interact during a linking reaction.

DNA *See* deoxyribonucleic acid.

DNA chip *See* DNA microarray.

DNA fingerprinting Technique in which DNA samples are used to distinguish between individuals of the same species.

DNA helicase An enzyme that catalyzes the unwinding of DNA template strands.

DNA hybridization Technique in which a gene or sequence of interest is identified in a set of clones when it base-pairs with a single-stranded DNA or RNA molecule called a nucleic acid probe.

DNA ligase In DNA replication, an enzyme that seals the nicks left after RNA primers are replaced with DNA.

DNA methylation Process in which a methyl group is added enzymatically to cytosine bases in the DNA.

DNA microarray A solid surface divided into a microscopic grid of thousands of spaces each containing thousands of copies of a DNA probe. DNA chips are used commonly for analysis of gene activity and for detecting differences between cell types. Also referred to as a *DNA chip*.

DNA polymerase An enzyme that assembles complementary nucleotide chains during DNA replication.

DNA repair mechanism Mechanism to correct base-pair mismatches that escape proofreading.

DNA technologies Techniques to isolate, purify, analyze, and manipulate DNA sequences.

dominance The masking effect of one allele over another.

dominant The allele expressed when more than one allele is present.

double helix Two nucleotide chains wrapped around each other in a spiral.

double-helix model Model of DNA consisting of two complementary sugar–phosphate backbones.

duplication Chromosomal alteration that occurs if a segment is broken from one chromosome and inserted into its homologue.

E site The site where an exiting tRNA binds prior to its release from the ribosome.

ecology The study of the interactions between organisms and their environments.

ecosystem A group of biological communities interacting with their shared physical environment.

ectoparasite A parasite that lives on the exterior of its host organism.

effector In signal transduction, a plasma membrane–associated enzyme, activated by a G protein, that generates one or more second messengers. In homeostatic feedback, the system that returns the condition to the set point if it has strayed away.

effector T cell A cell involved in effecting—bringing about—the specific immune response to an antigen.

electrochemical gradient A difference in chemical concentration and electric potential across a membrane.

electromagnetic spectrum The range of wavelengths or frequencies of electromagnetic radiation extending from gamma rays to the longest radio waves and including visible light.

electron Negatively charged particle outside the nucleus of an atom.

electron microscope Microscope that uses electrons to illuminate the specimen.

electron transfer system Stage of cellular respiration in which high-energy electrons produced from glycolysis, pyruvate oxidation, and the citric acid cycle are delivered to oxygen by a sequence of electron carriers.

electronegativity The measure of an atom's attraction for the electrons it shares in a chemical bond with another atom.

element A pure substance that cannot be broken down into simpler substances by ordinary chemical or physical techniques.

embryo An organism in its early stage of reproductive development, beginning in the first moments after fertilization.

enantiomers Isomers that are mirror images of each other. Also referred to as *optical isomers*.

endangered species A species in immediate danger of extinction throughout all or a significant portion of its range.

endergonic reaction Reaction that can proceed only if free energy is supplied.

endocytic vesicle Vesicle that carries proteins and other molecules from the plasma membrane to destinations within the cell.

endocytosis In eukaryotes, the process by which molecules are brought into the cell from the exterior involving a bulging in of the plasma membrane that pinches off to form an endocytic vesicle.

endomembrane system In eukaryotes, a collection of interrelated internal membranous sacs that divide a cell into functional and structural compartments.

endoparasite A parasite that lives in the internal organs of its host organism.

endoplasmic reticulum (ER) In eukaryotes, an extensive interconnected network of cisternae that is responsible for the synthesis, transport, and initial modification of proteins and lipids.

endosymbiont hypothesis The proposal that the membranous organelles of eukaryotic cells (mitochondria and chloroplasts) may have originated from symbiotic relationships between two prokaryotic cells.

endothermic Reactions that absorb energy.

end-product inhibition *See* feedback inhibition.

energy The capacity to do work.

energy coupling The process by which ATP is brought in close contact with a reactant molecule involved in an endergonic reaction, and when the ATP is hydrolyzed, the terminal phosphate group is transferred to the reactant molecule.

energy levels Regions of space within an atom where electrons are found. Also referred to as *energy shells*.

enhancer In eukaryotes, a region at a significant distance from the beginning of a gene containing regulatory sequences that determine whether the gene is transcribed at its maximum possible rate.

enthalpy Potential energy in a system.

entropy Disorder, in thermodynamics.

enzyme Protein that accelerates the rate of a cellular reaction.

enzyme specificity The ability of an enzyme to catalyze the reaction of only a single type of molecule or group of closely related molecules.

epistasis Interaction of genes, with one or more alleles of a gene at one locus inhibiting or masking the effects of one or more alleles of a gene at a different locus.

equilibrium point A state of balance between opposing factors that push a reaction in either direction.

ER (endoplasmic reticulum) lumen The enclosed space surrounded by a cisterna.

essential amino acid Any amino acid that is not made by the human body but must be taken in as part of the diet.

euchromatin In eukaryotes, regions of loosely packed chromatin fibres in interphase nuclei.

eukaryote Organism in which the DNA is enclosed in a nucleus.

eukaryotic chromosome A DNA molecule, with its associated proteins, in the nucleus of a eukaryotic cell.

euploid An individual with a normal set of chromosomes.

exchange diffusion *See* antiport.

excretion The process that helps maintain the body's water and ion balance while ridding the body of metabolic wastes.

exergonic reaction Reaction that has a negative ΔG because it releases free energy.

exocytosis In eukaryotes, the process by which a secretory vesicle fuses with the plasma membrane and releases the vesicle contents to the exterior.

exon An amino acid–coding sequence present in pre-mRNA that is retained in a spliced mRNA that is translated to produce a polypeptide.

exon shuffling Process by which existing amino acid–coding regions or domains are mixed into novel combinations to create new proteins.

exothermic Processes that release energy.

extinction The death of the last individual in a species or the last species in a lineage.

eye The organ animals use to sense light.

F pilus Structure on the cell surface that allows an F^+ donor bacterial cell to attach to an F^- recipient bacterial cell. Also referred to as a *sex pilus*.

F^- cell Recipient cell in conjugation between bacteria.

F^+ cell Donor cell in conjugation between bacteria.

F1 generation The first generation of offspring from a genetic cross.

F2 generation The second generation of offspring from a genetic cross.

facilitated diffusion Mechanism by which polar and charged molecules diffuse across membranes with the help of transport proteins.

facultative anaerobe An organism that can live in the presence or absence of oxygen, using oxygen when it is present and living by fermentation under anaerobic conditions.

fat Neutral lipid that is semisolid at biological temperatures.

fatty acid One of two components of a neutral lipid, containing a single hydrocarbon chain with a carboxyl group linked at one end.

feather A sturdy, lightweight structure of birds, derived from scales in the skin of their ancestors.

feedback inhibition In enzyme reactions, regulation in which the product of a reaction acts as a regulator of the reaction. Also referred to as *end-product inhibition*.

fermentation Process in which electrons carried by NADH are transferred to an organic acceptor molecule rather than to the electron transfer system.

fertilization The fusion of the nuclei of an egg and sperm cell, which initiates development of a new individual.

fibre In sclerenchyma, an elongated, tapered, thick-walled cell that gives plant tissue its flexible strength.

first law of thermodynamics The principle that energy can be transferred and transformed but cannot be created or destroyed.

first messenger The extracellular signal molecule in signal transduction pathways controlled by G protein–coupled receptors.

flagellum (plural, flagella) A long, threadlike, cellular appendage responsible for movement; found in both prokaryotes and eukaryotes, but with different structures and modes of locomotion.

fluid mosaic model Model proposing that the membrane consists of a fluid phospholipid bilayer in which proteins are embedded and float freely.

food chain A depiction of the trophic structure of a community, a portrait of who eats whom.

food web A set of interconnected food chains with multiple links.

formula The name of a molecule written in chemical shorthand.

fossil The remains or traces of an organism of a past geologic age embedded and preserved in Earth's crust.

frameshift mutation Mutation in a protein-coding gene that causes the reading frame of an mRNA transcribed from the gene to be altered, resulting in the production of a different, and nonfunctional, amino acid sequence in the polypeptide.

free energy The energy in a system that is available to do work.

freeze-fracture technique Technique in which experimenters freeze a block of cells rapidly and then fracture the block to split the lipid bilayer and expose the hydrophobic membrane interior.

functional genomics The study of the functions of genes and of other parts of the genome.

functional groups The atoms in reactive groups.

furrow In cytokinesis, a groove that girdles the cell and gradually deepens until it cuts the cytoplasm into two parts.

fusiform initial A cell derived from cambium inside a vascular bundle; gives rise to secondary xylem and phloem cells.

futile cycle Occurs when two metabolic pathways run simultaneously in opposite directions and have no overall effect other than wasting energy.

G0 phase The phase of the cell cycle in eukaryotes in which many cell types stop dividing.

G1 phase The initial growth stage of the cell cycle in eukaryotes, during which the cell makes proteins and other types of cellular molecules but not nuclear DNA.

G2 phase The phase of the cell cycle in eukaryotes during which the cell continues to synthesize proteins and grow, completing interphase.

gamete A haploid cell, and egg or sperm. Haploid cells fuse during sexual reproduction to form a diploid zygote.

gametophyte An individual of the haploid generation produced when a spore germinates and grows directly by mitotic divisions in organisms that undergo alternation of generations.

gap junction Junction that opens direct channels allowing ions and small molecules to pass directly from one cell to another.

gastric juice A substance secreted by the stomach that contains the digestive enzyme pepsin.

gated channel Ion transporter in a membrane that switches between open, closed, or intermediate states.

germ-line gene therapy Therapy in which a gene is introduced into germ-line cells of an animal to correct a genetic disorder.

gene A unit containing the code for a protein molecule or one of its parts, or for functioning RNA molecules such as tRNA and rRNA.

gene therapy Correction of genetic disorders using genetic engineering techniques.

general transcription factor (basal transcription factor) In eukaryotes, a protein that binds to the promoter of a gene in the area of the TATA box and recruits and orients RNA polymerase II to initiate transcription at the correct place.

generalized transduction Transfer of bacterial genes between bacteria using virulent phages that have incorporated random DNA fragments of the bacterial genome.

genetic code The nucleotide information that specifies the amino acid sequence of a polypeptide.

genetic counselling Counselling that allows prospective parents to assess the possibility that they might have a child affected by a genetic disorder.

genetic engineering The use of DNA technologies to alter genes for practical purposes.

genetic recombination The process by which the combinations of alleles for different genes in two parental individuals become shuffled into new combinations in offspring individuals.

genetic screening Biochemical or molecular tests for identifying inherited disorders after a child is born.

genetically modified organism (GMO) A transgenic organism.

genomic imprinting Pattern of inheritance in which the expression of a nuclear gene is based on whether an individual organism inherits the gene from the male or the female parent.

genomic library A collection of clones that contains a copy of every DNA sequence in a genome.

genotype The genetic constitution of an organism.

genus A Linnaean taxonomic category ranking below a family and above a species.

germ-line gene therapy Experiment in which a gene is introduced into germ-line cells of an animal to correct a genetic disorder.

gland A cell or group of cells that produces and releases substances nearby, in another part of the body, or to the outside.

glycocalyx A carbohydrate coat covering the cell surface.

glycogen Energy-providing carbohydrates stored in animal cells.

glycolysis Stage of cellular respiration in which sugars such as glucose are partially oxidized and broken down into smaller molecules.

glycosidic bond Bond formed by the linkage of two-glucose molecules with oxygen as a bridge between a carbon of the first glucose unit and a carbon of the second glucose unit.

Golgi complex In eukaryotes, the organelle responsible for the final modification, sorting, and distribution of proteins and lipids.

G protein–coupled receptor In signal transduction, a surface receptor that responds to a signal by activating a G protein.

guanine A purine that base-pairs with cytosine in nucleic acids.

haploid An organism or cell with only one copy of each type of chromosome in its nuclei.

head The anteriormost part of the body, containing the brain, sensory structures, and feeding apparatus.

heat of vaporization The heat required to give water molecules enough energy of motion to break loose from liquid water and form a gas.

herbicide A compound that, at proper concentration, kills plants.

herbivore An animal that obtains energy and nutrients primarily by eating plants.

heterochromatin In eukaryotes, regions of densely packed chromatin fibres in interphase nuclei.

heterozygote An individual with two different alleles of a gene.

heterozygous The state of possessing two different alleles of a gene.

Hfr cell A special donor cell that can transfer genes on a bacterial chromosome to a recipient bacterium.

histone A small, positively charged (basic) protein that is complexed with DNA in the chromosomes of eukaryotes.

homologous Similar.

homozygote An individual with two copies of the same allele.

homozygous State of possessing two copies of the same allele.

hormone A signalling molecule secreted by a cell that can alter the activities of any cell with receptors for it; in animals, typically a molecule produced by one tissue and transported via the bloodstream to another specific tissue to alter its physiological activity.

host A species that is fed upon by a parasite.

human immunodeficiency virus (HIV) A retrovirus that causes acquired immune deficiency syndrome (AIDS).

hydration layer A surface coat of water molecules that covers other polar and charged molecules and ions.

hydrocarbon Molecule consisting of carbon linked only to hydrogen atoms.

hydrogen bond Noncovalent bond formed by unequal electron sharing between hydrogen atoms and oxygen, nitrogen, or sulphur atoms.

hydrolysis Reaction in which the components of a water molecule are added to functional groups as molecules are broken into smaller subunits.

hydrophilic Polar molecules that associate readily with water.

hydrophobic Nonpolar substances that are excluded by water and other polar molecules.

hydrosphere The component of the biosphere that encompasses all of the waters on Earth, including oceans, rivers, and polar ice caps.

hydroxyl group Group consisting of an oxygen atom linked to a hydrogen atom on one side and to a carbon chain on the other side.

hypertonic Solution containing dissolved substances at higher concentrations than the cells it surrounds.

hypothesis A "working explanation" of observed facts.

hypotonic Solution containing dissolved substances at lower concentrations than the cells it surrounds.

incomplete dominance Condition in which the effects of recessive alleles can be detected to some extent in heterozygotes.

independent assortment Mendel's principle that the alleles of the genes that govern two characters segregate independently during formation of gametes.

inducer Concerning regulation of gene expression in bacteria, a molecule that turns on the transcription of the genes in an operon.

inducible operon Operon whose expression is increased by an inducer molecule.

inheritance The transmission of DNA (that is, genetic information) from one generation to the next.

initial A plant cell that remains permanently as part of a meristem and gives rise to daughter cells that differentiate into specialized cell types.

initiator codon *See* start codon.

initiator RNA The aminoacyl–tRNA used for initiation, with an anticodon to the methionine-specifying AUG start codon.

inner boundary membrane Membrane lying just inside the outer boundary membrane of a chloroplast, enclosing the stroma.

inner mitochondrial membrane Membrane surrounding the mitochondrial matrix.

inorganic molecule Molecule without carbon atoms in its structure.

inositol triphosphate (IP3) In particular, signal transduction pathways, a second messenger that activates transport proteins in the endoplasmic reticulum to release Ca^{2+} into the cytoplasm. IP_3 is involved in one of two major G protein–coupled receptor–response pathways.

insertion sequence A transposable element that contains only genes for its transposition.

integral membrane protein Protein embedded in a phospholipid bilayer.

interkinesis A brief interphase separating the two meiotic divisions.

intermediate filament A cytoskeletal filament about 10 nm in diameter that provides mechanical strength to cells in tissues.

interphase The first stage of the mitotic cell cycle, during which the cell grows and replicates its DNA before undergoing mitosis and cytokinesis.

intestine The portion of digestive system where organic matter is hydrolyzed by enzymes secreted into the digestive tube. As muscular contractions of the intestinal wall move the mixture along, cells lining the intestine absorb the molecular subunits produced by digestion.

intron A non–protein-coding sequence that interrupts the protein-coding sequence in a eukaryotic gene. Introns are removed by splicing in the processing of pre-mRNA to mRNA.

inversion Chromosomal alteration that occurs if a broken segment reattaches to the same chromosome from which it was lost, but in reversed orientation, so that the order of genes in the segment is reversed with respect to the other genes of the chromosome.

invertebrate An animal without a vertebral column.

inverted repeat Enables the transposase enzyme to identify the ends of the transposable element when it catalyzes transposition.

ion A positively or negatively charged atom.

ionic bond Bond that results from electrical attractions between atoms that have lost or gained electrons.

iris Of the eye, the coloured muscular membrane that lies behind the cornea and in front of the lens, which by opening or closing determines the size of the pupil and hence the amount of light entering the eye.

isomers Two or more molecules with the same chemical formula but different molecular structures.

isotonic Equal concentration of water inside and outside cells.

isotope A distinct form of the atoms of an element, with the same number of protons but a different number of neutrons.

karyotype A characteristic of a species consisting of the shapes and sizes of all of the chromosomes at metaphase.

ketone Molecule in which the carbonyl group is linked to a carbon atom in the interior of a carbon chain.

kilocalorie (kcal) The scientific unit equivalent to a calorie and equal to 1000 small calories.

kinesis A change in the rate of movement or the frequency of turning movements in response to environmental stimuli.

kinetic energy The energy of motion.

kinetochore A specialized structure consisting of proteins attached to a centromere that mediates the attachment and movement of chromosomes along the mitotic spindle.

kingdom Animalia The taxonomic kingdom that includes all living and extinct animals.

Krebs cycle *See* citric acid cycle.

lactate fermentation Reaction in which pyruvate is converted into lactate.

lagging strand A DNA strand assembled discontinuously in the direction opposite to DNA unwinding.

landscape ecology The field that examines how large-scale ecological factors—such as the distribution of plants, topography, and human activity—influence local populations and communities.

leading strand A DNA strand assembled in the direction of DNA unwinding.

lens The transparent, biconvex intraocular tissue that helps bring rays of light to a focus on the retina.

light The portion of the electromagnetic spectrum that humans can detect with their eyes.

light microscope Microscope that uses light to illuminate the specimen.

light-dependent reaction The first stage of photosynthesis, in which the energy of sunlight is absorbed and converted into chemical energy in the form of ATP and NADPH.

light-independent reaction The second stage of photosynthesis, in which electrons are used as a source of energy to convert inorganic CO_2 to an organic form. Also referred to as the *Calvin cycle*.

linkage The phenomenon of genes being located on the same chromosome.

linkage map Map of a chromosome showing the relative locations of genes based on recombination frequencies.

linked genes Genes on the same chromosome.

linker A short segment of DNA extending between one nucleosome and the next in a eukaryotic chromosome.

lithosphere The component of the biosphere that includes the rocks, sediments, and soils of the crust.

liver A large organ whose many functions include aiding in digestion, removing toxins from the body, and regulating the chemicals in the blood.

locus The particular site on a chromosome at which a gene is located.

loss of imprinting A phenomenon in which the imprinting mechanism for a gene does not work, resulting in both alleles of the gene being active.

lung One of a pair of invaginated respiratory surfaces, buried in the body interior where they are less susceptible to drying out; the organs of respiration in mammals, birds, reptiles, and most amphibians.

lysogenic cycle Cycle in which the DNA of the bacteriophage is integrated into the DNA of the host bacterial cell and may remain for many generations.

lysosome Membrane-bound vesicle containing hydrolytic enzymes for the digestion of many complex molecules.

lytic cycle The series of events from infection of one bacterial cell by a phage through the release of progeny phages from lysed cells.

macromolecule A very large molecule assembled by the covalent linkage of smaller subunit molecules.

magnification The ratio of an object as viewed to its real size.

mammary glands Specialized organs of female mammals that produce energy-rich milk, a watery mixture of fats, sugars, proteins, vitamins, and minerals.

map unit The unit of a linkage map, equivalent to a recombination frequency of 1%. Also referred to as a *centimorgan*.

maritime climate Climate tempered by ocean winds.

mass number The total number of protons and neutrons in the atomic nucleus.

maternal chromosome The chromosome derived from the female parent of an organism.

mating The pairing of a male and a female for the purpose of sexual reproduction.

matter Anything that occupies space and has mass.

meiocytes Cells that are destined to divide by meiosis.

meiosis The division of diploid cells to haploid progeny, consisting of two sequential rounds of nuclear and cellular division.

meiosis I The first division of the meiotic cell cycle in which homologous chromosomes pair and undergo an exchange of chromosome segments, and then the homologous chromosomes separate, resulting in two cells, each with the haploid number of chromosomes and with each chromosome still consisting of two chromatids.

meiosis II The second division of the meiotic cell cycle in which the sister chromatids in each of the two cells produced by meiosis I separate and segregate into different cells, resulting in four cells each with the haploid number of chromosomes.

membrane potential An electrical voltage that measures the potential inside a cell membrane relative to the fluid just outside; it is negative under resting conditions and becomes positive during an action potential.

messenger RNA (mRNA) An RNA molecule that serves as a template for protein synthesis.

metabolism The biochemical reactions that allow a cell or organism to extract energy from its surroundings and use that energy to maintain itself, grow, and reproduce.

metaphase The phase of mitosis during which the spindle reaches its final form and the spindle microtubules move the chromosomes into alignment at the spindle midpoint.

micelle A sphere composed of a single layer of lipid molecules.

microbody A small, membrane-bound organelle that carries out vital reactions linking metabolic pathways.

microclimate The abiotic conditions immediately surrounding an organism.

microfilament A cytoskeletal filament composed of actin.

microscope Instrument of microscopy with different magnifications and resolutions of specimens.

microscopy Technique for producing visible images of objects that are too small to be seen by the human eye.

microtubule A cytoskeletal component formed by the polymerization of tubulin into rigid, hollow rods about 25 nm in diameter.

microtubule organizing centre (MTOC) An anchoring point near the centre of a eukaryotic cell from which most microtubules extend outward.

migration The predictable seasonal movement of animals from the area where they are born to a distant and initially unfamiliar destination, returning to their birth site later.

minimal medium A growth medium containing the minimal ingredients that enable a nonmutant organism, such as *E. coli*, to grow.

mismatch repair Repair system that removes mismatched bases from newly synthesized DNA strands.

missense mutation A base-pair substitution mutation in a protein-coding gene that results in a different amino acid in the encoded polypeptide than the normal one.

mitochondrial electron transfer system Series of electron carriers that alternately pick up and release electrons, ultimately transferring them to their final acceptor, oxygen.

mitochondrial matrix The innermost compartment of the mitochondrion.

mitochondrion Membrane-bound organelle responsible for synthesis of most of the ATP in eukaryotic cells.

mitosis Nuclear division that produces daughter nuclei that are exact genetic copies of the parental nucleus.

mobile elements Particular segments of DNA that can move from one place to another; they cut and paste DNA backbones using a type of recombination that does not require homology.

model organism An organism with characteristics that make it a particularly useful subject of research because it is likely to produce results widely applicable to other organisms.

molarity (M) The number of moles of a substance dissolved in 1 L of solution.

mould Asexual, spore-producing stage of many multicellular fungi.

mole (mol) The atomic weight of an element or the molecular weight of a compound.

molecular weight The weight of a molecule in grams, equal to the total mass number of its atoms.

molecule A unit composed of atoms combined chemically in fixed numbers and ratios.

monohybrid An F1 heterozygote produced from a genetic cross that involves a single character.

monohybrid cross A genetic cross between two individuals that are each heterozygous for the same pair of alleles.

monomers Identical or nearly identical subunits that link together to form polymers during polymerization.

monosaccharides The smallest carbohydrates, containing three to seven carbon atoms.

monounsaturated Fatty acids with one double bond.

monsoon cycle A wind pattern that brings seasonally heavy rain to a region by blowing moisture-laden air from the sea to the land.

morphology The form or shape of an organism or of part of an organism.

motif A highly specialized region in a protein produced by the three-dimensional arrangement of amino acid chains within and between domains.

mRNA splicing Process that removes introns from pre-mRNAs and joins exons together.

multicellular organism Individual consisting of interdependent cells.

multiple alleles More than two different alleles of a gene.

mutation A spontaneous and heritable change in DNA.

Na$^+$/K$^+$ pump Pump that pushes 3 Na$^+$ out of the cell and 2 K$^+$ into the cell in the same pumping cycle. Also referred to as the *sodium–potassium pump*.

Nanoarchaeota A group of Archaea that was proposed based on rRNA sequence analysis of a thermophilic archaean found in a symbiotic relationship with another thermophilic archaean; most probably a subgroup of the Euryarchaeota.

nerve A bundle of axons enclosed in connective tissue and all following the same pathway.

nerve cord A bundle of nerves that extends from the central ganglia to the rest of the body, connected to smaller nerves.

neutral lipid Energy-storing molecule consisting of a glycerol backbone and three fatty acid chains.

neutron Uncharged particle in the nucleus of an atom.

nitrogenous base A nitrogen-containing molecule with the properties of a base.

noncompetitive inhibition Inhibition of an enzyme reaction by an inhibitor molecule that binds to the enzyme at a site other than the active site and, therefore, does not compete directly with the substrate for binding to the active site.

noncyclic electron flow Pathway in photosynthesis in which electrons travel in a one-way direction from H$_2$O to NADP$^+$.

nondisjunction The failure of homologous pairs to separate during the first meiotic division or of chromatids to separate during the second meiotic division.

nonhistone protein All of the proteins associated with DNA in a eukaryotic chromosome that are not histones.

nonpolar association Association that occurs when nonpolar molecules clump together.

nonpolar covalent bond Bond in which electrons are shared equally.

nonsense codon *See* stop codon.

nonsense mutation A base-pair substitution mutation in a gene in which the base-pair change results in a change from a sense codon to a nonsense codon in the mRNA. The polypeptide translated from the mRNA is shorter than the normal polypeptide because of the mutation.

N-terminal end The end of a polypeptide chain with an —NH$_3$ group.

nuclear envelope In eukaryotes, membranes separating the nucleus from the cytoplasm.

nuclear pore Opening in the membrane of the nuclear envelope through which large molecules, such as RNA and proteins, move between the nucleus and the cytoplasm.

nucleoid The central region of a prokaryotic cell with no boundary membrane separating it from the cytoplasm, where DNA replication and RNA transcription occur.

nucleolus The nuclear site of rRNA transcription, processing, and ribosome assembly in eukaryotes.

nucleoplasm The liquid or semiliquid substance within the nucleus.

nucleosome The basic structural unit of chromatin in eukaryotes, consisting of DNA wrapped around a histone core.

nucleosome core particle An eight-protein particle formed by the combination of two molecules each of H2A, H2B, H3, and H4, around which DNA winds for almost two turns.

nucleotide The monomer of nucleic acids consisting of a five-carbon sugar, a nitrogenous base, and a phosphate.

nucleus The central region of eukaryotic cells, separated by membranes from the surrounding cytoplasm, where DNA replication and messenger RNA transcription occur.

nutrition The processes by which an organism takes in, digests, absorbs, and converts food into organic compounds.

oil Neutral lipid that is liquid at biological temperatures.

omnivore An animal that feeds at several trophic levels, consuming plants, animals, and other sources of organic matter.

oncogene A gene capable of inducing one or more characteristics of cancer cells.

one gene–one enzyme hypothesis Hypothesis showing the direct relationship between genes and enzymes.

one gene–one polypeptide hypothesis Restatement of the one gene–one enzyme hypothesis, taking into account that some proteins consist of more than one polypeptide and not all proteins are enzymes.

operator A DNA regulatory sequence that controls transcription of an operon.

operon A cluster of prokaryotic genes and the DNA sequences involved in their regulation.

opsin One of several different proteins that bond covalently with the light-absorbing pigment of rods and cones (retinal).

optical isomers *See* enantiomers.

orbital The region of space where the electron "lives" most of the time.

organelles The nucleus and other specialized internal structures and compartments of eukaryotic cells.

organic molecule Molecule based on carbon.

origin of replication (ori) A specific region at which replication of a bacterial chromosome commences.

osmosis The passive transport of water across a selectively permeable membrane in response to solute concentration gradients, a pressure gradient, or both.

outer mitochondrial membrane The smooth membrane covering the outside of a mitochondrion.

overexploitation The excessive harvesting of an animal or plant species, potentially leading to its extinction.

oxidation The removal of electrons from a substance.

oxidative phosphorylation Synthesis of ATP in which ATP synthase uses an H$^+$ gradient built by the electron transfer system as the energy source to make the ATP.

oxidized Substance from which the electrons are removed during oxidation.

P generation The parental indi\viduals used in an initial cross.

P site The site in the ribosome where the tRNA carrying the growing polypeptide chain is bound.

pairing Process in meiosis in which homologous chromosomes come together and pair. Also referred to as *synapsis*.

paleobiology The study of ancient organisms.

parental Phenotypes identical to the original parental individuals.

partial diploid A condition in which part of the genome of a haploid organism is diploid. Recipients in bacterial conjugation between an Hfr and an F cell become partial diploids for part of the Hfr bacterial chromosome.

passive transport The transport of substances across cell membranes without expenditure of energy, as in diffusion.

paternal chromosome The chromosome derived from the male parent of an organism.

pedigree Chart that shows all parents and offspring for as many generations as possible, the sex of individuals in the different generations, and the presence or absence of a trait of interest.

pelagic province The water in a marine biome.

pepsinogen The inactive precursor molecule for pepsin.

peptide bond A link formed by a dehydration synthesis reaction between the —NH$_2$ group of one amino acid and the —COOH group of a second.

peptidyl transferase An enzyme that catalyzes the reaction in which an amino acid is cleaved from the tRNA in the P site of the ribosome and forms a peptide bond with the amino acid on the tRNA in the A site of the ribosome.

peptidyl–tRNA A tRNA linked to a growing polypeptide chain containing two or more amino acids.

peripheral membrane protein Protein held to membrane surfaces by noncovalent bonds formed with the polar parts of integral membrane proteins or membrane lipids.

permafrost Perpetually frozen ground below the topsoil.

peroxisome Microbody that produces hydrogen peroxide as a by-product.

pH scale The numerical scale used by scientists to measure acidity.

phagocytosis Process in which some types of cells engulf bacteria or other cellular debris to break them down.

phenotype The outward appearance of an organism.

phosphate group Group consisting of a central phosphorus atom held in four linkages: two that bind —OH groups to the central phosphorus atom, a third that binds an oxygen atom to the central phosphorus atom, and a fourth that links the phosphate group to an oxygen atom.

phosphodiester bond The linkage of nucleotides in polynucleotide chains by a bridging phosphate group between the 5 carbon of one sugar and the 3 carbon of the next sugar in line.

phospholipid A phosphate-containing lipid.

phosphorylation The addition of a phosphate group to a molecule.

photoautotroph A photosynthetic organism that uses light as its energy source and carbon dioxide as its carbon source.

photons Discrete particles or packets of energy.

photophosphorylation The synthesis of ATP coupled to the transfer of electrons energized by photons of light.

photopsin One of three photopigments in which retinal is combined with different opsins.

photorespiration A process that metabolizes a by-product of photosynthesis.

photosynthesis The conversion of light energy to chemical energy in the form of sugar and other organic molecules.

photosystem A large complex into which the light-absorbing pigments for photosynthesis are organized with proteins and other molecules.

photosystem I In photosynthesis, a protein complex in the thylakoid membrane that uses energy absorbed from sunlight to synthesize NADPH.

photosystem II In photosynthesis, a protein complex in the thylakoid membrane that uses energy absorbed from sunlight to synthesize ATP.

phototroph An organism that obtains energy from light.

physiological respiration The process by which animals exchange gases with their surroundings—how they take in oxygen from the outside environment and deliver it to body cells and remove carbon dioxide from body cells and deliver it to the environment.

phytosterol A sterol that occurs in plant cell membranes.

pigment A molecule that can absorb photons of light.

pilus (plural, pili) A hair or hairlike appendage on the surface of a prokaryote.

pinacoderm In sponges, an unstratified outer layer of cells

pinocytosis *See* bulk-phase endocytosis.

plasma membrane The outer limit of the cytoplasm responsible for the regulation of substances moving into and out of cells.

plasmid A DNA molecule in the cytoplasm of certain prokaryotes, which often contains genes with functions that supplement those in the nucleoid and which can replicate independently of the nucleoid DNA and be passed along during cell division.

pleiotropy Condition in which single genes affect more than one character of an organism.

ploidy The number of chromosome sets of a cell or species.

polar covalent bond Bond in which electrons are shared unequally.

poly(A) tail The string of A nucleotides added posttranscriptionally to the 3′ end of a pre-mRNA molecule and retained in the mRNA produced from it that enables the mRNA to be translated efficiently and protects it from attack by RNA-digesting enzymes in the cytoplasm.

polygenic inheritance Inheritance in which several to many different genes contribute to the same character.

polymerase chain reaction (PCR) Process that amplifies a specific DNA sequence from a DNA mixture to an extremely large number of copies.

polymerization Process in which monomers link together to form a polymer.

polypeptide The chain of amino acids formed by sequential peptide bonds.

polyploid An individual with one or more extra copies of the entire haploid complement of chromosomes.

polyploidy The condition of having one or more extra copies of the entire haploid complement of chromosomes.

polysaccharide Chain with more than 10 linked monosaccharide subunits.

polysome The entire structure of an mRNA molecule and the multiple associated ribosomes that are translating it simultaneously.

polyunsaturated Fatty acid with more than one double bond.

potential energy Stored energy.

precursor mRNA (pre-mRNA) The primary transcript of a eukaryotic protein-coding gene, which is processed to form messenger RNA.

prediction A statement about what the researcher expects to happen to one variable if another variable changes.

pregnancy The period of mammalian development in which the embryo develops in the uterus of the mother.

prenatal diagnosis Techniques in which cells derived from a developing embryo or its surrounding tissues or fluids are tested for the presence of mutant alleles or chromosomal alterations.

primary active transport Transport in which the same protein that transports a substance also hydrolyzes ATP to power the transport directly.

primary consumer A herbivore, a member of the second trophic level.

primary producer An autotroph, usually a photosynthetic organism, a member of the first trophic level.

primase An enzyme that assembles the primer for a new DNA strand during DNA replication.

primer A short nucleotide chain made of RNA that is laid down as the first series of nucleotides in a new DNA strand or made of DNA for use in the polymerase chain reaction (PCR).

Principle of Independent Assortment Mendel's principle that the alleles of the genes that govern two characters segregate independently during formation of gametes.

Principle of Segregation Mendel's principle that the pairs of alleles that control a character segregate as gametes are formed and that half the gametes carry one allele and the other half carry the other allele.

probability The possibility that an outcome will occur if it is a matter of chance.

product An atom or molecule leaving a chemical reaction.

product rule Mathematical rule in which the final probability is found by multiplying individual probabilities.

prokaryote Organism in which the DNA is suspended in the cell interior without separation from other cellular components by a discrete membrane.

prokaryotic flagellum A long, threadlike protein fibre that rotates in a socket in the plasma membrane and cell wall to push a prokaryotic cell through a liquid medium.

prometaphase A transition period between prophase and metaphase during which the microtubules of the mitotic spindle attach to the kinetochores and the chromosomes shuffle until they align in the centre of the cell.

promoter The site to which RNA polymerase binds for initiating transcription of a gene.

promoter proximal region Upstream of a eukaryotic gene, a region containing regulatory sequences for transcription called promoter proximal elements.

proofreading mechanism Mechanism of DNA polymerase to back up and remove mispaired nucleotides from a newly synthesized DNA strand.

prophase The beginning phase of mitosis during which the duplicated chromosomes within the nucleus condense from a greatly extended state into compact, rodlike structures.

protein Molecules that carry out most of the activities of life, including the synthesis of all other biological molecules. A protein consists of one or more polypeptides depending on the protein.

protein chip *See* protein microarray.

protein kinase Enzyme that transfers a phosphate group from ATP to one or more sites on particular proteins.

protein microarray Similar in concept to a DNA microarray, a solid surface with a microscopic grid with thousands of spaces containing probes for analyzing the proteome, the complete set of proteins encoded by the genome of an organism. Also referred to as a *protein chip*.

protein phosphatase Enzyme that removes phosphate groups from target proteins.

proteome The complete set of proteins that can be expressed by the genome of an organism.

proteomics The study of the proteome.

protobiont The term given to a group of abiotically produced organic molecules that are surrounded by a membrane or membranelike structure.

proton Positively charged particle in the nucleus of an atom.

proton pump Pump that moves hydrogen ions across membranes and pushes hydrogen ions across the plasma membrane from the cytoplasm to the cell exterior. Also referred to as H^+ *pump*.

proton-motive force Stored energy that contributes to ATP synthesis and to the cotransport of substances to and from mitochondria.

proto-oncogene A gene that encodes various kinds of proteins that stimulate cell division. Mutated proto-oncogenes contribute to the development of cancer.

prototrophs Strains that are able to synthesize the necessary amino acids.

provirus The inserted viral DNA.

Punnett square Method for determining the genotypes and phenotypes of offspring and their expected proportions.

pupil The dark centre in the middle of the iris through which light passes to the back of the eye.

purine A type of nitrogenous base with two carbon–nitrogen rings.

pyrimidine A type of nitrogenous base with one carbon–nitrogen ring.

pyruvate oxidation (pyruvic acid oxidation) Stage of cellular respiration in which the three-carbon molecule pyruvate is converted into a two-carbon acetyl group that is completely oxidized to carbon dioxide.

quaternary structure The arrangement of polypeptide chains in a protein that contains more than one chain.

radioactivity The giving off of particles of matter and energy by decaying nuclei.

radioisotope An unstable, radioactive isotope.

rain shadow An area of reduced precipitation on the leeward side of a mountain.

reactants The atoms or molecules entering a chemical reaction.

reaction centre Part of photosystems I and II in chloroplasts of plants. In the light-dependent reactions of photosynthesis, the reaction centre receives light energy absorbed by the antenna complex in the same photosystem.

reading frame A particular grouping of triplet bases read by transfer RNA during translation.

reception In signal transduction, the binding of a signal molecule with a specific receptor in a target cell.

receptor protein Protein that recognizes and binds molecules from other cells that act as chemical signals.

receptor tyrosine kinase In signal transduction, a surface receptor with built-in protein kinase activity.

receptor-mediated endocytosis The selective uptake of macromolecules that bind to cell surface receptors concentrated in clathrin-coated pits.

recessive An allele that is masked by a dominant allele.

recombinant Phenotype with a different combination of traits from those of the original parents.

recombinant DNA DNA from two or more different sources joined together.

recombination The physical exchange of segments between the chromatids of homologous chromosomes or between the chromosomes of prokaryotic cells or viruses.

recombination frequency In the construction of linkage maps of diploid eukaryotic organisms, the percentage of testcross progeny that are recombinants.

redox reaction Coupled oxidation–reduction reaction in which electrons are removed from a donor molecule and simultaneously added to an acceptor molecule.

reduced Substance that receives electrons during reduction.

reduction The addition of electrons to a substance.

release factor A protein that recognizes stop codons in the A site of a ribosome translating an mRNA and terminates translation. Also referred to as the *termination factor*.

replica plating Technique for identifying and counting genetic recombinants in conjugation, transformation, or transduction experiments in which the colony pattern on a plate containing solid growth medium is pressed onto sterile velveteen and transferred to other plates containing different combinations of nutrients.

replication fork The region of DNA synthesis where the parental strands separate and two new daughter strands elongate.

replication origin The site at which DNA replication begins.

repressible operon Operon whose expression is prevented by a repressor molecule.

repressor A regulatory protein that prevents the operon genes from being expressed.

reproduction The process in which parents produce offspring.

response In signal transduction, the last stage in which the transduced signal causes the cell to change according to the signal and to the receptors on the cell. In the nervous system, the output resulting from the integration of neural messages.

restriction endonuclease (restriction enzyme) An enzyme that cuts DNA at a specific sequence.

restriction fragment A DNA fragment produced by cutting a long DNA molecule with a restriction enzyme.

restriction fragment length polymorphisms When comparing different individuals, restriction enzyme–generated DNA fragments of different lengths from the same region of the genome.

retina A light-sensitive membrane lining the posterior part of the inside of the eye.

retrotransposon A transposable element that transposes via an intermediate RNA copy of the transposable element.

retrovirus A virus with an RNA genome that replicates via a DNA intermediate.

reverse transcriptase An enzyme that uses RNA as a template to make a DNA copy of the retrotransposon. Reverse transcriptase is used to make DNA copies of RNA in test tube reactions.

reversible The term indicating that a reaction may go from left to right or from right to left, depending on conditions.

ribonucleic acid (RNA) A polymer assembled from repeating nucleotide monomers in which the five-carbon sugar is ribose. Cellular RNAs are mRNA (which is translated to produce a polypeptide), tRNA (which brings an amino acid to the ribosome for assembly into a polypeptide during translation), and rRNA (which is a structural component of ribosomes). The genetic material of some viruses is RNA.

ribose A five-carbon sugar to which the nitrogenous bases in nucleotides link covalently.

ribosomal RNA (rRNA) The RNA component of ribosomes.

ribosome A ribonucleoprotein particle that carries out protein synthesis by translating mRNA into chains of amino acids.

ribosome binding site In translation initiation in prokaryotes, a sequence just upstream of the start codon that directs the small ribosomal subunit to bind and orient correctly for the complete ribosome to assemble and start translating in the correct spot.

ribozyme An RNA-based catalyst that is part of the biochemical machinery of all cells.

RNA *See* ribonucleic acid.

RNA interference (RNAi) The phenomenon of silencing a gene posttranscriptionally by a small, single-stranded RNA that is complementary to part of an mRNA.

RNA polymerase An enzyme that catalyzes the assembly of nucleotides into an RNA strand.

rough ER Endoplasmic reticulum with many ribosomes studding its outer surface.

RuBP carboxylase/oxygenase (rubisco) An enzyme that catalyzes the key reaction of the Calvin cycle, carbon fixation, in which CO_2 combines with RuBP (ribulose 1,5-bisphosphate) to form 3-phosphoglycerate.

ruminant An animal that has a complex, four-chambered stomach.

S phase The phase of the cell cycle during which DNA replication occurs.

saturated fatty acid Fatty acid with only single bonds linking the carbon atoms.

second law of thermodynamics Principle that for any process in which a system changes from an initial to a final state, the total disorder of the system and its surroundings always increases.

second messenger In particular, signal transduction pathways, an internal, nonprotein signal molecule that directly or indirectly activates protein kinases, which elicit the cellular response.

secondary active transport Transport indirectly driven by ATP hydrolysis.

secondary structure Regions of alpha helix, beta strand, or random coil in a polypeptide chain.

secretion A selective process in which specific small molecules and ions are transported from the body fluids (in animals with open circulatory systems) or blood (in animals with closed circulatory systems) into the excretory tubules.

secretory vesicle Vesicle that transports proteins to the plasma membrane.

selectively permeable Membranes that selectively allow, impede, or block the passage of atoms and molecules.

self-fertilization (self-pollination) Fertilization in which sperm nuclei in pollen produced by anthers fertilize egg cells housed in the carpel of the same flower.

semen The secretions of several accessory glands in which sperm are mixed prior to ejaculation.

semiconservative replication The process of DNA replication in which the two parental strands separate and each serves as a template for the synthesis of new progeny double-stranded DNA molecules.

senescence The biologically complex process of aging in mature organisms that leads to the death of cells and eventually the whole organism.

sense codon A codon that specifies an amino acid.

sensor A tissue or organ that detects a change in an external or internal factor such as pH, temperature, or the concentration of a molecule such as glucose.

sex chromosomes Chromosomes that are different in male and female individuals of the same species.

sex pilus *See* F pilus.

sex-linked gene Gene located on a sex chromosome.

sexual reproduction The mode of reproduction in which male and female parents produce offspring through the union of egg and sperm generated by meiosis.

shells *See* energy levels.

signal peptide A short segment of amino acids to which the signal recognition particle binds, temporarily blocking further translation. A signal peptide is found on polypeptides that are sorted to the endoplasmic reticulum. Also referred to as *signal sequence*.

signal recognition particle (SRP) Protein–RNA complex that binds to signal sequences and targets polypeptide chains to the endoplasmic reticulum.

signal sequence *See* signal peptide.

signal transduction The series of events by which a signal molecule released from a controlling cell causes a response (affects the function) of target cells with receptors for the signal. Target cells process the signal in the three sequential steps of reception, transduction, and response.

silencing Phenomenon in which methylation of cytosines in eukaryotic promoters inhibits transcription and turns the genes off.

silent mutation A base-pair substitution mutation in a protein-coding gene that does not alter the amino acid specified by the gene.

simple diffusion Mechanism by which certain small substances diffuse through the lipid part of a biological membrane.

single-lens eye An eye type that works by changing the amount of light allowed to enter into the eye and by focusing this incoming light with a lens.

single-stranded binding protein Protein that coats single-stranded segments of DNA, stabilizing the DNA for the replication process.

sister chromatid One of two exact copies of a chromosome duplicated during replication.

small interfering RNA (siRNA) A class of single-stranded RNAs that cause RNA interference.

small ribonucleoprotein particle A complex of RNA and proteins.

smooth ER Endoplasmic reticulum with no ribosomes attached to its membrane surfaces. Smooth ER has various functions, including synthesis of lipids that become part of cell membranes.

sodium–potassium pump *See* Na^+/K^+ pump.

solenoid *See* 30 nm chromatin fibre.

solute The molecules of a substance dissolved in water.

solution Substance formed when molecules and ions separate and are suspended individually, surrounded by water molecules.

solvent The water in a solution in which the hydration layer prevents polar molecules or ions from reassociating.

somatic cell Any of the cells of an organism's body other than reproductive cells.

somatic gene therapy Gene therapy in which genes are introduced into somatic cells.

Southern blot analysis Technique in which labelled probes are used to detect specific DNA fragments that have been separated by gel electrophoresis.

specialized transduction Transfer of bacterial genes between bacteria using temperate phages that have incorporated fragments of the bacterial genome as they make the transition from the lysogenic cycle to the lytic cycle.

species A group of populations in which the individuals are so closely related in structure, biochemistry, and behaviour that they can successfully interbreed.

spindle The structure that separates sister chromatids and moves them to opposite spindle poles.

spindle pole One of the pair of centrosomes in a cell undergoing mitosis from which bundles of microtubules radiate to form the part of the spindle from that pole.

spliceosome A complex formed between the pre-mRNA and small ribonucleoprotein particles, in which mRNA splicing takes place.

spontaneous reaction Chemical or physical reaction that occurs without outside help.

spore A haploid reproductive structure, usually a single cell, that can develop into a new individual without fusing with another cell; found in plants, fungi, and certain protists.

sporophyte An individual of the diploid generation produced through fertilization in organisms that undergo alternation of generations; it produces haploid spores.

SRP (signal recognition particle) receptor A protein on the membrane of the endoplasmic reticulum that binds the signal recognition particle.

starch Energy-providing carbohydrates stored in plant cells.

start codon The first codon read in an mRNA in translation—AUG. Also referred to as the *initiator codon*.

steroid A type of lipid derived from cholesterol.

steroid hormone receptor Internal receptor that turns on specific genes when it is activated by binding a signal molecule.

steroid hormone response element The DNA sequence to which the hormone receptor complex binds.

sterol Steroid with a single polar —OH group linked to one end of the ring framework and a complex, nonpolar hydrocarbon chain at the other end.

sticky end End of a DNA fragment, with a single-stranded structure that can form hydrogen bonds with a complementary sticky end on any other DNA molecule cut with the same enzyme.

stomach The portion of the digestive system in which food is stored and digestion begins.

stop codon A codon that does not specify amino acids. The three nonsense codons are UAG, UAA, and UGA. Also referred to as the *nonsense codon* and *termination codon*.

strict aerobe Cell with an absolute requirement for oxygen to survive, unable to live solely by fermentations.

strict anaerobe Organism in which fermentation is the only source of ATP.

stroma An inner compartment of a chloroplast, enclosed by two boundary membranes and containing a third membrane system.

stromatolite Fossilized remains of ancient cyanobacterial mats that carried out photosynthesis by the water-splitting reaction.

structural genomics The sequencing of genomes and the analysis of the nucleotide sequences to locate genes and other functionally important sequences within the genome.

structural isomers Two molecules with the same chemical formula but atoms that are arranged in different ways.

substrate The particular reacting molecule or molecular group that an enzyme catalyzes.

substrate-level phosphorylation An enzyme-catalyzed reaction that transfers a phosphate group from a substrate to ADP.

sugar–phosphate backbone Structure in a polynucleotide chain that is formed when deoxyribose sugars are linked by phosphate groups in an alternating sugar–phosphate–sugar–phosphate pattern.

sulfhydryl group A group that works as a molecular fastener, consisting of a sulphur atom linked on one side to a hydrogen atom and on the other side to a carbon chain.

sum rule Mathematical rule in which final probability is found by summing individual probabilities.

surface tension The force that places surface water molecules under tension, making them more resistant to separation than the underlying water molecules.

symmetry (adj., symmetrical) Exact correspondence of form and constituent configuration on opposite sides of a dividing line or plane.

symport The transport of two molecules in the same direction across a membrane. Also referred to as *cotransport*.

synapse A site where a neuron makes a communicating connection with another neuron or an effector such as a muscle fibre or gland.

synapsis *See* pairing.

synaptonemal complex A protein framework that tightly holds together homologous chromosomes as they pair.

systems biology An area of biology that studies the organism as a whole to unravel the integrated and interacting network of genes, proteins, and biochemical reactions responsible for life.

TATA box A regulatory DNA sequence found in the promoters of many eukaryotic genes transcribed by RNA polymerase II.

telomerase An enzyme that adds telomere repeats to chromosome ends.

telomeres Repeats of simple-sequence DNA that maintain the ends of linear chromosomes.

telophase The final phase of mitosis, during which the spindle disassembles, the chromosomes decondense, and the nuclei re-form.

temperate bacteriophage Bacteriophage that may enter an inactive phase (lysogenic cycle) in which the host cell replicates and passes on the bacteriophage DNA for generations before the phage becomes active and kills the host (lytic cycle).

template A nucleotide chain used in DNA replication for the assembly of a complementary chain.

template strand The DNA strand that is copied into an RNA molecule during gene transcription.

termination codon *See* stop codon.

termination factor *See* release factor.

terminator Specific DNA sequence for a gene that signals the end of transcription of a gene. Terminators are common for prokaryotic genes.

tertiary structure The overall three-dimensional folding of a polypeptide chain.

testcross A genetic cross between an individual with the dominant phenotype and a homozygous recessive individual.

tetrad Homologous pair consisting of four chromatids.

theory of endosymbiosis States that mitochondria developed from ingested prokaryotes that were capable of using oxygen for aerobic respiration; chloroplasts developed from ingested cyanobacteria.

thermodynamics The study of the energy flow during chemical and physical reactions.

thylakoids Flattened, closed sacs that make up a membrane system within the stroma of a chloroplast.

thymine A pyrimidine that base-pairs with adenine.

Ti (tumour-inducing) plasmid A plasmid used to make transgenic plants.

topoisomerase An enzyme that relieves the overtwisting and strain of DNA ahead of the replication fork.

trace element An element that occurs in organisms in very small quantities (0.01%); in nutrition, a mineral required by organisms only in small amounts.

tracer Isotope used to label molecules so that they can be tracked as they pass through biochemical reactions.

trait A particular variation in a genetic or phenotypic character.

transcription The mechanism by which the information encoded in DNA is made into a complementary RNA copy.

transcription factor Proteins that recognize and bind to the TATA box and then recruit the polymerase.

transcription initiation complex Combination of general transcription factors with RNA polymerase II.

transcription unit A region of DNA that transcribes a single primary transcript.

transcriptional regulation The processes that directly control gene activity.

transduction In cell signalling, the process of changing a signal into the form necessary to cause the cellular response. In prokaryotes, the process in which DNA is transferred from donor to recipient bacterial cells by an infecting bacteriophage.

transfer RNA (tRNA) The RNA that brings amino acids to the ribosome for addition to the polypeptide chain.

transformation The conversion of the hereditary type of a cell by the uptake of DNA released by the breakdown of another cell.

transgenic An organism that has been modified to contain genetic information from an external source.

transition state An intermediate arrangement of atoms and bonds that both the reactants and the products of a reaction can assume.

translation The use of the information encoded in the RNA to assemble amino acids into a polypeptide.

translocation In genetics, a chromosomal alteration that occurs if a broken segment is attached to a different, nonhomologous chromosome. In vascular plants, the long-distance transport of substances by xylem and phloem.

transport The controlled movement of ions and molecules from one side of a membrane to the other.

transposable element (TE) A sequence of DNA that can move from one place to another within the genome of a cell.

transposase An enzyme that catalyzes some of the reactions inserting or removing the transposable element from the DNA.

transposition Mechanism of movement of transposable elements involving nonhomologous recombination.

transposon A bacterial transposable element with an inverted repeat sequence at each end enclosing a central region with one or more genes.

tricarboxylic acid cycle *See* citric acid cycle.

triglyceride A nonpolar compound produced when a fatty acid binds by a dehydration synthesis reaction at each of glycerol's three —OH-bearing sites.

tropical forest Any forest that grows between the Tropics of Capricorn and Cancer, a region characterized by high temperature and rainfall and thin, nutrient-poor topsoil.

tropics The latitudes between 23.5° N and 23.5° S, the Tropics of Cancer and Capricorn.

true-breeding Individual that passes traits without change from one generation to the next.

tumour-suppressor gene A gene that encodes proteins that inhibit cell division.

umbilical cord A long tissue with blood vessels linking the embryo and the placenta.

unicellular organism Individual consisting of a single cell.

universal A feature of the nucleic acid code, with the same codons specifying the same amino acids in all living organisms.

unsaturated Fatty acid with one or more double bonds linking the carbons.

vagina The muscular canal that leads from the cervix to the exterior.

valence electron An electron in the outermost energy level of an atom.

van der Waals forces Weak molecular attractions over short distances.

vein In a plant, a vascular bundle that forms part of the branching network of conducting and supporting tissues in a leaf or other expanded plant organ. In an animal, a vessel that carries the blood back to the heart.

vertebrate A member of the monophyletic group of tetrapod animals that possess a vertebral column.

vesicle A small, membrane-bound compartment that transfers substances between parts of the endomembrane system.

vibrio Any of various short, motile, S-shaped or comma-shaped bacteria of the genus *Vibrio*.

virulent bacteriophage Bacteriophage that kills its host bacterial cells during each cycle of infection.

virus An infectious agent that contains either DNA or RNA surrounded by a protein coat.

vitamin An organic molecule required in small quantities that the animal cannot synthesize for itself.

water lattice An arrangement formed when a water molecule in liquid water establishes an average of 3.4 hydrogen bonds with its neighbours.

wavelength The distance between two successive peaks of electromagnetic radiation.

wax A substance insoluble in water that is formed when fatty acids combine with long-chain alcohols or hydrocarbon structures.

wobble hypothesis Hypothesis stating that the complete set of 61 sense codons can be read by fewer than 61 distinct tRNAs because of particular pairing properties of the bases in the anticodons.

X chromosome Sex chromosome that occurs paired in female cells and single in male cells.

X-linked recessive inheritance Pattern in which displayed traits are due to inheritance of recessive alleles carried on the X chromosome.

X-ray diffraction Method for deducing the position of atoms in a molecule.

Y chromosome Sex chromosome that is paired with an X chromosome in male cells.

zygote A fertilized egg.

Credits

This page constitutes an extension of the copyright page. We have made every effort to trace the ownership of all copyrighted material and to secure permission from copyright holders. In the event of any question arising as to the use of any material, we will be pleased to make the necessary corrections in future printings. Thanks are due to the following authors, publishers, and agents for permission to use the material indicated.

CHAPTER 1 1: (top left) The Bridgeman Art Library/Getty Images 1: (top right) © The London Art Archive / Alamy 2: NASA 6: (a) NASA 6: (b) Photo in 2004 by L. Lodwick 7: (bottom right) PLANT CELL. ONLINE by Melanie Schmidt, Gunther Geßner, Matthias Luff, Ines Heiland, Volker Wagner, Marc Kaminski, Stefan Geimer, Nicole Eitzinger, Tob. Copyright 2006 by American Society of Plant Biologists. Reproduced with permission of American Society of Plant Biologists in the format Textbook, CD-ROM and DVD via Copyright Clearance Center. 8: (top left) Photo: M.B. Fenton 9: (top) © E. R. Degginger 9: (bottom) © Chris Newbert 13: Photo: M.B. Fenton 15: (a) Photo: M.B. Fenton 15: (b) Photo: M.B. Fenton 15: (c) Photo: M.B. Fenton 15: (bottom left) Corel 16: (all photos) M.B. Fenton 17: (a–c) Corel 17: (bottom right) Image collection of the University of Wisconsin-La Crosse. Image used with permission 18: (top left) Photo: Thomas Hawk 18: (top right) Reprinted by permission from Macmillan Publishers Ltd: Nature, vol. 427, Issue 6973, copyright 2004. 19: (top left a, b) W. R. Jeffery, "Adaptive Evolution of Eye Degeneration in the Mexican Blind Cavefish", The Journal of Heredity, 2004, vol. 96, issue number 3, pp. 186, by permission of Oxford University Press. 19: ((bottom left) a) Steve Miller/Naval Research Lab 19: (bottom left) b) Photo: Steven Haddock 19: ((bottom left) c) Cas Liber 19: ((bottom left) d) Photo: Mike Sauder

CHAPTER 2 23: Time & Life Pictures/Getty Images 24: (top right) Art Wolfe/Stone/Getty Images 24: (bottom right) Credit: US Government Public Domain 24: (top left) Sascha Burkard/Shutterstock 24: (top right) Steve Byland/Shutterstock 24: (top right) harmeet/StockXchng 24: (top right) © Karin Duthie / Alamy 24: (top right) © PHOTOTAKE Inc. / Alamy 24: (top right) © Tim Pannell/ CORBIS 24: (top right) © Visuals Unlimited/ Corbis 25: (top left) US Government Public Domain 25: (a) Tony Brain /SPL/Photo Researchers 25: (b) M. Abbey/Visuals Unlimited 25: (c) Wim van Egmond/ Visuals Unlimited 25: (d) Manfred Kage/Peter Arnold 25: (e) C. E. Jeffree, et al, Planta, 172 (1):20–37, 1987. Reprinted. 26: (left) From Freeman, S. Biological Science, 2/E. Published by Benjamin Cummings. Copyright © 2004 by Pearson Education. Adapted by permission of the publisher. 26: (right) World Perspectives/Getty Images 27: Photo by Chesley Bonestell 28: (top left) Dr. Ken Macdonald/SPL/Photo Researchers, Inc. 28: (bottom right) Dr. W. Hargreaves and D. Deamer 32: (a) Bill Bachmann, Photo Researchers, Inc. 32: (b) Stanley M. Awramik 33: Dr. G. Cohen-Bazire 34: (top left) Yuri Arcurs/ Shutterstock 34: a) © Visuals Unlimited/Corbis 34: b) © Visuals Unlimited/Corbis 34: c) Ed Reschke / Peter Arnold Inc. 39: (a) J. U. Shuler/ Photo Researchers 39: (b) Courtesy of Mary Osborn, Max Planck Institute for Biophysical Chemistry, Goettingen FRG 39: (c) Courtesy of Dr. Vincenzo Cirulli, Lab. of Developmental Biology, The Whittier Inst. for Diabetes, Univ. of Cal.-San Diego, La Jolla, CA 41: (b) Don Fawcett/Photo Researchers 42: (top) Lennart Nilsson 42: (bottom) CNRI/SPL/Photo Researchers 43: Gary Carlson / Photo Researchers, Inc.

CHAPTER 3 47: From Russell et al., SCIENCE 320, p. 340–346 (18 April 2008). Reprinted with permission from AAAS. 48: Edward Snow/ Bruce Coleman USA 48: Jamie and Judy Wild/ Danita Delimont. com 48: Jamie and Judy Wild/ Danita Delimont. com 48: Ron Sefton/ Bruce Coleman USA 48: © Bryan Allen/ Corbis 49: (a) Photo: UBC Botanical Garden and Centre for Plant Research. 49: (b) Photo by M.B. Fenton 49: (c) Stephen Sharnoff 49: (d) Image: Natural History Museum 49: (e) Photo by M.B. Fenton 49: (f) Photo by M.B. Fenton 49: (g) Photo by M.B. Fenton 49: (h) Photo by M.B. Fenton 53: From Miller, J.D., Scott, E.C., Okamoto, S., Public Acceptance of Evolution, Science, Vol. 313, 11 August 2006: pp. 765–766. Reprinted with permission from AAAS. 55: Reprinted by permission from Macmillan Publishers Ltd: Nature, Vol. 389: pp. 33–39. The origin and early evolution of plants on land by Paul Kenrick, Peter R. Crane, copyright (1997). 56: From Francesca D. Ciccarelli, Tobias Doerks, Christian von Mering, Christopher J. Creevey, Berend Snel, Peer Bork, "Public Toward Automatic Reconstruction of a Highly Resolved Tree of Life", Science, Vol. 311, 3 March 2006: pp. 1283–1287. Reprinted with permission from AAAS. 61: Photo: Skip Pierce 62: (a, b) Photo by M.B. Fenton 62: (bottom right) Photo by Andy Didyk 63: (top left) © DLILLC/Corbis 63: (center left) Photo by M.B. Fenton 63: (bottom left) Photo by M.B. Fenton 63: (bottom right) Photo by M.B. Fenton 64: (a) Photo by M.B. Fenton 64: (b) Photo by M.B. Fenton 64: (c) Photo by M.B. Fenton 64: (d) Photo by M.B. Fenton 64: (e) Photo by M.B. Fenton 64: (f) Photo by M.B. Fenton 64: (g) Photo by M.B. Fenton 64: (h) Photo by M.B. Fenton 66: (top left) Yuri Arcurs/Shutterstock 66: Clare et al. 2007. Molecular Ecology notes, 7:184–190. Reprinted by permission of Blackwell Publishing 67: Alex Borisenko, © 2006, Royal Ontario Museum 68: Barcode of Life

CHAPTER 4 73: © Corel 74: (a) © Lehtikuva [2005] all rights reserved 74: (b) © Wally McNamee/ CORBIS 74: (bottom right) © David Young-Wolff / PhotoEdit 75: Monkey Business Images/Shutterstock 76: Anna Lyubimtseva/iStockPhoto 82: (top left) Yuri Arcurs/Shutterstock 82: (a, b) Photo: Denis Maxwell 89: Douglas Faulkner/ Sally Faulkner Collection

CHAPTER 5 96: Don W. Fawcett/ Photo Researchers, Inc. 105: (all photos) M. Sheetz, R. Painter, and S. Singer. Journal of Cell Biology, 70:493 (1976). By permission of Rockefeller University Press 108: (d) M. M. Perry and A. M. Gilbert 109: Mike Abbey/Visuals Unlimited 111: (top left) Yuri Arcurs/Shutterstock

CHAPTER 6 115: Professors P. Motta & T. Naguro/ SPL/ Photo Researchers, Inc. 123: Micrographs, M. Sheetz, R. Painter, and S. Singer. Journal of Cell Biology, 70:493, 1976. By permission of Rockefeller University Press. 127: (top left) Yuri Arcurs/Shutterstock 133: David M. Phillips/ Visuals Unlimited

CHAPTER 7 139: NASA/Goddard Space Flight Centre 141: Craig Tuttle/CORBIS 150: (top left) Yuri Arcurs/Shutterstock 154: © PHOTOTAKE Inc. / Alamy 156: (top right) PhotoDisc/ Getty Images 156: (bottom right) Chris Heller/Corbis

CHAPTER 8 161: © Russell Kightley Media 162: Visuals Unlimited 164: (top left) Yuri Arcurs/ Shutterstock

CHAPTER 9 179: Dr. Paul Andres, University of Dundee/Science Photo Library/Photo Researchers, Inc. 180: (top left) Photo used with permission from Damn Funny Pictures 180: (a) © John Cancalosi / Alamy 180: (b) © M.Brodie / Alamy 181: Conly Rieder 183: Photo provided by Fengtang Yang and Malcolm Ferguson-Smith of Cambridge University. 184–185: (all photos) Ed Reschke 186: (left, all) Ed Reschke 186: (right) Leonard Lessin / Peter Arnold Inc. 187: (top) D.M. Phillips / Visuals Unlimited 187: (bottom) R. Calentine / Visuals Unlimited 189: Photograph by Dr. Conly L. Rieder, Wadsworh Center, Albany, New York 12201-0509 192: Courtesy of Professor Pierre Chambon, Institut Clinique de la Souris, University of Strasbourg. Reprinted by permission from Nature 348:699. Copyright 1990 Macmillan Magazines, Ltd. 193: Courtesy of Dr. Sydney Brenner 196: (top left) Yuri Arcurs/Shutterstock

CHAPTER 10. 199: © VOLVOX Inc. Tsuneo Nakamura Marine Photo Office 203: (left, a) © Dennis Kunkel 203: (left, b) Courtesy of L. G. Caro and Academic Press, Inc. (London) Ltd. from Journal of Molecular Biology 16.269.1966 203: (right, a) Dr. Huntington Porter and Dr. David Dressler 203: (right, b) Prof. Stanley Cohen/SPL/Photo Researchers, Inc. 214–215: Micrographs with thanks to the John Innes Foundation Trustees 216: (top row, left) Marc Henrie/Dorling Kindersley/Getty Images 216: (top row, centre) Dave King/Dorling Kindersley/Getty Images 216: (top row, right) Elena Butinova/Shutterstock 216: (bottom row, left) Dave King/Dorling Kindersley/Getty Images 216: (bottom row, centre) Lexx/Shutterstock 216: (bottom row, right) Dave King/Dorling Kindersley/ Getty Images 217: (top left) Yuri Arcurs/Shutterstock 217: (top right) Photo by Oana Marcu 220: Courtesy Diter von Wettstein 223: Nik Kleinberg

CHAPTER 11 229: Carolyn A. McKeone/Science Photo Library/Photo Researchers, Inc. 230: (a, b) Stanley Flegler/Visuals Unlimited 230: (bottom left) Moravian Museum, Brno 239: (a) Dr. P. Marazzi/Photo Researchers, Inc. 239: (b) St. Bartholomew's Hospital/Photo Researchers, Inc. 239: (c) David Frazier/Photo Researchers, Inc. 240: (top left) William Ferguson 240: (top right) William Ferguson 240: (bottom) Francese Muntada/CORBIS 243: (a) Michael Stuckey/ Comstock, Inc. 243: (b) Bosco Broyer, Photo by Gary Head 243: (c) Michael Stuckey/Comstock, Inc. 244: Dan Fairbanks/Brigham Young University 246: (top left) Yuri Arcurs/Shutterstock

CHAPTER 12 249: Regents of University of California 2005/Dr. Uli Weier/Photo Researchers, Inc. 250: Eddie Adams/AP Wide World Photos 255: (right) Eyewire/ Getty Images 255: (left) Photodisc/Getty Images 256: (a) © Carolina Biological Supply/Visuals Unlimited 256: (b) © Terry Gleason/Carolina Biological Supply 258: © Bettman/CORBIS 259: Ulrike Schanz/ Animals, Animals—Earth Scenes 262: (top left) © 1997, Hironao Numabe, M.D., Tokyo Medical University 262: (top right) Permission of Carol Lafrate 263: (top left) Yuri Arcurs/Shutterstock 264: © Abraham Menashe 270: (bottom) Bonnie Kamin/ Stuart Kenter Associates 270: (top) Carolina Biological Supply Company

CHAPTER 13 271: Kenneth Edward/ Photo Researchers, Inc. 272: A. C. Barrington Brown © 1968 J.D. Watson 277: SPL/Photo Researchers, Inc 289: (top left) Yuri Arcurs/Shutterstock 290: (left) O.L. Miller, Jr. Steve McKnight 290: (right) B. Hamkalo

CHAPTER 14 295: © LookatSciences/Phototake 296: (left) Dennis Hallinan 296: (right) Bob Evans/ Peter Arnold, Inc. 307: (left) Yuri Arcurs/ Shutterstock 307: (right) From: Structure and in vitro activity of group II introns (G. Bassi, M. Costa, F. Michel), CNRS. 313: © Arco Images GmbH / Alamy 314: Courtesy Barbara A. Hamkalo

Index

complementary DNA (cDNA), **349**
complex molecules
    assembly of, 78, 79
    breakdown of, 78
compound eyes, 8–9
compounds, 36, **F-3**
concentration, **F-14**
concentration gradient
    as active transport energy source, 107*i*
    diffusion rate based on, 101
cones
    degeneration of, 20
    function of, 7
conifers
    mitotic spindle formation in, 188
conjugated system, **4**
conjugation, **202–206**
    F factor and, 203–205, 204*i*
    genes, mapping by, 205–206
conservation of energy, principle of, 72–73
conservative replication model of DNA,
    278–279, 280*i*
consumers as trophic role, 61
contact inhibition, **191–192**
continental climate, **59**
contractile proteins. *See* motor proteins
controlling cells, **162**
Convention for Trade in Endangered
    Species (CITES), 68
co-option of organisms, 61
Coriolis effect, **58**
corn *(Zea mays)*
    chromosomes, 221
    colour patterns, 223*i*
Correns, Carl, 237
cotransport, **106**
covalent bonds, 87, **F-7**, **F-8**
crassulacean acid metabolism, 156, **707**
Crick, Francis H.C., 272, 272*i*, 276,
    277–278, 308
crop plants
    engineered, 360
crossbreeding, 397
crosses, genetic, 233*i*, 234–235,
    235*i*, 250
crossing-over, **217**
crossovers, **217**, 225
cross-pollination, **231**
cross-talk, **174–175**, 174*i*
Crown gall disease, 360, 360*i*
crustaceans (subphylum
    Crustacea)
    eyes of, 9
cut-and-paste transposition, 222*i*
cyanide, 87, **135**
cyanide-resistant respiration, 135
cyanobacteria, 34*i*
    chloroplasts compared to, 38
    eukaryotic cells taking up, 37
    metabolism of, 32
    oxygen formation, role in, 34
cyclin:CDK complexes, 191, 192
cyclin-dependent kinases (CDK), **190**
    inhibition of, 193
cyclins, **190**, 193
cystic fibrosis, **93–94**
    children with, 264*i*
    defective gene in, 93, 93*i*, 111
    inheritance patterns in, 239, 264–265
    lung infections in, 164
cytochrome complex
    electron transfer from, 147
    proton migration to, 147–148
cytochrome oxidase, 134
    alternatives to, 135
    inhibition of, 87
cytochrome oxidase inhibitors, 135
cytogenetics, 263
cytokinesis, **180**, **185–186**

cell plate formation role in, 187*i*
centrioles received by daughter cells
    during, 188
mitotic spindle role in, 187
preparation for, 182
cytoplasm, **33**
    division of, 39, 194
    of eukaryotic cells, 35
    vesicle traffic in, 37*i*
cytoplasmic inheritance, 266–267
cytoplasmic streaming, **39**
cytoskeleton
    cell structures supported and moved
        by, **38–39**
    components of, 39*i*
    interphase, 187
cytosol, **33**
Czech, Thomas, 29

Dai, Hongjie, 110
dark–light distinction, visual devices
    aiding, 20
darkness, life forms existing in, 18, 28
Darwin, Charles
    climbing plants studied by, 52
    evolution theory of, 52
    eye evolution studied by, 9
    travels of, 54, 343
death factors, 191
decarboxylation reaction, 122–123
decomposers as trophic role, 61
deer fly, 9*i*
degeneracy, **300**
dehydration, F-19, F-19*i*
dehydrogenases, food oxidation in -pres-
    ence of, 118
dehydrogenation reaction, 123
deletion (chromosome), 260, 260*i*
deoxyribonucleic acid (DNA)
    contamination of, 271–272
    damage to, 133, 191, 192,
        271–272, 289
    degeneration of, 194
    degradation of, 272
    digital model of, 271*i*
    discovery of, 272
    double helix of, F-32, F-32*i*
    of eukaryotic cells, 33, 35, 181
    evolution of, 30–31
    formation of, 27
    function of, F-30
    as genetic material, 52
    as hereditary molecule, 272–275, 275*i*
    information stored in, 29, 29*i*, 30*i*
    mammalian retrovirus insertion into,
        224*i*
    of mitochondria and chloroplasts, 38
    molecules and cells, relationship
        to, 25
    nucleotide subunits of, 276*i*, 282
    of prokaryotic cells, 33
    protection of, 13
    recombination of, 200–201, 200*i*,
        206–208
    repair of, 134, 191, 288–289, 288*i*
    RNA synthesis directed by, 301–304,
        302*i*, 303*i*
    strands of, 280*i*, 282–283, 282*i*, 283*i*
    structure of, 272, 272*i*, 276–278, 277*i*,
        F-31, F-31*i*
    synthesis of, 282–283, 366
    ultraviolet light damage to, 12, 12*i*
    X-ray diffraction of, 276–277
deoxyribonucleic acid (DNA) replication,
    180, 182, 183, 188, 191, 193, 194, 200
    circadian control of, 13
    DNA sequencing techniques based
        on, 363

enzymes of, 279–280, 282, 283,
    285, 285*i*
error-correcting mechanisms for,
    287–289
models of, 278–279, 279*i*, 280*i*, 281*i*
in prokaryotes, 291, 291*i*, 292*i*
steps of, 284*i*
of strands, 283*i*
telomerase role in, 285–287
deoxyribonucleic acid (DNA) sequence
of genomes, 253
    inverted repeat sequence, **221**
    meiosis effect on, 210–211
    mutations of, 200, 289, 366
    sequencing techniques, 68, 363, 364*i*
desaturases, **97–98**, 99*i*
Desmostylus teeth (mammal), 64*i*
diabetes, 168
diabetes type 1, 116
diacylglycerol (DAG), 170, 171, 175
diarrhea, 169
Dick, John, 196
dideoxy DNA sequencing, **363**, 364*i*
dideoxyribonucleotides, **363**
diffusion
    as entropy-driven process, 101*i*
    passive transport based on, **101**
    rate, factors affecting, 101, 101*i*
    types of, 101–102, 103*i*, 106
    of water, 103–104
dihybrid, **236**
dihybrid cross, **236**
dimers, **12**, 167–168
dinoflagellates
    bioluminescence in, 19
    mitosis in, 195
dinosaurs
    extinction of, 26
diploids, **181**, 209, 210, 237
direct channels of cell communication,
    162
disaccharides
    breakdown of, 130
    structure of, F-22, F-22*i*
discontinuous DNA strand replication,
    283
diseases
    phenotypes of, 246
    sex-linked genes and, 258–259
    susceptibility, epistasis role in, 243–244
    transmission, differences in, 51
dispersive replication model of DNA,
    279, 280*i*
diversification of life. *See* biodiversity
DNA chips, **367**
DNA cloning, **344–349**
DNA fingerprinting, **353**, **355–356**, 355*i*
DNA fragments. *See also* cloned DNA
    fragments
    identifying, 354*i*
    separation of, 351*i*
DNA helicase, **282**
DNA hybridization, 348*i*, 354*i*
DNA libraries, **346**, 349
DNA ligase, **283**, 285
DNA methylation, 333–334
DNA microarrays, **366–367**, 368*i*
DNA packing, histones and, 290
DNA polymerases, 279–280, 282, 282*i*,
    283, 283*i*, 294
DNA technologies
    application of, 352–361
public concern over, 361–362
Doheny Eye Institute, 20
Dolly (cloned sheep), 359, 359*i*
dominance, **232**
dormancy
    in spores, 32
d'Ortous de Mairan, Jean-Jacques, 13

lowering, 83
kinetic energy, **72**, 73, 73*i*
kinetic motion, temperature effect on, 89
kinetochore, **184**, 190*i*
kinetochore microtubules, 188, 189, 190*i*
knifefish *(Notopterus notopterus)*, 179
knockout mice, F-40
Kramer, David, 157
Krebs cycle, 119, 119*i*, 123, 123*i*, 124*i*, 128, 130, 130*i*, 132, 134

L1 ligase ribozyme, 31
Labrador current, 59–60
Labrador retrievers, 243, 243*i*
Lacks, Henrietta, 182
lactate fermentation, **131–132**, 132*i*
Lactobacillus bacteria, 133
lactones, 164, 475
lagging DNA strand, **283**
lagging strand template, **283**
lambda phage (l), 207, 208, 208*i*
land, organism migration onto, 54
land breezes, 60*i*
land plants
    origin and evolution of, 26, 53
Landsteiner, Karl, 242
large ribosomal subunits, **308**
leading DNA strand, **283**
Lederberg, Joshua, 201
lens (eye), cataract effect on, 2
Leopold, Duke of Albany, 259
Lester, Diane, 240
leukemia, 196
lianas, 52
lichens, 64*i*
life, **24–25**
    chemical origins of, 25–29, 31
    early, 32–35
    and second law of thermodynamics, 74–75
light, **2–3**
    absorption of, 4–5, 18, 143–144, 148
    artistic depiction of, 1–2
    damage by, 11–13, 11*i*
    ecology and behaviour, role in, 13–18
    as energy source, 5–6, 50, 142
    as information source, 6–10
    physical nature of, 2–5
    sensing, 7–8 (*see also* eye; photoreceptors)
    wavelengths of, 3, 5
lightning, life origin role, possible of, 27
light pollution, 17–18, 18*i*
linear DNA molecules, 285–287
linkage map, 251, 253
lipids, **F-33–F-35**
    bilayers, 100*i*
    damage of, 133
    in membranes, 95, 96–98
    modifaction of, 37*i*
    molecular layers of, 94
    molecules of, 97*i*
    movement of, 42
    oxidation of, 130
    repair of, 134
    synthesis of, 6, 36
    transport of, 37*i*
liposomes, 29
living things, composition of, 11
local climates, 59–60
lock-and-key hypothesis, **83–84**
locomotion, circadian rhythm role in, 13
locus, **238**, 239*i*
loss of imprinting, 268
low-affinity state (of enzyme -conformation), 88
low-density lipoprotein (LDL) receptor, encoding of, 241
low-latitude circulation cells, 57

Luft, Rolf, 115
Luft syndrome, **115–116**
lung infections, in cystic fibrosis, 164
lungs
    mucus in, 93–94
lux operon, 327
lysogenic cycle, 208, 208*i*
lysosomes, 37*i*
lytic cycle, **206**, 208*i*

macromolecules, 28, 78
macular degeneration, 20
male sex chromosomes, 255
maltose, F-22*i*
mammalian cells
    contact inhibition in, 191–192
    cultures of, 182
    cycles of, 183
    microfilaments in, 39*i*
    mitotic spindles in, 189*i*
    substances taken in by, 107, 109
mammalian retrovirus, 224*i*
mammals
    alternative splicing in, 306
    body temperature regulation in, 129
    cell communication in, 162
    cloning in, 334
MAP kinases. *See* mitogen-activated protein (MAP) kinases
map unit, 253
marine life
    bioluminescence in, 19
    diversity of, 343–344
maritime climate, **59**
Mars, life on, 23–24
Mars Climate Orbiter, F-2
Martin, David, 240
mass number, F-4*t*
maternal chromosome, 211
maternal inheritance, 267
mating
    circadian rhythm role in, 13
    mate attraction, light role in, 19
matter, **F-3**
    conversion into energy, 2
    light interaction with, 3–4, 3*i*
    organization of, F-3–F-6
Maxam, Allan M., 363
M blood type, 241
McCarty, Maclyn, 274
McClintock, Barbara, 221, 223*i*
McLeod, Colin, 274
measurement, non-SI units of, F-2*t*
measurement and scale, F-1–F-2
meiosis, **181**, **195**, 214*i*–215*i*
    abnormalities in, 261, 261*i*, 262–263
    discovery of, 237
    gene and allele behaviour in, 238*i*
    genetic recombination associated with, 201, 209–218
    mitosis compared to, 218*i*
    recombination effects during, 245
    regulating mechanisms for, 225
    time and place, variations in, 209–210, 209*i*
meiosis II, 218, 219*i*
melanin, **12–13**
    absorption spectrum of, 12*i*
    amount, variations in, 13*i*
    in dogs, 243
melanocytes, 13
melatonin, 14, 14*i*
Mello, Craig, 335
membrane asymmetry, 95
membrane bilayer, **96**
    phospholipid, 97*i*
    splitting, 96*i*
membrane fluidity, 96–97, 97*i*
membrane potential, **105–106**

membrane proteins, **99–101**
    functions of, 100*i*
    integral, 96*i*, 99–100, 165
    peripheral, 100–101
    prion proteins as, 494
    structure of, 100*i*
membrane receptors, **164**
membrane structures, **94–95**, 94*i*
membrane transport
    active, 104–106, 109
    passive, 101–104, 109
Mendel, Gregor, **230–237**, 230*i*, 238–239, 246, 250, 272
    mice studies of, F-40
Mendel's hypotheses, modifications and additions to, 239–245
mental retardation, 265
Menten, Maud, 82
Meselson, Matthew, 279
mesophyll cells, 155
mesopredators, **61**
messenger RNA (mRNA), 295*i*, **297**, 299*i*
    aminoacyl-tRNAs, bringing together with, 308
    availability, factors affecting, 334–335
    breakdown rate, variations in, 335
    degradation of, 336
    eukaryote processing of, 304–306, 305*i*
    function of, F-30
    polypeptide synthesis role of, 307–317
    splicing, 304–305, 306*i*
    transcription of, 334
    translation impact on, 310, 313
metabolic activities, 162
metabolic disorders, 115
metabolic pathways
    development of, 29
    regulation of, 129
    types of, 78, 78*i*
metabolic processes, circadian rhythm role in, 13
metabolic regulation, enzyme inhibitor role in, 87, 88
metabolic wastes, excretion of, 1060–1061
metabolism
    anaerobic, 33, 34
metagenomic studies, 369
metals as cofactors, 84
metaphase as meiosis stage, 211, 213
metaphase cell, 183*i*
metaphase stage of mitosis, 183, 184, 185*i*
metastasis, **192**
meteorites of Martian origin, 23–24, 23*i*
methane
    burning of, 117–118, 117*i*
    C-H bonds of, 118
    potential energy of, 76
    in primordial atmosphere, 27, 28
    shared orbitals of, F-8*i*
    space-filling model of, F-8*i*
Mexican cavefish *(Astyanax mexicanus)*, 18, 19*i*
mice. *See also Mus musculus* (house mouse)
    coat colour variation in, 229*i*
    human hematopoietic cells in, 196
micelle, **96**, 97*i*
Michaelis, Leonor, 82
Michaelis-Menten equation, 82
microclimate, **60**
microfilaments, **38**, 39, 39*i*
micro-RNAs (miRNAs), 335
microscopic organism species, number of, 49
microtubule organizing centre (MTOC), **188**
microtubules, **38**

as open systems, 72
types and groupings of, 48–50, 50i
organs
specialization of, 42
origin of replication (ori), **194**
osmotic water movement, 104, 105i
outer membrane (of chloroplast), 142
oxidation, 50, **116–117**
oxidation-reduction reactions, 31
oxidative damage repair, 134
oxidative phosphorylation, 119i, 120, 125i, 126, 127, 128, 130
alternatives to, 132
defects of, 134
electron transport chain of, 131
oxidative stress, 217
oxidizing agents, 133
oxidizing atmosphere, **27**
oxygen consumption, 131–132, 152
elevation in, 115
rate of, 129
oxygenic photosynthesis, **33–35**, 37
by animals, 61
development of, 53, 145
oxygen (O_2)
atmosphere impacted by, 27
atmospheric, rise in, 33–35, 37, 53
cellular respiration and, 131–134
death in presence of, 133, 134
diffusion and availability of, 54, 54t
lifestyles dictated by, 133
properties of, F-3
reduction of, 133i
release of, 145, 145i
solubility, temperature effect on, 154, 154t
survival in absence of, 131
ozone layer, 12, 27, 53

P680 (chlorophyll), 144–145, 146, 148
oxidation of, 147
P680* (chlorophyll), 146, 148
P680+ (chlorophyll), 146
P700 (chlorophyll), 144, 145
oxidation-reduction of, 147
pairing, **212**
pancreatic cells, 39i
pangolin, scales of, 49i
panspermia, **32**, 34
Paralecithodendrium chilostomum -(endoparasite), 62i
parasites
types of, 62
parasitism, **61**, 62
Parkinson disease
mitochondrial disorder role in, 116
reactive oxygen formation in, 134
partial diploid, **205**, 206
paternal chromosome, 211
paternity, determining, 242, 356
pathogenesis, quorum sensing regulation of, 164
pedigree, **258**
penicillin
as competitive enzyme inhibitor, 86
Penicillium (mould), 86
peppered moth (*Biston betularia*), 14–15, 15i
pepsin, 314
pepsinogen, 314
peptide hormones
steroid hormones compared to, 174
peptides, 165
cell cycle regulation, role in, 191
molecular structure of, F-26, F-26i
as signal molecules, 163, 164
peptidoglycan, 86
peptidyl transferase, **311**, 312i
peptidyl-tRNA, 310

pesticides
resistance to, 50
P generation, **231**
pH
ammonia impact on balance of, 65
buffer impact on, F-16
enzyme activity affected by, 85, 88, 89i
water ionization and, F-14–F-15
phages. *See* bacteriophages
phagocytes, **109**
phagocytosis, **109**, 109i
phenotype, **233**, 242, 254i
phenylketonuria, 353
as autosomal recessive disease, 265
understanding of, 246
phenylthiocarbamide (PTC), **241**
pheophytin (pheo), 145i
phosphatases, 71–72
phosphate groups, 79, 79i, 169
phosphatidyl choline, 97i
phosphodiesterase, 170
phosphodiester linkage, 282i
phosphofructokinase, 130
phospholipid bilayers, 97i
phospholipids, **F-34**
in membranes, 96
membranes, new, assembly into, 110
molecular structure of, 97i, F-35i
phosphorylation, 166i
photoautographs
abundance, estimating, 139i
carbon dioxide (CO_2) fixation catalysis in, 152
environmental change sensors of, 150
examples of, 140i
photoautotrophs, 50, 50i, 61
photoheterotrophs, 50i
photomorphogenesis, **8**, 8i
photons, **3**
absorption of, 4–5, 20
energy of transferred to electrons, 18
as kinetic energy, 72
photoperiod, 14
photoreceptor cells
degeneration of, 20
of ocellus, 8
on retina, 9
photoreceptors, **7**
photorespiration, **152–157**, 156i
photosynthesis, **140**, **142**
action spectrum for, 5i
in algae, 2
as anabolic pathway, 78
in animals, 61
apparatus of, 142–145
applications, practical of, 157
chemical reaction of, F-10
chlorophyll involvement in, 3, 4i
development of, 53
efficiency, regulating, 157
electron transport in, 145–150
energy entry into biosphere through, 139
eyespot *versus*, 7
light damage effect on, 11–12
light-dependent and light-independent reactions, 140i
light energy converted to chemical energy through, 72
light reactions of, 149i
O_2 release rate in, 5i
overview of, 5i
photoautotroph use of, 61
processes, timing of, 13
regulation of, 150
in trees, 63
wavelengths used for, 11
photosynthetic organisms, light--harvesting properties in, 13, 33

photosynthetic pigments
absorption spectra, 144i
photosystem organization of, 144–145
photosystem I, **144**, 149i
photosystem II, **144–145**
excitation pressure, measuring on, 150
photosynthesis light reactions in, 149i
proton migration from, 147
structure and function of, 145–146, 145i
photosystems
components of, 145i
damage and repair of, 11–12, 11i
photosynthetic pigments organized into, 144–145
phototaxis, **8**, 11
phototrophs, **50**
phycoerythrobilin, structure of, 4i
phytochrome, **8**
phytoerythrin in aquatic plants, 17
phytoplankton, 139
piebaldism, receptor tyrosine kinase gene mutations as cause of, 176
pigment molecules
electrons within, 142i
in photosynthesis, 143i
pigments, **3–4**
colours, factors determining, 5
eye colours determined through, 256
light absorption by, 18, 20
molecules, electrons within, 142–143
oxidation of, 11
structures of, 4i
pineal gland
melatonin secretion from, 14
Pinguicula, insects caught by, 49i
pinocytosis, 107
pinta, 51
pituitary gland cells, 165
planarians
eye of, 8, 8i
planets, formation of, 26
plant cells, 25i
communication in, 162
cultures of, 182
division of, 187i
genetic engineering of, 182
plant cytokinin hormones, compounds related to, 193
plant pharming, 360
plants. *See also* under plant category, *e.g.* land plants
action spectrum in, 144i
animals emulating, 62
cyanide production in, 135
diversity of, 52
evolution of, 37, 53, 54
gas exchange by, 154i
genetic engineering of, 359–361
genetic recombination in, 210
life cycle of, 210
lineage of, 42
photoreceptors of, 7
polyploidy in, 263
signal transduction pathways found in, 166
water loss by, 154i
plasma membrane, 33, 35–36, 41, 52, **94**
ATP-dependent bicarbonate (HCO_3) pump on, 153i
growth, inward of, 194
materials of, 95
plasmid cloning vector, 347i
plasmids, **203**, 203i, **205**, 291
plastocyanin, 147
plastoquinone pool, 147
pleiotropy, **239**, **245**, 245i
Pleodorina californica, 43i
pneumonia
causes of, 206

	P	P
P	PP	PP
P	Pp	Pp

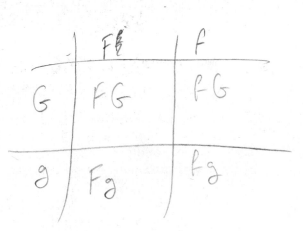

	F	f
G	FG	FG
g	Fg	Fg

Just What You Need to Know and Do NOW!

CengageNOW is an online teaching and learning resource that provides you more control in less time and delivers better student outcomes—NOW!

What instructors are saying...

CENGAGENOW IS AN ONLINE TEACHING AND LEARNING RESOURCE.

CengageNOW offers all of your teaching and learning resources in one intuitive program organized around the essential activities you perform for class - lecturing, creating assignments, grading, quizzing, and tracking student progress and performance. CengageNOW's intuitive "tabbed" design allows you to navigate to all key functions with a single click and a unique homepage tell you just what needs to be done and when. CengageNOW, in most cases, provides students access to an integrated eBook, interactive tutorials, videos, animations, games, and other multimedia tools to help them get the most out of your course.

CENGAGENOW PROVIDES MORE CONTROL IN LESS TIME

CengageNOW's flexible assignment and grade book options provides you more control while saving you valuable time in planning and managing your course assignments. With CengageNOW, you can automatically grade all assignments, weigh grades, choose points or percentages and set the number of attempts and due dates per problem to best suit your overall course plan.

CENGAGENOW DELIVERS BETTER STUDENT OUTCOMES

CengageNOW Personalized Study; a diagnostic tool (featuring a chapter specific Pre-test, Study Plan, and Post-test) empowers students to master concepts, prepare for exams, and be more involved in class. It's easy to assign and if you want, results will automatically post to your grade book. Results to Personalize Study provide immediate and ongoing feedback regarding what students are mastering and why they're not - to both you and the student. In most cases, Personalized Study links to an integrated eBook so students can easily review topics.

CengageNOW MAKES IT EASIER TO DO WHAT YOU ALREADY DO.

Designed by instructors for instructors, CengageNOW mirrors your natural workflow and provides time-saving, performance-enhancing tools for you and your students—all in one program!

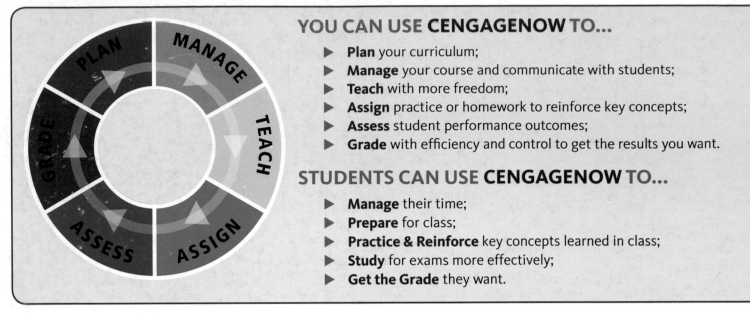

YOU CAN USE CENGAGENOW TO...

- ▶ **Plan** your curriculum;
- ▶ **Manage** your course and communicate with students;
- ▶ **Teach** with more freedom;
- ▶ **Assign** practice or homework to reinforce key concepts;
- ▶ **Assess** student performance outcomes;
- ▶ **Grade** with efficiency and control to get the results you want.

STUDENTS CAN USE CENGAGENOW TO...

- ▶ **Manage** their time;
- ▶ **Prepare** for class;
- ▶ **Practice & Reinforce** key concepts learned in class;
- ▶ **Study** for exams more effectively;
- ▶ **Get the Grade** they want.

The flexibility of CengageNOW allows you to use a single aspect of the program, or for maximum power and effectiveness, to use all of the teaching and learning resources to create and customize your own material to match your course objectives.

CENGAGENOW SEAMLESSLY INTEGRATES WITH POPULAR COURSE MANAGEMENT PROGRAMS

CengageNOW on Blackboard, WebCT, and eCollege provides students with seamless single sign-on access to CengageNOW through the school's course management system (CMS). After entering a simple access code just once at the beginning of the term, students get seamless access to both their CMS and CengageNOW textbook specific assignments and activities, with results flowing to your Blackboard, WebCT, or eCollege gradebook. Rich content, seamless integration with CengageNOW functionality, and only one gradebook to manage.

INTERESTED IN GIVING CENGAGENOW A TEST DRIVE IN YOUR CLASS?

Contact your Cengage Learning sales representative for more information about the **CengageNOW Class Test Program**.

academic.cengage.com/now